DEWEY

DEWEY

The Small-Town Library Cat
Who Touched the World

$\sim$

Vicki Myron

with Bret Witter

$\sim$

GRAND CENTRAL
PUBLISHING

New York   Boston

Grand Central Publishing
Hachette Book Group USA
237 Park Avenue
New York, NY 10017

Visit our Web site at www.HachetteBookGroupUSA.com.

Printed in the United States of America

Grateful acknowledgment is given to W. P. Kinsella for permission to quote in Chapter 14 from *Shoeless Joe* by W. P. Kinsella (Boston: Houghton Mifflin, 1982).

Endpaper photos of Dewey courtesy of Vicki Myron

First Edition: September 2008
10 9 8 7 6 5 4 3 2 1

Grand Central Publishing is a division of Hachette Book Group USA, Inc.
The Grand Central Publishing name and logo is a trademark of Hachette Book Group USA. Inc.

Library of Congress Cataloging-in-Publication Data

Myron, Vicki.
    Dewey : the small-town library cat who touched the world / Vicki Myron, with Bret Witter.—1st ed.
        p. cm.
    ISBN-13: 978-0-446-40741-0
    ISBN-10: 0-446-40741-0
    1. Dewey (Cat) 2. Cats—Iowa—Spencer—Biography. I. Witter, Bret. II. Title.
    SF445.5.M97 2008
    636.8092'9—dc22
                                            20088004498

ISBN-10: 0-446-54516-3 (Special Scholastic Edition)
ISBN-13: 978-0-446-54516-7 (Special Scholastic Edition)

Book design and text composition by Le3G McRee
Front jacket photo of Dewey by Rick Krebsbach

To Gran, Mom, and Jodi—
three amazing women who loved
Dewey almost as much as I do

Contents ⟶

DEWEY

Introduction

Welcome to Iowa

There is a thousand-mile table of land in the middle of the United States, between the Mississippi River on the east and the deserts on the west. Out here, there are rolling hills, but no mountains. There are rivers and creeks, but few large lakes. The wind has worn down the rock outcroppings, turning them first to dust, then dirt, then soil, and finally to fine black farmland. Out here, the roads are straight, stretching to the horizon in long, unbroken lines. There are no corners, only occasional, almost imperceptible bends. This land was surveyed and plotted for farms; the bends are corrections in the survey line. Exactly every mile, every road is intersected by another almost perfectly straight road. Inside is a square mile of farmland. Take a million of those square miles, lace them together, and you have one of the most important agricultural regions in the world. The Great Plains. The Bread Basket. The Heartland. Or, as many people think of it, the place you fly over on your way to somewhere else. Let them have the oceans and mountains, their beaches and their ski resorts. I'll take Iowa.

In northwest Iowa, in winter, the sky swallows the
farmhouses. On a cold day, the dark clouds that blow in
across the plains seem to churn the land under like a
plow. In the spring, the world is flat and empty, full of
brown dirt and hacked-off cornstalks waiting to be
plowed under, the sky and land perfectly balanced like a
plate on a stick. But if you come in the late summer, you
would swear the ground is about to push up and tip the
sky right out of the picture. The corn is nine feet high,
bright green leaves topped with brilliant gold tassels.
Most of the time you are buried in it, lost in the walls of
corn, but top a small rise in the road, just a few feet of elevation, and you can see endless fields of gold atop green,
silken threads sparkling in the sun. Those silks are the
sex organs of the corn, trapping pollen, flying golden
yellow for a month and then slowly drying up and
browning out under the stiff summer heat.

That's what I love about northwest Iowa: it is always
changing. Not in the way the suburbs change as one chain
restaurant replaces another or the way cities change as
buildings crowd each other ever higher, but in the way
the country changes, slowly back and forth in a gentle
motion that is always sliding forward, but never very
fast. There aren't many roadside businesses out here. No
crafts stores. No farmers' markets. The farmhouses,
which are fewer every year, hug the road. The towns
pop up suddenly, bearing signs announcing THE JEWEL
IN THE CROWN OF IOWA or THE GOLD BUCKLE ON THE
CORN BELT, and disappear just as quickly. Two minutes,
and they're gone. A grain elevator or a processing plant,
maybe a downtown strip with a convenience store, a
place to eat. Every ten miles or so, there's a roadside

cemetery, small plain markers behind low stone walls. These are pioneer plots that grew into extended family plots and eventually into town cemeteries. Nobody wants to be buried far from home, and nobody wants to waste much land. Use what you have. Make it simple. Keep it local.

Then, just when you're sliding away, when you're drifting into complacency like a corn row down the back side of a rise, the road widens and you pass a strip of stores: Matt Furniture, the Iron Horse Hotel, the Prime Rib restaurant, but also a Wal-Mart, a McDonald's, a Motel 6. Turn north at the stoplight, the first turn in fifty miles no matter which direction you've been driving, not to mention the first stoplight, and within a minute you've left the chains behind and you're driving the beautiful low bridge over the Little Sioux River right into the heart of Spencer, Iowa, a town that hasn't changed much since 1931.

Downtown Spencer is picture postcard small-town America: rows of storefronts in connecting two-and-three-story buildings where people pull their cars to the curb, get out, and walk. White Drug, Eddie Quinn's Men's Clothing, and Steffen Furniture have been in business for decades. The Hen House sells decorating items to farmwives and the occasional tourist on her way to the Iowa lake country twenty miles north. There's a hobby shop specializing in model airplanes, a card shop, and a store that rents oxygen tanks and wheelchairs. The Vacuum Cleaner Store. Arts on Grand. The old movie theater is still in business, although it shows only second-run movies since a seven-screen cineplex opened south of the bridge.

The downtown ends at The Hotel, eight blocks from the bridge. The Hotel. That's the actual name. It was known as the Tagney in the late 1920s when it was the area's best accommodation, bus depot, train station, and only sit-down restaurant. By the end of the Great Depression, it had become a flophouse and, according to legend, the town bordello. The five-story building, plain redbrick and built to last, was eventually abandoned, then rehabilitated in the 1970s, but by then the real action had moved five blocks down Grand Avenue to Sister's Main Street Café, a no-frills diner with Formica tables, drip coffee, and smoky booths. Three groups of men congregate every morning at Sister's: the old guys, the older guys, and the really old guys. Together, they have run Spencer for the past sixty years.

Around the corner from Sister's Café, across a small parking lot and just half a block off Grand Avenue, is a low gray concrete building: the Spencer Public Library. My name is Vicki Myron, and I've been working in that library for twenty-five years, the last twenty as director. I've overseen the arrival of the first computer and the addition of the reading room. I've watched children grow up and leave, only to walk back through the doors ten years later with their own children. The Spencer Public Library may not look like much, at least not at first, but it is the centerpiece, the middle ground, the heart of this heartland story. Everything I'm going to tell you about Spencer—and about the surrounding farms, the nearby lakes, the Catholic church in Hartley, the Moneta School, the box factory, and the wonderful old white Ferris wheel up at Arnold's Park—all flows back eventually to this small gray building and to the cat who lived here for more than nineteen years.

How much of an impact can an animal have? How many lives can one cat touch? How is it possible for an abandoned kitten to transform a small library into a meeting place and tourist attraction, inspire a classic American town, bind together an entire region, and eventually become famous around the world? You can't even begin to answer those questions until you hear the story of Dewey Readmore Books, the beloved library cat of Spencer, Iowa.

Chapter 1 ⟋

The Coldest Morning

January 18, 1988, was a bitterly cold Iowa Monday. The night before, the temperature had reached minus fifteen degrees, and that didn't take into account the wind, which cut under your coat and squeezed your bones. It was a killing freeze, the kind that made it almost painful to breathe. The problem with flat land, as all of Iowa knows, is that there's nothing to stop the weather. It blows out of Canada, across the Dakotas, and straight into town. The first bridge in Spencer across the Little Sioux, built in the late 1800s, had to be taken down because the river became so jammed with ice everyone worried the pylons would collapse. When the town water tower burned down in 1893—the straw packing used to keep the riser pipe from freezing caught fire, and all the nearby fire hydrants were frozen solid—a two-foot-thick, ten-foot-wide circle of ice slid out the top of the tank, crushed the community recreation center, and shattered all over Grand Avenue. That's winter in Spencer for you.

I have never been a morning person, especially on a dark and cloudy January day, but I have always been dedicated. There were a few cars on the road at seven thirty, when I drove the ten blocks to work, but as usual mine was the first car in the parking lot. Across the street, the Spencer Public Library was dead—no lights, no movement, no sound until I flipped a switch and brought it to life. The heater switched on automatically during the night, but the library was still a freezer first thing in the morning. Whose idea was it to build a concrete and glass building in northern Iowa? I needed my coffee.

I went immediately to the library staff room—nothing more than a kitchenette with a microwave and a sink, a refrigerator too messy for most people's taste, a few chairs, and a phone for personal calls—hung up my coat, and started the coffee. Then I scanned the Saturday newspaper. Most local issues could affect, or could be affected by, the library. The local newspaper, the *Spencer Daily Reporter*, didn't publish on Sunday or Monday, so Monday was catch-up morning for the Saturday edition.

"Good morning, Vicki," said Jean Hollis Clark, the assistant library director, taking off her scarf and mittens. "It's a mean one out there."

"Good morning, Jean," I said, putting aside the paper.

In the center of the staff room, against the back wall, was a large metal box with a hinged lid. The box was two feet high and four feet square, about the size of a two-person kitchen table if you sawed the legs in half. A metal chute rose out of the top of the box, then disappeared into the wall. At the other end, in the alley behind the building, was a metal slot: the library's after-hours book return.

You find all kinds of things in a library drop box — garbage, rocks, snowballs, soda cans. Librarians don't talk about it, because it gives people ideas, but all libraries deal with it. Video stores probably have the same problem. Stick a slot in a wall and you're asking for trouble, especially if, as it did at the Spencer Public Library, the slot opened onto a back alley across the street from the town's middle school. Several times we had been startled in the middle of the afternoon by a loud pop from the drop box. Inside, we'd find a firecracker.

After the weekend, the drop box would also be full of books, so every Monday I loaded them onto one of our book carts so the clerks could process and shelve them later in the day. When I came back with the cart on this particular Monday morning, Jean was standing quietly in the middle of the room.

"I heard a noise."

"What kind of noise?"

"From the drop box. I think it's an animal."

"A what?"

"An animal. I think there's an animal in the drop box."

That was when I heard it, a low rumble from under the metal cover. It didn't sound like an animal. It sounded more like an old man struggling to clear his throat. But I doubted it was an old man. The opening at the top of the chute was only a few inches wide, so that would be quite a squeeze. It was an animal, I had little doubt of that, but what kind? I got down on my knees, reached over to the lid, and hoped for a chipmunk.

The first thing I felt was a blast of freezing air. Someone had jammed a book into the return slot, wedging it open. It was as cold in the box as it was outside; maybe colder, since the box was lined with metal. You could have kept frozen meat in there. I was still catching my breath when I saw the kitten.

It was huddled in the front left corner of the box, its head down, its legs tucked underneath it, trying to appear as small as possible. The books were piled haphazardly to the top of the box, partially hiding it from view. I lifted one gingerly for a better look. The kitten looked up at me, slowly and sadly. Then it lowered its head and sank down into its hole. It wasn't trying to appear tough. It wasn't trying to hide. I don't even think it was scared. It was just hoping to be saved.

I know melting can be a cliché, but I think that's what actually happened to me at that moment: I lost every bone in my body. I am not a mushy person. I'm a single mother and a farm girl who has steered her life through hard times, but this was so, so . . . unexpected.

I lifted the kitten out of the box. My hands nearly swallowed it. We found out later it was eight weeks old, but it looked no more than eight days old, if that. It was so thin I could see every rib. I could feel its heart beating, its lungs pumping. The poor kitten was so weak it could barely hold up its head, and it was shaking uncontrollably. It opened its mouth, but the sound, which came two seconds later, was weak and ragged.

And cold. That's what I remember most, because I couldn't believe a living animal could be so cold. It felt like there was no warmth at all. So I cradled the kitten in my arms to share my heat. It didn't fight. Instead, it snuggled into my chest, then laid its head against my heart.

"Oh, my golly," said Jean.

"The poor baby," I said, squeezing tighter.

"It's adorable."

Neither of us said anything for a while. We were just staring at the kitten. Finally Jean said, "How do you think it got in there?"

I wasn't thinking about last night. I was only thinking about right now. It was too early to call the veterinarian, who wouldn't be in for an hour. But the kitten was so cold. Even in the warmth of my arms, I could feel it shaking.

"We've got to do something," I said.

Jean grabbed a towel, and we wrapped the little fellow up until only its nose was sticking out, its huge eyes staring from the shadows in disbelief.

"Let's give it a warm bath," I said. "Maybe that will stop the shivering."

I filled the staff room sink with warm water, testing it with my elbow as I clutched the kitten in my arms. It slid into the sink like a block of ice. Jean found some shampoo in the art closet, and I rubbed the kitten slowly and lovingly, almost petting it. As the water turned grayer and grayer, the kitten's wild shivering turned to soft purring. I smiled. This kitten was tough. But it was so very young. When I finally lifted it out of the sink, it looked like a newborn: huge lidded eyes and big ears sticking out from a tiny head and an even smaller body. Wet, defenseless, and meowing quietly for its mother.

We dried it with the blow dryer we used for drying glue at craft time. Within thirty seconds, I was holding a beautiful, long-haired orange tabby. The kitten had been so filthy, I had thought it was gray.

By this time Doris and Kim had arrived, and there were four people in the staff room, each cooing over the kitten. Eight hands touched it, seemingly at once. The other three staffers talked over one another while I stood silently cradling the kitten like a baby and rocking back and forth from foot to foot.

"Where did it come from?"

"The drop box."

"No!"

"Is it a boy or a girl?"

I glanced up. They were all looking at me. "A boy," I said.

"He's beautiful."

"How old is he?"

"How did he get in the box?"

I wasn't listening. I only had eyes for the kitten.

"It's so cold."

"Bitterly cold."

"The coldest morning of the year."

A pause, then: "Someone must have put him in the box."

"That's awful."

"Maybe they were trying to save him. From the cold."

"I don't know . . . he's so helpless."

"He's so young."

"He's so beautiful. Oh, he's breaking my heart."

I put him down on the table. The poor kitten could barely stand. The pads on all four of his paws were frost-bitten, and over the next week they would turn white and peel off. And yet the kitten managed to do something truly amazing. He steadied himself on the table and slowly looked up into each face. Then he began to hobble. As each person reached to pet him, he rubbed his tiny head against her hand and purred. Forget the horrible events in his young life. Forget the cruel person who shoved him down that library drop box. It was as if, from that moment on, he wanted to personally thank every person he ever met for saving his life.

By now it had been twenty minutes since I pulled the kitten out of the drop box, and I'd had plenty of time to think through a few things—the once common practice of keeping library cats, my ongoing plan to make the library more friendly and appealing, the logistics of bowls and food and cat litter, the trusting expression on the kitten's face when he burrowed into my chest and looked up into my eyes. So I was more than prepared when someone finally asked, "What should we do with him?"

"Well," I said, as if the thought had just occurred to me, "maybe we can keep him."

Chapter 2

A Perfect Addition

The most amazing thing about the kitten was how happy he was that first day. Here he was in a new environment, surrounded by eager strangers who wanted nothing more than to squeeze him, fondle him, and coo over him, and he was perfectly calm. No matter how many times we passed him from hand to hand, and no matter what position we held him in, he was never jumpy or fidgety. He never tried to bite or get away. Instead, he just melted into each person's arms and stared up into her eyes.

And that was no small feat, because we didn't leave him alone for a second. If someone had to set him down—for instance, because there was actual work to do—there were always at least five sets of hands ready to grab him, hold him, and love him. In fact, when I set him down at closing time that first night, I had to watch him for five minutes to make sure he could totter all the way to his food dish and litter box. I don't think his poor frostbitten feet had touched the ground all day.

The next morning, Doris Armstrong brought in a warm pink blanket. Doris was the grandparent on staff, our mother hen. We all watched as she bent down and scratched the kitten under the chin, then folded the blanket and put it in a cardboard box. The kitten stepped gingerly into the box and curled his legs underneath his body for warmth. His eyes closed in blissful contentment, but he had only a few seconds to rest before someone snatched him up and wrapped him in her arms. A few seconds, but it was enough. The staff had been polarized for years. Now we were all making accommodations, coming together as a family, and the kitten was clearly happy to call the library home.

It wasn't until late the second morning that we finally shared our little guy with someone outside the staff. That person was Mary Houston, Spencer's local historian and a member of the library board. The staff may already have accepted the kitten, but keeping him wasn't our decision. The previous day I had called the mayor, Squeege Chapman, who was in his last month in office. As I suspected, he didn't care. Squeege wasn't a reader; I'm not even sure he knew Spencer had a library. The city attorney, my second call, didn't know of any statutes barring animals from the library and didn't feel compelled to spend time looking for one. Good enough for me. The library board, a panel of citizens appointed by the mayor to oversee the library, had the final say. They didn't object to the idea of a library cat, but I can't say they were enthusiastic. Their response was more "Let's give it a try" than "Heck, yeah, we're behind you a hundred percent."

That's why meeting a board member like Mary was so important. Agreeing to have an animal in the library was one thing; agreeing on *this* animal was another thing entirely. You can't just put any cute cat in a library. If he's not friendly, he's going to make enemies. If he's too shy or scared, nobody will stand up for him. If he's not patient, he's going to bite. If he's too rambunctious, he's going to make a mess. And above all, he has to love being around people, and he has to make those people love him back. In short, it has to be the right cat.

I had no doubt about our boy. From the moment he looked up into my eyes that first morning, so calm and content, I knew he was right for the library. There wasn't a flutter in his heart as I held him in my arms; there wasn't a moment of panic in his eyes. He trusted me completely. He trusted everyone on staff completely. That's what made him so special: his complete and unabashed trust. And because of it, I trusted him, too.

But that doesn't mean I wasn't a little apprehensive when I motioned Mary into the staff area. As I took the kitten in my arms and turned to face her, I felt a flutter in *my* heart, a moment of doubt. When the kitten had looked into my eyes, something else had happened, too; we had made a connection. He was more than just a cat to me. It had only been a day, but already I couldn't stand the thought of being without him.

"There he is," Mary exclaimed with a smile. I held him a little more tightly as she reached out to pet him on the top of the head, but Dewey didn't even stiffen. Instead, he stretched out his neck to sniff her hand.

"Oh, my," Mary said. "He's handsome."

Handsome. I heard it over and over again the next few days because there was no other way to describe him. This was a handsome cat. His coat was a mix of vibrant orange and white with subtle darker stripes. It grew longer as he got older, but as a kitten it was thick and stylishly long only around his neck. A lot of cats have pointy noses, or their mouths jut out a bit too far, or they're a little lopsided, but this kitten's face was perfectly proportioned. And his eyes, those huge golden eyes.

But it wasn't just his looks that made him beautiful; it was also his personality. If you cared at all about cats, you just had to hold him. There was something in his face, in the way he looked at you, that called out for love.

"He likes to be cradled," I said, gently sliding him into Mary's arms. "No, on his back. That's right. Like a baby."

"A one-pound baby."

"I don't think he even weighs that much."

The kitten shook his tail and nestled down into Mary's arms. He didn't just trust the library staff instinctively, it turned out; he trusted everyone.

"Oh, Vicki," Mary said. "He's adorable. What's his name?"

"We're calling him Dewey. After Melville Dewey. But we haven't really decided on a name yet."

"Hi, Dewey. Do you like the library?" Dewey stared into Mary's face, then pushed his head against her arm. Mary looked up with a smile. "I could hold him all day."

But, of course, she didn't. She put Dewey back into my arms, and I took him around the corner. The entire staff was waiting for us. "That went well," I said. "One down, ten thousand to go."

Slowly we started introducing Dewey to a few regulars known to love cats. He was still weak, so we passed him directly into their arms. Marcie Muckey came in that second day. Instantly smitten. Mike Baehr and his wife, Peg, loved him. "This is a great idea," they said, which was nice to hear since Mike was on the library board. Pat Jones and Judy Johnson thought him adorable. Actually there were four Judy Johnsons in Spencer. Two were regular library users, and both were Dewey fans. How big is a town of 10,000 people? Big enough to have four Judy Johnsons, three furniture stores, two commercial streets with stoplights, but only one mansion. Everyone calls it The Mansion. Typical Iowa—no fuss, no bother, just the facts.

A week later, Dewey's story ran on the front page of the *Spencer Daily Reporter* under the headline "Purr-fect Addition Made to Spencer Library." The article, which took up half the page, told the story of Dewey's miraculous rescue and was accompanied by a color photograph of a tiny orange kitten staring shyly but confidently into the camera from atop an old-fashioned pull-drawer card catalog.

Publicity is a dangerous thing. For a week, Dewey had been a secret between the library staff and a few select patrons. If you didn't come into the library, you didn't know about him. Now everyone in town knew. Most people, even library regulars, didn't give Dewey a second thought. There were two groups, though, that were thrilled by his arrival: the cat lovers and the children. Just the smiles on the faces of the children, their excitement and laughter, were enough to convince me Dewey should stay.

Then there were the complainers. I was a little disappointed, I must admit, but not surprised. There is nothing on God's green earth that someone won't complain about, including both God and green earth.

One woman took particular offense. Her letter, sent to me and every member of the city council, was pure fire and brimstone, full of images of children keeling over from sudden asthma attacks and pregnant mothers spontaneously miscarrying when exposed to kitty litter. According to the letter, I was a murderous madwoman who was not only threatening the health of every innocent child in town, born or unborn, but also destroying the social fabric of the community. An animal! In a library! If we let that stand, what was to stop people from walking a cow down Grand Avenue? In fact, she threatened to show up in the library one morning very soon with her cow in tow. Fortunately nobody took her seriously. I have no doubt she spoke for others in the community, in her overblown way, but general anger wasn't my concern. None of those people, as far as I could tell, ever visited the library.

Far more important to me, though, were the worried phone calls. "My child has allergies. What am I going to do? He loves the library," one woman said. I knew that would be the most common concern, so I was prepared. A year earlier, Muffin, the beloved cat-in-residence at the Putnam Valley Library in upstate New York, had been banished after a library board member developed a severe cat allergy. As a consequence, the library lost $80,000 in promised donations, mostly from the estates of local citizens. I had no intention of letting my cat, or my library, go the way of Muffin.

Spencer didn't have an allergist, so I solicited the advice of two general practice doctors. The Spencer Public Library, they noted, was a large, open space sectioned off by rows of four-foot-high shelves. The staff area, my office, and the supply closets were enclosed by a temporary wall, leaving six feet open to the ceiling. There were two door-size openings in that wall, and since neither had a door, they were always accessible. Even the staff area was an open space, with desks pushed back-to-back or separated by bookshelves.

Not only did this layout allow Dewey easy access to the safety of the staff area at all times, but the doctors assured me it would also prevent the buildup of dander and hair. The library, apparently, was perfectly designed to prevent allergies. If anyone on staff had been allergic it might have been a problem, but a few hours of exposure every couple of days? The doctors agreed there was nothing to worry about.

I spoke personally with each concerned caller and passed on this professional assessment. The parents were skeptical, of course, but most brought their children to the library for a trial run. I held Dewey in my arms for each visit. I not only didn't know how the parents would react, I didn't know how Dewey would react because the children were so excited to see him. Their mothers would tell them to be quiet, be gentle. The children would approach slowly, tentatively, and whisper, "Hi, Dewey," and then explode with squeals as their mothers ushered them away with a quick, "That's enough." Dewey didn't mind the noise; he was the calmest kitten I'd ever seen. He did mind, I think, that these children weren't allowed to pet him.

But a few days later, one family was back, this time with a camera. And this time the allergic little boy, the object of such concern for the mother, was sitting beside Dewey, petting him, while his mother took pictures.

"Justin can't have pets," she told me. "I never knew how much he missed them. He loves Dewey already."

I loved Dewey already, too. We all loved Dewey. How could you resist his charm? He was beautiful, loving, social—and still limping on his tiny frostbitten feet. What I couldn't believe was how much Dewey loved us. How comfortable he seemed around strangers. His attitude seemed to be, how can anyone not love a cat? Or more simply, how can anyone resist me? Dewey didn't think of himself, I soon realized, as just another cat. He always thought of himself, correctly, as one of a kind.

Chapter 3 —◦

Dewey
Readmore
Books

Dewey was a fortunate cat. He not only survived the freezing library drop box, but also fell into the arms of a staff that loved him and a library perfectly designed to care for him. There were no two ways about it, Dewey led a charmed life. But Spencer was also lucky, because Dewey couldn't have fallen into our lives at a better time. That winter wasn't just bitterly cold; it was one of the worst times in Spencer's history.

Those who lived in larger cities may not remember the farm crisis of the 1980s. Maybe you remember Willie Nelson and Farm Aid. Maybe you remember reading about the collapse of family farming, about the nation moving from small growers to large factory farms that stretch for miles without a farmhouse, or even a farm-worker, in sight. For most people, it was just a story, not something that affected them directly.

In Spencer, you could feel it: in the air, in the ground,

in every spoken word. We had a solid manufacturing base, but we were still a farm town. We supported, and were supported by, farmers. And on the farms, things were falling apart. These were families we knew, families that had lived in the area for generations, and we could see the strain. First they stopped coming in for new parts and machinery, making do with bootstrap repairs. Then they cut back on supplies. Finally they stopped making mortgage payments, hoping for a booming harvest to set the account books right. When a miracle didn't come, the banks foreclosed. Almost half the farms in northwest Iowa went into foreclosure in the 1980s. Most of the new owners were giant farming conglomerates, out-of-state speculators, or insurance companies.

The farm crisis wasn't a natural disaster like the Dust Bowl of the 1930s. This was primarily a financial disaster. In 1978, farmland in Clay County was selling for $900 an acre. Then the price of land took off. In 1982, farmland was selling for $2,000 an acre. A year later, it was $4,000 an acre. Farmers borrowed up and bought more land. Why not, when the price was going up forever and you could make more money selling off land every few years than you could farming it?

Then the economy took a downturn. The price of land began to drop and credit dried up. The farmers couldn't borrow against their land to buy new machinery, or even new seed for the planting season. Crop prices weren't high enough to pay the interest on the old loans, many of which had rates of more than 20 percent a year. It took four or five years to reach bottom, years with false bottoms and false hopes, but economic forces were pulling our farmers steadily down.

In 1985, Land O'Lakes, the giant butter and margarine manufacturer, pulled out of the plant on the north edge of town. Soon after, unemployment reached 10 percent, which doesn't sound too bad until you realize that the population of Spencer had fallen from 11,000 to 8,000 in just a few years. The value of houses dropped 25 percent seemingly overnight. People were leaving the county, even the state of Iowa, looking for jobs.

The price of farmland plummeted further, forcing more farmers into foreclosure. But selling the land at auction couldn't cover the loans; the banks were stuck with the loss. These were rural banks, the backbones of small towns. They made loans to local farmers, men and women they knew and trusted. When the farmers couldn't pay, the system collapsed. In towns all across Iowa, banks failed. Banks were failing across the entire Midwest. The savings and loan in Spencer was sold to outsiders for pennies on the dollar, and the new owners didn't want to make new loans. Economic development stalled. As late as 1989, there wasn't a single housing permit issued in the city of Spencer. Not one. Nobody wanted to put money into a dying town.

Every Christmas, Spencer had a Santa Claus. The retailers sponsored a raffle and gave away a trip to Hawaii. In 1979, there wasn't a vacant storefront in town for Santa to set up shop in. In 1985, there were twenty-five empty storefronts downtown, a 30 percent vacancy rate. No trip to Hawaii was offered. Santa barely made it to town. There was a running joke: the last store owner out of downtown Spencer, please turn off the lights.

The library did what it could. When Land O'Lakes skipped town, we set up a job bank that contained all our job listings and books on job skills, job descriptions, and technical training. We set up a computer so local men and women could create résumés and cover letters. This was the first computer most of these people had ever seen. It was almost depressing how many people used the job bank. And if it was depressing for an employed librarian, just think how depressing it was for a laid-off factory worker, bankrupt small business owner, or out-of-work farmhand.

Then into our laps fell Dewey. I don't want to make too much of this one turn of events, because Dewey didn't put food on anyone's table. He didn't create jobs. He didn't turn our economy around. But one of the worst things about bad times is the effect on your mind. Bad times drain you of energy. They occupy your thoughts. They taint everything in your life. Bad news is as poisonous as bad bread. At the very least, Dewey was a distraction.

But he was so much more. Dewey's story resonated with the people of Spencer. We identified with it. Hadn't we all been shoved down the library drop box by the banks? By outside economic forces? By the rest of America, which ate our food but didn't care about the people who grew it?

Here was an alley cat, left for dead in a freezing drop box, terrified, alone, and clinging to life. He made it through that dark night, and that terrible event turned out to be the best thing that ever happened to him. He never lost his trust, no matter what the circumstances, or his appreciation for life. He was humble. Maybe *humble* isn't the right word—he was a cat, after all—but he wasn't arrogant. He was confident. Maybe it was the confidence of the near-death survivor, the serenity you find when you've been to the end, beyond hope, and made it back. All I knew was that, from the moment we found him, Dewey believed everything was going to be fine.

And when he was around, he made others believe that, too. It took him ten days to get healthy enough to explore the library on his own, and once he did it was clear he had no interest in books, shelves, and other inanimate objects. His interest was people. If there was a patron in the library, he'd walk straight up to him—still slow on his sore feet but no longer hobbling—and jump into his lap. More often than not he was pushed away, but rejection never deterred him. Dewey kept jumping, kept looking for laps to lie in and hands to pet him, and things started to change.

I noticed it first with the older patrons, who often came to the library to flip through magazines or browse for books. Once Dewey started spending time with them, they showed up more frequently and stayed longer. A few seemed better dressed, with more care given to their appearance. They had always given the staff a friendly wave or good morning, but now they engaged us in conversation, and that conversation was usually about Dewey. They couldn't get enough Dewey stories. They weren't just killing time now; they were visiting friends.

One older man in particular came in at the same time every morning, sat in the same big, comfortable chair, and read the newspaper. His wife had recently died, and I knew he was lonely. I didn't expect him to be a cat person, but from the first moment Dewey climbed into his lap the man was beaming. Suddenly he wasn't reading the newspaper alone. "Are you happy here, Dewey?"

the man would ask every morning as he petted his new friend. Dewey would shut his eyes and, more often than not, drop off to sleep.

And then there was the man at the job bank. I didn't know him personally, but I knew his type—proud, hard-working, resilient—and I knew he was suffering. He was from Spencer like most of the men who used the job bank, a laborer not a farmer. His job-hunting outfit, like his former work outfit, was jeans and a standard-issue shirt, and he never used the computer. He studied the résumé books; he looked through our job listings; he never asked for help. He was quiet, steady, unflappable, but as the weeks passed I could see the strain in the hunch of his back and the deepening lines on his always clean-shaven face. Every morning, Dewey approached him, but the man always pushed him away. Then one day I saw Dewey sitting on his lap, and for the first time in weeks the man was smiling. He was still bent, and there was still sadness in his eyes, but he was smiling. Maybe Dewey couldn't give much, but in the winter of 1988 he gave exactly what Spencer needed.

So I gave our kitten to the community. The staff understood. He wasn't our cat, not really. He belonged to the patrons of the Spencer Public Library. I put a box by the front door, right next to the job bank, and told people, "You know the cat who sits on your lap and helps with your résumé? The one who reads the newspaper with you? Who steals the lipstick out of your purse and helps you find the fiction section? Well, he's your cat, and I want you to help name him."

I had been library director for only six months, so I was still enthusiastic about contests. Every few weeks we put a box in the lobby, made an announcement on the local radio station, offered a prize for the winning entry, and tried to stoke interest in the latest bit of library news. A good contest with a good prize might draw fifty entries. If the prize was expensive, like a television set, we might scrape up seventy. Usually we got about twenty-five. Our Name the Kitty contest, which wasn't mentioned on the radio because I wanted only regular patrons to participate, and which didn't even offer a prize, received three hundred ninety-seven entries. Three hundred ninety-seven entries! That's when I realized the library had stumbled onto something important. Community interest in Dewey was off all our charts.

Lasagna-loving Garfield was at the height of his popularity, so Garfield was a popular choice. There were nine votes for Tiger. Tigger was almost as popular. Morris was another multiple vote-getter, after the Nine Lives spokescat. Even cultural blips like ALF (a cuddly alien puppet with his own television show) and Spuds (after Spuds MacKenzie, the hard-drinking party dog of beer commercial fame) received votes. There were a few mean-spirited entries, like Fleabag, and some that tripped over the thin line between clever and weird, like Catgang Amadeus Taffy (a sudden sweet tooth?), Ladybooks (an odd name for a male cat), Hopsnopper, Boxcar, and Nukster.

By far the most entries, more than fifty, were for Dewey. Apparently the patrons had already grown attached to this kitten, and they didn't want him to change. Not even his name. And to be honest, the staff didn't, either. We, too, had grown attached to Dewey just the way he was.

Still, the name needed something. Our best option, we decided, was to think of a last name. Mary Walk, our children's librarian, suggested Readmore. A commercial running during the Saturday morning cartoons—this was back when cartoons were only for children and shown only before noon on Saturdays—featured a cartoon cat named O. G. Readmore who encouraged kids to "read a book and take a look at the TV in your head." I'm sure that's where the name came from. Dewey Readmore. Close, but not quite. I suggested the last name Books.

Dewey Readmore Books. One name for the librarians, who live by the Dewey decimal system. One for the children. One for everyone.

Do We Read More Books? A challenge. A name to put us all in the mood to learn. The whole town was going to be well-read and well-informed in no time.

Dewey Readmore Books. Three names for our regal, confident, beautiful cat. I'm sure we'd have named him Sir Dewey Readmore Books if we had thought of it, but we were not only librarians, we were from Iowa. We didn't stand on pomp and circumstance. And neither did Dewey. He always went by his first name or, occasionally, just "the Dew."

Chapter 4 ⌁

A Day
in the
Library

C ats are creatures of habit, and it didn't take long for Dewey to develop a routine. When I arrived at the library every morning, he was waiting for me at the front door. He would take a few bites of his food while I hung up my jacket and bag, and then we would walk the library together, making sure everything was in place and discussing our evenings. Dewey was more a sniffer than a talker, but I didn't mind. The library, once so cold and dead first thing in the morning, was alive and well.

After our walk, Dewey would visit the staff. If someone was having a bad morning, he'd spend extra time with her. Jean Hollis Clark had recently married and commuted forty-five minutes from Estherville to the library. You'd think that would frazzle her, but Jean was the calmest person you've ever met. The only thing that bothered her was the friction between a couple people on staff.

She'd still be carrying the tension when she arrived the next morning, and Dewey was always there to comfort her. He had an amazing sense of who needed him, and he was always willing to give his time. But never for too long. At two minutes to nine, Dewey would drop whatever he was doing and race for the front door.

A patron was always waiting outside at nine o'clock when we opened the doors, and she would usually enter with a warm, "Hi, Dewey. How are you this morning?"

Welcome, welcome, I imagined him saying from his post to the left of the door. *Why don't you pet the cat?*

No response. The early birds were usually there for a reason, which meant they didn't have time to stop and chat with a cat.

No petting? Fine. There's always another person where you came from — wherever that is.

It wouldn't take long for him to find a lap, and since he'd been up for two hours that usually meant it was time for a quick nap. Dewey was already so comfortable in the library he had no problem falling asleep in public places. He preferred laps, of course, but if they weren't available he would curl up in a box. The cards for the catalog came in small boxes about the size of a pair of baby shoes. Dewey liked to cram all four feet inside, sit down, and let his sides ooze over the edge. If the box was a little bigger, he buried his head and tail in the bottom. The only thing you could see was a big blob of back fur sticking out of the top. He looked like a muffin. One morning I found Dewey sleeping beside a box full of cards with one paw resting inside. It probably took him hours to reluctantly admit there wasn't room for anything else.

Soon after, I watched him slowly wind his way into a half-empty tissue box. He put his two front feet through the slit on top, then delicately stepped in with the other two. Slowly he sat down on his hind legs and rolled his back end until it was wedged into the box. Then he started bending his front legs and working the front of his body into the crease. The operation took four or five minutes, but finally there was nothing left but his head sticking out in one direction and his tail sticking out in the other. I watched as he stared half-lidded into the distance, pretending the rest of the world didn't exist.

In those days, Iowa provided envelopes with its tax forms, and we always put a box of them out for patrons. Dewey must have spent half his first winter curled up in that box. "I need one envelope," a patron would say nervously, "but I don't want to disturb Dewey. What should I do?"

"Don't worry. He's asleep."

"But won't it wake him up? He's lying on top of them."

"Oh, no, Dew's dead to the world."

The patron gently rolled Dewey to the side and then, far more carefully than necessary, slid out an envelope. He could have jerked it like a magician pulling a tablecloth from under a dinner setting, it wouldn't have mattered.

"Cat hair comes with the envelope, no charge."

Dewey's other favorite resting spot was the back of the copier. "Don't worry," I told the confused patrons, "you can't disturb him. He sleeps there because it's warm. The more copies you make, the more heat the machine produces, the happier he'll be."

If the patrons weren't quite sure what to do with Dewey yet, the staff had no such hesitation. One of my first decisions was that no library funds, not one penny, would ever be spent on Dewey's care. Instead, we kept a Dewey Box in the back room. Everyone on staff tossed in their loose change. Most of us also brought in soda cans from home. Recycling soda cans was all the rage, and one of the clerks, Cynthia Behrends, would take the cans to a drop-off point every week. The whole staff was "feeding the kitty" to feed the kitty.

In return for these small contributions, we'd get endless hours of pleasure. Dewey loved drawers, and he developed a habit of popping out of them when you least expected. If you were shelving books, he'd jump onto the cart and demand a trip around the library. And when Kim Peterson, the library secretary, started typing, you knew a show was about to begin. As soon as I heard those keys, I'd put down my work and wait for the signal.

"Dewey's after the clacker thingies again!" Kim would call out.

I'd hurry out of my office to find Dewey hunched on the back edge of Kim's big white typewriter. His head would be jerking from side to side as the disk moved left to right, then back again, until finally he couldn't take it anymore and lunged at the clacker thing-ies, which were nothing more than the keys rising up to strike the paper. The whole staff would be there, watching and laughing. Dewey's antics always drew a crowd.

This was important. Everyone at the library was well-intentioned, but over the years the staff had become splintered and cliquish. Only Doris Armstrong, who was older and possibly wiser than the rest of us, had managed to stay friends with everyone. She had a large desk in the middle of the staff area where she covered each new book with a plastic protective sleeve, and her humor and good cheer held us together. She was also our biggest cat lover, and soon her desk was one of Dewey's favorite spots. He would sprawl there in the late morning, batting at her big sheets of plastic, the new center of attention and the mutual friend of everyone on staff. Here, finally, was something we could share. Just as important, he was a friend to all our children (or in Doris's case, grandchildren), too. Nothing concrete happened—no one apologized or discussed their issues, for instance—but once Dewey arrived the tension began to lift. We were laughing; we were happier; Dewey had brought us together.

But no matter how much fun Dewey was having, he never forgot his routine. At exactly ten thirty, he would hop up and head for the staff room. Jean Hollis Clark ate yogurt on her break, and if he hung around long enough she'd let him lick the lid. Jean was quiet and hardworking, but she always found ways to accommodate Dewey. If Dewey wanted downtime, he would lie limply over Jean's left shoulder—and only her left shoulder, never her right—while she filed papers. After a few months, Dewey wouldn't let us hold him cradled in our arms anymore (too much like a baby, I suppose) so the whole staff adopted Jean's over the shoulder technique. We called it the Dewey Carry.

Dewey helped me with downtime, too, which was nice since I had a tendency to work too hard. Many days I'd be hunched over my desk for hours, so intent on budget numbers or progress reports that I wouldn't even realize Dewey was there until he sprang into my lap.

"How you doing, baby boy?" I'd say with a smile. "So nice to see you." I'd pet him a few times before turning back to my work. Unsatisfied, he'd climb on my desk and start sniffing. "Oh, you just happened to sit on the paper I'm working on, didn't you? Purely a coincidence."

I put him on the floor. He hopped back up. "Not now, Dewey. I'm busy." I put him back down. He hopped back up. Maybe if I ignored him.

He pushed his head against my pencil. I pushed him aside. *Fine*, he thought, *I'll knock these pens to the ground.* Which he proceeded to do, one pen at a time, watching each one fall. I couldn't help but laugh.

"Okay, Dewey, you win." I wadded up a piece of paper and threw it to him. He ran after it, sniffed it, then came back. Typical cat. Always one to play, never one to fetch. I walked over, picked up the paper, tossed it a few more times. "What am I going to do with you?"

But it wasn't all jokes and games. I was the boss, and I had responsibilities—like giving the cat a bath. The first time I bathed Dewey, I was confident things would go well. He loved the bath that first morning, right? This time, Dewey slid into the sink like a block of ice dropped . . . into a vat of acid. He thrashed. He screamed. He put his feet on the edge of the sink and tried to throw his body over the side. I held him down with both arms. Twenty minutes later, I was covered with water. My hair looked like I had stuck my tongue in a light socket. Everybody laughed, including, eventually, me.

The third bath was just as bad. I managed to get

Dewey scrubbed, but I didn't have the patience for toweling and blow-drying. Not this crazy kitten.

"Fine," I told him. "If you hate it that much, just go."

Dewey was a vain cat. He would spend an hour washing his face until he got it just right. The funniest part was the way he would ball up his fist, lick it, and shove it into his ears. He would work those ears until they were sparkling white. Now, soaking wet, he looked like a Chihuahua crushed by a wave of toupees. It was pathetic. The staff was laughing and taking pictures, but Dewey looked so genuinely upset that after a few minutes the pictures stopped.

"Have a sense of humor, Dew," I teased him. "You brought this on yourself." He curled up behind a shelf of books and didn't come out for hours. After that, Dewey and I agreed that two baths a year were plenty.

"The bath is nothing," I told Dewey a few months into his stay at the library, wrapping him up in his green towel. "You're not going to like this at all." Dewey never rode in a cage; it was too much like that night in the box. Whenever I took him out of the library, I just wrapped him up in his green towel.

Five minutes later, we arrived at Dr. Esterly's office at the other end of town. There were several veterinarians in Spencer—after all, we lived in an area prone to breech-birth cows, distressed hogs, and sick farm dogs—but I preferred Dr. Esterly. He was a quiet, self-effacing man with an extremely deliberate way of speaking. His voice was deep and slow like a lazy river. He didn't rush. He was always tidy. He was a big man but his hands were gentle. He was conscientious and efficient. He knew his job. He loved animals. His authority came from his lack of words, not his use of them.

"Hi, Dewey," he said, checking him over.

"Do you think this is absolutely necessary, Doctor?"

"Cats need to be neutered."

I looked down at Dewey's tiny paws, which had finally healed. There were tuffs of fur sticking out from between his toes. "Do you think he's part Persian?"

Dr. Esterley looked at Dewey. His regal bearing. The glorious ruff of long orange fur around his neck. He was a lion in alley cat clothing.

"No. He's just a good-looking alley cat."

I didn't believe it for a second.

"Dewey is a product of survival of the fittest," Dr. Esterly continued. "His ancestors have probably lived in that alley for generations."

"So he's one of us."

Dr. Esterly smiled. "I suppose so." He picked Dewey up and held him under his arm. Dewey was relaxed and purring. The last thing Dr. Esterly said before they disappeared around the corner was, "Dewey is one fine cat."

He sure was. And I missed him already.

When I picked Dewey up the next morning, my heart almost broke in two. He had a faraway look in his eyes, and a little shaved belly. I took him in my arms. He pushed his head against my arm and started purring. He was so happy to see his old pal Vicki.

Back at the library, the staff dropped everything. "Poor baby. Poor baby." I gave him over to their care— he was our mutual friend, after all—and went back to work. One more set of hands and he might be crushed. Besides, the trip to the vet's office had put me behind, and I had a mountain of work. I needed two of me to do this job right, but the city would never have paid for it, so I was stuck with myself.

But I wasn't alone. An hour later, as I was hanging up the phone, I looked up to see Dewey hobbling through my office door. I knew he'd been getting love and attention from the rest of the staff, but I could tell from his determined wobbling that he needed something more.

Sure, cats can be fun, but my relationship with Dewey was already far more complex and intimate. He was so intelligent. He was so playful. He treated people so well. I didn't yet have a deep bond with him, but even now, near the beginning, I loved him.

And he loved me back. Not like he loved everyone else, but in a special and deeper way. The look he gave me that first morning meant something. It really did. Never was that more clear than now, as he pushed toward me with such determination. I could almost hear him saying, *Where have you been? I missed you.*

I reached down, scooped him up, and cradled him against my chest. I don't know if I said it out loud or to myself, but it didn't matter. Dewey could already read my moods, if not my mind. "I'm your momma, aren't I?"

Dewey put his head on my shoulder, right up against my neck, and purred.

Chapter 5 ⟶

Catnip and Rubber Bands

D on't get me wrong, everything wasn't perfect with the Dew. Yes, he was a sweet and beautiful cat, and yes, he was extraordinarily trusting and generous, but he was still a kitten. He'd streak maniacally through the staff room. He'd knock your work to the floor out of pure playfulness. He was too immature to know who really needed him, and he sometimes wouldn't take no for an answer when a patron wanted to be left alone. At Story Hour, his presence made the children so rambunctious and unpredictable that Mary Walk, our children's librarian, banned him from the room. Then there was Mark, a large puppet of a child with muscular dystrophy. We used Mark to teach schoolchildren about disabilities. There was so much cat hair on Mark's legs that we finally had to put him in a closet. Dewey worked all night until he figured out how to open that closet and went right back to sleeping on Mark's lap. We bought a lock for the closet the next day.

But nothing compared to his behavior around catnip. Doris Armstrong was always bringing Dewey presents, such as little balls or toy mice. Doris had cats of her own, and like the consummate mother hen she always thought of Dewey when she went to the pet store for their litter and food. One day near the end of Dewey's first summer, she quite innocently brought in a bag of fresh catnip. Dewey was so excited by the smell I thought he was going to climb her leg. For the first time in his life, the cat actually begged.

When Doris finally crumbled a few leaves on the floor, Dewey went crazy. He started smelling them so hard I thought he was going to inhale the floor. After a few sniffs, he started sneezing, but he didn't slow down. Instead, he started chewing the leaves, then alternating back and forth: chewing, sniffing, chewing, sniffing. His muscles started to ripple, a slow cascade of tension flowing out of his bones and down his back. When he finally shook that tension out the end of his tail, he flopped over on the ground and rolled back and forth in the catnip. He rolled until he lost every bone in his body. Unable to walk, he slithered on the floor, undulating as he rubbed his chin along the carpet like a snowplow blade. I mean, the cat oozed. Then, gradually, his spine bent backward, in slow motion, until his head was resting on his behind. He formed figure eights, zigzags, pretzels. I swear the front half of his body wasn't even connected to the back half. When he finally, and accidentally, ended up flat on his tummy, he rippled his way back to the catnip and started rolling in it again. Most of the leaves were by now stuck in his fur, but he kept sniffing and chewing. Finally he stretched out on his back and started kicking his chin with his back legs. This lasted until, with a few flailing kicks hanging feebly in the air, Dewey passed out right on top of the last of the catnip. Doris and I looked at each other in amazement, then burst out laughing. My goodness, it was funny.

Dewey never tired of catnip. He would often sniff halfheartedly at old, worn-out leaves, but if there were fresh leaves in the library, Dewey knew it. And every time he got hold of catnip, it was the same thing: the undulating back, the rolling, the slithering, the bending, the kicking, and finally one very tired, very comatose cat. We called it the Dewey Mambo.

Dewey's other interest—besides puppets, drawers, boxes, copiers, typewriters, and catnip—was rubber bands. Dewey was absolutely fanatical about rubber bands. He didn't even need to see them; he could smell them across the library. As soon as you put a box of rubber bands on your desk, he was there.

"Here you go, Dewey," I would say as I opened a new bag. "One for you and one for me." He would take his rubber band in his mouth and happily skip away.

I would find it the next morning . . . in his litter box. It looked like a worm poking its head out of a chunk of dirt. I thought, "That can't be good."

Dewey always attended staff meetings, but fortunately he wasn't yet able to understand what we were talking about. A few years down the road that cat and I were able to have long philosophical conversations, but for right now it was easy to wrap up the meeting with a simple reminder. "Don't give Dewey any more rubber bands. I don't care how much he begs. He's been eating them, and I have a feeling rubber isn't the healthiest food for a growing kitten."

The next day, there were more rubber band worms in Dewey's litter. And the next. And the next. At the next staff meeting, I was more direct. "Is anyone giving Dewey rubber bands?"

No. No. No. No. No.

"Then he must be stealing them. From now on, don't leave rubber bands lying out on your desk."

Easier said than done. Much, much easier said than done. You would be amazed how many rubber bands there are in a library. We all put our rubber band holders away, but that didn't even dent the problem. Rubber bands apparently are sneaky critters. They slide under computer keyboards and crawl into your pencil holder. They fall under your desk and hide in the wires. One evening I caught Dewey rummaging through a stack of work on someone's desk. There was a rubber band lurking every time he pushed a piece of paper aside.

"Even the hidden ones need to go," I said at the next staff meeting. "Let's clean up those desks and put them away. Remember, Dewey can smell rubber." In a few days, the staff area looked neater than it had in years.

So Dewey started raiding the rubber bands left out on the circulation desk for patrons. We stashed them in a drawer. He found the rubber bands by the copier, too. The patrons were just going to have to ask for rubber bands. A small price to pay, I thought, in exchange for a cat who spent most of his day trying to make them happy.

Soon, our counteroperation was showing signs of success. There were still worms in the litter box but not nearly as many. And Dewey was being forced into brazenness. Every time I pulled out a rubber band, he was watching me.

"Getting desperate, are we?"

No, no, just seeing what's going on.

As soon as I put the rubber band down, Dewey pounced. I pushed him away, and he sat on the desk waiting for his chance. "Not this time, Dewey," I said with a grin. I admit it, this game was fun.

Dewey became more subtle. He waited for you to turn your back, then pounced on the rubber band left innocently lying on your desk. It had been there five minutes. Humans forget. Not cats. Dewey remembered every drawer left open a crack, then came back that night to wiggle his way inside. He never messed up the contents of the drawer. The next morning, the rubber bands were simply gone.

One afternoon I was walking past our big floor-to-ceiling supply cabinet. I was focused on something else, probably budget numbers, and only noticed the open door out of the corner of my eye. "Did I just see . . ."

I turned around and walked back to the cabinet. Sure enough, there was Dewey, sitting on a shelf at eye level, a huge rubber band hanging out of his mouth.

You can't stop the Dew! I'm going to be feasting for a week.

I had to laugh. In general, Dewey was the best-behaved kitten I had ever seen. He never knocked books or displays off shelves. If I told him not to do something, he usually stopped. He was unfailingly kind to stranger and staffer alike. For a kitten, he was downright mellow. But he was absolutely incorrigible when it came to rubber bands. The cat would go anywhere and do anything to sink his teeth into a rubber band.

"Hold on, Dewey," I told him, putting down my pile of work. "I'm going to get a picture of this." By the time I got back with the camera, the cat and his rubber band were gone.

"Make sure all the cabinets and drawers are completely closed," I reminded the staff. Dewey was already notorious. He had a habit of getting closed inside cabinets and drawers and then leaping out at the next person to open them. We weren't sure if it was a game or an accident, but Dewey clearly enjoyed it.

A few mornings later I found file cards sitting suspiciously unbound on the front desk. Dewey had never gone for tight rubber bands before; now, he was biting them off every night. As always, he was delicate even in defiance. He left perfectly neat stacks, not a card out of place. The cards went into the drawers; the drawers were shut tight.

By the fall of 1988, you could spend an entire day in the Spencer Public Library without seeing a rubber band. Oh, they were still there, but they were squirreled away where only those with an opposable thumb could get to them. It was the ultimate cleaning operation. The library looked beautiful, and we were proud of our accomplishment. Except for one problem: Dewey was still chewing rubber bands.

I put together a crack investigative team to follow all leads. It took us two days to find Dewey's last good source: the coffee mug on Mary Walk's desk.

"Mary," I said, flipping a notebook like the police detective in a bad television drama, "we have reason to believe the rubber bands are coming from your mug."

"That's impossible. I've never seen Dewey around my desk."

"Evidence suggests the suspect is intentionally avoiding your desk to throw us off the trail. We believe he only approaches the mug at night."

"What evidence?"

I pointed to several small pieces of chewed rubber band on the floor. "He chews them up and spits them out. He eats them for breakfast. I think you know all the usual clichés."

Mary shuddered at the thought of the garbage on the floor having passed into and out of the stomach of a cat. Still, it seemed so improbable. . . .

"The mug is six inches deep. It's full of paper clips, staples, pen, pencils. How could he possibly pluck out rubber bands without knocking everything over?"

"Where there's a will, there's a way. And this suspect has proven, in his eight months at the library, that he has the will."

"But there are hardly any rubber bands in there! Surely this isn't his only source!"

"How about an experiment? You put the mug in the cabinet, we'll see if he pukes rubber bands near your desk."

"But this mug has my children's pictures on it!"

"Good point. How about we just remove the rubber bands?"

Mary decided to put a lid on the mug. The next morning, the lid was lying on her desk with suspicious teeth marks along one edge. No doubt about it, the mug was the source. The rubber bands went into a drawer. Convenience was sacrificed for the greater good.

We never completely succeeded in wiping out Dewey's rubber band fixation. He'd lose interest, only to go back on the prowl a few months or even a few years later. In the end, it was more a game than a battle, a contest of wits and guile. While we had the wits, Dewey had the guile. And the will. He was far more intent on eating rubber bands than we were on stopping him. And he had that powerful, rubber-sniffing nose.

But let's not make too much of it all. Rubber bands were a hobby. Catnip and boxes were mere distractions. Dewey's true love was people, and there was nothing he wouldn't do for his adoring public. I remember standing at the circulation desk one morning talking with Doris when we noticed a toddler wobbling by. She must have recently learned to walk, because her balance was shaky and her steps uneven. It wasn't helping that her arms were wrapped tightly across her chest, clutching Dewey in a bear hug. His rear and tail were sticking up in her face, and his head was hanging down toward the floor. Doris and I stopped talking and watched in amazement as the little girl toddled in slow motion across the library, a very big smile on her face and a very resigned cat hanging upside down from her arms.

"Amazing," Doris said.

"I should do something about that," I said. But I didn't. I knew that, despite appearances, Dewey was completely in control of the situation. He knew what he was doing and, no matter what happened, he could take care of himself.

We think of a library, or any single building really, as a small place. How can you spend all day, every day, in a 13,000-square-foot room and not get bored? But to

Dewey, the Spencer Public Library was a huge world full of drawers, cabinets, bookshelves, display cases, rubber bands, typewriters, copiers, tables, chairs, backpacks, purses, and a steady stream of hands to pet him, legs to rub him, and mouths to sing his praises. And laps. The library was always graciously, gorgeously full of laps.

By the fall of 1988, Dewey considered all of it his.

Chapter 6 ⟶

Moneta

S ize is a matter of perspective. For an insect, one stalk of corn, or even one ear of corn, can be the whole world. For Dewey, the Spencer Public Library was a labyrinth that kept him endlessly fascinated — at least until he started to wonder what was outside the front door. For most of the people in northwest Iowa, Spencer is the big city. In fact, we are the biggest city for a hundred miles in any direction. People from nine counties funnel into Spencer for entertainment and shopping. We have stores, services, live music, local theater, and, of course, the county fair. What more do you need? If there was a front door leading from Grand Avenue to the rest of the world, most people around here wouldn't have any interest in going through it.

In junior high school, I remember being scared of girls from Spencer, not because I'd ever met any but because they were from the big city. Like most people around here, I grew up on a farm. My great-great-aunt Luna was the first schoolteacher in Clay County. She taught class out of a one-room sod house. There have never been trees out here on the prairie, so the settlers built with what they could find: grass. Roots, soil, and all. My great-grandfather Norman Jipson was the one who amassed enough land to grant a farmstead to each of his six children. No matter where I went as a kid, I was surrounded by my father's family. Most of the Jipsons were staunch Baptists, and they didn't wear pants. All right, the men wore pants. Religiously. The women wore dresses. I never saw a pair of slacks on any woman on my father's side.

In time, my father inherited his land and started the hard work of running a family farm, but first he learned to dance. Dancing was off-limits to most Baptists, but Verlyn "Jipp" Jipson was fifteen years younger than his four siblings, and his parents indulged him. As a young man, Jipp would slip out and drive the truck an hour to the Roof Garden, a 1920s gilded-era resort on the edge of Lake Okoboji, for their Friday-night dances. Okoboji is a mystical name in Iowa. West Okoboji, the centerpiece of a chain of five lakes, is the only blue-water, spring-fed lake in the state, and people come from Nebraska and even Minnesota, a state with a few lakes of its own, to the hotels along its shore. In the late 1940s, the hottest spot in the area, maybe even the whole state of Iowa, was the Roof Garden. Every big-name swing band played the joint, and often the ballroom was so packed you couldn't move. World War II was over, and the party seemed like it would go on forever. Outside, on the boardwalk, there was a roller coaster, a Ferris wheel, and enough lights, sounds, and pretty girls to make you forget that Lake Okoboji was a brilliant blue pinprick in the vast emptiness of the Great American Plains.

And there, in that little circle of light, Jipp Jipson met Marie Mayou. They danced the night away, and just about every other night for the next six months. My father kept the relationship a secret because he knew his family would never approve. The Mayous weren't like the Jipsons. They were full-blooded French by way of Montreal, and they were fiery, passionate people. They loved hard, fought hard, drank hard, and even churched hard, with a no-nonsense midwestern Catholicism that almost scorched the earth.

The Mayous owned the town café in Royal, Iowa, about ten miles from Dad's farm. My mother's father was a wonderful man: gregarious, honest, kind. He was also a full-blown alcoholic. As a child, Mom would leave school to work the lunch rush, then head back to school for a few hours in the afternoon. Often her father would be passed out in one of the booths, so Mom would have to get him off to bed and out of the way of the paying customers.

It wasn't that Marie Mayou's family was notorious. Ten miles was a long way in 1940s Iowa. The problem was that they were Catholic. So Mom and Dad ran away to Minnesota to get married. The wound from the elopement took a few years to heal, but practical always prevails in Iowa. If a deed is done, it's time to move on. Mom and Dad settled down on the family farm and soon had the first three of their six children, two boys (David and Mike) and a girl. I was the middle child.

The family farm. The idea has been romanticized, but for most of the history of the world family farming has been a difficult, poorly paid, backbreaking enterprise. The Jipson farm was no different. We had a cold water hand pump in the kitchen that you physically had to prime. We had a washing machine in the root cellar, but you had to heat the water on the stove upstairs. After the clothes were washed, you cranked them one by one through rollers to wring out the excess water, then hung them outside on the line. We had a shower in the corner of the root cellar. The walls were concrete, but we had tile on the floor. That was our luxury.

Air-conditioning? I didn't know such a thing existed. Mom worked in her kitchen six hours a day over an open flame, even in hundred-degree heat. The kids slept upstairs, and it was so hot on humid summer nights we'd take our pillows downstairs and sleep on the dining room floor. Linoleum was the coolest surface in the house.

Indoor plumbing? Until I was ten years old, we used a one-hole outhouse. When the outhouse became full, you simply dug a new hole and moved the shack. Hard to believe now, looking back, but it's true.

It was the best childhood, the very best. I wouldn't trade it for all the money in Des Moines. Why worry about new toys and clothes? No one we knew had those. We handed down clothes. We handed down toys. There was no television, so we talked to each other. Our big trip was once a year to the municipal swimming pool in Spencer. Every morning we woke up together, and then we worked together.

When I was ten, Mom and Dad had their second set of three children—Steven, Val, and Doug. I raised those children alongside Mom. We were Jipsons. We were there for each other. It's dark on a farm at night, and empty, and lonely, but I knew there was nothing out there in the world that could harm me—not Russians, not rockets, not thieves. I had my family. And if things got really bad, I had the cornfield. I could always run into it and disappear.

We weren't really alone, of course. Each square mile of farmland, bordered on all sides by those perfectly straight Iowa roads, was called a section. In those days, most sections held four family-owned farms. Three and a half of the families in our section were Catholic (we were the half), and there were seventeen children among them, so we had our own baseball game. Even if only four kids showed up, we played baseball. I can't remember thinking about any other game. I was small, but by the time I was twelve, I could hit a baseball across the ditch and into the corn. Every night we huddled around the Jipson family table and gave thanks to God that we'd gone another day without losing our baseball in the corn.

Two miles from our eastern field, at the end of the second section, was the town of Moneta, Iowa. Spencer and Moneta were only twenty miles apart, but they might as well have been different worlds. Some might call that twenty-mile stretch nondescript, but if you drive it in September, when the sky is darkening with blue storm clouds and the crops form patches in every glorious shade of brown, you'd be hard-pressed not to call it beautiful. The highlight is probably the faded wooden billboard outside the town of Everly saluting the 1966 Iowa Girl's Basketball Champions. I remember that team. Everly beat us by a point in the regional finals, which were held in Spencer. I'd tell you about the game, but it's already taken longer to mention the sign than it takes to pass through Everly, which has only five hundred people.

The population of Moneta never reached five hundred, but it topped that number if you included all the farmers, like my family, who thought of themselves as members of that wonderful community. In the 1930s, Moneta was the gambling capital of northwest Iowa. The restaurant on Main Street was a speakeasy, and there was a gambling hall in the back accessible through a secret door. By the time I was a child, those legends were long gone, replaced in our imaginations by the baseball field and the bees. Every community has something the children remember. Come to Spencer in sixty years and the older people will say, "We had a cat. He lived in the library. What was his name? Oh, yes, Dewey. I'll always remember Dewey." In Moneta, it was the bees. A local family had sixty hives, and the honey was famous in four counties, which seemed like the whole world.

The centerpiece of town, though, was the Moneta School, a ten-room, two-story redbrick building just down the road from the baseball field. Almost everyone in town had attended the Moneta School, at least for a few years. There were only eight children in my grade, but what we lacked in size we made up for in amenities. Two local women cooked homemade meals for the whole school every day. Janet and I, the only girls in our class, often got special permission to go over in the morning and frost the cinnamon rolls. If you had a problem, a teacher would walk you to the hidden circle in the grove of trees behind the school where you could talk it out one-on-one. If you wanted to be alone, or with a special someone, you went to the grove, too. That's where I got my first kiss. The Moneta School had a party at the end of every school year with sack races, horse races, and, of course, baseball games. The whole town brought picnics. Everybody participated. In the middle of the summer, when the corn was so high it surrounded the town like a wall, there was the Moneta School reunion, which in the 1950s drew several thousand people. Everyone was proud of that school. Everyone.

Then, in 1959, the state of Iowa shuttered the Moneta School. The town had been on a long population slide, and the state could no longer justify the expense. Moneta had always been a hub for local farmers, but farming was changing. In the early 1950s, the first generation of giant harvesters and combines allowed farmers to plow and harvest larger fields. Some farmers bought new machines, then bought out their neighbors and doubled their production, then used that money to buy out more neighbors. Farm families began to disappear, moving away to local population centers like Spencer, and with them went the farmhouses, the family gardens, and the rows of trees the original settlers had planted to protect the house from the summer sun and the winter wind. These were huge trees, five feet around and a hundred years old. When larger farmers moved in, they bulldozed everything—trees, buildings, everything—piled it up, and burned it to the ground. Why keep a house nobody's living in when you could have a field? The land went back, but not to nature. It went to corn.

The old family farmers raised livestock. They planted gardens. They grew crops in distinct, smaller fields. On the large new farms, there was only corn and its companion crop, soybeans. Every year Iowa grew more corn, but we ate less and less of the crop, at least as kernels and cobs. Most was used as animal feed. Some eventually became ethanol. The rest was separated, broken down, and processed. Have you ever wondered what xanthan gum is? It's processed corn, like almost everything else in that long list of unidentifiable ingredients printed on the packaging of your dinner. Seventy percent of the average American diet—70 percent!—is corn.

But life in farm country isn't easy. A few large farms are worth a fortune, but for most farmers and the people who rely on them—farmhands, salesmen, storage facilities, processing plants, local merchants—the money is tight, the work is hard, and life is often beyond your control. If it doesn't rain; if it doesn't stop raining; if it gets too hot or too cold; if prices don't hold up when your product hits market, there's not much you can do. Farm life isn't forty acres and a mule anymore. Farmers need large combines to plow big fields, and they can cost $500,000 or more. Throw in seed, chemicals, and living expenses, and a farmer's debt can easily top a million. If they stumble, or fall behind the times, or simply have a run of bad luck, most can't make it.

The same is true of the towns in farm country. Towns are, after all, a collection of people. The town relies on the people; the people rely on the town. Like the pollen and the corn silk, they are interdependent. That's why the people of northwest Iowa take such pride in their towns. That's why they invest so much energy in making their towns work. They plant trees; they build parks; they join community organizations. They know if a town is not constantly looking ahead, it can fall behind, and then it can die.

Some people think the grain elevator burning down in the 1930s ruined the town of Moneta. I think it was the closing of the Moneta School. After the Jipson kids started being bused ten miles away to Hartley in 1959, Dad lost interest in struggling against the farm. Our land didn't produce, and Dad couldn't afford big new machinery. He joined a cattle-buying business, then started selling insurance. The Jipsons had been on the farmstead for three generations, but two years after the Moneta School closed Dad sold out to a neighbor and went into insurance full-time. He hated it, hated having to use scare tactics and lowball families in their time of need. He ended up working as a salesman for Crow brand seed. The neighbor who bought our land leveled our farmhouse, chopped down our trees, and turned the entire 160 acres into farmland. He even straightened the creek. I often drive by now without even recognizing it. The first four feet of our dirt driveway is all that remains of my childhood.

Drive fifteen miles west of Spencer today and there's still a sign on the side of the road for Moneta. Turn left. Two miles down the pavement ends, leaving only a dirt track running between the fields. But there isn't a town. There are maybe fifteen houses, at least half of them abandoned. There isn't a single business to be seen. Almost all the buildings on the old downtown strip I remember from my childhood are gone, replaced by a cornfield. You can stand at the former spot of the Moneta general store, where kids would stand transfixed in front of the giant counter full of penny candies and whistles, and watch the cultivators, cone-shaped chutes in front and barrels of fertilizer and poison strapped on the back, crawl across fields like tiny grasshoppers tiptoeing across a vast emptiness. The dance hall remains, and the old speakeasy, but both are shuttered. In a few years, they'll probably be gone, too.

The Moneta School still stands behind, but volunteer trees are growing between the bricks. Most of the windows are broken. Goats lived in the building for a decade, wrecking the floors and biting holes in the walls, and you can still smell them. The only thing left is the reunion. Forty years after the closing of the Moneta School, the annual reunion still drew a thousand people a year back to the field where we used to hold those baseball games and end-of-the-year parties. Now the reunion is down to a hundred or so. The school has been closed fifty years; there aren't that many graduates left. Soon the sign on Highway 18 will be the last thing standing, still pointing two miles down the lonely road to Moneta.

Chapter 7 ⌒

Grand Avenue

The farm crisis of the 1980s was hard, but most of us never truly believed Spencer would go the way of Moneta. We never believed it would give up, blow away, disappear. Throughout its history, after all, the town had proved its resilience. Nothing had ever been handed to Spencer or its citizens. What we'd gotten, we'd earned.

Spencer started as a sham town. In the 1850s, a developer sold numbered lots on a large parcel near a bend in the Little Sioux River. The settlers expected a prosperous town in a fertile river valley, but they never found it. There was nothing but a lazy river and a single cabin—four miles away. The only place a town existed was on paper.

The homesteaders decided to stay. Instead of coming to an established town, they scratched a community out of the dirt. Spencer incorporated in 1871 and immediately petitioned the government for a railroad depot, which it wouldn't get for almost fifty years. Later that year, it wrested the seat of Clay County away from Petersen, a larger town thirty miles to the south. Spencer was a blue-collar town. It didn't have pretensions, but it knew that out here on the Plains, you have to keep moving, modernizing, and growing.

In June 1873, the grasshoppers arrived, devouring the crops down to the stalks before moving on to the harvested grain. In May 1874, the grasshoppers returned. They came again in July 1876, just as the wheat was ripening and the corn coming into tassel and silk. As described in *The Spencer Centennial*, an account of the community written for our hundredth anniversary, "the grasshoppers ate the heads off the grain and settled on the corn until they broke it down with their weight. There was complete destruction."

Farmers abandoned the area. Town residents turned their homes and businesses over to their creditors and left the county. Those who remained pulled together and helped one another through a long and hungry winter. In the spring they scraped together enough credit to buy seed for a full planting. The grasshoppers ate their way to the western edge of Clay County, about forty miles away, but they came no farther. The crop of 1877 was the best the area had ever produced. The grasshoppers never returned.

When the first generation of homesteaders became too old to farm, they moved into Spencer. They built small Craftsman bungalows north of the river, mixing with the merchants and hired hands. When the railroad finally arrived, local farmers no longer had to drive a horse and buggy fifty miles to market. Now other farmers drove twenty miles to Spencer. The town celebrated by widening the road from the river to the train depot.

Those eight blocks, christened Grand Avenue, became the main retail corridor for the entire region. There was a savings and loan downtown, a popcorn factory on the north side near the fairgrounds, a concrete block factory, a brick works, and a lumberyard. But Spencer was not an industrial town. There were no large industrial facilities. There were no diamond-studded, twenty-dollar-bill-smoking frontier financiers. There was no row of Victorian mansions. There were the fields, the farmers, and the eight blocks of businesses under our enormous blue Iowa sky.

And then came June 27, 1931.

The temperature was 103 degrees when, at 1:36 p.m., an eight-year-old boy lit a sparkler outside Otto Bjornstad's drugstore at Main and West Fourth Street. Someone screamed, and the startled boy dropped the sparkler into a large display of fireworks. The display exploded and the fire, whipped by a hot wind, spread across the street. Within minutes the blaze was burning down both sides of Grand Avenue, completely beyond the control of Spencer's small fire department. Fourteen surrounding towns sent equipment and men, but water pressure was so low river water had to be pumped into the mains. At the height of the blaze, the pavement on Grand Avenue caught fire. By the end of the day, thirty-six buildings housing seventy-two businesses, well more than half the businesses in town, were destroyed.

I can't imagine what those people were thinking as they looked at the smoke floating out over the fields and the smoldering remains of their beloved town. That afternoon northwest Iowa must have felt like a lonely, isolated place. Out here, towns die. The businesses shutter;

the people move on. Most of the families in Spencer had scratched out a living in the area for three generations. Now, on the cusp of the Great Depression — it had already started on the coasts but wouldn't spread to inland areas like northwest Iowa until the mid-1930s — Spencer's heart was in ashes. The cost, just over $2,000,000 in Depression-era dollars, makes it still the most expensive man-made disaster in the history of Iowa.

How do I know all this? Everyone in Spencer knows it. The fire is our legacy. It defines us. The only thing we don't know is the name of the boy who started the fire. Somebody knows it, of course, but a decision was made to keep the identity secret. The message: we're a town. We're in this together. Let's not point a finger. Let's fix the problem. Around here, we call that progressive. If you ask anyone in Spencer about the town, they'll tell you, "It's progressive." That's our mantra. If you ask what *progressive* means, we'll say, "We have parks. We volunteer. We always look to improve." If you dig deeper, we'll think for a minute and finally say, "Well, there was a fire. . . ."

It's not the fire that defines us; it's what the town did afterward. Two days after the fire, a commission was meeting to make the new downtown as modern and accident-proof as possible, even as stores reopened out of houses and outbuildings. Nobody quit. Nobody said, "Let's just put it back the way it was." Our community leaders had traveled to the large cities of the Midwest, like Chicago and Minneapolis. They had seen the cohesive planning and sleek style of places like Kansas City. Within a month, a master plan was created for a modern Art Deco downtown in the style of the most prosperous cities of the day. Each destroyed building was individually owned, but each was also part of a town. The owners bought into the plan. They understood that they lived, worked, and survived together.

If you visit downtown Spencer today, you might not think Art Deco. Most of the architects were from Des Moines and Sioux City, and they built in a style called Prairie Deco. The buildings are low to the ground. They are mostly brick. A few have Mission-style turrets, like the Alamo. Prairie Deco is a practical style. It's quiet but elegant. It's not flashy. It doesn't show off. It suits us. We like to be modern in Spencer, but we don't like to draw attention to ourselves.

When you come downtown, maybe for a pastry at Carroll's Bakery or shopping at The Hen House, you probably won't notice the low storefronts and long, clean lines. Instead, you'll park along Grand Avenue, stroll under the large flat overhangs and in front of the glass windows. You'll notice the metal streetlights and brick inlay on the sidewalks, the way the stores seem to flow one after the other, and you'll think to yourself, "I like it here. This is a downtown that works."

Our downtown is the legacy of the fire of 1931, but it is also the legacy of the farm crisis of the 1980s. When times are tough, you either pull together or fall apart. That's true of families, towns, even people. In the late 1980s, Spencer once again pulled together. And once again, the transformation occurred from the inside out when the merchants on Grand Avenue, many in stores run by their grandparents in 1931, decided they could make the city better. They hired a business manager for the entire downtown retail corridor; they made infrastructure improvements; they spent heavily on advertising even when there seemed to be no money left in the community to spend.

Slowly the wheels of progress began to turn. A local couple bought and began to restore The Hotel, the largest and most historic building in town. The run-down building had been an eyesore, a drain on our collective energy and goodwill. Now it became a source of pride, a promise of better days to come. Along the commercial section of Grand Avenue, the shopkeepers paid for new windows, better sidewalks, and summer evening entertainment. They clearly believed the best days of Spencer were ahead, and when people came downtown, heard the music, and walked the new sidewalks, they believed it, too. And if that wasn't enough, at the south end of downtown, just around the corner on Third Street, was a clean, welcoming, newly remodeled library.

At least, that was my plan. As soon as I was made director in 1987, I started pressing for money to remodel the library. There was no city manager, and even mayor was a part-time, largely ceremonial position. The city council made all the decisions. So that's where I went, again and again and again.

The Spencer city council was a classic good ole boy network, an extension of the power brokers who met at Sister's Café. Sister's was only twenty feet from the library, but I don't think a single member of that crowd had ever stepped foot in our building. Of course, I never frequented Sister's Café, so the problem cut both ways.

"Money for the library? What's that going to do? We need jobs, not books."

"The library isn't a warehouse," I told the council. "It's a vital community center. We have job placement resources, meeting rooms, computers."

"Computers! How much are we spending on computers?"

That was always the danger. Start asking for money and sooner or later someone was going to say, "What does the library need money for, anyway? You've already got enough books."

I told them, "Newly paved roads are nice, but they don't lift our community's spirits. Not like a warm, friendly, welcoming library. Wouldn't it be great for morale to have a library we're proud of?"

"I got to be honest. I don't see how prettier books make a difference."

After almost a year of being put on the shelf, I was frustrated, but certainly not defeated. Then a funny thing happened: Dewey started to make my argument for me. By the late summer of 1988, there was a noticeable change at the Spencer Public Library. Our visitor numbers were up. People were staying longer. They were leaving happy, and that happiness was being carried to their homes, their schools, and their places of employment. Even better, people were talking.

"I was down at the library," someone would comment while window-shopping on the new, improved Grand Avenue.

"Was Dewey there?"

"Of course."

"Did he sit in your lap? He always sits on my daughter's lap."

"Actually, I was reaching for a book on a high shelf,

not really paying attention, and instead of a book I grabbed a handful of Dewey. I was so startled I dropped a book right on my toe."

"What did Dewey do?"

"He laughed."

"Really?"

"No, but I sure did."

The conversation must have reached Sister's Café, because eventually even the city council started to notice. Slowly their attitude shifted. First they stopped laughing at me. Then they started listening.

"Vicki," the city council finally said, "maybe the library does make a difference. There's a financial crunch right now, as you know, and we don't have any money. But if you have the funds, you have our support." It wasn't much, I admit, but it was the most the library had gotten from the city in a long, long time.

Chapter 8 —◦

A Cat's Best Friends

The whisper the city council heard in the autumn of 1988 wasn't mine. Or at least not mine alone. It was the voice of the people bubbling up, the voices that were usually never heard: those of the older residents, the mothers, the children. Some patrons came to the library for a purpose—to check out a book, to read the newspaper, to find a magazine. Other patrons considered the library a destination. They enjoyed spending time there; they were sustained and strengthened. Every month there were more of these people. Dewey wasn't just a novelty; he was a fixture in the community. People came to the library to see him.

Not that Dewey was an especially fawning animal. He didn't just rush up to each person who came through the door. He made himself available at the front door if people wanted him; if they didn't, they could step around and be on their way. That's the subtle difference between dogs and cats, and especially a cat like Dewey: cats may need you, but they aren't needy.

When regular patrons came in and Dewey wasn't there to greet them, they often walked the library looking for him. First they searched the floor, figuring Dewey was hiding around a corner. Then they checked the top of the bookshelves.

"Oh, how are you, Dewey? I didn't see you there," they would say, reaching up to pet him. Dewey would give them the top of his head to pet, but he wouldn't follow them. The patrons always looked disappointed.

But as soon as they forgot about him, Dewey jumped into their laps. That's when I saw the smiles. It wasn't just that Dewey sat with them for ten or fifteen minutes; it was that he had singled them out for special attention. By the end of his first year, dozens of patrons were telling me, "I know Dewey likes everyone, but I have a special relationship with him."

I smiled and nodded. "That's right, Judy," I thought. "You and everyone else who comes into this library."

Of course, if Judy Johnson (or Marcy Muckey or Pat Jones or any of Dewey's other fans) hung around long enough, she was sure to be disappointed. Many times I had that conversation only to see the smile drop half an hour later when, leaving the library, she happened to notice Dewey sitting on someone else's lap.

"Oh, Dewey," Judy would say. "I thought it was all about me."

She would look at him for a few seconds, but Dewey wouldn't look up. Then she would smile. I knew what

Judy was thinking. "That's just his job. He still loves me best."

Then there were the children. If you wanted to understand the effect Dewey had on Spencer, all you had to do was look at the children. The smiles when they came into the library, the joy as they searched and called for him, the excitement when they found him. Behind them, their mothers were smiling, too.

I knew families were suffering, that for many of these children times were hard. The parents never discussed their problems with me or anyone on staff. They probably didn't discuss them with their closest friends. That's not the way we are around here; we don't talk about our personal circumstances, be they good, bad, or indifferent. But you could tell. One boy wore his old coat from the previous winter. His mother stopped wearing her makeup and, eventually, her jewelry. The boy loved Dewey; he clung to Dewey like a true friend; and his mother never stopped smiling when she saw them together. Then, around October, the boy and his mother stopped coming to the library. The family, I found out, had moved away.

That wasn't the only boy who wore an old coat that fall, and he certainly wasn't the only child who loved Dewey. They all wanted, even craved, his attention, so much so that they learned enough control to spend Story Hour with him. Every Tuesday morning, the murmur of excited children in the Round Room, where Story Hour was held, would be suddenly punctuated by a cry of "Dewey's here!" A mad rush would ensue as every child in the room tried to pet Dewey at the same time.

"If you don't settle down," our children's librarian, Mary Walk, would tell them, "Dewey has to go."

A barely contained hush would fall over the room as the children took their seats, trying their best to contain their excitement. When they were relatively calm, Dewey would begin sliding between them, rubbing against each child and making them all giggle. Soon kids were grabbing at him and whispering, "Sit with me, Dewey. Sit with me."

"Children, don't make me warn you again."

"Yes, Mary." The children always called Mary Walk by her first name. She never got into the habit of Miss Mary.

Dewey, knowing he had pushed the limit, would stop wandering and curl up in the lap of one lucky child. He didn't let a child grab him and hold him in her lap; he *chose* to spend time with her. And every week it was a different child.

Once he had chosen a lap, Dewey usually sat quietly for the whole hour. Unless a movie was being shown. Then he would jump on a table, curl his legs under his body, and watch the screen intently. When the credits rolled he feigned boredom and jumped down. Before the children could ask, "Where's Dewey?" he was gone.

There was only one child Dewey couldn't win over. She was four years old when Dewey arrived, and she came to the library every week with her mother and older brother. Her brother loved Dewey. The girl hung back as far as possible, looking tense and nervous. Her mother eventually confided in me that the girl was afraid of four-legged animals, especially cats and dogs.

What an opportunity! I knew Dewey could do for this girl what he had done for the children with cat allergies, who finally had a cat to spend time with. I suggested exposing her gently to Dewey, first by looking through the window at him and then with supervised meetings.

"This is an ideal job for our gentle, loving Dewey," I told her mother. I was so enthusiastic, I even researched the best books to help the girl overcome her fear.

Her mother didn't want to go that route, so instead of trying to change the girl's feelings about cats, I accommodated her. When the girl came to the door and waved at the clerk on the front desk, we found Dewey and locked him in my office. Dewey hated being locked in my office, especially when patrons were in the library. *You don't have to do this*, I could hear him howling. *I know who she is! I won't go near her!*

I hated to lock him away, and I hated to miss the opportunity for Dewey to make this little girl's life better, but what could I do? "Don't force it, Vicki," I told myself. "It will come."

With that in mind I planned a low-key celebration for Dewey's first birthday: just a cake made out of cat food for Dewey, and a normal one for the patrons. We didn't know exactly when he was born, but Dr. Esterly had estimated he was eight weeks old when we found him, so we counted back to late November and chose the eighteenth. We found Dewey on January 18, so we figured that was his lucky day.

A week before the celebration, we put out a card for signatures. Within days there were more than a hundred. At the next Story Hour, the children colored pictures of birthday cakes. Four days before the party, we strung the pictures on a clothesline behind the circulation desk. Then the newspaper ran a story, and we started receiving birthday cards in the mail. I couldn't believe it, people were sending birthday cards to a cat!

By the time the party rolled around, the kids were jumping up and down with excitement. Another cat would have been frightened, no doubt, but Dewey took it all in with his usual calm. Instead of interacting with the kids, though, he kept his eyes on the prize: his cat-food cake in the shape of a mouse, covered with Jean Hollis Clark's brand of full-fat yogurt (Dewey hated the diet stuff). As the kids smiled and giggled, I looked out at the adults gathered at the back of the crowd, most of them parents. They were smiling as much as the children. Once again I realized how special Dewey was. Not just any cat would have this kind of fan club. And I realized a few other things, too: that Dewey was having an impact; that he had been accepted as part of the community; and that although I spent all day with him I would never know all the relationships he developed and all the people he touched. Dewey didn't play favorites; he loved everyone equally.

But even as I say that, I know it wasn't true. Dewey did have special relationships, and one I'll always remember was with Crystal. For decades the library had hosted a special Story Hour every week for local elementary and middle school special education classes. Before Dewey, the kids were poorly behaved. This was their big outing for the week, and they were excited:

screaming, yelling, jumping up and down. But Dewey changed that. As they got to know him, the children learned that if they were too noisy or erratic, Dewey left. They would do anything to keep Dewey with them; after a few months, they became so calm you couldn't believe it was the same group of kids.

The children couldn't pet very well, since most were physically disabled. Dewey didn't care. As long as the children were somewhat quiet, Dewey spent the hour with them. He walked around the room and rubbed their legs. He jumped in their laps. The children became so fixated on him, they didn't notice anything else. If we had read them the phone book they couldn't have cared less.

Crystal was one of the more disabled members of the group. She was a beautiful girl of about eleven, but she had no speech and very little control of her limbs. She was in a wheelchair, and the wheelchair had a wooden tray on the front. When she came into the library, her head was always down and her eyes were staring at that tray. The teacher took off her coat or opened her jacket, and she didn't move. It was like she wasn't even there.

Dewey noticed Crystal right away, but they didn't form an immediate bond. She didn't seem interested in him, and there were plenty of children who desperately wanted his attention. Then one week Dewey jumped on Crystal's wheelchair tray. Crystal squealed. She had been coming to the library for years, and I didn't even know she could vocalize. That squeal was the first sound I ever heard her make.

Dewey started visiting Crystal every week. Every time he jumped onto her tray, Crystal squealed with delight. It was a loud, high-pitched squeal, but it never scared Dewey. He knew what it meant. He could feel her excitement, or maybe he could see the change in her face. Whenever she saw Dewey, Crystal glowed. Her eyes had always been blank. Now they were on fire.

Soon it wasn't just seeing Dewey on her tray. The moment the teacher pushed her into the library, Crystal was alive. When she saw Dewey, who waited for her at the front door, she immediately started to vocalize. It wasn't her usual high-pitched squeal but a deeper sound. I believed she was calling to Dewey. Dewey must have thought so, too, because as soon as he heard it, he was at her side. Once her wheelchair was parked, he jumped on her tray, and happiness exploded from within her. She started to squeal, and her smile, you couldn't believe how big and bright it was. Crystal had the best smile in the world.

Usually Crystal's teacher picked up her hand and helped her pet Dewey. That touch, the feel of his fur on her skin, always brought on a round of louder and more delighted squeals. I swear, one day she looked up and made eye contact with me. She was overcome with joy, and she wanted to share the moment with someone, with everyone. This from a girl who for years never lifted her eyes from the floor.

One week I picked Dewey off Crystal's tray and put him inside her coat. She didn't even squeal. She just stared down at him in awe. She was so happy. Dewey was so happy. He had a chest to lean on, and it was warm, and he was with somebody he loved. He wouldn't come out of her coat. He stayed in there for twenty minutes, maybe more. The other children checked out books.

Dewey and Crystal sat together in front of the circulation desk. The bus was idling in front of the library, and all the other children were on it, but Dewey and Crystal were still sitting where we had left them, alone together. That smile, that moment, was worth the world.

I can't imagine Crystal's life. I don't know how she felt when she was out in the world, or even what she did. But I know that whenever she was in the Spencer Public Library with Dewey, she was happy. And I think she experienced the kind of complete happiness very few of us ever feel. Dewey knew that. He wanted her to experience that happiness, and he loved her for it. Isn't that a legacy worthy of any cat, or human being?

The list on the opposite page was written on a big orange piece of poster board and hung at the Spencer Public Library circulation desk for Dewey's first birthday, November 18, 1988.

DEWEY'S LIKES AND DISLIKES

Category	Loves	Hates
Food	Purina Special Dinners, Dairy Flavor!	Anything else
Place to sleep	Any box or someone's lap	Alone or in his own basket
Toy	Anything with catnip	Toys that don't move
Time of day	8 a.m. when the staff arrives	When everybody leaves
Body position	Stretched out on his back	Standing up for very long
Temperature	Warm, warm, warm	Cold, cold, cold
Hiding place	Between the Westerns on the bottom shelf	The lobby
Activity	Making new friends, watching the copier	Going to the vet
Petting	On the head, behind his ears	Scratched or touched on stomach
Equipment	Kim's typewriter, the copier	Vacuum cleaner
Animal	Himself!	
Grooming	Cleaning his ears	Being brushed or combed
Medicine	Felaxin (for hair balls)	Anything else
Game	Hide-and-seek, push the pen on the floor	Wrestling
People	Almost everyone	People who are mean to him
Noise	A snack being opened, paper rustling	Loud trucks, construction, dogs barking
Book	The Cat Who Would Be King	101 Uses for a Dead Cat

Chapter 9 ⟋

Dewey
and Jodi

The relationship between Dewey and Crystal is important not just because it changed her life but because it illustrates something about Dewey. It shows his effect on people. His love. His understanding. The extent to which he cared. Take this one person, I'm saying every time I tell that story, multiply it by a thousand, and you'll begin to see how much Dewey meant to the town of Spencer. It wasn't everybody, but it was another person every day, one heart at a time. And one of those people, one very close to my own heart, was my daughter, Jodi.

I was a single mother, so when she was young Jodi and I were inseparable. We walked our cockapoo Brandy. We went window-shopping at the mall. We had sleepovers in the living room, just the two of us. Whenever a movie came on television we wanted to see, we had a picnic on the floor. *The Wizard of Oz*—over the rainbow where everything is in color and you have the power to do what you've always wanted and that power has always been with you if only you knew how to tap into it—came on once a year, and it was our favorite. When Jodi was nine, we went every afternoon, weather permitting, to hike in a nearby wilderness area. At least once a week, we hiked all the way to the top of a lime-stone cliff, where we sat and looked down on the river, a mother and her daughter, talking together.

We lived in Mankato, Minnesota, but we spent a lot of time at my parents' house in Hartley, Iowa. For two hours, as the cornfields of Minnesota turned into the cornfields of Iowa, we sang along to the old eight-track, mostly corny 1970s songs by John Denver and Barry Manilow. And we always played a special game. I would say, "Who's the biggest man you know?"

Jodi would answer, and then ask me, "Who's the strongest woman you know?"

I would answer and ask, "Who's the funniest woman you know?"

We asked questions back and forth until eventually I could think of only one more question, the one I had been waiting to ask. "Who's the smartest woman you know?"

Jodi always answered, "You, Mommy." She had no idea how much I looked forward to hearing that.

Then Jodi turned ten. At ten, Jodi stopped answering the question. This behavior was typical of a girl that age, but I couldn't help being disappointed.

At thirteen, after we had moved to Spencer, she stopped letting me kiss her good night. "I'm too old for that, Mommy," she said one night.

"I know," I told her. "You're a big girl now." But it broke my heart.

I remember walking out into the living room of our two-bedroom, 1,200-square-foot bungalow, which was only a mile from the library. Of course, half of Spencer was only a mile from the library. I looked out the window at the quiet, square houses on their nice square lawns. As in the rest of Iowa, most of the roads in Spencer were perfectly straight. Why wasn't life like that?

Brandy tottered up and nuzzled my hand. Brandy had been with me since I was pregnant with Jodi, and the dog was clearly feeling her age. She was lethargic, and for the first time in her life she was having accidents on the floor. Poor Brandy. Not you, too. I held out as long as I could, but eventually I took her to see Dr. Esterly, who diagnosed an advanced stage of kidney failure.

"She's fourteen years old. It's not unexpected."

"What should we do?"

"I can treat it, Vicki, but there's no hope for recovery."

I looked down at the poor, tired dog. She had always been there for me; she had given me everything. I took her head in my hands and scratched behind her ears. "I can't afford much, girl, but I'll do what I can."

Several weeks of pills later, I was sitting in my living room with Brandy on my lap when I felt something warm. Then I realized it was wet. Brandy was peeing all over me. I could tell she was not just embarrassed; she was in pain.

"It's time," Dr. Esterly said.

I didn't tell Jodi, at least not everything. Partly to

protect her. Partly because I didn't want to acknowledge it myself. I felt as if Brandy had been with me my whole life. I loved her; I needed her. I couldn't bring myself to put her down.

I called my sister, Val, and told her husband, Don, "Please come by the house and pick her up. Don't tell me when, just do it."

A few days later I came home for lunch and Brandy wasn't there. I knew what that meant. She was gone. I called Val and asked her to pick Jodi up from school and take her to dinner. I needed time to compose myself. At dinner Jodi could tell something was wrong. Eventually Val broke down and told her Brandy had been put to sleep.

I had done so many things wrong by this point. I had tried to treat Brandy's pain. I had left her to die with my brother-in-law. I hadn't been completely honest with Jodi. And I had allowed my sister to tell my daughter about the death of the dog she loved. But my biggest mistake was what I did when Jodi came home. I didn't cry. I didn't show any emotion. I told myself that I needed to be strong for her. I didn't want her to see how much I hurt. When Jodi went to school the next day, I broke down. I cried so hard I made myself sick. I was so distraught I couldn't even drive to work until the afternoon. But Jodi didn't see that. To her thirteen-year-old mind, I was the woman who killed her dog and didn't even care.

Brandy's death wasn't a turning point in our relationship. It was more a symptom of the gulf developing between us. Jodi wasn't a little child anymore, but part of me still treated her like one. She also wasn't an adult, but part of her thought she was all grown up and didn't need me any longer. Even as I realized, for the first time, the distance between us, Brandy's death pushed us further apart.

By the time Dewey arrived, Jodi was sixteen, and like many mothers of girls that age I felt we were living separate lives. Much of that was my fault. I was working very hard planning the library remodeling I had finally pushed through the city council, and I didn't have much time to spend at home. But it was her fault, too. Jodi spent most of her time out with friends or locked in her room. Most of the week, we interacted only at dinner. Even then we rarely had much to talk about.

Until Dewey. With Dewey, I had something to talk about that Jodi wanted to hear. I'd tell her what he did; who came to see him; whom he played with; what local newspaper or radio station called for an interview. A few staff members alternated feeding Dewey on Sunday morning. Although I was never able to get Jodi out of bed for those Sunday-morning visits, we'd often drop by the library Sunday night on our way back from dinner at Mom and Dad's house.

You wouldn't believe Dewey's excitement when Jodi walked in that library door. The cat pranced. He would literally do flips off bookshelves just to impress her. While I was alone in the back room cleaning his litter and refilling his food dish, Dewey and Jodi played. She wasn't just another person spending time with him; Dewey was absolutely crazy for Jodi.

I've said Dewey never followed anyone around, that his style was to retain some distance, at least for a while. That wasn't true with Jodi. Dewey followed her like a dog. She was the only person in the world from whom he wanted and needed affection. Even when Jodi came to the library during work hours, Dewey sprinted to her side. He didn't care who saw him; he had no pride around that girl. As soon as she sat down, Dewey was in her lap.

On holidays, when the library was closed for a few days, I brought Dewey home with me. He didn't like the car ride—he always assumed it meant Dr. Esterly, so he spent the first couple minutes in the backseat on the floor—but as soon as he felt me turn off Grand Avenue onto Eleventh Street, he bounced up to stare out the window. As soon as I opened the door, he rushed into my house to give everything a nice long sniff. Then he ran up and down the basement stairs. He lived in a one-floor world at the library, so he couldn't get enough of stairs.

Once he ran his excitement out on the stairs, Dewey would often settle in beside me on the sofa. Just as often, though, he sat on the back of the sofa and stared out the window. He was watching for Jodi. When she came home, he jumped right up and ran to the door. As soon as she walked in, Dewey was like Velcro. He never left Jodi's side. He got between her legs and almost tripped her, he was so excited. When Jodi took her shower, Dewey waited in the bathroom with her, staring at the curtain. If she closed the door, he sat right outside. If the shower stopped and she didn't come out quickly enough, he cried. As soon as she sat down, he was on her lap. It didn't matter if she was at the dinner table or on the toilet. He jumped on her, kneaded her stomach, and purred, purred, purred.

Jodi's room was an absolute mess. When it came to her appearance, the girl was immaculate. Not a hair out of place, not a speck of dirt anywhere. Put it this way: she ironed her socks. So who would believe her room looked like the lair of a troll? Only a teenager could live in a room where you couldn't see the floor or close the closet door, where crusty plates and glasses were buried under dirty clothes for weeks. I refused to clean it up, but I also refused to stop nagging her about it. A typical mother-daughter relationship, I know, but that's only easy to say after the fact. It's never easy when you're going through it.

But everything was easy for Dewey. Dirty room? Nagging mother? What did he care? *That's Jodi in there,* he said to me with one last look as he disappeared behind her door for the night. *What does that other stuff matter?*

Sometimes, just before turning in for the night, Jodi would call me to her room. I'd walk in and find Dewey guarding Jodi's pillow like a pot of gold or lying over the top half of her face. I'd look at him for a second, so desperate for her touch, and then we'd both start laughing. Jodi was silly and funny around her friends, but for all those high school years she was so serious with me. Dewey was the only thing that made our relationship lighthearted and playful. With Dewey around, we laughed together, almost like we had when Jodi was a child.

Jodi and I weren't the only ones Dewey was helping. Spencer Middle School was across the street from the library, and about fifty students were regularly staying with us after school. On the days they blew in like a hurricane, Dewey avoided them, especially the rowdy ones, but usually he was out mingling. He had many friends among the students, both boys and girls. They petted him and played games with him, like rolling pencils off the table and watching his surprise when they disappeared. One girl would wiggle a pen out the end of her coat sleeve. Dewey would chase the pen up the sleeve and then, deciding he liked that warm, dark place, he'd sometimes lie down for a nap.

Most of the kids left just after five when their parents got off work. A few stayed as late as eight. Spencer wasn't immune to problems—alcoholism, neglect, abuse—but our regulars were the children of blue-collar parents. They loved their kids but had to work extra jobs or extra shifts to make ends meet.

These parents, who came in for only a moment, rarely had time to pet Dewey. They worked long days, and they had meals to prepare and houses to clean before falling into bed. But their children spent hours with Dewey; he entertained and loved them. I never realized how much that meant, or how deep those bonds were, until I saw the mother of one of our boys bend down and whisper, "Thank you, Dewey," as she tenderly stroked his head.

I figured she was thanking him for spending time with her son, for filling up what could have been an awkward and lonely time for him.

She stood up and put her arm around her son. Then, as they were walking out the door, I heard her ask him, "How was Dewey today?" Suddenly, I knew exactly how she felt. Dewey had turned a difficult time apart into common ground; he was her road back to so much of what she had left behind. I never considered this boy one of Dewey's close companions—he spent most of his time goofing off with friends or playing games on the computer—but clearly Dewey was having an impact on his life beyond the library walls. And it wasn't just this boy. The more I looked, the more I noticed that the ember that had ignited my relationship with Jodi was felt by other families, too. Like me, parents all over Spencer were spending their one hour a day with their teenagers talking about Dewey.

The staff didn't understand. They saw Jodi and Dewey together and thought I'd be offended that Dewey loved someone more than me. After Jodi left, someone would usually say, "Her voice sounds just like yours. That's why he loves her so much."

But I didn't feel jealous at all. Dewey and I had a complex relationship, one that involved baths, brushings, veterinary visits, and other unpleasant experiences. Dewey's relationship with Jodi was pure and innocent. It was fun and good times, uncomplicated by responsibility. If I wanted to put a Vicki spin on their relationship, I could say Dewey realized how important Jodi was to me, and that made her important to him. I could even stretch to say that maybe, just maybe, Dewey understood the significance of those moments the three of us shared, how much I missed laughing with my daughter, and he was therefore happy to throw himself over the chasm and serve as the bridge between us.

But I don't think that was it at all. Dewey loved Jodi because she was Jodi—warm, friendly, wonderful Jodi. And I loved him for loving my daughter.

Chapter 10

A Long Way from Home

In Hartley, Iowa, where my family moved when I was fourteen, I was a straight arrow, the head student librarian, and the second smartest girl in my grade, after Karen Watts. It was all As for Vicki Jipson, except in typing, where I got a C. But that didn't keep me from having a reputation. One night I went with my parents to a dance in Sanborn, a little town nine miles from Hartley. When the dance hall closed at eleven, we went to the restaurant next door, where I promptly passed out. Dad took me outside for some fresh air, and I threw up. The next morning at eight thirty, my grandfather called the house and said, "What the hell is going on over there? I heard Vicki was drunk in Sanborn last night." The cause turned out to be an abscessed tooth, but there was no beating a bad reputation in a small town like Hartley.

My older brother, meanwhile, was considered one of the smartest kids ever to attend Hartley High School.

Everyone called him the Professor. David graduated a year ahead of me and went to college a hundred miles away in Mankato, Minnesota. I figured I'd follow him there. When I mentioned my plans to my guidance counselor, he said, "You don't need to worry about college. You're just going to get married, have kids, and let a man take care of you." What a jerk. But it was 1966. This was rural Iowa. I didn't get any other advice.

After graduation from high school, I got engaged to the third boy I'd ever dated. We'd been going out for two years, and he adored me. But I needed to get away from the microscope of small-town Iowa; I needed to be out on my own. So I broke off the engagement, which was the hardest thing I'd ever done, and moved to Mankato with my best friend, Sharon.

While David went to college on the other side of town, Sharon and I worked at the Mankato Box Company. Mankato Box packaged products like Jet-Dry, the dishwashing liquid, and Gumby, who was a star at the time. I worked mostly on Punch and Grow, a container of potting soil with seeds attached to the lid. My job was to grab potting soil containers off a conveyor belt, snap on the plastic lid, slide them into a cardboard sleeve, and put them in a box. Sharon and I worked side by side, and we were always singing goofy lyrics about Punch and Grow to the tune of popular songs. We would get the whole line laughing, the Laverne and Shirley of Mankato Box. After three years, I worked my way up to feeding the empty plastic cups into the machine. The job was more isolated, so I didn't get to sing as much, but at least I didn't get filthy from all the potting soil.

Sharon and I developed a routine, which happens with line work. We would get off work exactly at five, ride the bus to our apartment for a quick dinner, then hit the dance clubs. We'd stay out, dancing our toes off, until they shut the dance halls down. If I wasn't dancing, I was usually out with my brother David and his friends. David was more than my brother, he was my best friend, and I can't count the number of times we stayed up talking about our lives. If I stayed home, which was rare, I'd put on a record and dance, all alone in my bedroom. I just had to dance. I loved to dance.

I met Wally Myron at a dance club, but he wasn't like the other guys I'd dated. He was very smart and very well-read, which impressed me immediately. And he had personality. Wally was always smiling, and everyone with him was always smiling, too. He was the kind of person who would go down to the corner store for milk and talk to the clerk for two hours. Wally could talk with anyone about anything. He didn't have a mean bone in his body. I say it to this day: Wally was incapable of intentionally hurting anyone.

We dated for a year and a half before getting married in July 1970. I was twenty-two, and I got pregnant right away. It was a tough pregnancy, with sickness morning, noon, and night. Wally spent evenings after work out with his friends, usually riding motorcycles, but he was always home by seven thirty. He wanted a social wife, but he would take a sick wife if that meant a baby on the way.

Sometimes one decision changes your life, and it doesn't have to be one you make yourself—or even know about. When I went into labor, the doctor decided to speed the process with two massive doses of Pitocin. I found out later he had a party to attend, and he wanted to get this darn procedure over with. I went from three centimeters dilated to crowning in two hours. The shock broke my afterbirth, so they put me back into labor. They didn't get all the pieces. Six weeks later I hemorrhaged, and they rushed me back to the hospital for emergency surgery.

I had always wanted a daughter named Jodi Marie. I had dreamed about it from a young age. Now I had that daughter, Jodi Marie Myron, and I was dying to spend time with her, to hug her and talk to her and look into her eyes. But the surgery knocked me flat on my back. My hormones went haywire, and I was racked with headaches, insomnia, and cold sweats. Two years and six operations later my health hadn't improved, so my doctor suggested exploratory surgery. I woke up in the hospital bed to discover he'd taken both ovaries and my uterus. The physical pain was intense, but worse was the knowledge that I couldn't have any more children. I had expected a peek inside; I wasn't prepared to be hollowed out. And I wasn't prepared to enter sudden and severe menopause. I was twenty-four going on sixty, with scarring through my gut, regret in my heart, and a daughter I couldn't hold. The curtain came down and everything went black.

When I came around a few months later, Wally wasn't there. Not like he used to be, anyway. That's when I noticed, suddenly, that everything meant drinking to Wally. If he went fishing, it meant drinking. If he went hunting, it meant drinking. Even motorcycle riding meant drinking.

Before long, he wasn't showing up when he promised. He would be out late and never call. He'd come home drunk, and I'd say, "What are you doing? You have a sick wife and a two-year-old child!"

"We just went fishing," he'd say. "I had a couple too many. It's no big deal."

I'd wake up the next morning, and he'd be gone to work. I'd find a note on the kitchen table. *I love you. I don't want to fight. I'm sorry.* Wally could never sleep, and he would stay up all night writing me long letters. The man was smart. He could write beautifully. And every morning, when I saw those letters, I loved him.

The realization that your husband is a problem drinker comes suddenly, but the admission takes a long, long time. Your insides tie themselves in knots, but your heart refuses to understand. You make explanations, then excuses. You dread the ringing of the telephone. Then you dread the silence when it doesn't ring. Instead of talking, you throw out the beer. You pretend not to notice things, like money. He always comes through, but only when the cupboard is bare. But you're scared to complain. What are the chances, you think, that it will get worse instead of better?

"I understand," he says when you mention it. "It's not a problem. But I'll quit. For you. I promise." But neither of you believes it.

Day by day, your world gets smaller. You don't want to open cabinets for fear of what you'll find. You don't want to search the pockets of his pants. You don't want to go anywhere. Where's he going to take you that doesn't involve drinking?

Many mornings I found beer bottles in the oven. Jodi found beer cans in her toy box. Wally was waking up early every morning, and if I dared to look out the window, I could see him sitting in his van drinking warm beer. He didn't even bother driving around the corner.

When Jodi was three, we went to Hartley for my brother Mike's wedding. Jodi and I were in the ceremony, so Wally had free time on his hands. He would disappear and not show up until late at night, when everyone was asleep.

"Are you trying to avoid us?" I asked him.

"No, I love your family. You know that."

The family was sitting around Mom's kitchen table one night, and as usual Wally was nowhere to be found. We ran out of beer, so Mom went to the cabinet where she was keeping extra beer for all the friends and relatives in town. Most of it was gone.

"What were you thinking, taking Mom's beer?"

"I don't know. I'm sorry."

"How do you think I feel? How do you think Jodi feels?"

"She doesn't know."

"She's old enough to know. You just don't know her."

Afraid to ask. Afraid not to ask. "Are you even working?"

"Of course I am. You see the paychecks, don't you?"

Wally's father had given him part ownership of the family construction business, which meant Wally didn't get a steady paycheck. I couldn't tell if the company was between projects or if the whole world was crashing down around us.

"It's not just money, Wally."

"I know. I'll spend more time at home."

"Quit drinking for one week."

"Why?"

"Wally."

"Okay, one week. I'll quit."

But again, neither of us believed it.

After Mike's wedding, I finally admitted to myself that Wally had a problem. That he was coming home less and less. That I almost never saw him sober. He wasn't a mean drunk, but he wasn't a functioning drunk, either. And yet he ran our lives. He drove our only car. I had to take the bus or ride with a friend to buy groceries. He cashed the paychecks. He paid the bills. Often I was too sick to follow the finances, much less raise a child on my own. I called our house the Blue Coffin because it was painted a hideous shade of blue and shaped like a casket. It started out as a joke—it was actually a fine house in a nice neighborhood—but within two years it felt like the truth. Jodi and I were stuck in that house, being buried alive.

My family came through for me. They never blamed me. They never lectured me. My parents didn't have money, but they took Jodi in, two weeks at a time, and raised her like their daughter. Whenever life smothered me, they gave me room to breathe.

Then there were my friends. If that delivery room doctor ruined my body, another stranger saved my mind. When Jodi was six months old, a woman knocked on my door. She had a daughter about Jodi's age in a stroller. She said, "I'm Faith Landwer. My husband has been friends with your husband since high school, so let's have coffee and get to know each other."

Thank goodness I agreed.

Faith got me involved in a newcomer's club that played cards once a month. I met Trudy over our regular game of Five Hundred, then met Barb, Pauli, Rita, and Idelle. Soon we were having coffee together at Trudy's house a couple days a week. We were all young mothers, and Trudy's house was the only one big enough to hold us. We would shove the children into her enormous playroom, sit at the kitchen table, and keep one another sane. I confided in them about Wally, and they didn't blink. Trudy just came around the table and gave me a hug.

What did my friends do for me in those years? What didn't they do for me? When I needed to run an errand, they drove me. When I was sick, they cared for me. When I needed someone to watch Jodi, they picked her up. I don't know how many times one of them dropped by with a plate of hot food just when I needed it.

"I just cooked a little extra casserole. Do you want it?"

And yet it wasn't my family or my friends who saved my life. Not really. My real motivation, my real reason for picking myself up every morning and struggling on, was my daughter, Jodi. She needed me to be her mother, to teach by example. We didn't have money, but we had each other. When I was confined to my bed, Jodi and I spent hours talking. When I was physically able, we walked in the park with the real third member of our family. Brandy and Jodi looked up to me; they adored me without question or doubt; they gave me unconditional love, which is the secret power of children and dogs. Every night when I put Jodi to bed, I kissed her, and that touch, that skin on my skin, sustained me.

"I love you, Mom."

"I love you, too. Good night."

A hero of mine, Dr. Charlene Bell, says everyone has a pain thermometer that goes from zero to ten. No one will make a change until they reach ten. Nine won't do it. At nine, you are still afraid. Only ten will move you, and when you're there, you'll know. No one can make that decision for you.

I saw that firsthand with one of my friends. She was pregnant, and her abusive husband was still beating her every day. We decided we had to get her out of there before it was too late, so we talked her into leaving him. We set her up in a trailer with her kids. Her parents came by every day. She had everything she needed. Two weeks later she went back to her husband. I realized then you can't make people do what you know is right. They have to come to it on their own. A year later my friend left her husband for good. She didn't need help from any of us.

I learned that lesson for myself, too, because a marriage unwraps slowly. Maybe it's not the slowness but the consistency that crushes you. Every day is a little bit worse, a little less predictable, until finally you're doing things you never, ever thought you'd do. I was looking for food in the kitchen one night, and I found a checkbook. It was for a secret banking account Wally had set up for himself. I turned on the grill at two in the morning, ripped out the checks one by one, and burned them.

Halfway through I thought, "Sane people don't live like this."

But I stayed. I was worn out. I was emotionally drained. My confidence was crippled. I was physically weak from the surgeries. And I was scared. But not scared enough to make a change.

The last year was the worst. It was so bad, I can't even remember the details. The whole year was black. Wally had stopped coming home before three in the morning, and since we were sleeping in different rooms, I never saw him. He left the house early every morning, but I didn't know where he went. He had been pushed out of the family business, and our money situation was drifting from bad to unbearable. Mom and Dad sent me what they could. Then they went to the rest of the family and collected several hundred dollars more. When that ran out, Jodi and I had nothing to eat. We lived on oatmeal, nothing but oatmeal, for two weeks. I finally went to Wally's mother, who I knew blamed me for her son's condition.

"Don't do it for me," I said. "Do it for your granddaughter." She bought one bag of groceries, set it on the kitchen table, and left.

A few nights later Wally came home. Jodi was asleep. I was in the living room reading *One Day at a Time*, the bible of Al-Anon, a support group for people affected by alcoholics. I didn't yell or hit him or anything like that. We both acted as if Wally came home all the time. I hadn't seen him in a year, and I was surprised how bad he looked. He was thin. He was sickly. He clearly wasn't eating. I could smell alcohol, and he still had the shakes. He sat down on the other side of the room without a word, this man who used to talk for hours to anyone, and watched me read. Eventually he dozed off, so it surprised me when he said, "What are you smiling about?"

"Nothing," I told him, but when he asked I knew. I had reached ten. No fireworks. No final injustice. The moment had slipped in as quiet as a stranger coming home.

I went to a lawyer the next day and started divorce proceedings. That's when I discovered we were six months behind on house payments, six months behind on car payments, and $6,000 in debt. Wally had even taken out a home-improvement loan, but of course no work had been done. The Blue Coffin was falling apart.

Grandma Stephenson—Mom's mother, who had divorced her own alcoholic husband—gave me the money to save the house. We let the bank repossess the car. It wasn't worth saving. My dad passed the hat in Hartley and came up with $800 to buy me a 1962 Chevy an old lady didn't even drive in the rain. I had never driven a car in my life. I took driving lessons for a month and passed my driver's test. I was twenty-eight years old.

The first place I drove that car was to the welfare office. I had a six-year-old daughter, a high school diploma, a medical history that can only be called a disaster, and a pile of debt. I didn't have a choice. I told them, "I need help, but I'm only going to take it if you let me go to college."

Thank goodness, welfare was different in those days. They agreed. I went straight to Mankato State and registered for the upcoming semester. Four years later, in 1981, I graduated summa cum laude, the highest level of honors, with a general studies degree, double majors in psychology and women's studies, and minors in anthropology and library science. Welfare paid for the whole thing: classes, housing, living expenses. My brothers David and Mike had dropped out without graduating, and so, at the age of thirty-two, I became the first Jipson to earn a diploma from a four-year college. Twelve years later Jodi would become the second.

Chapter 11

Hide-and-Seek

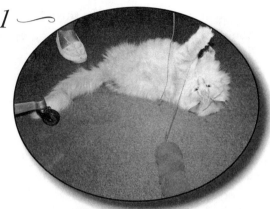

After graduation I found out it takes more than a college degree to become a psychologist. To make ends meet, I took a job as a secretary for my friend Trudy's husband, Brian. After a week, I told him, "Don't waste any more money training me. I'm not going to stay." I hated filing. I hated typing. After thirty-two years, I was tired of taking orders. For most of my adult life I had tried to be the person my guidance counselor predicted I'd be way back at Hartley High School. I had followed the path set out for me and just about every other woman of my generation. I didn't want to do that anymore.

My sister, Val, who lived in Spencer, mentioned an opening at the local library. At that moment I had no intention of returning home. Despite my minor in library science, I had never really considered working in a library. But I took the interview, and I loved the people.

A week later, I was on my way back to northwest Iowa, the new assistant director of the Spencer Public Library.

I wasn't expecting to love the job. Like most people, I thought being a librarian meant stamping due dates in the back of books. But it was so much more. Within months, I was neck-deep in marketing campaigns and graphic design. I started a homebound program, which took books to people unable to visit the library, and developed a major initiative to interest teens in reading. I developed programs for nursing homes and schools; I started answering questions on the radio and speaking to social clubs and community organizations. I was a big-picture person, and I was beginning to see the difference a strong library made in a community. Then I got involved in the business side of running a library — the budgeting and long-range planning — and I was hooked. This was a job, I realized, I could love for the rest of my life.

In 1987, my friend and boss, Bonnie Pluemer, was promoted to a regional library management position. I spoke confidentially to several members of the library board and told them I wanted to be the new director. Unlike the rest of the applicants, who interviewed at the library, I interviewed secretly at a board member's house. After all, a small town can turn quickly from nurturing nest to nettle bush when it looks like you're getting too big for your britches.

Most of the members of the library board were fond of me but skeptical. They kept asking me, "Are you sure you can *handle* this job?"

"I've been assistant director for five years, so I know

the position better than anyone. I know the staff. I know the community. I know the library's problems. The last three directors have moved on to regional positions. Do you really want another person who views this job as a stepping-stone?"

"No, but do you really *want* the job?"

"You have no idea how much I want this job."

Life is a journey. After all I'd been through, it was inconceivable this wasn't my next step, or that I wasn't the best person for the job. I was older than past directors. I had a daughter. I wasn't going to take an opportunity lightly.

"This is my place," I told the board. "There's nowhere else I want be."

The next day they offered me the position.

I wasn't qualified. That's not an opinion, it's a fact. I was smart, experienced, and hardworking, but the job required a master's degree in library science and I didn't have one. The board was willing to overlook this fact as long as I started a master's program within two years. That seemed more than fair, so I accepted the offer.

Then I found out the nearest American Library Association–accredited master's program was five hours away in Iowa City. I was a single mother. I had a full-time job. That wasn't going to work.

Today you can earn an accredited master's degree in library science on the Internet. But in 1987 I couldn't even find a long-distance learning program. And believe me, I looked. Finally, at the urging of my regional administrator, John Houlahan, Emporia State University in Emporia, Kansas, took the plunge. The first American Library Association–accredited long-distance master's program in the nation met in Sioux City, Iowa, in the fall of 1988. And I was the first student in the door.

I loved the classes. This wasn't cataloging and checking out books. This was demographics; psychology; budgeting and business analysis; the methodology of information processing. We learned community relations. We spent twelve grueling weeks on community analysis, which is the art of figuring out what patrons want. On the surface, community analysis is easy. In Spencer, for instance, we didn't carry books on snow skiing, but we always had the latest information on fishing and boating because the lakes were only twenty minutes away.

A good librarian, though, digs deeper. What does your community value? Where has it been? How and why has it changed? And most important, where is it going? A good librarian develops a filter in the back of her brain to catch and process information. Farm crisis in full swing? Don't just stock up on résumé builders and career manuals; purchase books on engine repair and other cost-saving measures. Hospital hiring nurses? Update the medical manuals and partner with the local community college to help them utilize your resources. More women working outside the home? Start a second Story Hour in the evening and concentrate on day-care centers during the day.

The material was complex, the homework brutal. All the students were working librarians, and there were several other single mothers. This program wasn't a casual decision; it was a last chance, and we were willing to work for it. In addition to attending class from five thirty on Friday to noon on Sunday—after a two-hour drive to Sioux City, no less—we were researching and

writing two papers a week, sometimes more. I didn't
have a typewriter at home, much less a computer, so I
would leave work at five, cook dinner for myself and
Jodi, then head back to the library and work until midnight or later.

At the same time I threw myself into the library remodeling. I wanted to complete it by the summer of
1989, and I had months of work to do before we could
even begin. I learned space planning, section organization, disability compliance. I chose colors, mapped furniture arrangements, and decided whether there was
enough money for new tables and chairs (there wasn't,
so we refurbished the old ones). Jean Hollis Clark and I
made exact scale models of the old library and the new
library to display on the circulation desk. It wasn't
enough to plan a great remodel; the public had to be enthusiastic and informed. Dewey helped out by sleeping
every day inside one of the models.

Once a design was determined, I moved on to the
next step: planning how to move more than 30,000 objects out of the building, then put them all back into their
correct places. I found warehouse space. I found moving
equipment. I organized and scheduled volunteers. And
every plan, every penny, had to be tallied and earmarked
and justified to the library board.

The hours at work and in class were wearing me
down, physically and mentally, and the school fees were
straining my budget. So I could hardly believe it when
the city council started an employee education fund. If
city employees went back to school to enhance their job
performance, the town would pay for it. Donna Fisher,
the city clerk, received a well-deserved degree. When I

mentioned my master's program at a city council meeting, the reception wasn't as accommodating.

Cleber Meyer, our new mayor, was sitting opposite me at the end of the table. Cleber was the epitome of a Sister's Café power broker, a blue-collar, salt-of-the-earth type. He had only an eighth-grade education, but he had a loud voice, broad shoulders, and his finger on the pulse of Spencer. Cleber owned and operated a gas station, Meyer Service Station, but you could tell from his huge rough hands that he grew up on the farms. In fact, he grew up outside Moneta; he and Dad had known each other all their lives. And yes, Cleber was his real name. His brother's name, if you can believe it, was Cletus.

For all his bluster, Cleber Meyer was the finest man you will ever meet. He would lend you the shirt off his back (gas stains included), and I don't believe he had it in him to hurt anyone. He meant well, and he always had the best interest of Spencer at heart. But he was a good ole boy, he was opinionated, and let's just say he could be gruff. When I mentioned my master's program, Cleber slammed his fist on the table and thundered, "Who do you think you are? A city employee?"

David Scott, a local attorney and council member, cornered me a few days later and said he'd go to bat for my expenses. After all, I *was* a city employee.

"Don't bother," I told him. "It will only hurt the library." I had no intention of undoing all the goodwill Dewey had begun to foster.

Instead, I worked harder. More hours on schoolwork: writing, researching, studying. More work on the remodeling project: planning, researching, budgeting.

More work running the day-to-day operations of the library. All of which meant, unfortunately, less time with my daughter. One Sunday Val's phone call caught me just as I was leaving Sioux City.

"Hi, Vicki. I hate to tell you this, but last night . . ."

"What happened? Where's Jodi?"

"Jodi's fine. But your house . . ."

"Yes?"

"Look, Vicki, Jodi had a party for a few friends and, well, it got a little out of control." She paused. "Just imagine the worst for the next two hours, and you'll be happy with what you find."

The house was a wreck. Jodi and her friends had spent the morning cleaning, but there were still stains on the carpet . . . and ceiling. The vanity door in the bathroom was ripped off its hinges. The kids threw all my records against the wall and broke them. Someone put beer cans down the heating vents. My pills were gone. A depressed kid had locked himself in the bathroom and tried to overdose—on estrogen. I found out later the police were called twice, but since the football team was at the party and since it was a winning season, they looked the other way. The mess didn't bother me, not really, but it reminded me once again that Jodi was growing up without me. The only thing I couldn't whip with more work, I realized, was my relationship with my daughter.

Ironically it was Cleber Meyer who put it all in perspective. He was pumping gas for me at his station one day—yes, he was the mayor, but it was a part-time position—when the subject of Jodi came up. "Don't worry," he told me. "When they turn fifteen, you become the dumbest person in the world. But when they turn twenty-two, you get smart again."

Work, school, home life, petty local politics, I did what I always did in times of stress: I took a deep breath, dug inside, and forced myself to stand up taller than ever before. I had been picking myself up by my bootstraps all my life. There wasn't anything about this situation, I told myself, that I couldn't handle. It was only late at night in the library, alone with my thoughts and staring at that blank computer screen, that I began to feel the pressure. It was only then, in my first quiet moment of the day, that I felt my foundation begin to shake.

A library after closing is a lonely place. It is heart-poundingly silent, and the rows of shelves create an almost unfathomable number of dark and creepy corners. Most of the librarians I know won't stay alone in a library after closing, especially after dark, but I was never nervous or scared. I was strong. I was stubborn. And most of all, I was never alone. I had Dewey. Every night, he sat on top of the computer screen as I worked, lazily swiping his tail back and forth. When I hit a wall, either from writer's block, fatigue, or stress, he jumped down into my lap or onto the keyboard. *No more,* he told me. *Let's play.* Dewey had an amazing sense of timing.

"All right, Dewey," I told him. "You go first."

Dewey's game was hide-and-seek, so as soon as I gave the word he would take off around the corner into the main part of the library. Half the time I immediately spotted the back half of a long-haired orange cat. For Dewey, hiding meant sticking your head in a bookshelf; he seemed to forget he had a tail.

"I wonder where Dewey is," I said out loud as I snuck up on him. "Boo!" I yelled when I got within a few feet, sending Dewey running.

Other times he was better hidden. I would sneak around a few shelves with no luck, then turn the corner to see him prancing toward me with that big Dewey smile.

You couldn't find me! You couldn't find me!

"That's not fair, Dewey. You only gave me twenty seconds."

Occasionally he curled up in a tight spot and stayed put. I'd look for five minutes, then start calling his name. "Dewey! Dewey!" A dark library can feel empty when you're bending over between the stacks and looking through rows of books, but I always imagined Dewey somewhere, just a few feet away, laughing at me.

"All right, Dewey, that's enough. You win!" Nothing. Where could that cat be? I'd turn around and there he was, standing in the middle of the aisle, staring at me.

"Oh, Dewey, you clever boy. Now it's my turn."

I'd run and hide behind a bookshelf, and invariably one of two things happened. I'd get to my hiding place, turn around, and Dewey would be standing right there. He had followed me.

Found you. That was easy.

His other favorite thing to do was run around the other side of the shelf and beat me to my hiding spot.

Oh, is this where you're thinking about hiding? Because, well, I've already figured it out.

I'd laugh and pet him behind the ears. "Fine, Dewey. Let's just run for a while."

We'd run between the shelves, meeting at the end of the aisles, nobody quite hiding and no one really seeking. After fifteen minutes I would completely forget my research paper, or the most recent budget meeting for the remodeling project, or that unfortunate conversation with Jodi. Whatever had been bothering me, it was gone. The weight, as they say, was lifted.

"Okay, Dewey. Let's get back to work."

Dewey never complained. I'd climb back into my chair, and he'd climb back to his perch on top of the computer and start waving his tail in front of the screen. The next time I needed him, he'd be there.

It's not a stretch to say those games of hide-and-seek with Dewey, that time spent together, got me through. Maybe it would be easier, right now, to tell you Dewey put his head on my lap and whimpered while I cried or that he licked the tears from my face. Anyone can relate to that. And it is almost true, because sometimes when the ceiling started falling in on me and I found myself staring blankly down at my lap, tears in my eyes, Dewey was there, right where I needed him to be.

But life isn't neat and tidy. Our relationship can't be tied up with a few tears. I'm not much of a crier, for one thing. And while Dewey was demonstrative with his love—he was always a soft touch for a late-night cuddle—he didn't bathe me with affection. Somehow Dewey knew when I needed a little nudge or a warm body, and he knew when the best thing for me was a stupid, mindless game of hide-and-seek. And whatever I needed, he'd give me, without thought, without wanting something in return, and without me asking. It wasn't just love. It was more than that. It was respect. It was empathy. And it went both ways. That spark Dewey and I had felt when we met? Those nights alone together in the library turned it into a fire.

I guess my final answer is that when everything in my life was so complex, when things were sliding in so many directions at once and it seemed at times the center wouldn't hold, my relationship with Dewey was so simple, and so natural, and that's what made it so right.

Chapter 12

Christmas

C hristmas is a holiday the town of Spencer cele-
brates together. It's the slow season for the
farmers and manufacturers, a time to relax and
spread our collected coins around to the merchants. The
activity of the season is the Grand Meander, a walking
tour of Grand Avenue that begins the first weekend in
December. The whole street is strung with white lights,
a coordinated display that shows off the fine lines of our
buildings. Christmas music is piped in; Santa Claus
comes out to receive wish lists from the children. His
elves, also in Santa suits, ring bells on corners and collect coins for charities. The whole town is out, laughing,
talking, clutching one another to share the warmth. The
stores stay open late, showing off their holiday selections
and offering cookies and hot chocolate to fight off the
biting cold.

Every storefront window is decorated. We call them
Living Windows, because in each one local residents act
out holiday scenes. The Parker Museum, which houses

a collection of Clay County artifacts, including a fire truck that battled the great fire of 1931, always creates a variation on the pioneers' Christmas. Other windows offer interpretations of Christmases not quite so long past, with Radio Flyers and porcelain dolls. Some have mangers. Others feature toy tractors and cars, a boy's view of Christmas morning. You can't look at the windows, playful or touching, funny or serious, and not think of the hundred fifty previous meanders up and down this stretch of stores, and the next hundred fifty to come. This, the windows all say, is Spencer.

The Festival of Trees, a Christmas-tree decorating contest, is held on the corner of First Avenue and Fifth Street, inside what used to be the Spencer Convention Center but is now the Eagles Club, a military-related social club that holds dances and dinners to raise money for charity. Since 1988 was Dewey's first Christmas, the library entered a tree under the title Do-We Love Christmas? The tree was decorated with—what else?— pictures of Dewey. It also featured puffy kitten ornaments and garlands of red yarn. The presents under the tree were appropriate books, like *The Cat-a-log* and *The Cat in the Hat*, tied in neat red bows. Visitors could wander through the trees for a small charitable donation. There was no official judging, but I don't think it's a stretch to say Do-We Love Christmas? was the winner, hands down.

Christmas at the library, like Christmas on Grand Avenue, was a time to put away other concerns and focus on the here and now. After a stressful fall, I was happy to stop thinking about school and remodeling and, for a change, focus on decorations. The Monday after the

Grand Meander, we took the boxes down from the top shelves of the storage room to prepare for the holiday season. The centerpiece was our big artificial Christmas tree next to the circulation desk. The first Monday in December, Cynthia Behrends and I always arrived early to set up and decorate the tree. Cynthia was the hardest worker on staff and eagerly volunteered for every job. But she didn't know what she was getting into because this year, when we slid the long thin Christmas tree box off its high shelf, we had company.

"Dewey's excited this morning. He must like the looks of this box."

"Or the smell of all that plastic." I could see his nose sniffing ninety odors a minute and his mind racing. *Could it be? All this time, could Mom have been hiding the world's largest, most spectacular, most deliciously smelly rubber band?*

When we pulled the Christmas tree out of the box, I could almost see Dewey's jaw drop.

It's not a rubber band, it's . . . it's . . . better.

As we pulled each branch out of the box, Dewey lunged at it. He wanted to sniff and chew every green piece of plastic sticking out of every green wire branch. He pulled a few plastic needles off the tree and started working them around in his mouth.

"Give me those, Dewey!"

He coughed a few pieces of plastic onto the floor. Then he leaped forward and thrust his head into the box just as Cynthia was pulling out the next branch.

"Back off, Dewey."

Cynthia pulled him out, but a second later he was back, a green needle stuck to the moist tip of his nose.

This time, his whole head disappeared inside the box. "This isn't going to work, Dewey. Do you want me to get the rest of the tree out or not?"

Apparently the answer was not, because Dewey wasn't moving.

"All right, Dewey, out you go. I'd hate for you to lose an eye." Cynthia wasn't scolding him, she was laughing. Dewey got the message and jumped back, only to start burrowing into the pile of branches on the floor.

"This is going to take all day," Cynthia said.

"I sure hope so."

As Cynthia pulled the last branches out of the box, I started to assemble the tree. Dewey was prancing and grinning, watching my every move. He came in for a sniff and a taste, then bounced back a few feet for perspective. The poor cat looked like he was about to explode with excitement. *Hurry up, hurry up. I want my turn.* This was the happiest I'd seen him all year.

"Oh, no, Dewey, not again."

I looked over to find Dewey buried in the Christmas tree box, no doubt sniffing and pawing at the scents clinging to the cardboard. He disappeared completely inside, and a few seconds later the box was rolling back and forth across the floor. He stopped, poked his head out, and looked around. He spotted the half-assembled tree and bolted back to chew on the lower branches.

"I think he's found a new toy."

"I think he's found a new *love*," I said as I put the top branches into the notches on the green pole that comprised the trunk of our tree.

It was true. Dewey loved the Christmas tree. He loved the smell of it. The feel of it. The taste of it. Once

I had it assembled and set up next to the circulation desk, he loved to sit under it. *Mine now*, he said as he rounded the base a few times. *Just leave us be, thanks.*

"Sorry, Dewey. Still work to do. We don't even have it decorated yet."

Out came the ornaments, the new tinsel in this year's color, the pictures and special embellishments for this year's theme. Angels on strings. Santa Clauses. Shiny balls with glitter all over them. Ribbons, ornaments, cards, and dolls. Dewey rushed up to each box, but he had little interest in cloth and metal, hooks and lights. He was distracted by our wreath, which I had made out of worn-out pieces of the library's previous Christmas tree, but old plastic was no match for the new, shiny stuff. Soon it was back to his spot under the tree.

We started hanging ornaments. One minute Dewey was in the boxes, finding out which ornaments came next. The next minute he was at our feet, playing with our shoelaces. Then he was stretching into the tree for another whiff of plastic. A few seconds later he was gone.

"What's that rustling sound?"

Suddenly Dewey came tearing by us with his head through the strap of one of the plastic grocery bags we used for storage. He ran all the way to the far side of the library, then came careening back toward us.

"Catch him!"

Dewey dodged and kept running. Soon he was on his way back again. Cynthia blocked the area near the front door. I took the circulation desk. Dewey sprinted right between us. I could see from the look in his eyes he was in a frenzy. He had no idea how to get the plastic bag from around his neck. His only thought was, *Keep running. Maybe I can lose this monster.*

Soon there were four or five of us chasing him, but he wouldn't stop dodging and sprinting away. It didn't help that we were all laughing at him.

"Sorry, Dewey, but you've got to admit this is funny."

I finally cornered him and, despite his terrified squirming, managed to free him from the bag. Dewey immediately went over to his new best friend, the Christmas tree, and lay down under the branches for a nice, comforting tongue bath, complete with his customary fist in the ears. There would be a hair ball, no doubt, either later today or tomorrow morning. But at least one lesson had been learned. From then on, Dewey hated plastic bags.

That first day with the library Christmas tree was one of our best. The staff spent the entire day laughing, and Dewey spent the entire day—plastic bag run excluded, of course—in a state of gooey, romantic bliss. His love for the Christmas tree never diminished. Every year when the box came off the shelf, he pranced.

The librarians usually received a few gifts from grateful patrons, but that year our small trove of chocolates and cookies was dwarfed by Dewey's enormous stack of balls, treats, and toy mice. It seemed that everyone in town wanted Dewey—and us—to know just how much he meant to them. There were some fancy toys in that stash, even some nice homemade items, but Dewey's favorite toy from that holiday season wasn't a gift at all; it was a skein of red yarn he found in a decorating box. That yarn skein was Dewey's constant companion, not just for the holiday season but for years to come. He batted it around the library until a few feet of yarn stuck out, which he then pounced on, wrestled, and, very soon, got wrapped around his body. More than once, I was almost run down by an orange cat streaking across the staff area, red yarn in mouth, dragging the bundle behind him. An hour later he'd be sacked out under the Christmas tree, all four feet clutching his red buddy.

The library was closed for a few days at Christmas, so Dewey came home with me. He spent much of his time alone, though, because Christmas in Hartley was a Jipson family tradition. Everyone came to Mom and Dad's house for Christmas; you might be disowned if you didn't. You weren't allowed to miss any of the holiday activities, and there were a lot of them: extravagant meals; decorating parties; games for children; holiday carols; desserts and cookies; games for adults; relatives dropping by with a plate of cookies or nothing much, just a little something I saw in Sioux City and thought you'd love; a year's worth of stories, told and retold. There was always a story to tell around the family tree. The presents weren't extravagant, but every Jipson got to spend a week in the arms of a large extended family, and that's the best gift of all.

Eventually someone always said, "Let's play 'Johnny M'Go.'"

Mom and Dad collected antiques, and a few years earlier we'd used them to form the Jipson family band. I played bass, which was a washtub with a broom handle attached to the top and a string running between them. My sister played the washboard. Dad and Jodi banged

out a rhythm with a couple of spoons. Mike blew on a
comb covered with wax paper. Doug blew across the
mouth of a moonshine jar. It was an antique jar, of course,
never used for its intended purpose. Mom turned an old
pioneer-era wooden butter churn upside down and
played it like a drum. Our song was "Johnny B. Goode"
When she was little, Jodi always said, "Play 'Johnny
M'Go'!" The name stuck. Every year we played "Johnny
M'Go" and other old rock-and-roll songs deep into the
night on our homemade instruments, a homage to a
country tradition that probably never existed in this part
of Iowa, laughing with one another the whole time.

After Midnight Mass on Christmas Eve, Jodi and I
headed home to Dewey, who as always was eager to see
us. We spent Christmas morning together in Spencer,
just the three of us. I hadn't even gotten Dewey a present.
What would be the point? He already had more stuff
than he needed. And after a year together, our relationship had gone well beyond token gifts and forced attention. We didn't have anything to prove. All Dewey
wanted or expected from me was a few hours a day of
my time. I felt the same way. That afternoon I dropped
Jodi at Mom and Dad's house and slipped home to
spend time with Dewey on the couch, doing nothing,
saying nothing, just two friends lounging around like a
couple of old socks waiting for a shoe.

Chapter 13

A Great Library

A great library doesn't have to be big or beautiful. It doesn't have to have the best facilities or the most efficient staff or the most users. A great library provides. It is enmeshed in the life of a community in a way that makes it indispensable. A great library is one nobody notices because it is always there, and it always has what people need.

The Spencer Public Library was founded in 1883 in Mrs. H. C. Crary's parlor. In 1890, the library moved to a small frame building on Grand Avenue. In 1902, Andrew Carnegie granted the town $10,000 for a new library. Carnegie was a product of the industrial revolution that had turned a nation of farmers into factory workers, oilmen, and iron smelters. He was a ruthless corporate capitalist who built his United States Steel into the nation's most successful business. He was also a Baptist, and by 1902 he was deep into the pursuit of giving away his money to worthwhile causes. One cause was providing grants to small towns for libraries. For a town like Spencer, a Carnegie library was a sign you had made it not exactly to the top, but farther than Hartley and Everly.

The Spencer Public Library opened on March 6, 1905, on East Third Street, half a block off Grand Avenue. It was typical of Carnegie libraries, since Carnegie had mandated a classical style and symmetry of design. There were three stained-glass windows in the entrance hall, two with flowers and one with the word *library*. The librarian perched behind a large central desk, surrounded by drawers of cards. The side rooms were small and cloistered, with bookshelves to the ceiling. In an era when public buildings were segregated by sex, men and women were free to enter any room. Carnegie libraries were also among the first to let patrons choose books off the shelves instead of making requests to the librarian.

Some historians describe Carnegie libraries as plain, but that is true only in comparison to the elaborate central libraries of cities like New York and Chicago, which had carved friezes, ornately painted ceilings, and crystal chandeliers. Compared to the parlor of a local woman's home or a storefront on Grand Avenue, the Spencer Carnegie library was impossibly ornate. The ceiling was high, the windows enormous. The half-underground bottom floor held the children's library, an innovation at a time when children were often kept locked away in their homes. Children could sit and read on a circular bench, while above them a window looked out at ground level on a flat grass lawn. The floorboards throughout the building were dark wood, highly polished and very wide. They creaked when you walked, and often that creaking was the only sound you could hear. The Carnegie was a library where books were seen, not heard. It was a museum. It was as quiet as a church. Or a monastery. It was a shrine to learning, and in 1902 learning meant books.

When many people think of a library, they think of a Carnegie library. These are the libraries of our childhood. The quiet. The high ceilings. The central library desk, complete with matronly librarian (at least in our memories). These libraries seemed designed to make children believe you could get lost in them, and nobody could ever find you, and it would be the most wonderful thing.

By the time I was hired in 1982, the old Carnegie library was gone. It had been beautiful but small. Too small for a growing town. The land deed specified the town must use it for a library or return it to the owner, so in 1971 the town tore down the old Carnegie building to build a bigger, more modern, more efficient library, one without squeaky floorboards, dim lighting, imposingly high bookshelves, and rooms to get lost in.

It was a disaster.

Spencer is built in a traditional style. The retail buildings are brick, the houses along Third Street two- and three-story frame boardinghouses. The new library was concrete. One story tall, it hunched on the corner like a bunker. Its original wide lawn was gone, replaced by two tiny gardens. Too shadowed to grow much, they were soon filled in with rocks. The glass front doors were set back from the street, but the entryway was enclosed and unwelcoming. The east wall, which faced the town middle school, was solid concrete. Grace Renzig lobbied herself onto the library board in the late 1970s with the goal of having vines planted along the east wall. She got her vines a few years later, but she ended up staying on the board for almost twenty years.

The new Spencer Public Library was modern, but with a brutish efficiency. And it was flat-out cold. A glass wall faced north, with a lovely view of the alley. In the winter, you couldn't keep the back of the library warm. The floor plan was open, leaving no space for storage. There was no designated staff area. There were only five electric outlets. The furniture, made by local craftsmen, was beautiful but impractical. The tables had prominent support bars so you couldn't pull up additional chairs, and they were solid oak with black laminate tops, so they were too heavy to move. The carpet was orange, a Halloween nightmare.

Or to put it more simply, the building wasn't right for a town like Spencer. The library had always been well run. The collection of books was exceptional, especially for a town the size of Spencer, and the directors had always been early adopters of new technologies and ideas. For enthusiasm, professionalism, and expertise, the library was top-notch. But after 1971, it was all squeezed into the wrong building. The exterior didn't fit the surrounding area. The interior wasn't practical or friendly. It didn't make you want to sit down and relax. It was cold in every sense of the word.

We started the remodel—let's call it the warming process—in May 1989, just as northwest Iowa was waking up and changing from brown to green. The lawns suddenly needed mowing, the trees on Grand Avenue were throwing out new leaves. On the farms, the plants were pushing through the soil and unfolding, and you could finally see the result of all that time spent fixing equipment, churning fields, and planting seeds. The weather turned warm. The kids brought out bicycles. At the library, after almost a year of planning, it was finally time to work.

The first stage of remodeling was painting the bare concrete walls. We decided to leave the nine-foot bookshelves bolted to the walls, so Tony Joy, our painter and the husband of staff member Sharon Joy, simply had to throw on some drop cloths and lean his ladder against the shelves. But as soon as he did, Dewey climbed up.

"All right, Dewey, down we go."

Dewey wasn't paying attention. He'd been in the library more than a year, but he'd never seen it from nine feet up. It was a revelation. Dewey stepped off the ladder and onto the top of the wall shelf. With a few steps, he was out of reach.

Tony moved the ladder. Dewey moved again. Tony climbed to the top, propped his elbow on the bookshelf, and looked at this stubborn cat.

"This is a bad idea, Dewey. I'm going to paint this wall, then you're going to rub against it. Vicki's going to see a blue cat, and then you know what's going to happen? I'm going to get fired." Dewey just stared down at the library. "You don't care, do you? Well, I warned you. Vicki!"

"Right here."

"You've been watching?"

"It's a fair warning. I won't hold you responsible."

I wasn't worried about Dewey. He was the most conscientious cat I'd ever known. He raced down bookshelves without a misstep. He intentionally brushed displays with his side, as cats do, without knocking them over. I knew he could not only walk a shelf without touching wet paint, but also tiptoe up a ladder without knocking off the can of paint at the top. I was more worried about Tony. It's not easy sharing a ladder with the king of the library.

"I'm fine with the arrangement if you are," I called up to him.

"I'll take my chances," Tony joked.

Within a few days, Tony and Dewey were fast friends. Or maybe I should say Tony and Dewkster, because that's what Tony always called him. Tony felt Dewey was too soft a name for such a macho cat. He worried the local alley cats were congregating outside the children's library window at night to make fun of his name. So Tony decided his real name wasn't Dewey, it was the Duke, like John Wayne. "Only his close friends call him Dewkster," Tony explained. He always called me Madame President.

"What do you think of this shade of red, Madame President?" he would ask when he saw me crossing the library.

"I don't know. It looks pink to me."

But pink paint wasn't our biggest worry. Suddenly we couldn't keep our polite, well-behaved cat off the top of the wall shelves. One day Tony looked across the library and saw Dewey on top of the wall shelves at the opposite end of the building. That was when things changed for Dewey, when he realized he could climb to the top of the wall shelves whenever he wanted. He had the run of the library up there, and some days he never wanted to come down.

"Where's Dewey?" each member of the genealogy club would ask as they settled in for their regular meeting on the first Saturday of the month. Like all the clubs that met in the library—our Round Room was the largest free meeting space in town, and it was usually booked— the club members were used to the Dewey treatment. This started with Dewey jumping into the center of the table at the beginning of every meeting. He would survey the meeting participants, then walk around to each person at the table, sniffing her hand or looking into his face. When he had made a full circuit, he chose one person and settled into his lap. It didn't matter what was going on in the meeting, Dewey never rushed or varied his routine. The only way to break his rhythm was to toss him out and close the door.

The Dewey treatment was met with resistance at first, especially by the business and political groups that often met in the Round Room, but after a few months even the salesmen treated it as a highlight. The genealogy club treated it almost like a game, since every month Dewey picked someone different to spend the meeting with. They would laugh and try to coax him into their laps, almost like the children at Story Hour.

"Dewey's distracted these days," I told them. "Ever since Tony started painting the library, he's been off his routine. But I'm sure once he realizes you're here . . ."

And as if on cue, Dewey walked in the door, jumped on the table, and started his rounds.

"Let us know if you need anything," I told them, turning back to the main part of the library. Nobody said anything; they were too busy focusing on Dewey. "No fair, Esther," I heard as the sound of the meeting faded into the distance, "you must have tuna in your pocket."

When Tony finished the painting three weeks later, Dewey was a changed cat. Maybe he thought he really was Duke, because suddenly he wasn't content with just naps and laps. He wanted to explore. And climb. And most important, explore new places to climb. We called this Dewey's Edmund Hillary phase, after the famous mountain climber. Dewey didn't want to stop climbing until he'd reached the top of his personal Mount Everest, which he managed to do not more than a month later.

"Any sign of Dewey this morning?" I asked Audrey Wheeler, who was working at the circulation desk. "He didn't come for breakfast."

"I haven't seen him."

"Let me know if you do. I want to make sure he's not sick."

Five minutes later I heard Audrey utter what around here was a surprising profanity: "Oh, my goodness!"

She was standing in the middle of the library, looking straight up. And there, on top of the lights, looking straight down, was Dewey.

When he saw us looking, Dewey pulled his head back. He was instantly invisible. As we watched, Dewey's head reappeared a few feet down the light. Then it disappeared again, only to appear a few feet farther on. The lights run in hundred-foot strips, and he had clearly been up there for hours, watching us.

"How are we going to get him down?"

"Maybe we should call the city," someone suggested. "They'll send someone with a ladder."

"Let's just wait him out," I said. "He's not doing any

harm up there, and he'll have to come down for food eventually."

An hour later Dewey trotted into my office, licking his lips from a late breakfast, and jumped into my lap for a pet. He was clearly keyed up about this new game, but didn't want to overplay his hand. I knew he was dying to ask, *What do you think of that?*

"I'm not even going to mention it, Dewey."

He cocked his head at me.

"I'm serious."

Okay then, I'll nap. Exciting morning, you know.

I asked around, but nobody had seen him come down. It took us a few weeks of constant surveillance to figure out his method of getting up. First Dewey jumped on the empty computer desk. Then he jumped on a filing cabinet, which gave him a long jump to the top of the temporary wall around the staff area, where he could hide behind a huge quilt of Spencer history. From there, it was only four feet to the light.

Sure, we could have rearranged the furniture, but once he became ceiling fixated we knew there wasn't much, except old age and creaky bones, that could stop Dewey from walking the lights. When cats don't know something exists, it's easy to keep them away. If they can't get to something and it's something they've made up their minds they want, it's almost impossible. Cats aren't lazy; they'll put in the work to thwart even the best-laid plans.

Besides, Dewey loved being up on the lights. He loved walking back and forth from end to end until he found an interesting spot. Then he would lie down, drape his head over the side, and watch. The patrons loved it, too. Sometimes when Dewey was pacing you could see them craning up at the ceiling, their heads going back and forth like the pendulum on a clock. They talked to him. When Dewey was pointed out to the children, his head just peaking over the edge of the lights, they screamed with excitement. They had so many questions.

"What's he doing?"

"How'd he get up there?"

"Why is he up there?"

"Will he get burned?"

"What if he falls off? Will he die?"

"What if he falls on somebody? Will they die?"

When the children found out they couldn't join him on the ceiling, they begged him to come down. "Dewey likes it up there," we explained. "He's playing." Eventually even the children understood that when Dewey was on the lights, he was coming down only on his terms. He had discovered his own little seventh heaven up there.

The official remodeling took place in July 1989, because July was the library's slow month. The children were out of school, which meant no class trips and no unofficial after-school child care. A local tax firm donated warehouse space across the street. The Spencer Public Library contained 55 shelving units, 50,000 books, 6,000 magazines, 2,000 newspapers, 5,000 albums and cassette tapes, and 1,000 genealogy books and binders, not to mention projectors, movie screens, televisions, cameras (16 mm and 8 mm), typewriters, desks, tables, chairs, card catalogs, filing cabinets, and office supplies. Everything was given a number. The number corresponded to a color-coordinated grid, which showed both its place in the warehouse and its new place in the library. On the new blue carpet, Jean Hollis Clark and I chalked the location of every shelf, table, and desk. If a shelf was put down an inch out of place, the workers had to move it because there were strict aisle width and ADA (Americans with Disabilities Act) requirements. If a shelf was off an inch, the next one could be off two inches. Next thing you knew, a wheelchair would be stuck in a back corner.

The move was truly a community effort. The Rotary Club helped move the books out; the Golden Kiwanis helped move them back. Our downtown development manager, Bob Rose, moved shelving. Doris Armstrong's husband, Jerry, spent more than a week bolting 110 new steel plates onto the ends of our shelving units, at least six bolts per plate, and never complained. Everybody volunteered: the genealogy club, the library board, teachers, parents, the nine-member board of Spencer's Friends of the Library. The downtown merchants pitched in, too, and there were free drinks and snacks for everyone.

The remodeling went like clockwork. In exactly three weeks, our Halloween horror was replaced with a neutral blue carpet and colorful reupholstered furniture. We added two-person gliders to the children's library so mothers could rock and read to their kids. In a closet, I found eighteen Grosvenor prints, along with seven old pen-and-ink sketches. The library didn't have enough money to frame them, so each print was adopted by a member of the community who paid for the framing. The newly arranged, angled shelves led the eye back into the books, where thousands of colorful spines invited patrons to browse, read, relax.

We unveiled the new library with a cookies and tea open house. Nobody was more excited that day than Dewey. He had been locked away at my house for three weeks, and during that time his whole world had changed. The walls were different; the carpet was different; all the chairs and tables and bookshelves were out of place. The books even smelled different after a trip to the warehouse across the street.

But as soon as people started arriving, Dewey dashed back to the refreshment table to be front and center again. Yes, the library had changed, but what he missed most after three weeks away was people. He hated being away from his friends at the library. And they had missed him, too. As they went for their cookies, they all stopped to pet Dewey. Some lifted him onto their shoulders for a tour through the newly arranged shelving units. Others just watched him, talked about him, and smiled. The library may have changed, but Dewey was still the king.

Between 1987, the year before Dewey fell into our arms, and 1989, the year of the remodel, visits to the Spencer Public Library increased from 63,000 a year to more than 100,000. Clearly something had changed. People were thinking differently about their library, appreciating it more. And not just the citizens of Spencer. That year, 19.4 percent of our visitors were from rural Clay County. Another 18 percent came from the surrounding counties. No one could argue, seeing those numbers, that the library wasn't a regional center.

The remodeling helped, there's no doubt about that. So did the revitalization of Grand Avenue; and the economy, which was picking up; and the energized staff; and our new outreach and entertainment programs. But most of the change, most of what brought the new people in and finally made the Spencer Public Library a meeting house, not a warehouse, was Dewey.

Chapter 14

Dewey's Great Escape

L ate July is the best time of year in Spencer. The corn is ten feet high, golden and green. It's so high, the farmers are required by state law to cut it to half height every mile, where the roads meet at right angles. Rural Iowa has too many intersections and not enough stop signs. The short corn helps, because at least you can see cars coming, and it doesn't hurt the farmers. Corn ears grow in the center of the stalk, not the top.

It's easy to neglect your job in an Iowa summer. The bright green, the warm sun, the endless fields. You leave the windows open, just to catch the scent. You spend your lunch hour down by the river, your weekends fishing near Thunder Bridge. It's hard, sometimes, to stay inside.

"Is this heaven?" I want to say every year.

"No," is the imaginary reply. "It's Iowa."

By August of 1989, the remodeling effort was over. Attendance was up. The staff was happy. Dewey had not only been accepted by the community, but was drawing people in and inspiring them. The Clay County Fair, the biggest event of the year, was just around the corner in September. I even had a month off from my master's classes. Everything was going perfectly—except for Dewey. My contented baby boy, our library hero, was a changed cat: distracted, jumpy, and most of all, trouble.

The problem was the three weeks Dewey had spent at my house during the remodeling, staring through my window screens at the world outside. He couldn't see the corn from my house, but he could hear the birds. He could feel the breeze. He could smell whatever cats smell when they direct their nose to the great outdoors. Now he missed those screens. There were windows in the library, but they didn't open. You could smell the new carpet but not the outdoors. You could hear trucks, but you couldn't make out the birds. *How can you show me something so wonderful,* he seemed to whine, *then take it away?*

Between the two sets of front doors at the Spencer Public Library was a tiny glass lobby that helped keep out the cold in the winter, since at least one set of doors was usually closed. For two years Dewey hated that lobby; when he returned from his three weeks at my house, he adored it. From the lobby, he could hear the birds. When the outer doors were open, he could smell fresh air. For a few hours in the afternoon, there was even a patch of sunlight. He pretended that was all he wanted, to sit in that patch of sunlight and listen to the birds. But we knew better. If he spent enough time in the lobby, Dewey would become curious about going through that second set of doors and into the outside world.

"Dewey, get back in here!" the front desk clerk would yell every time he followed a patron out the first set of doors. The poor cat had no chance. The circulation desk faced into the lobby, and the desk clerk always spotted him immediately. So Dewey stopped listening, especially if the clerk was Joy DeWall. Joy was the newest and youngest member of the staff and the only one who wasn't married. She lived with her parents in a duplex where the lease didn't allow pets, so she had a soft spot in her heart for Dewey. Dewey knew that, and he wouldn't listen to a word she said. So Joy started coming back to get me. I was the Mom voice. Dewey always listened to me, although in this case he was so intent on disobeying I was forced to back up my threat.

"Dewey, do you want me to get the squirt bottle?"

He just stared at me.

I brought the squirt bottle out from behind my back. With the other arm, I held open the door to the library. Dewey slunk back inside.

Ten minutes later I heard: "Vicki, Dewey's in the lobby again."

That was it. Three times in one day. It was time to put my foot down. I stormed out of my office, screwed up my best Mom voice, threw open the lobby door, and demanded, "You get in here right now, young man."

A man in his early twenties almost jumped out of his skin. Before the last word was out of my mouth, he had rushed into the library, grabbed a magazine, and buried his head in it all the way up to the fine print. Talk about embarrassing. I was holding the door open in stunned silence, unable to believe I hadn't seen this kid right in front of my face, when Dewey came trotting past like nothing out of the ordinary had happened. I could almost see him smiling.

A week later, Dewey didn't come for his morning meal, and I couldn't find him anywhere. Nothing unusual there; Dewey had plenty of places to hide. There was a cubbyhole behind the display case by the front door that I swear was the size of a box of crayons—the old sixty-four pack with the sharpener built in. There was the brown lounge chair in the children's area, although his tail usually stuck out of that one. One afternoon Joy was shelving the bottom row of books in the Westerns section when, to her amazement, Dewey popped out. In a library, books fit on both sides of a shelf. Between the two rows is four inches of space. Between the books was Dewey's ultimate hiding place: quick, handy, and secure. The only way to find him was to lift books at random and look behind them. That doesn't sound so difficult until you consider that the Spencer Public Library contained more than four hundred shelves of books. Between those books was an enormous labyrinth, a long, narrow world all Dewey's own.

Fortunately he almost always stuck to his favorite place in the bottom rows of Westerns. Not this time. He wasn't under the brown lounger, either, or in his cubbyhole. I didn't notice him peeking down from the lights. I opened the doors to the bathrooms to see if he had been locked inside. Not this morning.

"Has anyone seen Dewey?"

No. No. No. No.

"Who locked up last night?"

"I did," Joy said, "and he was definitely here." I knew Joy would never have forgotten to look for Dewey. She was the only staffer, besides me, who would stay late with him to play hide-and-seek.

"Good. He must be in the building. Looks like he's found a new hiding place."

But when I returned from lunch, Dewey was still missing. And he hadn't touched his food. That's when I began to worry.

"Where's Dewey?" a patron asked.

We had already heard that question twenty times, and it was only early afternoon. I told the staff, "Tell them Dewey's not feeling well. No need to alarm anyone." He'd show up. I knew it.

That night, I drove around for half an hour instead of heading straight home. I wasn't expecting to see a fluffy orange cat prowling the neighborhood, but you never know. The thought going through my mind was, "What if he's hurt? What if he needs me, and I can't find him? I'm letting him down." I knew he wasn't dead. He was so healthy. And I knew he hadn't run away. But the thought kept creeping up. . . .

He wasn't waiting for me at the front door the next day. I stepped inside and the place felt dead. A cold dread walked up my spine, even though it was ninety degrees outside. I knew something was wrong.

I told the staff, "Look everywhere."

We checked every corner. We opened every cabinet and drawer. We pulled books off the shelves, hoping to find him in his crawl space. We shone a flashlight behind the wall shelves. Some of them had pulled an inch or two away from the wall; Dewey could have been making his rounds, fallen in, and gotten stuck. Clumsiness wasn't like him, but in an emergency you check every possibility.

The night janitor! The thought hit me like a rock, and I picked up the phone. "Hi, Virgil, it's Vicki at the library. Did you see Dewey last night?"

"Who?"

"Dewey. The cat."

"Nope. Didn't see him."

"Is there anything he could have gotten into that made him sick? Cleaning solution maybe?"

He hesitated. "Don't think so."

I didn't want to ask, but I had to. "Do you ever leave any doors open?"

He really hesitated this time. "I prop open the back door when I take the garbage to the Dumpster."

"How long?"

"Maybe five minutes."

"Did you prop it open two nights ago?"

"I prop it every night."

My heart sank. That was it. Dewey would never just run out an open door, but if he had a few weeks to think about it, peek around the corner, sniff the air . . .

"Do you think he ran out?" Virgil asked.

"Yes, Virgil, I do."

I told the staff the news. Any information was good for our spirits. We set up shifts so that two people could cover the library while the rest looked for Dewey. The regular patrons could tell something was wrong. "Where's Dewey?" went from an innocent inquiry to an expression of concern. We continued to tell most patrons nothing was wrong, but we took the regulars aside and told them Dewey was missing. Soon a dozen people were walking the sidewalks. "Look at all these people. Look at all this love. We'll find him now," I told myself again and again.

I was wrong.

I spent my lunch hour walking the streets, looking for my baby boy. He was so sheltered in the library. He wasn't a fighter. He was a finicky eater. How was he going to survive?

On the kindness of strangers, of course. Dewey trusted people. He wouldn't hesitate to ask for help.

I dropped in on Mr. Fonley at Fonley Flowers, which had a back entrance off the alley behind the library. He hadn't seen Dewey. Neither had Rick Krebsbach at the photo studio. I called all the veterinarians in town. We didn't have an animal shelter, so a vet's office was the place someone would take him. If they didn't recognize him, that is. I told the vets, "If someone brings in a cat who looks like Dewey, it probably is Dewey. We think he's escaped."

I told myself, "Everyone knows Dewey. Everyone loves Dewey. If someone finds him, they'll bring him back to the library."

I didn't want to spread the news that he was missing. Dewey had so many children who loved him, not to mention the special needs students. Oh, my goodness, what about Crystal? I didn't want to scare them. I knew Dewey was coming back.

When Dewey wasn't waiting for me at the front door on the third morning, my stomach plummeted. I realized that, in my heart, I had been expecting to see him sitting there. When he wasn't, I was devastated. That's when it hit me: Dewey was gone. He might be dead. He probably wasn't coming back. I knew Dewey was important, but only at that moment did I realize how big a hole he would leave. To the town of Spencer, Dewey was the library. How could we go on without him?

When Jodi was three, I lost her at the Mankato Mall. I looked down and she was gone. I almost choked on my own heart, it jumped into my throat so fast. When I couldn't find her, I became absolutely frantic. My baby. My baby. I couldn't even think. All I could do was rip clothes off hangers, run the aisles faster and faster. I finally found her hiding in the middle of a circular rack of clothes, laughing. She had been there all along. But, oh, how I died when I thought she was gone.

I felt the same way now. That's when I realized Dewey wasn't just the library's cat. My grief wasn't for the town of Spencer, or for its library, or even for its children. The grief was for me. He might live at the library, but Dewey was my cat. I loved him. That's not just words. I didn't just love something about him. I loved him. But my baby boy, my baby Dewey, was gone.

The mood in the library was black. Yesterday we had hope. We believed it was only a matter of time. Now we believed he was gone. We continued to search, but we had looked everywhere. We were out of options. I sat down and thought about what I was going to tell the community. I would call the radio station, which was the information nexus of Spencer. They would immediately make an announcement. They could mention an orange cat without saying his name. The adults would understand, but maybe that would buy time with the children.

"Vicki!"

Then the newspaper. They would definitely run the story tomorrow. Maybe someone had taken him in.

"Vicki!"

Should we put up flyers? What about a reward?

"Vicki!"

Who was I kidding? He was gone. If he was here, we would have found . . .

"Vicki! Guess who's home!"

I stuck my head out of the office and there he was, my big orange buddy, wrapped in the arms of Jean Hollis Clark. I rushed over and hugged him tight. He laid his head on my chest. Out of the circular clothes rack, right under my nose, my child had appeared!

"Oh, baby boy, baby boy. Don't ever do that again."

Dewey didn't need me to reassure him. I could tell immediately this was no joke. Dewey was purring like he had on our first morning. He was so happy to see me, so thankful to be in my arms. He seemed happy. But I knew him so well. Underneath, in his bones, he was still shaking.

"I found him under a car on Grand Avenue," Jean was saying. "I was going over to White Drug, and I happened to catch a glimpse of orange out of the corner of my eye."

I wasn't listening. I would hear the story many times over the next few days, but at that moment I wasn't listening. I only had eyes and ears for Dewey.

"He was hunched against the wheel on the far side of the car. I called to him, but he didn't come. He looked like he wanted to run, but he was too afraid. He must have been right there all along. Can you believe that?

All those people looking for him, and he was right there all along."

The rest of the staff was crowding around us now. I could tell they wanted to hold him, to cuddle him, but I didn't want to let him go.

"He needs to eat," I told them. Someone put out a fresh can of food, and we all watched while Dewey sucked it down. I doubt the cat had eaten in days.

Once he had done his business—food, water, litter box—I let the staff hold him. He was passed from hand to hand like a hero in a victory parade. When everyone had welcomed him home, we took him out to show the public. Most of them didn't know anything had happened, but there were a few wet eyes. Dewey, our prodigal son, gone but now returned to us. You really do love something more when it's been lost.

That afternoon I gave Dewey a bath, which he tolerated for the first time since that cold January morning so long ago. He was covered in motor oil, which took months to work out of his long fur. He had a tear in one ear and a scratch on his nose. I cleaned them gently and lovingly. Was it another cat? A loose wire? The undercarriage of a car? I rubbed his cut ear between my fingers, and Dewey didn't even flinch. "What happened out there?" I wanted to ask him, but the two of us had already come to an understanding. We would never talk about this incident again.

Years later, I would make it a habit to prop open a side door during library board meetings. Cathy Greiner, a board member, asked me every time, "Aren't you worried Dewey will run out?"

I looked down at Dewey, who was there as usual to

attend the meeting, and he looked up at me. That look told me, as clearly as if he'd crossed his heart and hoped to die, that he wasn't going to run. Why couldn't everyone else see it?

"He's not going anywhere," I told her. "He's committed to the library."

And he was. For sixteen years, Dewey never went into the lobby again. He lounged by the front door, especially in the morning, but he never followed patrons out. If the doors opened and he heard trucks, he sprinted to the staff area. He didn't want to be anywhere near a passing truck. Dewey was completely done with the outdoors.

Chapter 15 ⟶

Spencer's Favorite Cat

About a month after Dewey's escape, Jodi left Spencer. I wasn't sure I could afford to send her to college, and she didn't want to stay home. Jodi wanted to travel, so she took a job as a nanny in California and saved money for college. I'm sure it didn't hurt that California was a long way from Mom.

I brought Dewey home for her last weekend. As always, he was stuck to Jodi's side like a flesh-hugging magnet. I think he loved nighttime with her most of all. As soon as Jodi pulled down the covers, Dewey was in her bed. Actually he beat her into bed. By the time she finished brushing her teeth, he was sitting on her pillow, ready to curl up beside her. As soon as she lay down, he was plastered against her face. He wouldn't even let her breathe. She shoved him down into the covers, but he came back. Shove. On her face. Shove. Across her neck.

"Stay down, Dewey."

He finally relented and slept by her side, locked onto her hip. She could breathe, but she couldn't turn over. Did he know our girl was leaving, maybe for good? When he slept with me, Dewey was in and out of bed all night, exploring the house one minute and snuggling the next. With Jodi, he never left. At one point, he wandered down to attack her feet, which were under the covers, but that was as far as he went. Jodi didn't get any sleep that night.

The next time Dewey came to my house, Jodi was gone. He found a way to stay close to her, though, by spending the night in Jodi's room, curled up on the floor next to her heater, no doubt dreaming of those warm summer nights spent snuggled up to Jodi's side.

"I know, Dewey," I said to him. "I know."

A month later I took Dewey for his first official photograph. I'd like to say it was for sentimental reasons, that my world was changing and I wanted to freeze that moment, or that I realized Dewey was on the cusp of something far bigger than either of us ever imagined. But the real reason was a coupon. Rick Krebsbach, the town photographer, was offering pet photographs for ten dollars.

Dewey was such an easygoing cat that I convinced myself getting a professional portrait made of him, in a professional portrait studio, would be easy. But Dewey hated the studio. As soon as we walked in, his head was swiveling, his eyes looking at everything. I put him in the chair, and he immediately hopped out. I picked him up and put him in the chair again. I took one step back, and Dewey was gone.

"He's nervous. He hasn't been out of the library much," I said as I watched Dewey sniff the photo backdrop.

"That's nothing," Rick said.

"Pets aren't easy?"

"You have no idea," he said as we watched Dewey dig his head under a pillow. "One dog tried to eat my camera. Another dog actually ate my fake flowers. Now that I think about it, he puked on that pillow."

I picked Dewey up quickly, but my touch didn't calm him. He was still looking around, more nervous than interested.

"There's been quite a bit of unfortunate peeing. I had to throw away a sheet. I sanitize everything, of course, but to an animal like Dewey it must smell like a zoo."

"He's not used to other animals," I said, but I knew that wasn't quite right. Dewey never cared about other animals. He always ignored the Seeing Eye dog who came into the library. He even ignored the Dalmatian. This wasn't fear; it was confusion. "He knows what's expected of him in the library, but he doesn't understand this place."

"Take your time."

A thought. "May I show Dewey the camera?"

"If you think it will help."

Dewey posed for photographs at the library all the time, but those were personal cameras. Rick's camera was a large, boxy, professional model. Dewey had never seen one of those before, but he was a fast learner.

"It's a camera, Dewey. Camera. We're here to get your picture taken."

Dewey sniffed the lens. He leaned back and looked at it, then sniffed it again. I could feel him getting less tense, and I knew he understood.

I pointed. "Chair. Sit in the chair."

I put him down. He sniffed up and down every leg, and twice on the seat. Then he jumped into the chair and stared right at the camera. Rick hurried over and snapped six photos.

"I can't believe it," he said as Dewey climbed down off the chair.

I didn't want to tell Rick, but this happened all the time. Dewey and I had a means of communicating even I didn't understand. He always seemed to know what I wanted, but unfortunately that didn't mean he was always going to obey. I didn't even have to say *brush* or *bath*; all I had to do was think about them, and Dewey disappeared. I remember passing him in the library one afternoon. He looked up at me with his usual lazy indifference. *Hi, how you doing?*

I thought, "Oh, there are two knots of fur on his neck. I should get the scissors and cut them off." As soon as the idea formed in my mind, *whoosh*, Dewey was gone.

But since his escape, Dewey had been using his powers for good, not mischief. He not only anticipated what I wanted, he did it. Not when a brushing or a bath was involved, of course, but for library business. That was one reason he was so willing to have his photograph taken. He wanted to do what was best for the library.

"He knows it's for the library," I told Rick, but I could tell he wasn't buying it. Why, after all, would a cat care about a library? And how could he connect a library with a photo studio a block away? But it was the truth, and I knew it.

I picked Dewey up and petted his favorite spot, the top of his head between the ears. "He knows what a camera is. He's not afraid of it."

"Has he ever posed before?"

"At least two or three times a week. For visitors. He loves it."

"That doesn't sound like a cat."

I wanted to tell him Dewey wasn't just any cat, but Rick had been taking pet photographs for the past week. He'd probably heard it a hundred times already.

And yet if you see Dewey's official photograph, which Rick shot that day (it's on the cover of this book), you can tell immediately he's not just another cat. He's beautiful, yes, but more than that, he's relaxed. He has no fear of the camera, no confusion about what's going on. His eyes are wide and clear. His fur is perfectly groomed. He doesn't look like a kitten, but he doesn't look like a grown cat, either. He's a young man getting his college graduation photograph taken, or a sailor getting a memento for his girl back home before shipping off on his first tour. His posture is remarkably straight, his head cocked, his eyes staring calmly into the camera. I smile every time I see that photo because he looks so serious. He looks like he's trying to be strong and handsome but can't quite pull it off because he's so darn cute.

A few days after receiving the finished photographs, I noticed the local Shopko, a large general merchandise chain like Wal-Mart or Kmart, was holding a pet photo contest to raise money for charity. You paid a dollar to vote, and the money was used to fight muscular dystrophy. This was typical of Spencer. There was always a fund-raiser, and it was always supported by local citizens. Our radio station, KCID, promoted these efforts. The paper often ran a story. The turnout was usually overwhelming. We don't have a ton of money in Spencer, but if someone needs a hand, we're happy to provide it. That's civic pride.

On a whim, I entered Dewey in the contest. The photo was for library promotion purposes, after all, and wasn't this a perfect opportunity to promote this special aspect of the library? A few weeks later, Shopko strung a dozen photos, all of cats and dogs, on a wire in the front of the store. The town voted, and Dewey won by a landslide. He got more than 80 percent of the votes, seven times as many as the runner-up. It was ridiculous. When the store called to tell me the results, I was almost embarrassed.

Part of the reason Dewey won so overwhelmingly was the photograph. Dewey is staring at you, asking you to look back at him. He makes a personal connection, even if there is a touch of stateliness in his pose.

Part of the reason was Dewey's looks. He's a 1950s matinee idol, suave and cool. He's so handsome you have to love him.

Part of the reason was Dewey's personality. Most cats in photographs look scared to death, desperate to sniff the camera, or disgusted by the whole process — or often all three. Most dogs look like they are about to go absolutely bonkers, knock over everything in the room, get themselves wound up in an electrical cord, and then eat the camera. Dewey looks calm.

But mostly, Dewey trounced the competition because the town had adopted him. Not just the regular library patrons, I realized for the first time, but the whole town. While I wasn't watching, while I was preoccupied with school and remodeling and Jodi, Dewey was quietly working his magic. The stories, not just about his rescue but about his life and relationships, were seeping down into the cracks and sprouting new life. He wasn't just the library's cat, not anymore. He was Spencer's cat. He was our inspiration, our friend, our survivor. He was one of us. And at the same time, he was ours.

Was he a mascot? No. Did he make a difference in the way the town thought about itself? Absolutely. Not to everyone, of course, but to enough. Dewey reminded us, once again, that we were a different kind of town. We cared. We valued the small things. We understood life wasn't about quantity but quality. Dewey was one more reason to love this hardy little town on the Iowa plains. The love of Spencer, the love of Dewey, it was all intermingled in the public mind.

Chapter 16

Iowa's Famous Library Cat

I can see now, in hindsight, that Dewey's escape was a turning point, a last fling at the end of youth. After that, he was content with his lot in life: to be the cat in residence at the Spencer Public Library, a friend, a confidant, and a goodwill ambassador to all. He greeted people with new enthusiasm. He perfected the fine art of lounging in the middle of adult nonfiction, where he could be seen from the whole library, but where there was plenty of room for people to walk without stepping on him. If he was in a contemplative mood, he would lie on his stomach with his head up and his front paws crossed casually in front. We called this his Buddha pose. Dewey could zone out in that pose for an hour like a fat little man at peace with the world. His other favorite position was to sprawl out full on his back, wide open, his paws sticking out in four directions. He went completely slack, letting it all hang out.

It's amazing how, when you stop running and start sprawling, the world comes to you. Or if not the world, then at least Iowa. Soon after the Shopko contest, Dewey was the subject of Chuck Offenburger's Iowa Boy column in the *Des Moines Register.* Iowa Boy was one of those columns that said things like, "It was the most shocking piece of news I'd come across since the time a few years ago I found out the Cleghorn Public Library, just down the road a ways, had started checking out cake pans to its patrons." In fact, that's exactly what the column said, and yes, the Cleghorn Public Library, just down the road, does check out cake pans to patrons. I know at least a dozen libraries in Iowa with extensive cake pan collections. The librarians hang them on the walls. If you want to bake a special cake, for instance, a Winnie the Pooh cake for a child's birthday party, you go to the library. Now, those are librarians who serve their communities!

When I read the article, I thought, "Wow, Dewey's really made it." It was one thing for a town to adopt a cat. It was even better for a region to adopt that cat, as northwest Iowa had with Dewey. The library received visitors every day from small towns and farms in surrounding counties. Summer residents of the Iowa lake country drove down to meet him, then spread the word to their neighbors and guests, who would drive down the following week. He appeared frequently in the newspapers of nearby towns. But the *Des Moines Register*! That was the daily newspaper in the state capital, which had a population of almost 500,000. The *Des Moines Register* was read all over the state. More than half a million people were probably reading about Dewey right now.

That was more people than attend the Clay County Fair!

After Iowa Boy, Dewey started making regular appearances on our local television newscasts, which originated out of Sioux City, Iowa, and Sioux Falls, South Dakota. Soon he began appearing on stations in other nearby cities and states. Every segment started the same way, with a voice-over: *The Spencer Library wasn't expecting anything more in their drop box than books on a freezing January morning. . . .* No matter how they framed it, the picture was the same. A poor feeble kitten, almost frozen to death, begging for help. The story of Dewey's arrival at the library was irresistible.

But so was his personality. Most news crews weren't used to filming cats—there were thousands of cats in northwest Iowa, no doubt, but none ever made it on camera—so they always started out with what seemed like a good idea: "Just have him act natural."

"Well, there he is, sleeping in a box with his tail hanging out and his stomach oozing over the side. That's as natural as it gets."

Five seconds later: "Maybe he can jump or something?"

Dewey always gave them what they wanted. He jumped over the camera for a flying action shot. He walked between two displays to show his dexterity. He ran and jumped off the end of a shelf. He played with a child. He played with his red yarn. He sat quietly on top of the computer and stared into the camera, the model of decorum. He wasn't showing off. Posing for the camera was part of Dewey's job as publicity director for the library, so he did it. Enthusiastically.

Dewey's appearance on *Living in Iowa*, an Iowa Public Television series that focuses on issues, events, and people in the state of Iowa, was typical. The *Living in Iowa* crew met me at the library at seven thirty in the morning. Dewey was ready. He rolled. He jumped between the shelves. He walked up and put his nose on the camera. He stuck right by the side of the host, a beautiful young woman, winning her over.

"Can I hold him?" she asked.

I showed her the Dewey Carry—over the left shoulder, with his behind in the crook of your arm, head over your back. If you wanted to hold him for any length of time, you had to use the Dewey Carry.

"He's doing it!" the host whispered excitedly as Dewey draped over her shoulder.

Dewey's head popped up. *What did she say?*

"How do I get him to calm down?"

"Just pet him."

The host stroked his back. Dewey lay his head on her shoulder and cuddled against her neck. "He's doing it! He's really doing it! I can feel him purring." She smiled at her cameraman and whispered, "Are you getting this?"

I was tempted to tell her, "Of course he's doing it. He does it for everyone," but why spoil her excitement?

Dewey's episode aired a few months later. It was called "A Tale of Two Kitties." (Yes, it's a pun on Charles Dickens.) The other kitty was Tom, who lived in Kibby's Hardware in Conrad, Iowa, a small town in the middle of the state. Like Dewey, Tom was found on the coldest night of the year. Store owner Ralph Kibby took the frozen stray to the vet's office. "They gave him sixty dollars' worth of shots," he said on the program, "and said if he's still alive in the morning he may have a chance." As I watched the show, I realized why the host was so happy that morning. There were at least thirty seconds of footage of Dewey lying on her shoulder; the best she could get from Tom was a sniff of her finger.

Dewey wasn't the only one expanding his horizons. During my master's program I had become very active in state library circles, and after graduation I was elected president of the Iowa Small Library Association, an advocacy group for libraries in towns of less than 10,000 people. Advocacy, at least when I joined, was a stretch. The group had a serious inferiority complex. "We're small," they thought. "Who cares about us? Let's just stick with milk, cookies, and a little gossip. That's all we're good for."

But I had seen firsthand that small didn't mean irrelevant, and I was inspired. "You don't think small towns matter?" I asked them. "You don't think your library can make a difference? Look at Dewey. Every librarian in the state knows Dewey Readmore Books. He's appeared on the cover of the Iowa library newsletter twice. He appeared twice in the National Library Cat Society newsletter, and he gets fan mail from England and Belgium. He was featured in the state library newsletter . . . of Illinois. I get calls every week from librarians wondering how they can convince their board to let them have a cat. Does that sound irrelevant to you?"

"So we should all get cats?"

"No. You should believe in yourselves."

And they did. Two years later, the Iowa Small Library Association was one of the most active and respected advocacy groups in the state.

Dewey's breakthrough, though, came not through my efforts but through the mail. One afternoon the library received a package containing twenty copies of the June/July 1990 issue of *Country*, a national magazine with a circulation of more than five million. It wasn't unusual for us to receive magazines from publishers hoping to drum up library subscriptions, but twenty copies? I had never read *Country*, and I had never spoken to anyone from *Country*, but I liked its slogan: For Those Who Live In or Long For The Country. I decided to flip through it. Right there, on page 57, was a two-page, full-color article about Dewey Readmore Books of the Spencer Public Library, complete with photographs sent in by a local woman I didn't even know but whose daughter frequented the library. Clearly she had been going home and telling her mother about the Dew.

It was just a small article, but its impact was extraordinary. For years, visitors told me how much it inspired them. Writers, calling for information for other articles about Dewey, often cited it. More than a decade later, I opened the mail to find a perfectly preserved copy of the article, neatly torn out of the magazine near the fold. The woman wanted me to know how much Dewey's story meant to her.

In Spencer, people who had forgotten about Dewey or who had never shown any interest in him took notice. Even the crowd at Sister's Café perked up. The worst of the farm crisis had passed, and our leaders were looking for a way to attract new business. Dewey was getting the kind of national exposure they could only dream of, and of course that energy and excitement was rubbing off on the town. Sure, nobody has ever built a factory because of a cat, but nobody has ever built a factory in a town they'd never heard of, either. Once again, Dewey was doing his part, not just in Spencer this time but out there in the larger world, beyond the cornfields of Iowa.

The biggest change, though, was pride. Dewey's friends were proud of him, and everyone was proud to have him in town. One man, back for his twentieth high school reunion, stopped by the library to flip through newspapers from that year. Dewey, of course, won him over immediately. But once he heard about Dewey's friends and saw the articles about him, he became truly impressed. He wrote later to thank us and say he'd been telling everyone in New York about his wonderful hometown and its beloved library cat.

He wasn't the only one. We had three or four people a week coming into the library to show Dewey off. "We're here to see the famous cat," an older man said, approaching the desk.

"He's sleeping in the back. I'll go get him."

"Thanks," he said, motioning to a younger woman with a little blond girl hiding behind her leg. "I wanted my granddaughter Lydia to meet him. She's in town from Kentucky."

When Lydia saw Dewey, she smiled and looked up at her grandfather as if for permission. "Go ahead, sweetie. Dewey won't bite." The girl tentatively stretched out her hand to Dewey; two minutes later she was stretched out on the floor, petting him.

"See?" her grandfather said to the little girl's mother. "I told you it was worth the trip." I suppose he could have meant Dewey or the library, but I suspect he was referring to something more.

Later, while the mother was petting Dewey with her daughter, the grandfather came up to me and said, "Thanks so much for adopting Dewey." It seemed he wanted to say more, but I think we both understood he had already said enough. Thirty minutes later, as they were leaving, I heard the young woman tell the older man, "You were right, Dad. That was great. I wish we had come by sooner."

"Don't worry, Mommy," the little girl said. "We'll see him next year, too."

Pride. Confidence. Assurance that this cat, this library, this experience, maybe even this town, really was special. Dewey wasn't any more beautiful or friendly after the *Country* article; in fact, fame never changed him. All Dewey ever wanted was a warm place to nap, a fresh can of food, and love and attention from every person who ever stepped foot in the Spencer Public Library. But at the same time, Dewey *had* changed, because now people looked at him differently.

The proof? Before the *Country* article, nobody took the blame for shoving poor Dewey into our book return. Everybody knew the story, but nobody confessed. After Dewey hit the media, eleven different people came up to me confidentially and swore on their mother's grave (or their mother's eye, if Mom was alive) that they had shoved Dewey down that hole. They weren't taking blame; they were taking credit. "I always knew it would turn out well," they said.

Eleven people! Can you believe it? That must have been one wild, cat-saving alley party.

THE DAILY ROUTINE

As developed by Dewey Readmore Books soon after
his regrettable romp outside the Spencer Public Library,
and followed for the rest of his life.

7:30 a.m. Mom Arrives. Demand food, but don't be too hasty. Watch everything she does. Follow at her heels. Make her feel special.

8:00 a.m. Staff Arrives. Spend an hour checking in with everyone. Find out who is having a tough morning and give them the honor of petting me for as long as they want. Or until . . .

8:58 a.m. Prep Time. Take up position by the front door, ready for first patron of the day. Also has the added benefit of alerting distracted staff to current time. I hate it when they open late.

9:00–10:30 a.m. Doors Open. Greet patrons. Follow the nice ones, ignore the mean ones, but give everyone a chance to brighten their day by paying attention to me. Petting me is a gift to you for visiting the library.

10:30 a.m. Find Lap for Nap. Laps are for naps, not playing. Playing in laps is for kittens.

11:30–11:45 a.m. Lounge. Middle of adult nonfiction, head up, paws crossed in front. The humans call this the Buddha pose. I call it the Lion. Hakuna Matata. No, I don't know what it means, but the kids keep talking about it.

11:45 a.m.–12:15 p.m. Sprawl. When it gets too tiring to hold my head up, assume the sprawl: full out on back, paws sticking out in four directions. Petting is assured. But don't fall asleep. Fall asleep, and you're vulnerable to a belly wrestle attack. I hate the belly wrestle attack.

12:15–12:30 p.m. Lunch in the Staff Room. Anybody got yogurt? No? Then never mind.

12:30–1:00 p.m. Cart Ride! When the afternoon clerks shelve books, jump on the cart and hitch a ride around the library. Oh, man, it's relaxing to go completely limp and let my legs hang down between the bars of the metal rack.

1:00–3:55 p.m. Afternoon Free Time. See how the day is going. Mix in a trip up to the lights with more lap time. Greet the afternoon crowd. Spend ten minutes with Mom. Fur licking is encouraged, not mandatory. And don't forget to find a nice box to nap in. As if it's possible to forget that!

3:55 p.m. Dinner. They keep thinking dinnertime is four o'clock. If I sit here long enough, they'll eventually learn.

4:55 p.m. Mom Leaves. Jump around so she'll remember you want to play. A running jump off a bookshelf, complete with somersault, works every time.

5:30 p.m. Play. Mom calls it Boodha track. I call it the ball thingy because there's nothing better than batting that ball around that track. Except for my red yarn. I absolutely love my red yarn. Does anyone want to dangle it for me?

8:55 p.m. Last Shift Leaves. Repeat 4:55 routine, but don't expect the same results unless Joy's working the night shift. Joy always finds time to wad up paper and toss it across the library. Sprint after the paper as fast as possible, but once you get there, always ignore it.

9:00 p.m.–7:30 a.m. My Time! None of your business, nosy.

Chapter 17 ⁓

Dewey in the Modern World

I'm not naive. I know not everyone in Spencer embraced Dewey. For instance, that woman still wrote regular letters threatening to bring her cow downtown if the city didn't stop the injustice, the horror, of a cat living in a public building. She was the most vocal, but she certainly wasn't the only person who didn't understand the Dewey phenomenon.

"What's so special about that cat?" they would say over a cup of coffee at Sister's Café. "He never leaves the library. He sleeps a lot. He doesn't *do* anything."

By which they meant Dewey didn't create jobs. Dewey was appearing regularly in magazines, newspapers, and on the radio around the country, but he wasn't improving our municipal parks. He wasn't paving roads. He wasn't out recruiting new businesses. The worst of the farm crisis had passed; spirits were rising; it was time

for Spencer to spread its wings and attract new employers to our plucky Midwest town fairly far off the
beaten track.

The Spencer economic development commission
scored its first big triumph in 1992 when Montfort, a
large meatpacking company headquartered in Colorado,
decided to lease the slaughterhouse on the north end of
town. In 1952, when local businessmen developed the
property, the plant was the pride of Spencer. It was locally owned, locally run, and employed local workers at
top wages. In 1974, the salary was fifteen dollars an
hour, the best-paying job in town. Trucks lined up for a
mile waiting to be unloaded. The company began packaging several products under a Spencer Foods label.
That label was a source of pride, especially when you'd
drive to Sioux Falls or down to Des Moines and see the
Spencer name in the big new grocery stores.

In 1968, sales started dropping. Processing conglomerates had moved into nearby towns with more efficient
plants and cheaper labor. The owners tried to rebrand
the products and retool the plant, but nothing worked.
In 1978, the Spencer Packing Company was sold to a
national competitor. When the workers wouldn't take
nonunion wages of five-fifty an hour, the company closed
the plant and moved the work to Skylar, Nebraska. Land
O'Lakes moved in next, but when the recession hit in
the mid-1980s, they closed up and left, too. They didn't
have ties to the community, and there was no economic
reason to stay.

Ten years later, Montfort negotiated a lease with the

absentee owner of the plant. They just needed the
building rezoned so they could expand and upgrade it.
Small towns all over the country were desperate for jobs,
but the jobs that had paid fifteen dollars in 1974 were
being offered by Montfort at five dollars an hour with
almost no benefits. This was slaughter work, which was
physically brutal and psychologically numbing, not to
mention smelly, noisy, dirty, and polluting. Locals didn't
want the work, at least not for long. Most of the people
who ended up in the jobs were Hispanic immigrants.
Towns around Spencer with slaughterhouses, such as
Storm Lake, were already 25 percent Hispanic, or
more.

Still, Montfort had steamrolled through dozens of
towns, and they didn't even bother addressing our concerns or offering concessions. The town leaders were for
the plant, why worry about the citizens? The city council
offered the usual public forum on the proposed zoning
changes. The forum usually took place in front of five
people in a little room at the council offices. The demand
was so great this time that they held this debate in the
largest room in town, the middle school gym. Three
thousand people showed up that night, more than 25
percent of the town. It wasn't much of a debate.

"Slaughterhouses are messy. What are they going to
do about the waste?"

"Slaughterhouses are loud. That factory is only a mile
from downtown."

"Don't even get me started on the smell."

"What about the hog trucks? Will they come straight

down Grand Avenue? Has anybody thought about the traffic?"

"We want local jobs. How are these jobs going to benefit our city?"

Outside of the economic development commission and the city council, there weren't a hundred people in that gymnasium who supported the slaughterhouse. The next day, the zoning change was voted down.

Some people—Montfort supporters in the city and economic development boards in nearby towns—hinted that the decision was racially motivated. "Lily-white Spencer," they snickered, "doesn't want Mexicans moving in."

I don't believe that at all. Spencer is not a racist town. In the 1970s, for instance, we welcomed one hundred refugee families from Laos. It's true we looked at the changes in towns like Storm Lake and Worthington and didn't like what we saw, but the problem was the slaughterhouses themselves, not the workers. Spencer banded together that day not against immigrants but against pollution, traffic, and environmental disaster. We weren't willing to sell our way of life for two hundred of the worst jobs in the country. If we did, it meant we had learned nothing from Land O'Lakes, who walked out of that very building when we needed them most. Maybe, as some suggested, we were turning our backs on economic progress to preserve the kind of town—a town based on local merchants, farmers, and small manufacturers—that can no longer survive in modern America. All I know is this: Spencer would be a different town if the first thing you saw (and smelled and heard) when you drove in from the north was a slaughterhouse, and I think we're better without it.

Spencer is not antibusiness. Within a year, the old slaughterhouse was turned into a refrigerated storage facility. Storage didn't provide as many jobs, but the wages were better and you didn't get pollution, noise, or traffic. You barely even noticed it was there.

Two years later, in 1994, Spencer welcomed with open arms what many consider the biggest, baddest conglomerate on the block: Wal-Mart. The downtown merchants were against Wal-Mart, especially a Wal-Mart superstore, so they brought in a consultant to advise them. After all, local businesses had carried this town. Why should they turn over what they had invested in and built to a national competitor?

"Wal-Mart will be the best thing to ever happen to the businesses in Spencer," the consultant told them. "If you try to compete with them, you will lose. But if you find a niche they aren't serving, for instance by providing specialty products or knowledgeable, hands-on service, you will win. Why? Because Wal-Mart will bring more customers to town. It's that simple."

The consultant was right. There were losers, most obviously Shopko, which packed up and left town, but business at the downtown merchants has increased significantly since Wal-Mart arrived. Wal-Mart did what the railroad depot had done decades before: it made Spencer a regional destination.

The same year, 1994, the Spencer Public Library entered the modern era. Out went the antiquated book-management system, with its cards, stamps, catalog drawers, checkout bins, late-notice slips, complex filing systems, and of course, dozens and dozens of boxes. In came a fully automated system complete with eight computers. The bins for the cards, where Dewey loved to lounge in the afternoon, were replaced with a circulation computer. Kim's typewriter, which Dewey had loved as a kitten, fell silent and motionless. We threw a party, pulled all the drawers out of our card catalogs, dumped thousands of cards on the floor, then turned on the one public-access computer that would replace them all. The three card catalog cabinets, with their hundreds of tiny drawers, were sold at auction. I bought one for my house. I keep it in my basement with a 1950s flip-top desk from the Moneta School. The card catalog holds all my craft supplies; the desk holds all Jodi's papers and artwork from elementary school, which I've kept care-fully preserved for thirty years.

After the technology update of 1994, people began using the library differently. Before computers, if a student was assigned a report on monkeys, she checked out every book we had on monkeys. Now she did research online and checked out one book. Patron visits to the Spencer Library rose between 1994 and 2006, but only a third as many books were checked out. In 1987, when Dewey arrived, it was common for the book drop to overflow with books. We haven't had a full drop box in a decade. Our most popular items for checkout are classic movies on DVD—the local video stores don't carry them—and video games. We have nineteen computers for public use, sixteen with Internet access. Even though we're small, we are tenth in the number of computers available to patrons in the entire Iowa library system.

A librarian clerk's job used to involve filing and answering reference questions. Now it's understanding computers and inputting data. To keep track of usage, the clerk working the circulation desk used to make a hash mark on a piece of paper every time a patron entered the library. You can imagine how accurate that system was, especially when the library was busy and the clerk was answering reference questions. Now we have an electronic clicker that records every person who comes through the door. The checkout system tells us exactly how many books, games, and movies come and go and tracks which items are the most popular and which haven't been touched in years.

And yet, for all that, the Spencer Public Library remains essentially the same. The carpet is different. The back window, which looked out on the alley, has been plastered over and covered with bookshelves. There's less wood, fewer drawers, and more electronics. But there are still children's groups laughing and listening to stories. Middle school students killing time. Older people thumbing through the newspaper. Businessmen reading magazines. This library has never been Carnegie's quiet cathedral to knowledge, but it's still a relaxed, and relaxing, place.

And when you walk into the library, you still notice

the books: shelf after shelf and row after row of books. The covers may be more colorful, the art more expressive, and the type more contemporary, but in general the books look the same as they did in 1982, and 1962, and 1942. And that's not going to change. Books have survived television, radio, talking pictures, circulars (early magazines), dailies (early newspapers), Punch and Judy shows, and Shakespeare's plays. They have survived World War II, the Hundred Years' War, the Black Death, and the fall of the Roman Empire. They even survived the Dark Ages, when almost no one could read and each book had to be copied by hand. They aren't going to be killed off by the Internet.

And neither is the library. We may not be the soothingly silent book depository of yesteryear, but we serve the community better than ever. We are connected to the wider world like never before. We can order any book at any time; we research at the touch of a button; we communicate on an electronic bulletin board with other librarians, swapping tips and information essential to making each library better and more efficient; and we access hundreds of newspapers and magazines for less than the cost of ten subscriptions only ten years ago. The number of people entering the Spencer Public Library keeps rising. Does it matter if they are checking out books, renting movies, playing video games, or visiting a cat?

Dewey didn't care about any of that, of course. He always focused on the here and now. And he loved the new library. Sure, he lost a few boxes, but there are always boxes in a library that orders books on an almost daily basis. Computers may seem cold compared to the old hands-on system of wood, paper, and ink, but to Dewey they were warm. Literally. He loved to sit on them and bask in the heat of their exhaust. I took a picture of him up there, which became the image on our new computerized checkout cards. The company that made the cards loved it. Every time I went to a library convention, I would see Dewey emblazoned on a huge banner above their booth.

Almost as good, at least from Dewey's perspective, were the new sensor posts beside the front door, which beeped if you tried to leave without checking out your library materials. Dewey's new favorite position was just inside the left post. (Just like the left shoulder for the Dewey Carry. Was Dewey left-pawed?) He sat by that post for the first hour of every day, starting promptly at two minutes to nine. With Dewey and the posts crowding the entranceway, there was almost no space for patrons to walk. Before, it was difficult to ignore Dewey when he was in front-door greeting mode; with the new sensors, it was impossible.

BASIC RULES FOR CATS WHO HAVE A LIBRARY TO RUN

(according to Dewey Readmore Books)

First printed in the Library Cat Society newsletter, and since reprinted numerous times around the world.

1. STAFF: If you are feeling particularly lonely and wanting more attention from the staff, sit on whatever papers, project, or computer they happen to be working on at the time—but sit with your back to the person and act aloof, so as not to appear too needy. Also, be sure to continually rub against the leg of the staff person who is wearing dark brown, blue, or black for maximum effect.

2. PATRONS: No matter how long the patron plans on staying at the library, climb into their briefcase or book bag for a long comfortable sleep until they must dump you out on the table in order to leave.

3. LADDERS: Never miss an opportunity to climb on ladders. It does not matter which human is on the ladder. It only matters that you get to the top and stay there.

4. CLOSING TIME: Wait until ten minutes before closing time to get up from your nap. Just as the staff is getting ready to turn out the lights and lock the door, do all your cutest tricks in an effort to get them to stay and play with you. (Although this doesn't work very often, sometimes they can't resist giving in to one short game of hide-and-seek.)

5. BOXES: Your humans must realize that all boxes that enter the library are yours. It doesn't matter how large, how small, or how full the box should be, it is yours! If you cannot fit your entire body into the box, then use whatever part of your body fits to assume ownership for naptime. (I have used one or two paws, my head, or even just my tail to gain entry and each works equally well for a truly restful sleep.)

6. MEETINGS: No matter the group, timing, or subject matter, if there is a meeting scheduled in the meeting room, you have an obligation to attend. If they have shut you out by closing the door, cry pitifully until they let you in or until someone opens the door to use the restroom or get a drink of water. After you gain entry, be sure to go around the room and greet each attendee. If there is a film or slide show, climb on any table close to the screen, settle in, and watch the film to conclusion. As the credits roll, feign extreme boredom and leave the meeting before it concludes.

And the library cat's golden rule for all time . . .

Never forget, nor let humans forget, that you own the joint!

Chapter 18 ⌒

Puss in Books

The computers weren't the only change in Dewey's life. Crystal, Dewey's friend from the special education class, graduated and began a life I can't imagine, but one I pray was happy. The little girl who had been afraid of Dewey overcame her fear of cats. She still approached the desk sometimes and asked us to lock Dewey up, but now she said it with a smile. Like any ten-year-old, she liked having adults do what she asked. The other children her age, the ones Dewey had spent Story Hour with that first year, were growing up, too. The middle school kids who had rolled pencils at him were leaving. He had been in the library six years, and it was inevitable that many of the children he had known were moving away or moving on.

Jean Hollis Clark, my assistant director, left for a new job. Eventually she was replaced by Kay Larson, whom I had known for years. Kay was laid-back and practical, a strong Iowa farm woman. She had been a chemical engineer and worked on oil rigs in the Gulf before marrying a farmer and moving back to Iowa. There were no engineering jobs in the area, so she did slaughter work for a time before landing a position at the tiny library in Petersen, about thirty miles south of Spencer. Maybe I should say *the* position, since the Petersen Library was a one-person show.

I hired Kay because she was good with computers, and we needed someone who could keep up with new technology. I also knew she was a cat person. In fact, twenty cats lived in her barn, as well as two in her house. "Typical tomcat," she'd say with Iowa practicality whenever Dewey copped a little attitude or refused to engage in a patron's two-armed hug. She thought Dewey was smart and beautiful, but she didn't think he was anything that special.

But Dewey never lacked for friends. Tony, our painter, scratched the Dewkster whenever he came to see his wife, Sharon, who was expecting their third child. It was an unplanned pregnancy, but it made them both happy. Sharon called from the hospital the day of the birth. She was crying. "Emmy has Down syndrome," she said. She had never suspected anything was wrong, and the surprise was shattering. Sharon took a few months off from the library, and by the time she came back she was head over heels in love with Emmy.

Dewey's old friend Doris Armstrong still brought him little gifts and surprises, and she loved to dangle his beloved red Christmas yarn while he jumped with delight. She was as gregarious and charming as ever, but shortly after the library remodel she began to have severe attacks of vertigo. The doctors couldn't determine the cause, so they guessed panic attacks. Then her hands began to tremble, and eventually she could barely put the covers on books. She no longer trusted herself to pet Dewey, but he didn't mind. The more she trembled, the more he brushed his back against her arm and lounged on her desk to keep her company.

Then one morning Dewey ran into my office crying. This was unusual, but he was leading me toward his food bowl so I thought he wanted a snack. Instead, I found Doris lying on the floor of the staff room. She was having such a severe vertigo attack she couldn't stand up. For days, she could barely eat she was so dizzy. The next time I found her on the floor, she not only had vertigo, but was sure she was having a heart attack. A few months later, Doris found a tiny black kitten. She brought the kitten to the library and, with trembling hands, held it out for me to hold. I could feel its heart racing and its lungs gasping for air. The kitten was weak, frightened, and sick.

"What should I do?" she asked me. I didn't know.

The next day Doris came into the library crying. She had taken the kitten home with her, and it had died during the night. Sometimes a cat is more than an animal, and sometimes the loss you mourn is not just the obvious one. Dewey sat with Doris the whole day, and she even managed to lay her hands on him and pet him, but his presence didn't soothe her. Not long after, Doris retired from the library and moved away to be near her family in Minnesota.

And yet, despite the changes, Dewey's life stayed essentially the same. Children grew up, but there were always new ones turning four. Staffers moved on, but even on our skimpy budget we managed new hires. Dewey may never again have had a friend like Crystal, but he still met the special education class at the door every week. He even developed relationships with patrons like Mark Carey, who owned the electronics store on the corner. Dewey knew Mark wasn't a cat lover, and he took fiendish delight in suddenly jumping on the table and scaring the bejeebers out of him. Mark took delight in kicking Dewey out of whatever chair he was lounging in, even if there was nobody else in the library.

One morning I noticed a businessman in a suit sitting at a table, reading the *Wall Street Journal*. It looked like he had stopped in to kill time before a meeting, so I wasn't expecting to see a fluffy orange tail sticking out at his side. I looked closer and saw that Dewey had plopped down on one page of his newspaper. Busy. Businessman. On his way to a meeting. "Oh, Dewey," I thought, "you're pushing it now." Then I realized the man was holding the newspaper with his right hand while petting Dewey with his left. One of them was purring; the other was smiling. That's when I knew Dewey and the town had fallen into a comfort zone, that the general outline of our lives had been set, at least for the next few years.

Maybe that's why I was so surprised when I arrived at the library one morning to find Dewey pacing. He was never agitated like that; even my presence didn't calm him. When I opened the door, he ran a few steps, then stopped, waiting for me to follow.

"Do you need to go to the bathroom, Dewey? You know you don't have to wait for me."

It wasn't the bathroom, and he didn't have any interest in breakfast, either. He kept pacing back and forth, crying for me. Dewey never cried unless he was in pain, but I knew Dewey. He wasn't in pain.

I tried fixing his food. Nope. I checked to see if he had poop stuck in his fur. Poop in his fur drove him absolutely nuts. I checked his nose to see if he had a temperature, and his ears to see if he had an infection. Nothing.

"Let's make the rounds, Dew."

Like all felines, Dewey had hair balls. Whenever it happened, our fanatically neat cat was mortified. But he had never acted this strangely, so I braced myself for the mother of all hair balls. I worked my way through fiction and nonfiction, checking every corner. But I didn't find anything.

Dewey was waiting for me in the children's library. The poor cat was in knots. But I didn't find anything there, either.

"I'm sorry, Dewey. I don't understand what you're trying to tell me."

When the staff arrived, I told them to keep an eye on Dewey. I was extremely busy, and I couldn't spend all morning playing charades with a cat. If Dewey was still acting strange in a few hours, I decided to take him to see Dr. Esterly. I knew he would love that.

Two minutes after the library opened, Jackie Shugars came back to my office. "You're not going to believe this, Vicki, but Dewey just peed on the cards."

I jumped up. "It can't be!"

The library automation wasn't yet complete. To check out a book, we still stamped two cards. One went home with you in the book; the other went into a big bin with hundreds of other cards. When you returned the book, we pulled that card and put the book back on the shelf. Actually there were two bins, one on each side of the front desk. Sure enough, Dewey had peed in the front right corner of one of them.

I wasn't mad at Dewey. I was worried about him. He'd been in the library for years; he'd never acted out. This was completely out of character. But I didn't have long to think the situation through before one of our regular patrons came up and whispered in my ear, "You better get down here, Vicki. There's a bat in the children's department."

Sure enough, there was the bat, hanging by his heels behind a ceiling beam. And there was Dewey at *my* heels.

I tried to tell you. I tried to tell you. Now look what you've done. You've let a patron find it. We could have taken care of this before anyone arrived. Now there are children in the library. I thought you were protecting them.

Have you ever been lectured by a cat? It's not a pleasant experience. Especially when the cat is right. And especially when a bat is involved. I hate bats. I couldn't stand the thought of having one in the library, and I couldn't imagine being trapped all night with that thing flying all over the place. Poor Dewey.

"Don't worry, Dewey. Bats sleep during the day. He won't hurt anybody."

Dewey didn't look convinced, but I couldn't worry about that now. I didn't want to scare the patrons, especially the children, so I quietly called the city hall janitor and told him, "Get down to the library right away. And bring your ladder."

He climbed up for a look. "It's a bat, all right."

"Shhh. Keep your voice down."

He climbed down. "You got a vacuum cleaner?"

I shivered. "Don't use the vacuum cleaner."

"How about Tupperware? Something with a lid."

I just stared at him. This was disgusting.

Someone said, "We've got an empty coffee can. It's got a lid."

The ordeal was over in a matter of seconds. Thank goodness. Now I had to sort out the mess in the cards.

"This is my fault," I told Jackie, who was still manning the circulation desk.

"I know." Jackie has a droll sense of humor.

"Dewey was trying to warn us. I'll clean this up."

"I figured you would."

I pulled out about twenty cards. Underneath them was a big pile of bat guano. Dewey hadn't just been trying to get my attention; he'd been using his scent glands to cover the stench of the intruder.

"Oh, Dewey, you must think I'm so stupid."

The next morning, Dewey started what I referred to as his sentry phase. Each morning, he sniffed three heating vents: the one in my office, the one by the front door, and the one by the children's library. He sniffed each one again after lunch. He knew those vents led somewhere and that therefore they were access points. He had taken it upon himself to use his powerful nose to protect us, to be our proverbial canary in the coal mine. His attitude was, *If you can't even figure out there's a bat in the library, how are you going to take care of all these people?*

I suppose there could be something funny about such a vigilant cat. What was Dewey worried about, a terrorist attack on the Spencer Public Library? Call me sentimental, but I found it very endearing. At one point in his life, Dewey wasn't content until he expanded his world to the street outside the library. Now that his story had gone all over the country, he wanted nothing more than to hunker down in the library and protect his friends. You would have to love a cat like that, right?

And the world apparently did, because Dewey's fame continued to grow. He was featured in all the cat magazines — *Cats*, *Cat Fancy*, *Cats & Kittens*. If the magazine had *cat* in the title, Dewey was probably in it. He even appeared in *Your Cat*, a leading publication of the British feline press. Marti Attoun, a young freelance writer, traveled to Spencer with a photographer. Her article appeared in *American Profile*, a weekend insert featured in more than a thousand newspapers. Then, in the summer of 1996, a documentary filmmaker from Boston turned up in out-of-the-way Spencer, Iowa, camera in tow, ready to put Dewey in his first movie.

Gary Roma was traveling the country, from the East Coast to North Dakota, to create a documentary about library cats. He arrived expecting the kind of footage he'd shot at other libraries: cats darting apprehensively behind bookshelves, walking away, sleeping, and doing everything possible to avoid looking into the camera. Dewey was exactly the opposite. He didn't ham it up, but he went about all his usual activities, and he performed them on command. Gary arrived early in the morning to catch Dewey waiting for me at the front door. He shot Dewey sitting by the sensor posts greeting patrons; lying in his Buddha pose; playing with his favorite toys, Marty Mouse and the red yarn; sitting on a patron's shoulder in the Dewey Carry; and sleeping in a box.

Gary said, "This is the best footage I've shot so far. If you don't mind, I'll come back after lunch."

After lunch I sat down for an interview. After a few introductory questions, Gary asked, "What is the meaning of Dewey?"

I told him, "Dewey's great for the library. He relieves stress. He makes it feel like home. People love him, especially children."

"Yes, but what's the deeper meaning?"

"There is no deeper meaning. Everyone enjoys spending time with Dewey. He makes us happy. He's one of us. What more to life is there than that?"

He kept pressing for meaning, meaning, meaning. Gary's first film was *Off the Floor & Off the Wall: A Doorstop Documentary*, and I could imagine him pressing all his subjects: "What does your doorstop mean to you?"

"It keeps the door from hitting the wall."

"Yes, but what about the deeper meaning?"

"Well, I can use it to hold the door open."

"Go deeper."

"Umm, it keeps the room drafty?"

Gary must have gotten deeper meaning out of doorstops because one review mentions linguists dissecting the etymology of the word and philosophers musing about a world without doors.

About six months after filming, in the winter of 1997, we threw a party for the inaugural showing of *Puss in Books*. The library was packed. The film started with a distant shot of Dewey sitting on the floor of the Spencer library waving his tail slowly back and forth. As the camera zoomed in and followed him under a table, across some shelves, and finally to his favorite cart for a ride, you heard my voice in the background: "We arrived at work one morning, and we went back to open the book drop and empty the books out, and there inside was this tiny little kitten. He was buried under tons of books, the book drop was just full of books. People will come in, and they'll hear the story of how we acquired Dewey, and they'll say, 'Oh, you poor little thing. You were thrown into that book drop on that day.' And I'll say, 'Poor little thing, my foot. That was the luckiest day of that boy's life, because he's king around here, and he knows it.'"

As the last words rolled out, Dewey stared right into the camera, and boy, could you tell I was right. He really was the king.

By this time, I was used to strange calls about Dewey. The library was getting a couple requests a week for interviews, and articles about our famous cat were turning up in our mail on an almost weekly basis. Dewey's official photograph, the one taken by Rick Krebsbach just after Jodi left Spencer, had appeared in magazines, newsletters, books, and newspapers from Minneapolis, Minnesota, to Jerusalem, Israel. It even appeared in a cat calendar; Dewey was Mr. January. But even I was surprised to receive a phone call from the Iowa office of a national pet food company.

"We've been watching Dewey," they said, "and we're impressed." Who wouldn't be? "He seems like an extraordinary cat. And obviously people love him." You don't say! "We'd like to use him in a print advertising campaign. We can't offer money, but we will provide free cat food for life."

I have to admit, I was tempted. Dewey was a finicky

eater, and we were indulgent parents. We were throwing out dishes full of food every day just because he didn't like the smell, and we were donating a hundred cans of out-of-favor cat food a year. Since the Feed the Kitty campaign of loose change and soda cans didn't cover the costs and I had vowed to never use a penny of city funds for Dewey's care, most of that money was coming out of my pocket. I was personally subsidizing the feeding of a good portion of the cats in Spencer.

"I'll talk to the library board."

"We'll send over samples."

By the time the next library board meeting rolled around, the decision had already been made. Not by me or the board, but by Dewey himself. Mr. Finicky completely rejected the free samples.

Are you kidding me? he told me with a disdainful sniff. *I can't shill for this junk.*

"I'm sorry," I told the manufacturer. "Dewey only eats Fancy Feast."

Chapter 19 ⟳

The World's Worst Eater

ewey's pickiness wasn't just a matter of personality. He had a disease. No, really, it's true. As far as digestive systems were concerned, that cat really got a lemon.

Dewey always hated being petted on the stomach. Stroke his back, scratch his ears, even pull his tail and poke him in the eye, but never pet his stomach. I didn't think much of it until Dr. Esterly tried to clean his anal glands when he was about two years old. "I just push down on the glands and squeeze them clean," he explained. "It will take thirty seconds."

Sounded easy enough. I held Dewey while Dr. Esterly prepared his equipment, which consisted of a pair of gloves and a paper towel. "Nothing to it, Dewey," I whispered. "It will be over before you know it."

But as soon as Dr. Esterly pressed down, Dewey screamed. This wasn't a mild complaint. This was a full-fledged, terrified cry that ripped out from the base of his stomach. His body bolted like it had been hit by lightning, and his legs scrambled frantically. Then he threw his mouth over my finger and bit down. Hard.

Dr. Esterly looked at my finger. "He shouldn't have done that."

I rubbed the sore. "It's not a problem."

"Yes, it is a problem. A cat shouldn't bite like that."

I wasn't worried. That wasn't Dewey. I knew Dewey; he wasn't a biter. And I could still see the panic in the poor cat's eyes. He wasn't looking at anything. He was just staring. The pain had been blinding.

After that, Dewey hated Dr. Esterly. He even hated the thought of getting in the car because it might lead to Dr. Esterly. As soon as we pulled into the veterinary office's parking lot, he started shaking. The smell of the lobby sent him into uncontrollable tremors. He would bury his head in the crook of my arm as if to say, *Protect me.*

As soon as he heard Dr. Esterly's voice, Dewey growled. Many cats hate the veterinarian in his office but treat him as any other human in the outside world. Not Dewey. He feared Dr. Esterly unconditionally. If he heard his voice in the library, Dewey growled and sprinted to the other side of the room. If Dr. Esterly managed to sneak up on him and reached out to pet him, Dewey sprang up, looked around in panic, and bolted away. I think he recognized Dr. Esterly's smell. That hand, to Dewey, was the hand of death. He had found his archenemy, and it happened to be one of the nicest men in town.

A few uneventful years went by after the anal gland incident, but Dewey eventually went back to prowling for rubber bands. As a kitten, his rubber band hunting had been halfhearted, and he was easily distracted. At about five years of age, Dewey became serious. I started finding the sticky remnants on the floor almost every morning. His litter box was filled not only with rubber worms but with the occasional drop of blood. Sometimes Dewey came tearing out of the back room like someone had lit a firecracker under his rear end.

Dr. Esterly diagnosed Dewey with constipation. Extreme constipation. "What kind of food does Dewey eat?"

I rolled my eyes. Dewey was well on his way to becoming the world's worst eater. "He's very picky. He has a remarkable sense of smell, so he can tell when the food is old or off in some way. Cat food isn't the highest quality, you know. It's just a bunch of leftover animal parts. So you can't blame him."

Dr. Esterly looked at me like a kindergarten teacher eyeing a parent who had just explained away her child's disruptive behavior. Overindulgent, are we?

"He always eats canned food?"

"Yes."

"Good. Does he drink much water?"

"Never."

"Never?"

"The cat avoids his water dish like poison."

"More water," Dr. Esterly assured me. "That should clear up the problem."

Thanks, Doc, nothing to it. Except have you ever tried to get a cat to drink water against his will? It's impossible.

I started with gentle coaxing. Dewey turned away in disgust.

I tried bribery. "No food until you drink some water. Don't look at me like that. I can last longer than you can." But I couldn't. I always gave in.

I started petting Dewey as he ate. Slowly the petting turned to pushing. "If I force his head down into the water," I thought, "he has to drink." Needless to say, that plan didn't work.

Maybe it was the water. We tried warm water. We tried cold water. We tried refreshing the water every five minutes. We tried different faucets. This was the mid-1990s, so there was no such thing as bottled water, at least not in Spencer, Iowa. We tried putting ice in the water dish. Everyone likes ice water, right? Actually, the ice worked. Dewey took a lick. But otherwise, nothing. How could an animal stay alive without water?

A few weeks later I rounded the corner into the staff bathroom and there was Dewey, on the toilet, his head completely buried in the bowl. All I could see was his rear end sticking straight up in the air. Toilet water! You sneaky son of a gun.

"Well," I thought, "at least he isn't going to die of dehydration."

The door was left open when the staff bathroom was unoccupied, so that toilet was Dewey's primary water source. But he also loved the women's bathroom in the front of the library. Joy DeWall was the library clerk who spent the most time shelving books. Dewey would watch her loading books onto the book cart, then hop on for a ride once it was full. He would stare at the bookshelves as the cart rolled past, and whenever he saw something he liked, he'd signal Joy that he wanted to get off, like he was riding a little cat trolley. He knew she was a soft touch, so he always begged her to let him into that bathroom. Once inside the sanctum, he jumped on the sink and begged for the water to be turned on. He didn't drink this water. He watched it. Something about the way it bounced off the drain plug fascinated him. He could watch that water for an hour, occasionally taking a quick slap at it with his paw.

But that didn't help his constipation, and neither did trips to his royal porcelain bowl. Whether he watched water or drank it, Dewey still couldn't go. When it got really bad, Dewey tended to hide. One morning, poor Sharon Joy reached into the top drawer of the circulation desk for a tissue, but instead grabbed a handful of hair. She literally fell out of her chair.

"How did he get in there?" she asked, staring down at Dewey's back. His head and rear were completely buried in the drawer.

Good question. The drawer hadn't been opened all morning, so Dewey must have climbed in during the night. I poked around under the desk. Sure enough, there was a small opening behind the drawers. But this was the top drawer, more than three feet off the ground. Mr. Rubber Spine had wiggled his way to the top of the crevice and turned a tight corner, all to curl up in a space of no more than a few inches.

I tried to rouse him, but Dewey shrugged me off and didn't move. This wasn't like him at all. Obviously something was wrong.

As I suspected, Dewey was constipated. Extremely constipated. Again. This time, Dr. Esterly performed a thorough exam, with lots of deep poking and prodding of Dewey's sensitive belly. Oh, it was painful to watch. This was definitely the end of the cat-doctor relationship.

"Dewey has megacolon."

"You're going to have to walk me through that, Doctor."

"Dewey's colon is distended. This causes his intestinal contents to pool inside his body cavity."

Silence.

"Dewey's colon is permanently stretched out. This allows it to store more waste. By the time Dewy tries to get rid of it, the opening to the outside world is too small."

"A little extra water isn't going to solve the problem, is it?"

"I'm afraid there's no cure. The condition is rare." In fact, they weren't even sure of the cause. Apparently, distended feline colons were not a top research priority.

If Dewey had lived in the alley, his megacolon would have shortened his life. In a controlled environment like the library, I could expect periodic but severe bouts of constipation, accompanied by very picky eating. When the plumbing tends to back up, cats get awfully choosy about what they put in the system. See, I told you he had a disease.

Dr. Esterly suggested an expensive cat food, the kind you could buy only from a veterinarian. I forget the name, maybe Laboratory Diet, Middle-aged Cat with Bowel Troubles Formula? The bill almost broke the budget. I hated to dish out thirty dollars for something I knew wasn't going to work.

I told Dr. Esterly, "Dewey's a picky eater. He's not going to like this."

"Put it in his bowl. Don't give him anything else. He'll eat it. No cat will starve itself to death." As I was packing up to leave, he added, as much to himself as to me, "We're going to have to watch Dewey carefully. There will be ten thousand unhappy people if something happens to him."

"There will be more people than that, Dr. Esterly. A lot more."

I put the fancy new food in the bowl. Dewey didn't eat it. He sniffed it once and walked away.

This food, it's no good. I want the usual, please.

The next day, he dropped the subtle approach. Instead of sniffing and walking away, he sat down by the food bowl and cried.

Whhhyyyy? What have I done to deserve this?

"Sorry, Dewey. Doctor's orders."

After two days, he was weak, but he didn't waver. He hadn't even batted the food with his paw. That's when I realized Dewey was stubborn. Painfully stubborn. He was a mellow cat. He was accommodating. But when it came to an important principle like food, Dewey would never roll over and play dog.

And neither would I. Mom could be stubborn, too.

So Dewey went behind my back to the rest of the staff. First he hit up Sharon by jumping on her desk and rubbing her arm. He had taken to sitting on Sharon's desk and watching her eat lunch, and she seemed appreciative of a good meal.

When that didn't work, he tried his old friend Joy, always a soft touch. Then he tried Audrey, Cynthia, Paula, everybody, right down the line. He tried Kay, even though he knew she was the no-nonsense, practical type.

Kay had no time for weakness. But I could see even she was beginning to waver. She tried to act tough, but she was developing a real warm spot in her heart for the Dew.

I didn't care, let them disapprove. I was going to win this round. It might break my heart now, but in the end Dewey would thank me. And besides, I was Mommy, and I said so!

On the fourth day, even the patrons turned on me. "Just feed him, Vicki! He's so hungry." Dewey had been shamelessly putting on a starving cat act for his fans, and it had clearly been working.

Finally, on the fifth day, I caved and gave Dewey his favorite can of Fancy Feast. He gobbled it down without even coming up for air. *That's it*, he said, licking his lips and then stepping to the corner for a long tongue bath of his face and ears. *We all feel better now, don't we?*

That night I went out and bought him an armful of cans. I couldn't fight anymore. "Better a constipated cat," I thought, "than a dead one."

For two months Dewey was happy. I was happy. All was right with the world.

Then Dewey decided he didn't like Fancy Feast, chunky chicken flavor. He wasn't going to eat another bite of it. He wanted something new, and make it snappy, thank you very much. I bought a new flavor, something in the moist smelly blob category. Dewey took one sniff and walked away. *Nope, not that one, either.*

"You'll eat it, young man, or no dessert for you."

At the end of the day, the food was still there, dried out and crusty. What was I supposed to do? The cat was sick! It took five tries, but I found a flavor he liked. It only lasted a few weeks. Then he wanted something new. Oh, brother. I hadn't just ceded the battlefield; I'd completely lost the war.

By 1997 the situation was completely absurd. How could you not laugh at an entire bookshelf full of cans of cat food? I'm not exaggerating. We kept Dewey's items on two shelves in the staff area, and one of them was only for food. We had at least five flavors on hand at all times. The Dew had Midwestern taste. His favorite flavors were beef, chunky chicken, beef & liver, and turkey, but you never knew when another flavor would strike his fancy. He hated seafood, but he fell in love with shrimp. For a week. Then he wouldn't touch it.

Unfortunately Dewey was still constipated, so on Dr. Esterly's orders I copied a page out of a calendar and hung it on the wall. Every time someone found a present in Dewey's litter box, they marked the date. The calendar was known throughout the office as Dewey's Poop Chart.

I can only imagine what someone like Sharon thought. She was very funny, and she loved Dewey, but she was also fastidious. Now we were discussing poop on a regular basis. She must have thought I was nuts. But she marked that chart, and she never complained. Of course, Dewey only pooped a couple times a week, so we weren't exactly wearing down the nibs of our pens.

When Dewey hadn't gone for three days, we locked him in the back closet for a romantic date with his litter. Dewey hated being locked anywhere, especially a closet. I hated it almost as much as Dewey, especially in the winter because the closet was unheated.

"It's for your own good, Dew."

After a half hour, I let him out. If no evidence turned

up in the litter box, I gave him an hour to roam and then locked him in for another half hour. No poop, back in the box. Three times was the limit. After three times, he wasn't holding out, he really couldn't go.

This strategy completely backfired. Dewey soon became so pampered he refused to use the bathroom unless someone took him to the box. He stopped going completely at night, which meant first thing in the morning I had to carry him—yes, carry him—to his litter. Talk about being the king!

I know, I know. I was a sucker. A spoiler of cats. But what could I do? I knew how bad Dewey felt. Not just because I had a connection with him, but because I was no stranger to lifelong illness. I'd been in and out of the hospital more times than most doctors. I'd been medevaced to Sioux Falls twice. And I had been through the Mayo Clinic for irritable bowel syndrome, hyperthyroidism, severe migraines, and Graves' disease, among others. At one point I had hives on my legs for two years. It turned out I was allergic to the prayer kneeler at church. A year later I suddenly froze. I couldn't move for half an hour. The staff had to carry me to a car, drive me home, and lay me out in bed. It happened again at a wedding. I had a forkful of wedding cake halfway to my mouth and I couldn't put my arm down. I couldn't even move my tongue to tell anyone. Thank God my friend Faith was there. The cause turned out to be a sudden, severe drop in blood pressure exacerbated by one of my medications.

But worst, by far, were the lumps in my breasts. Even now, I don't feel entirely comfortable talking about it.

I've shared this experience with very few people, and it's difficult to break that silence. I don't want anyone to look at me as less than a complete woman or, even worse, some kind of fraud.

Of all the things in my life—the alcoholic husband, the welfare, the surprise hysterectomy—my double mastectomy was by far the hardest. The worst part wasn't the procedure, although it was probably the most physically painful thing I've ever endured. The worst part was the decision. I agonized over it for more than a year. I traveled to Sioux City, Sioux Falls, and Omaha, more than three hours away, to consult physicians, but I couldn't make up my mind.

Mom and Dad encouraged me to have the procedure. They said, "You have to do it. You have to get healthy. Your life is at stake."

I talked to my friends, who had helped me through the end of my marriage and so many problems since, but for the first time they didn't talk back. They couldn't deal with it, they admitted later. Breast cancer hit too close to the bone.

I needed to have the surgery. I knew that. If I didn't, it was only a matter of time before I heard the word *cancer*. But I was a single woman. I dated fairly regularly, if not particularly successfully. My friend Bonnie and I still laugh about the Cowboy, whom I met at a dance in West Okoboji. We met up in Sioux City, and he took me to one of those country places with sawdust on the floor. I can't tell you about the food because a fight broke out, someone pulled a knife, and I spent twenty minutes huddled in the women's bathroom. The Cowboy graciously took me back to his house and showed me—I kid you not—how to make bullets. On the way back, he drove me through the stockyards. He found it romantic to see the holding pens in the moonlight.

And yet despite the flops, I still hoped for the right man. I didn't want that hope to die. But who could love me without my breasts? It wasn't losing my sexuality I was worried about. It was losing my femininity, my identity as a woman, my self-image. My parents didn't understand; my friends were too scared to help. What could I do?

One morning there was a knock on my office door. It was a woman I had never met. She came in, closed the door, and said, "You don't know me, but I'm a patient of Dr. Kolegraff's. He sent me to see you. Five years ago, I had a double mastectomy."

We talked for two hours. I don't remember her name, and I haven't seen her since (she wasn't from Spencer), but I remember every word. We talked about everything—the pain, the procedure, the recovery, but mostly the emotions. Did she still feel like a woman? Was she still herself? What did she see when she looked in the mirror?

When she left, I not only knew the right decision, I was ready to make it.

The double mastectomy was a multistep process. First, they took my breasts. Then they installed temporary implants called expanders. I had ports under my arms—literally tubes that stuck out from my flesh—and every two weeks I received a saline injection to expand the size of my chest and stretch the skin. Unfortunately the dangers of silicone implants exploded into the news during my first weeks of recovery, and the FDA placed a temporary ban on new implants. I ended up keeping my four-week temporary expanders for eight months. I had so much scar tissue under my armpits that I got shooting pains down my sides whenever the barometric pressure changed. For years, Joy asked me every time she saw a dark cloud, "Vicki, is it going to rain?"

"Yes," I'd say, "but not for another thirty minutes." I could tell when the rain was coming to within ten minutes just by the level of pain. Once it reached crippling, the rain was almost here. Joy and I would laugh, because I was almost always right, but I really just wanted to sit down, right where I was, and cry.

Nobody knew my pain: not my parents, my friends, or my staff. The doctor dug inside my body and scraped out every ounce of flesh he could find. That hollow, sore, scraped-out feeling was always with me, every minute, but sometimes the pain would wash over me so suddenly and so savagely that I would drop to the floor. I was out of the library, on and off, for most of a year. Many of the days I struggled to my desk I knew I shouldn't have been there at all. With Kay in charge, the library could run without me, but I wasn't sure I could run without it. The routine. The company. The feeling of accomplishment. And most of all, Dewey.

Whenever I had needed him in the past, Dewey had always been by my side. He had perched on my computer when I thought life might overwhelm me, and he had sat beside me on the sofa and waited for Jodi to spend time with us. Now he moved from sitting beside me to climbing up, one paw at a time, and sitting on my lap. He stopped walking beside me and started insisting on climbing into my arms. That might seem like a small thing, but it made all the difference to me because, you see, I didn't have anybody to touch. There was a distance between me and the world, and there was no one to hug me, to tell me it was going to be okay. It wasn't just the surgery. For two years, while I agonized over my decision, mourned my loss, and endured the physical pain, Dewey touched me every day. He sat on me. He snuggled in my arms. And when it was over, when I was finally back to something resembling my normal self, he went right back to sitting at my side. Nobody understood what I was going through for those two years; nobody, that is, but Dewey. He seemed to understand that love was constant, but that it could be raised to a higher level when it really mattered.

Every morning since his first week in the library, Dewey had waited for me at the front door. He would stare at me as I approached, then turn and run for his food bowl when I opened the door. Then, on one of the worst mornings of that terrible two years, he started waving. Yes, waving. I stopped and looked at him. He stopped and looked at me, then started waving again.

It happened the next morning, too. And the next. And the next, until finally I understood this was our new routine. For the rest of his life, as soon as Dewey saw my car pull into the parking lot, he started scratching his right paw on the front door. The wave continued as I crossed the street and approached the door. It wasn't frantic. He wasn't meowing or pacing. He was sitting very still and waving at me, as if welcoming me to the library and, at the same time, reminding me he was there. As if I could ever forget. Every morning, Dewey waving at me as I walked toward the library made me feel better:

about the job, about life, about myself. If Dewey was waving, everything was all right.

"Good morning, Dewey," I would say, my heart singing and the library bursting with life, even on the darkest and coldest mornings. I would look down at him and smile. He would rub against my ankle. My buddy. My boy. Then I would cradle him in my arms and carry him to his litter box. How could I deny him that?

Chapter 20 ⌐

Dewey's
New Friends

O
n the afternoon of June 7, 1999, I received a phone call from a Dewey fan. "Vicki, turn on the radio. You're not going to believe this."

I turned it on to hear "and now you know . . . the rest of the story."

Anyone raised on radio knows that sign-off. Paul Harvey's *The Rest of the Story* is one of the most popular programs in the history of radio. Each broadcast relates a minor but telling incident in the life of a well-known person. The gimmick is that you don't know whom Paul Harvey is talking about until his famous closing.

"And that little boy," he might say, "the one who so wanted to cut down that cherry tree, grew up to be none other than George Washington, the father of our country. And now you know . . . the rest of the story."

Now Paul Harvey was telling the story of a cat who inspired a town and became famous around the world . . . and it all started in a library book drop on a cold January morning in a small Iowa town. And now you know . . .

Who cares if nobody from Paul Harvey's staff called to check the facts? Who cares if they didn't know 10 percent of the rest of the story, the part that made Dewey so special? I sat down at the end of the broadcast and thought, "That's it. Dewey's really made it now." And then, because I was so used to the unexpected with Dewey, I wondered what was going to happen next.

For years I had gone to the newspaper and the radio station to pass on Dewey news. With Paul Harvey, I decided to hold back. It wasn't that there weren't plenty of Dewey fans. Patrons asked every day for the latest bit of Dewey news. Children ran into the library, eager and smiling, looking for their friend. But good news about Dewey no longer seemed to impress the rest of the town. In fact, I was beginning to worry it was pushing some people away. Dewey, I suspected, might be a little overexposed.

But only in Spencer. The rest of the world still couldn't get enough. In addition to being on several state boards, I was one of six continuing-education instructors in the Iowa library system. I taught the courses using the Iowa Communication Network (ICN), a teleconferencing system connecting libraries, military depots, hospitals, and schools around the state. Every time I sat down in our ICN room to teach the opening class of a course, the first question was, "Where's Dewey?"

"Yes," another librarian would pipe up, "can we see him?"

Fortunately, Dewey attended all meetings in the ICN room. He preferred meetings of actual people, but teleconferences were acceptable, too. I put Dewey on the table and pushed a button so he appeared on viewing screens all over the state. You could probably hear the gasp in Nebraska.

"He's so cute."

"Do you think my library should get a cat?"

"Only if it's the right cat." That's what I always told them. "You can't get just any cat. He has to be special."

"Special?"

"Calm, patient, dignified, intelligent, and above all, outgoing. A library cat has to love people. It also helps if he's gorgeous and comes with an unforgettable story." I didn't mention loving, absolutely loving with his whole heart, being the library cat.

"Okay," I told them eventually. "Enough fun. Back to censorship and collection development."

"One more minute. Please. I want my staff to meet Dewey."

I looked over at my big orange buddy, who was sprawled out in his favorite spot on the table. "You're loving this, aren't you?"

He gave me an innocent look. *Who, me? I'm just doing my job.*

It wasn't just librarians who loved Dewey. I was working in my office one morning when Kay called me to the front desk. Standing there was a family of four, two young parents and their children.

"This nice family," Kay said, with barely disguised

amazement, "is from Rhode Island. They've come to meet Dewey."

The father extended his hand. "We were in Minneapolis, so we decided to rent a car and drive down. The kids just love Dewey."

Was this man crazy? Minneapolis was four and half hours away. "Wonderful," I said, shaking their hands. "How did you find out about Dewey?"

"We read about him in *Cats* magazine. We're cat lovers."

Obviously.

"Okay," I said, because I couldn't think of anything else. "Let's go meet him."

Dewey was, thank goodness, as eager to please as always. He played with the children. He posed for photographs. I showed the little girl the Dewey Carry, and she walked him all around the library on her left shoulder (always the left). I don't know if it was worth the nine-hour round trip, but the family left happy.

"That was weird," Kay said once the family was gone.

"It sure was. I bet that never happens again."

It happened again. And again. And again. And again. They came from Utah, Washington, Mississippi, California, Maine, and every other corner of the map. Older couples, younger couples, families. Many were traveling cross-country and drove one hundred, two hundred miles out of their way to stop in Spencer for the day. I can remember many of their faces, but the only names I remember are Harry and Rita Fein's from New York City because after meeting Dewey they sent both a birthday present and a Christmas present of twenty-five dollars every year for food and supplies. I wish I had thought to write down information on the others, but at first it seemed so unlikely more people would ever come. Why bother? By the time we realized the power of Dewey's appeal, visitors were so common they no longer seemed unusual enough to take note of.

How were these people finding out about Dewey? I have no idea. The library never pursued publicity for Dewey. We never contacted a single newspaper, with the exception of the *Spencer Daily Reporter*. We never hired a publicity agent or marketing manager. After Shopko, we never entered Dewey in any contests. We were Dewey's answering service, nothing more. We picked up the phone, and there was another magazine, another television program, another radio station wanting an interview. Or we opened the mail and found an article about Dewey from a magazine we'd never heard of or a newspaper halfway across the country. A week later, another family popped up at the library.

What were these pilgrims expecting to find? A wonderful cat, of course, but there are wonderful cats sitting homeless in every shelter in America. Why come all this way? Was it love, peace, comfort, acceptance, a reminder of the simple joys of life? Did they just want to spend time with a star?

Or were they hoping to find a cat, a library, a town, an experience that was genuine, that wasn't from the past or for the moment, that was different from their lives but somehow familiar? Is that what Iowa is all about? Maybe the heartland isn't just the place in the middle of the country; maybe it's also the place in the middle of your chest.

Whatever they were after, Dewey delivered. The magazine articles and newscasts touched people. We received letters all the time that started, "I've never written to a stranger before, but I heard Dewey's story and . . ." His visitors, all of them, left smitten. I know this not only because they told me or because I saw their eyes and their smiles but because they went home and told people the story. They showed them the pictures. At first they sent letters to friends and relatives. Later, when the technology caught on, they sent e-mails. Dewey's face, his personality, his story, it all magnified. He received letters from Taiwan, Holland, South Africa, Norway, Australia. He had pen pals in half a dozen countries. A ripple started in a little town in northwest Iowa, and somehow the human network carried it all over the world.

Whenever I think of Dewey's popularity, I think of Jack Manders. Jack is now retired, but when Dewey arrived he was a middle school teacher and the president of our library board. A few years later, when his daughter was accepted at Hope College in Holland, Michigan, Jack found himself attending a reception for the parents of incoming freshmen. As he stood there in an elegant Michigan nightspot slowly sipping a martini, he fell into conversation with a couple from New York City. Eventually they asked where he was from.

"A small town in Iowa you've never heard of."

"Oh. Is it near Spencer?"

"Actually," he told them with surprise, "it is Spencer."

The couple perked up. "Do you ever go to the library?"

"All the time. In fact, I'm on the board."

The charming, well-dressed woman turned to her husband and, with an almost girlish giggle, exclaimed, "It's Dewey's daddy!"

A similar thing happened to another board member, Mike Baehr, on a cruise in the South Pacific. During the meet and greet, Mike and his wife realized many of their fellow passengers had never even heard of Iowa. At about the same time, they realized cruises had a social hierarchy based on how many cruises you'd been on, and since this was their first cruise, they were at the bottom of the pecking order. Then a woman came up to them and said, "I hear you're from Iowa. Do you know Dewey, the library cat?" What an icebreaker! Mike and Peg were off the outcast list, and Dewey was the talk of the cruise.

This is not to say everyone knew Dewey. No matter how famous and popular Dewey became, there was always someone with no idea Spencer Public Library had a cat. A family would drive from Nebraska to see Dewey. They would bring gifts, spend two hours playing with him, taking pictures, talking with the staff. Ten minutes after they left, someone would come up to the desk, obviously worried, and whisper, "I don't want to alarm you, but I just saw a cat in the building."

"Yes," we would whisper back. "He lives here. He's the world's most famous library cat."

"Oh," they'd say with a smile, "then I guess you already know."

The visitors who truly touched me, though, the ones I remember clearly, were the young parents from Texas and their six-year-old daughter. As soon as they entered the library, it was clear this was a special trip for her. Was she sick? Was she dealing with a trauma? I don't know why, but I had the feeling the parents offered her one wish, and this was it. The girl wanted to meet Dewey. And, I noticed, she had brought a present.

"It's a toy mouse," her father told me. He was smiling, but I could tell he was intensely worried. This was no ordinary spur-of-the-moment visit.

As I smiled back at him, only one thought was going through my mind: "I hope that toy mouse has catnip in it." Dewey would regularly go through periods where he wanted nothing to do with any toy that didn't contain catnip. Unfortunately this was one of those times.

All I said was, "I'll go get Dewey."

Dewey was asleep in his new fake fur–lined bed, which we kept outside my office door in front of a heating unit. As I woke him up I tried a little mental telepathy: "Please, Dewey, please. This one's important." He was so tired, he barely opened his eyes.

The little girl was hesitant at first, as many children are, so the mother petted Dewey first. Dewey lay there like a sack of potatoes. The girl eventually reached out to pet him, and Dewey woke up enough to lean into her hand. The father sat down and put both Dewey and the girl on his lap. Dewey immediately snuggled up against her.

They sat like that for a minute or two. Finally the girl showed him the present she had brought, with its carefully tied ribbon and bow. Dewey perked up, but I could tell he was still tired. He would have preferred to snooze in the girl's lap all morning. "Come on, Dewey," I thought. "Snap out of it." The girl unwrapped the gift, and sure enough, it was a plain toy mouse, no catnip in sight. My heart sank. This was going to be a disaster.

The girl dangled the mouse in front of Dewey's sleepy eyes to get his attention. Then she delicately tossed it a few feet away. As soon as it hit the ground, Dewey jumped on it. He chased that toy; he threw it in the air; he batted it with his paws. The girl giggled with delight. Dewey never played with it again, but while that little girl was here, he loved that little mouse. He gave that mouse every ounce of energy he had. And the little girl beamed. She just beamed. She had come hundreds of miles to see a cat, and she was not disappointed. Why did I ever worry about Dewey? He always came through.

DEWEY'S JOB DESCRIPTION

*Written in response to the question, "So what is Dewey's job?"
which was often asked after people found out Dewey received
a 15 percent library employee discount from Dr. Esterly.*

1. Reducing stress for all humans who pay attention to him.

2. Sitting by the front door every morning at nine to greet the
   public as they enter the library.

3. Sampling all boxes that enter the library for security problems and comfort level.

4. Attending all meetings in the Round Room as official library
   ambassador.

5. Providing comic relief for staff and visitors.

6. Climbing in book bags and briefcases while patrons are
   studying or trying to retrieve needed papers.

7. Generating free national and worldwide publicity for Spencer
   Public Library. (This entails sitting still for photographs,
   smiling for the camera, and generally being cute.)

8. Working toward status as world's most finicky cat by refusing
   all but the most expensive, delectable foods.

Chapter 21 ⌒

What Makes
Us Special?

I'll always remember the former city manager. Every time he saw me, he said with a smile, "Are you girls at the library still mooning over that cat?" Maybe he was trying to be funny, but I couldn't help but feel offended. *Girls!* That word might be a term of endearment, but I got the feeling he was putting me in my place, that he was speaking for a large block of community leaders who couldn't even conceive of making a fuss over things like books, libraries, and cats. That was *girl* stuff.

Did the town even need a cat anymore? It was the twenty-first century, after all, and Spencer was thriving. In the late 1990s, the YMCA completed a $2 million renovation. The Spencer Regional Hospital expanded twice. Thanks to $170,000 in donations and 250 volunteers, the modest new playground planned for East Lynch Park turned into a 30,000-square-foot megaplayground called the Miracle on South Fourth Street. Why not just take the next step and attract . . . a casino?

When Iowa decided to issue a few casino licenses in 2003, some community leaders sensed an opportunity to catapult Spencer into the biggest little small town in America. They courted developers, even picked out a location along the river on the southwest edge of town, and drew up plans. But for many of us, the casino in 2003 looked like the slaughterhouse in 1993—a chance to put on economic muscle, but at a high cost. Sure, the casino would generate good jobs and, according to estimates, more than a million dollars in mandatory charitable contributions a year, but would we ever be the same town again? Would we lose our identity and become, in our own eyes and everyone else's around, the casino town? The debate went back and forth, but in the end the casino met the same fate as the Montfort plant: the community voted it down. The casino was authorized in Palo Alto County, the county east of us, and built in Emmetsburg, only twenty-five miles away.

Maybe when we voted down the casino we once again turned our backs on the future. Maybe we were selling out our history as a progressive town. Maybe we were being naive. But in Spencer we believe in building on what we have.

We have the Clay County Fair, one of the best county fairs in the United States and a tradition for almost a hundred years. Clay County has fewer than 20,000 residents, but the fair attracts more than 300,000 people for nine days of rides, concerts, food, and fun. We have a full-size track for races and tractor pulls, a separate ring for horses, and long metal barns for everything from chickens to llamas. There are hay wagons to take you from the parking lot (a grass field) to the front gate.

We've even installed a sky bucket system to carry people from one end of the fair to the other. There's a year-round sign about ten miles south of Spencer, on the main road (and only road if you're driving more than a few miles), that counts down the weeks to the fair. It's painted on a brick building built on the highest hill in the area.

We have Grand Avenue, a historic treasure, rebuilt in 1931 and revived in 1987. In the late 1990s, our city planner, Kirby Schmidt, spent two years researching our downtown strip. Kirby was one of the native sons who almost left Spencer during the crisis of the 1980s. His brother left for the East Coast, his sister for the West Coast. Kirby sat down at the kitchen table with his young family, and they decided to stick it out. The economy turned; Kirby got a job with the city. A few years later, I gave him the key to the library, and he started coming in at six every morning to search through microfiche files, old newspapers, and local histories. Dewey mostly slept through these early visits; in the morning, he only had eyes for me.

In 1999, Grand Avenue between Third Street and Eighth Street was placed on the National Register of Historic Places. The area was cited as a remarkable example of Prairie Deco and one of the few surviving comprehensive models of Depression-era urban planning. It usually took two or three applications to make the Registry, but thanks to Kirby Schmidt, Grand Avenue made it by unanimous vote on the first application. Around the same time, Kirby's sister moved her family back to Spencer from Seattle. She wanted to raise her kids the old-fashioned way: in Iowa.

That's another of Spencer's unique and valuable assets: its people. We are good, solid, hardworking midwesterners. We are proud but humble. We don't brag. We believe your worth is measured by the respect of your neighbors, and there is no place we'd rather be than with those neighbors right here in Spencer, Iowa. We are woven not just into this land, which our families have worked for generations, but to one another. And a bright shining thread, popping up in a hundred places in that tapestry, is Dewey.

In our society, people believe you have to *do* something to be recognized, by which we mean something "in your face," and preferably caught on camera. We expect a famous town to survive a tsunami and a forest fire or produce a president or cover up some horrible crime. We expect a famous cat to save a child from a burning building, find his way home after being left behind on the other side of the country, or meow "The Star-Spangled Banner." And that cat better be not just heroic and talented, but media savvy, attractive, and have a good press agent, too, or he's never going to make it onto the *Today* show.

Dewey wasn't like that. He didn't perform spectacular feats. There was nobody pushing him to success. We didn't want him to be anything more than the beloved library cat of Spencer, Iowa. And that's all he wanted, too. He ran away only once, and he went only two blocks, and even that was too far.

Dewey wasn't special because he *did* something extraordinary but because he *was* extraordinary. He was like one of those seemingly ordinary people who, once you get to know them, stand out from the crowd. They are the ones who never miss a day of work, who never complain, who never ask for more than their share. They are those rare librarians, car salesmen, and waitresses who provide excellent service on principle, who go beyond the job because they have a passion for the job. They know what they are meant to do in life, and they do it exceptionally well. Some win awards; some make a lot of money; most are taken for granted. The store clerks. The bank tellers. The auto mechanics. The mothers. The world tends to recognize the unique and the loud, the rich and the self-serving, not those who do ordinary things extraordinarily well. Dewey came from humble beginnings (an Iowa alley); he survived tragedy (a freezing drop box); he found his place (a small-town library). Maybe that's the answer. He found his place. His passion, his purpose, was to make that place, no matter how small and out of the way it may have seemed, a better place for everyone.

I don't want to take anything away from the cat who falls out of the Winnebago, then spends five months trudging home through snowdrifts and scorching heat. That cat is an inspiration: never give up, always remember the importance of home. In his quiet way, Dewey taught those lessons, too. He never gave up during his long night in the box, and he was devoted to the library that became his home. Dewey didn't do one heroic thing; he did something heroic every day. He spent his time changing lives right here in Spencer, Iowa, one lap at a time.

You've no doubt noticed the strings on a fresh ear of corn. Those are the silks. Each one is connected to a particular spot on the ear. The spot grows a kernel only if that particular string is fertilized by pollen. The ear is made piece by piece, one kernel at a time. For an ear of corn to be whole, every silk must be fertilized. That's the way Dewey operated. He won hearts day by day, one person at a time. He never left anyone out or took anyone for granted. If you were receptive, he was there for you. If you weren't receptive, he worked to bring you around. Surely you know Wilbur, the pig in *Charlotte's Web*. Dewey had that personality: enthusiastic, honest, charming, radiant, humble (for a cat), and above all, a friend to anyone and everyone. It wasn't just beauty. It wasn't just a great story. Dewey had charisma, like Elvis or any of the other people who will live in our minds forever. There are dozens of library cats in the United States, but none come close to accomplishing what Dewey accomplished. He wasn't just another cat for people to pet and smile about. Every regular user of the library, *every single one*, felt they had a unique relationship with Dewey. He made everyone feel special.

Sharon often brought her daughter Emmy, who had Down syndrome, to see Dewey, especially on Sunday when it was her turn to feed him. Every Saturday night Emmy asked her, "Is tomorrow a Dewey day?" The first thing Emmy did every "Dewey day" was search for Dewey. When he was younger, he would usually be waiting by the door, but as he aged Emmy often found him lying in the sun by a window. She would pick him up and bring him to Mommy so they could pet him together. "Hi, Dewey. I love you," Emmy would say in a soft, kind voice, the way her own mother talked to her. For Emmy, that was the voice of love. Sharon was always afraid Emmy would pet him too hard, but Emmy and Dewey were friends, and she understood him as well as any of us. She was always wonderfully gentle.

Yvonne Berry, a single woman in her late thirties, came to the library three or four times a week. Every time, Dewey sought her out and spent fifteen minutes on her lap. Then he tried to coax her to open the bathroom door so he could play with the water. It was their ritual. But on the day Yvonne had to put her own cat to sleep, Dewey sat with her for more than two hours. He didn't know what had happened, but he knew something was wrong. Years later, when she told me that story, I could tell it was still important to her.

The century was turning, changing over, and Dewey was mellowing. He spent more time in his cat bed, and strenuous play was replaced by quiet book cart rides with Joy. Instead of jumping onto the cart, he would meow for Joy to pick him up so he could ride at the front of the cart like the captain of a ship. He stopped jumping to the ceiling lights, more out of boredom, I believe, than physical necessity. He couldn't abide rough handling, but he loved a gentle touch, like that of the homeless man who became one of his best friends. It is difficult to be invisible in a town like Spencer, but this man came close. He simply appeared at the library every day, unshaven, uncombed, and unwashed. He never said a word to anyone. He never looked at anyone. He wanted only Dewey. He would pick Dewey up and drape him over his shoulder; Dewey would lie there, purring, for twenty minutes while the man unburdened himself of secrets.

When Dewey gave up walking the top of the wall shelves, Kay took his old cat bed and put it on top of her desk hutch. Dewey would snuggle up in that bed and watch Kay work. Kay was attentive to Dewey's needs, changing his food, brushing his tangles, giving him Vaseline for fur balls, helping me with his bath. She wasn't as patient or gentle as I was, but even her roughest handling ended with a tender moment and a soft chuck on the head. One day not too long after Kay set up the new arrangement, Dewey jumped up to the bed and the shelf collapsed. The cat flew one way, four legs flailing. Notepads and paper clips flew the other. Before the last paper clip had hit the floor, Dewey was back to survey the damage.

"Not scared of too much in this library, are you?" Kay joked, a smile that I could tell reached all the way down to her heart curling the corners of her mouth.

Only the brush and the bath, Dewey would have said if he was being honest. The older Dewey got, the more he hated being groomed.

He also didn't have as much patience for preschool children, who tended to poke and pull at him. He was stiffening up, and he could no longer tolerate the small knocks and bruises. He never lashed out at children, and he rarely ran from them. He simply began to scoot away and hide when certain children came looking for him, avoiding a situation before it began.

Babies were a different story. One day I watched Dewey plop himself down a few feet from an infant girl who was on the floor in a baby carrier. I had often seen Dewey interact with infants, so I wasn't apprehensive. But babies are delicate, and new moms even more so. Especially this one. Dewey just sat with a bored expression, looking off into the distance as if to say, *Just happened to be walking by.* Then, when he thought I wasn't looking, he squirmed an inch closer. *Just adjusting my position*, his body language said, *nothing to see here.* A minute later, he did it again. Then again. Slowly, inch by inch, he crept closer, until finally he was pressed right up against the carrier. He popped his head over the edge, as if to confirm the child was inside, then settled down with his head on his paws. The infant reached her little hand over the edge and snatched his ear. Dewey adjusted his head so she could get a better grip. She laughed, kicking her legs and squeezing his ear. Dewey sat quietly, a contented look on his face.

We hired a new assistant children's librarian, Donna Stanford, in 2002. Donna had been around the world as a Peace Corps recruiter, and she had recently returned to northwest Iowa to care for her mother, who was suffering from Alzheimer's. Donna was quiet and conscientious, which I thought at first was the reason Dewey spent a few hours every day with her over in the children's section. It took me a long time to realize that Donna didn't know anyone in town besides her mother, and that even a place like Spencer — or maybe especially a close-knit place like Spencer — could seem cold and intimidating to an outsider. The only local resident who reached out to Donna was Dewey, who would ride on her shoulder while she rolled around in her office chair shelving books. When he tired of that, he would climb down onto her lap so Donna could pet him. Sometimes she read him children's books. I caught them by surprise one day, Dewey resting with his eyes closed, Donna deep in thought. I could tell she was startled.

"Don't worry," I said. "It is part of your job description to hold the kitty."

Then there was Jodi's boyfriend, Scott. Poor Scott was thrown right into the fire on his first trip to Spencer: my parents' fiftieth wedding anniversary. And this wasn't just a family party. The event was held at the Spencer Convention Center, which had a seating capacity of 450 people. Even the convention center couldn't contain the crowd. When the Jipson children descended on the stage to perform—in this case "You Are My Sunshine" with family-themed lyrics and Vince Gill's "Look at Us," complete with my brother Doug's flat, off-key warbling—there were still more than a hundred people lined up outside, waiting to congratulate Mom and Dad. All their lives they had treated the whole world as their family; now the world had come to honor them.

As soon as she left home, my relationship with Jodi improved dramatically. We were great friends, we realized, and terrible roommates. But while we laughed about the present, we still didn't talk about the past. Maybe mothers and daughters never do. That didn't mean I couldn't try.

"I know we've had some hard times, Jodi."

"What are you talking about, Mom?"

Where should I start? My health. My absences. Her messy room. Brandy. "In Mankato. Remember? We would walk by a store and you'd say 'I really want that shirt, Mommy, but I know we don't have any money, so that's okay.' You didn't want it, you needed it, but you never wanted me to feel bad." I sighed. "You were only five years old."

"Oh, Mom, that's just life."

And right then I realized that she was right. The good, the bad, that's just life. Let it go. There's no need to fret about the past. The question is: who are you going to share it with tomorrow?

That night, after the party, Jodi and I took Scott to the library to meet Dewey. That's when I knew this relationship was serious; Jodi had never introduced Dewey to one of her boyfriends before, and none of her other boyfriends, as far as I knew, had ever been interested in meeting him. Dewey was, of course, overjoyed to see Jodi. She was forever his love. Scott gave the two of them time together, then gently picked Dewey up and petted him. Not on the stomach, which Dewey hated, but along the back. He walked him around the empty library in the Dewey Carry. He pulled out his camera and took a snapshot for his mother. She had heard the Dewey stories, and she was a big fan. My heart warmed to see the two of them together. Scott was so loving and tender. And how could I not fall for a guy thoughtful enough to take a photograph for his mom?

It never occurred to me there was anything unusual about taking a grown woman's boyfriend to a library to meet her mother's cat. Dewey was part of the family; his opinion mattered. How could anyone seriously consider being a part of this family without knowing him? And I trusted Dewey to sniff out a rat; he was my sentry, always protecting the ones he loved. Seeing Scott with Dewey, and Dewey with Scott, told me everything I needed to know.

It also never crossed my mind, at this point, to think of Dewey as the library's cat. Dewey was my cat. I was the person he came to for love. I was the person he came to for comfort. And I went to him for love and comfort, too. He wasn't a substitute husband or a substitute child.

I wasn't lonely; I had plenty of friends. I wasn't unful-
filled; I loved my job. I wasn't looking for someone special. It wasn't even that I saw him every day. We lived
apart. We could spend whole days in the library together
and hardly see each other. But even when I didn't see
him, I knew he was there. We had chosen, I realized, to
share our lives, not just tomorrow, but forever.

Dewey was more special to me than any animal I had
ever known. He was more special to me than I ever believed an animal could be. However, that didn't change a
fundamental truth. He was my cat, but he belonged in the
library. His place was with the public. Dewey was happy
at my house for a day or two, but as soon as we got in the
car and headed downtown to the library, he put his front
feet on the dashboard and stared excitedly out the window.
I had to take the turns slowly, or he'd slide right off. When
he smelled Sister's Café, Dewey knew we were a few
blocks away. That's when he got really excited. He'd move
to the armrest and put his paws on the side window, practically willing the door to open. *We're here! We're here!* He'd
look over his shoulder and practically yell it to me when
we entered the alley. As soon as the door opened, he
jumped into my arms and I carried him across the
threshold. And then . . . bliss.

There was nothing Dewey loved more than being
home.

Chapter 22 ⌒⌐

Dewey Goes to Japan

W e received the e-mail from Japan in early 2003. Actually, the e-mail came from Washington, D.C., on behalf of people in Tokyo. Tomoko Kawasumi represented Japanese Public Television, which wanted to film Dewey. The company was making a documentary to introduce some new high-definition technology, and they wanted as wide an audience as possible. They decided first on a documentary about animals, then narrowed the focus to cats. They discovered Dewey through a feature in the Japanese magazine *Nekobiyori*. Would we mind if a film crew came to Spencer for a day?

That's funny, we had no idea Dewey had appeared in a Japanese magazine.

A few months later, in May, six people from Tokyo arrived at the Spencer Public Library. They had flown to Des Moines, rented a van, and driven to Spencer. Iowa in May is beautiful. The corn is just below eye level, three or four feet tall, so you can see the fields spreading into the distance. Of course, it's two hundred miles from Des Moines to Spencer, and that's all you can see, mile after mile. What were six people from Tokyo thinking after three and a half hours of looking at Iowa corn? We'd have to ask them, because they were probably the only people from Tokyo ever to make that drive.

The crew had one day to film, so they asked me to arrive at the library before seven. It was a miserably rainy morning. The interpreter, the only woman in the group, asked me to open the first set of doors so they could set up their cameras in the lobby. As they were carting equipment, around the corner came Dewey. He was half asleep, stretching his back legs as cats often do when they first wake up. When he saw me, he trotted over and gave me a wave. *Oh, it's you. What are you doing here so early? I wasn't expecting you for twenty minutes.* You could have set your watch by that cat.

Once the crew set up the cameras, the interpreter said, "We'd like him to wave again."

Oh, brother. I tried to explain, as best I could, that Dewey waved only once, when he saw me first thing in the morning. The director, Mr. Hoshi, wouldn't hear of it. He was used not only to giving orders but to having them obeyed. He was definitely the man in charge. And right now, he wanted that wave.

So I went back to my car and approached the library again, pretending I hadn't been in that morning. Dewey just stared at me.

What? You were just here five minutes ago.

I entered the library, turned on the lights, turned off the lights, went back to the car, waited five minutes, and approached the library again. Mr. Hoshi thought this might fool Dewey into thinking it was the next day.

It didn't.

We tried for an hour to get footage of Dewey waving. Finally I said, "Look, the poor cat has been sitting there this whole time waiting for his food. I have to feed him." Mr. Hoshi agreed. I scooped Dewey up and rushed to the litter box. The last thing I wanted the Japanese to get on film was flying poop. Dewey relieved himself, then ate a leisurely breakfast. By the time he was finished, the camera crew was set up inside. They had come halfway around the world, and they never got their wave.

But they got everything else. Dewey was almost fifteen years old and he was slowing down, but he hadn't lost his enthusiasm for strangers. Especially strangers with cameras. He approached each member of the crew and greeted him with a rub on the leg. They were petting him, horsing around, and one cameraman lay down on the floor for a Dewey-eye view. The interpreter politely asked me to put Dewey on a bookshelf. He sat there and let them film. He jumped from shelf to shelf. Then she said, "Have him walk down the shelf between the books and jump off the end."

I thought, "Wait a second. He's a cat, not a trained animal in the circus, and that's a pretty specific request. I hope you didn't come all this way expecting a show because there's no way he's going to walk that shelf, slalom between the display books, and jump off at command."

I trudged down to the far end of the shelf and called, "Come here, Dewey. Come here." Dewey walked down the shelf, slalomed between the books, and jumped down to my feet.

For five hours Mr. Hoshi gave orders and Dewey complied. He sat on a computer. He sat on a table. He sat on the floor with his feet crossed and stared into the camera. He rode on his favorite book cart with his feet hanging down through the openings in the metal grill, completely relaxed. No time to dally; move, move, move. A three-year-old girl and her mother agreed to appear in the film, so I put Dewey on the glider chair with them. The girl was nervous, grabbing and pulling at Dewey. Dewey didn't mind. He sat through the whole five-minute ordeal and never forgot to stare sweetly at the camera.

I had been telling the interpreter all morning that people came from all over the United States to visit Dewey, but I don't think Mr. Hoshi believed me. Then, just after lunch, in walked a family from New Hampshire. Talk about timing! The family was at a wedding in Des Moines and decided to rent a car and drive up to see Dewey. Need I remind you that's a three-and-a-half-hour drive?

Mr. Hoshi was all over the visitors. He interviewed them extensively. He took footage of them shooting their own footage of Dewey with their camcorder (probably manufactured in Japan). I taught the girl, who was five or six, the Dewey Carry, and how to gently rock back and forth until he put his head down on her back and closed his eyes. The family stayed an hour; the Japanese crew left soon after. As soon as they were gone, Dewey fell asleep and was out the rest of the day.

We received two copies of the DVD. After sixteen years, I was reluctant to talk about Dewey too much, but this seemed special. I called the newspaper. The electronics store on the corner loaned us a giant projection television, and we packed the library. By this time, Dewey had been on the radio in Canada and New Zealand. He had appeared in newspapers and magazines in dozens of countries. His photograph had been all over the world. But this was different. This was worldwide television!

I had sneaked a peak at the video, so I was a little nervous. The documentary turned out to be an alphabetic trip through the world of cats. There were twenty-six featured cats, one for each letter of the alphabet. Yes, our alphabet, even though the documentary was in Japanese.

I told the audience, "There are a lot of other cats in this documentary. Dewey is near the end, and the whole thing is in Japanese, so let's take a vote. Should we fast-forward to Dewey's part or watch the whole thing?"

"Watch the whole thing! Watch the whole thing!"

Ten minutes late the crowd was shouting, "Fast-forward! Fast-forward!" Let's just say it was extremely boring to watch jump cuts of cats and interviews in Japanese. We stopped for especially cute cats, or every time there was an American on screen — we stopped twice for that reason, but one of the women turned out to be British — but most of the footage was of Japanese people and their pets.

When we hit the letter *W*, a cry went up around the room, no doubt waking the snoozers. There was our Dewey, along with the words *Working Cat* in English and Japanese. There I was walking up to the library in the rain, while the announcer said something in Japanese. We understood only three words: "America, Iowa-shun, Spencer." Another loud cheer. A few seconds later we heard: "Dewey a-Deedamore Booksa."

And there was Dewey, sitting at the front door (I have to admit, a wave would have been nice), followed by Dewey sitting on a bookshelf, Dewey walking through two bookshelves, Dewey sitting, and sitting, and sitting and being petted by a little boy under a table and . . . sitting. One and a half minutes, and it was over. No little girl with Dewey on her lap. No riding the shoulder. No book cart. No family from New Hampshire. They didn't even use the shot of Dewey walking on top of the bookshelf, slaloming between the books, and jumping off the end. They came halfway around the world for a minute and a half of sitting.

Silence. Stunned silence.

And then a huge burst of cheering. Our Dewey was an international star. Here was the proof. So what if we didn't have a clue what the announcer was saying? So what if Dewey's portion lasted barely longer than a typical commercial break? There was our library. There was our librarian. There was our Dewey. And the announcer definitely said, "America, Iowa-shun, Spencer."

The town of Spencer has never forgotten that Japanese documentary. Maybe its contents. We have two copies for checkout in the library, but nobody ever watches them. *Puss in Books* is much more popular. But the fact that a film crew came from Tokyo to Spencer, that's something we'll never forget. The local radio station and the newspaper both ran long features, and for months people came into the library to talk about it.

"What was the crew like?"

"What did they do?"

"Where did they go while in town?"

"What else did they film?"

"Can you believe it?"

"Can you believe it?"

"Can you believe it?"

Japanese television put Dewey over the top. Even today, when locals talk about Dewey, the conversation always comes around to, "And those Japanese people came here, to Spencer, to film him." What more needs to be said?

Spencer residents aren't the only ones who remember that documentary. After it aired, we received several letters from Japan and forty requests for Dewey postcards. Our library Web site tallies the origin of visitors, and every month since the documentary aired in the summer of 2004 Japan has been the second most popular country of origin, after the United States—more than 150,000 visitors in three years. Somehow, I don't think they're interested in checking out books.

But the Japanese invasion wasn't the only special thing that happened during the summer of 2003, at least for me. The previous year, Scott had proposed to Jodi on Christmas Eve at my parents' house. She asked me to take charge of the flowers and decorations, since both were hobbies of mine.

But there was something nagging at me. My sister, Val, was Jodi's maid of honor, and I knew the two of them were discussing dresses. I didn't have a chance to choose my own wedding dress. A girl in Hartley had called off her wedding at the last minute, and Mom bought her dress for me. I wanted more than anything to help Jodi pick her wedding dress. I wanted the dress to be special. I wanted to be a part of it. I called Jodi and said, "I've dreamed all my life of helping you pick out your wedding dress. Val has two daughters of her own. She'll have her chance."

"I would love to do this with you, Mom."

My heart leaped into my throat. I could tell by the quiver in Jodi's voice that she felt it, too. We are both sentimental fools.

But I'm also practical. "You narrow down the choices," I told her. "When you find half a dozen you like, I'll drive there to help you make the final decision." Jodi could never make up her mind about clothes. She kept most of her garments in their original boxes, because she was always returning them. Jodi lived more than three hours away in Omaha, Nebraska, and I didn't want to kill myself making that drive every weekend for the next six months.

Jodi shopped for dresses with her friends. Weeks later I drove to Omaha to help her make the final decision. We couldn't decide. Then we spotted one she'd never tried on. As soon as we saw her in the dress, we knew. Jodi and I stood in the dressing room together and cried.

We went shopping together a few months later, and she chose a beautiful dress for me. Then Jodi called me and said, "I just bought a dress for Grandma."

"That's funny," I told her. "I was in Des Moines on library business, and I bought her one, too." When we got together, we realized we had bought Mom the same dress on the same day at the same time. We really laughed about that one.

The wedding took place in July at St. Joseph Catholic Church in Milford, Iowa. Jodi planned the wedding from Omaha; I did the legwork. My old friends from Mankato, Trudy, Barb, Faith, and Idelle, came down a few days before the ceremony to help me set up. Jodi and I were perfectionists; we didn't want a flower out of place. Trudy and Barb were nervous wrecks when we decorated Mom and Dad's garage for the reception, but they did a beautiful job. When they finished, it didn't even resemble a garage. The next day we decorated the church, then the restaurant for the rehearsal dinner.

There were thirty-seven guests at the wedding, just family members and close friends. My friends didn't attend the ceremony; they were in a back room heating butterflies. The butterflies were supposed to be kept on ice, in suspended animation, then warmed up and "awoken" fifteen minutes before being called upon to fly. Faith called herself the BBBBB—the Beautiful Big-Boobed Butterfly Babysitter—but she took her job quite seriously. She was so nervous about the butterflies, the night before the wedding she took them to Trudy's house in Worthington, Minnesota, an hour away, and kept them beside her bed.

When the guests came out of the wedding, Scott's parents handed each of them an envelope. My brother Mike, who was standing next to the bride, immediately started squeezing. Jodi gave him a look.

"What?" Mike said. "Is it alive?"

"Well, it *was*."

I read the legend of the butterflies, which have no voices. When released, they rise to heaven and whisper our wishes to God.

When the guests opened their envelopes, butterflies

of all sizes and colors flew up into a beautiful clear blue sky, a whisper away from God. Most of them disappeared on the wind. Three settled back down on Jodi's dress. One stayed on her bridal bouquet for more than an hour.

After wedding photos, the guests piled into a bus. While my friends cleaned up, the rest of us rode to West Okoboji for a lake tour on the *Queen II*, the area's famous sightseeing boat. Afterward Jodi and Scott decided to ride the Arnold Park Ferris wheel, the same one that had glistened in the night when Mom and Dad were falling in love to the sound of Tommy Dorsey at the Roof Garden so many decades before. As the rest of us watched, the Ferris wheel took Jodi and Scott, along with the ring bearer and the flower girl, up, up, up into that clear blue sky, like butterflies slipping out of their envelopes and taking flight.

The letter Jodi sent after the honeymoon said it all: "Thank you, Mom. It was the perfect wedding." No eight words could ever make me happier.

If only life were that easy. If only Dewey, Jodi, and the whole Jipson family could be frozen right there, in the summer of 2003. But even as that Ferris wheel rose, even as Dewey became a star in Japan, there was a stain on the picture. Only a few months before, Mom had been diagnosed with leukemia, the latest in a long line of illnesses to try to strike her down. They say cancer, like luck, runs in a family. Unfortunately, cancer runs deep in the Jipson line.

Chapter 23

Memories of Mom

My brother Steven was diagnosed with stage four non-Hodgkin's lymphoma, the most advanced form of a lethal cancer, in 1976. The doctors gave him two months to live. He was nineteen years old.

Steven dealt with his cancer with more dignity than anybody I have ever known. He battled it, but not desperately. He lived his life, too. He never lost his sense of self. But the cancer was in his chest, and they couldn't beat it. They knocked it down, but it came back. The treatment was painful, and it ate through Steven's kidneys. My brother Mike, Steven's best friend, offered to give him one of his kidneys, but Steven told him, "Don't bother. I'll just ruin that one, too."

As I struggled with a divorce, welfare, and college, Steven struggled with cancer. By 1979, he had lived longer than anyone in Iowa had ever lived with stage four non-Hodgkin's lymphoma. The doctors had given him so much chemotherapy, he had no blood left in his extremities. There was no hope left in chemo, so Steven enrolled in an experimental treatment center in Houston. He was scheduled to start in January, and before the trip he wanted a full-scale, no-holds-barred Jipson Christmas. Steven wanted the clam chowder Dad always made on Christmas Eve. He wanted me to make his favorite caramel popcorn. He sat under a blanket and smiled along as we played our homemade instruments in the Jipson Family Band. It was eighteen below zero on Christmas Eve; Steven couldn't even stand, he was so weak, but he insisted we all go to Midnight Mass. On his last night at Mom and Dad's house, he made me drive him to Aunt Marlene's house at two in the morning to say good-bye. Afterward, he wanted me to stay up with him and watch *Brian's Song*, a movie about a football player with cancer.

"No thanks, Stevie. I've already seen it."

But he insisted, so I stayed up with him. He fell asleep in the first five minutes.

A week later, on January 6, Steven woke his wife at 5:00 a.m. and asked her to help him down the stairs to the sofa. When she came back down a few hours later, she couldn't wake him. We found out later he hadn't been enrolled in an experimental treatment program in Houston. The day before Thanksgiving, the doctors had told him there were no more treatment options left. He hadn't told anyone because he wanted one last Jipson family Christmas, free from crying and pity, before he died.

My parents took Steven's death hard. Death can drive two people apart, but it drove Mom and Dad together. They cried together. They talked together. They leaned on each other. My father converted to Catholicism, Mom's religion, and started attending church regularly for the first time in his adult life.

And they adopted a cat.

Three weeks after Steven's death, Dad bought Mom a blue Persian and named him Max. Those were terrible days for them, just terrible, but Max was a sainted cat, full of personality but not wild. He would sleep in the bathroom sink; with the exception of snuggling up against Mom's side, that sink was his favorite place in the house. If ever a cat changed a couple, it was Max. He raised my parents' spirits. He made them laugh. He kept them company in their empty home. The children loved Max for his personality, but we loved him more for taking care of Mom and Dad.

My older brother David, my dear friend and inspiration, was also deeply affected by Steven's death. David had dropped out of college six weeks before graduation and after a few false starts ended up in Mason City, Iowa, about a hundred miles east of Spencer. When I think of David, though, I think of Mankato, Minnesota. The two of us were so close in Mankato. We had a wonderful time together, simply wonderful. But one night, shortly before he dropped out of college and moved away, he knocked on my door at one in the morning. It was ten below zero, and he had walked ten miles.

He said, "There's something wrong with me, Vicki. In my head. I think I'm having a breakdown. But you can't tell Mom and Dad. Promise me you'll never tell Mom and Dad."

I was nineteen years old, young and stupid. I promised. I never told anyone about that night, but I know now that mental illness often strikes young men, especially bright and talented young men in their early twenties like David. I know David was ill. He was as ill as Steven had been, but it wasn't as obvious. Slowly, his condition pulled his life downward. Within a few years, he was a different person. He couldn't hold a job. He couldn't laugh, even with me. He started taking drugs, downers mostly, to combat depression. He fathered a child out of wedlock. He called me every few months, and we talked for hours, but over the years I heard from him less and less.

When Steven died in January 1980, David coped with drugs. He said he couldn't function without them. His daughter, Mackenzie, was four, and her mother cut David off from contact with her until he kicked his habit. Eight months after Steven died, David phoned me in the middle of the night to tell me he had lost his daughter.

"You haven't lost Mackenzie," I told him. "If you're straight, you can visit her. If you're high, you can't. It's that simple."

He couldn't see it. We talked about a million things that night, but nothing I suggested was possible. He had a blank wall in front of him. He couldn't see any future at all. I was scared to death, but he swore he wouldn't do anything until we talked again. He loved his daughter, he assured me, and he would never leave her. But sometime later that night or early the next morning, my brother David, my childhood buddy, picked up a shotgun and pulled the trigger.

My friend Trudy drove me to Hartley at two in the morning. I could barely breathe; there was no way I could drive. My parents were no better. None of us wanted to face David's death, especially so soon after Steven's, but it was there whether we wanted it or not. A few days after the funeral, David's landlord started calling my parents' house and pestering them. He was screaming at us to come get David's things, to clean out the apartment, so he could rent it again. It was another reminder that David didn't live in the best area or associate with the kindest people.

We drove to Mason City in two vehicles. Dad, my brothers Mike and Doug, and two of David's old friends drove ahead in the car. My mother, Val, and I followed in a truck. When we arrived, the men were standing at the curb.

"You're not going in there," Dad said. "Wait here. We'll bring everything out."

We didn't know it until Dad opened the door, but nobody had touched the apartment since David's death. The mess from what David had done, it was everywhere. Dad, Mike, and Doug had to wipe everything down before bringing it out to pack in the truck. I can still see the stains. David's possessions were meager, to say the least, but it took all day to move them. Dad, Mike, and Doug didn't say a word, and they've never spoken about that day since. When I told him I was writing this book, Dad asked me not to mention David. It wasn't shame or secrecy. There were tears in his eyes. Even after all this time, it's too painful for him to talk about. But talk we must.

Two weeks after David's death, it was time to have Max fixed. The vet gave him the anesthetic and left for ten minutes to give it time to work. Unfortunately he didn't remove the water dish from his cage. The dish held only half an inch of water, but Max fell in and drowned.

I happened to be there when the veterinarian came to the house. He knew my family. He knew what my parents were going through. Now he had to tell them he had killed their cat. We all stared at him for half a minute, speechless. "I loved that cat with a passion," Dad finally said, calmly but firmly. "You son of a bitch." Then he turned and walked upstairs. He couldn't even speak to the guy. He couldn't look at him. Dad still feels bad about his outburst, but Max's death was too much. It was simply too much.

When Mom was diagnosed with leukemia in the spring of 2003, she and Dad adopted a kitten. Mom hadn't owned a Persian in twenty years, since the death of Max. But instead of adopting a Persian as they intended, they came back with a Himalayan, a cross between a Persian and a Siamese. He was a gray beauty with silky blue eyes, the spitting image of Max right down to the outgoing and loving personality. They named him Max II.

Max II was the first admission Mom was going to die. Not from Dad. My mother was so strong, Dad believed she could survive anything. The admission came from

Mom. She knew this illness was the one to beat her, and she didn't want Dad to be alone.

Mom was a force of nature. I suspect she started out running from life, from her alcoholic father and the long hours she worked in the family restaurant, even as a five-year-old child. When my grandmother divorced, she and Mom took jobs in a women's clothing store. That was her life, her future, until she met Dad.

After she met Verlyn Jipson, Marie Mayou turned around and spent every moment running toward life. My mother and father loved each other deeply. Their love was so great it can't be contained in this or any book. They loved their children. They loved to sing and dance. They loved their friends, their town, their lives. They were great ones for celebrations. They would throw a party for every accomplishment and milestone. Mom would get up early to do the cooking, and she'd stay up until three in the morning when everyone finally left. At six the next morning, she'd start cleaning. By eight, the house was immaculate. Mom's house was always immaculate.

Mom was diagnosed with breast cancer in the early 1970s. The doctors gave her no chance to live, but she beat it. She beat it not once but five times, twice in one breast and three times in the other. She beat it with a whole lot of strength and a whole lot of faith. My friend Bonnie and I used to call Mom "the number two Catholic in the world." When Jodi was eight, she and I were riding our bikes in Hartley when we happened to pass the small building that used to house St. Joseph Catholic Church. Mom had been on the planning committee for the new building, and the two trees in front were planted in memory of Steven and David. Jodi looked at the old wooden building and said, "Mom, was Grandma as crazy about church when you were growing up as she is now?"

"Yes," I told her, "she sure was."

Mom's faith came from the church, but her strength came from inside. She simply wouldn't give in to anything. Not pain, not tiredness, not sorrow. When Mom fought her third bout with breast cancer, her stepmother, Lucille, drove her every day to Sioux City, four hours round-trip, for eight weeks. Radiation treatment in those days was much worse than it is today. They basically blasted you until your body couldn't take any more. Mom was burned to a crisp. She had an open wound the size of a large pancake under her arm, and it was so chewed up Dad would get physically sick when he changed the bandages. After more than twenty years in Hartley, my parents were retiring to a house on the lake. Dad wanted to postpone the move, but Mom wouldn't hear of it. She came home from Sioux City every night and cooked, cleaned, then packed boxes until she fell asleep, dead tired. In the middle of radiation treatment, she organized an auction to sell off most of the possessions she and Dad had gathered in a lifetime. The auction took two days, and Mom was there to say good-bye to every last spoon.

Mom raised me to have that kind of strength. She knew there were no promises in life. Even when things went well, they never went easy. Mom raised six children, and she didn't have a bathroom in the house or running water until the fifth one, my sister, Val. She had boundless energy but limited time. She had chores, meals to cook, a house full of children, her chicken and egg business, and an entire community of local kids who thought of her as their mother. Mom never turned anyone away. If a child needed a meal, he'd sit with us at our table. If a family was struggling and she knew their little one liked peanut butter, the jar of peanut butter would disappear from our pantry. She had room in her heart for everyone, which didn't leave much time for any one person. Most of the time I spent with Mom growing up, I was working beside her. I was her alter ego, her other half, which was both a treasure and a burden. When Val arrived at the house after Steven's death, Mom and Dad ran out to hug her, and they all cried together. When I arrived, Dad hugged me and cried. Mom hugged me and said, "Don't you cry. You have to be strong." Mom knew if I was strong, she could be, too. And I knew what was expected of me.

Mom said she loved me all the time. There was never any doubt about that. Dad was the sentimental one; Mom showed her love through pride. She cried at my college graduation when she saw my summa cum laude sash. She was that proud of me for kicking off the shackles, standing up, and walking. That was her adult daughter up there, and in a way, that was her up there, too. A college graduate. With honors.

Dad couldn't attend my graduation because he was working, so my parents threw a graduation party for two hundred people back in Hartley. Dad had worked for a month to make me an apron out of a hundred one-dollar bills. One hundred dollars was a huge amount of money for my parents. In those days you were considered rich if you had two five-dollar bills to rub together.

I loved that apron. It represented Dad's love and pride, just like Mom's tears. But I was so poor, it lasted only a week before I took it apart and spent it.

When my mother rallied from leukemia, no one was surprised. She had survived breast cancer five times, after all, and she was a fighter. She was on radiation treatments for years, but they never broke her. When radiation stopped working, she switched to IGG, in which parts of someone else's immune system are injected into your body. She'd have good periods, but eventually it became clear she wasn't going to win this time. She was almost eighty years old, and her strength was running out.

Mom wanted a huge party for her wedding anniversary, which was still months away. The biggest parties of our lives were for Mom and Dad's anniversaries. We four remaining children put our heads together. We didn't think Mom was going to make it to her anniversary, and besides, in her condition a huge party was out of the question. We decided to throw a small party for Mom's seventy-ninth birthday, which was only three days before Dad's eightieth birthday, just the family and a few close friends. The Jipson Family Band got together one last time and played "Johnny M'Go." All the children wrote poems in honor of Mom and Dad. Poems are a Jipson family tradition. Dad wrote poetry at the drop of a hat. We made fun of him for it, but we kept his poems framed on our walls or buried in our drawers, always within arm's reach.

The children agreed the poems would be silly. Here's the poem I wrote for Dad. It refers all the way back to the time I broke my engagement just out of high school.

MEMORIES OF DAD

I had broken my engagement,
John and I would never marry.
It was the hardest thing I'd every done,
Emotional and scary.

Mom was quite upset,
What would the neighbors say?
I shut myself up in my room
To cry the pain away.

Dad could hear my sobs;
This was the solace he gave:
Leaning on my doorknob, he said,
"Honey, do you want to come and watch me shave?"

But I couldn't write a silly poem for Mom. She had done too much for me; there was too much to say. Would I get another chance? I broke down and wrote the kind of poem Dad was famous for, the awkwardly sentimental kind.

MEMORIES OF MOM

When I began to pick a memory,
One day, one incident, one chat,
I realized my fondest memory
Had more substance than that.

The 70s lost my marriage—lost everything,
I could feel my life unwind.

I was depressed and struggling,
Quite literally losing my mind.

Friends and family got me through,
But with a daughter under five,
Jodi paid for all my pain
As I struggled to survive.

Thank God for Mom.
Her strength showed I could recover,
But her most important role
Back then was Jodi's second mother.

When I had no more to give,
When I fought to get out of bed,
Mom took Jodi in her arms
And kept her soul fed.

Unconditional love and stability
In that Hartley home;
Swimming lessons, silly games,
Jodi didn't have to be alone.

While I built my life back,
Studied, worked, and found my way,
Mom gave Jodi what I missed,
Special attention every day.

I was a mess while raising Jodi,
But when she fell, you caught her.
So, thank you, Mom, most of all
For helping shape our daughter.

Two days after the party, Mom woke Dad in the middle of the night and told him to drive her to the hospital. She couldn't take the pain anymore. A few days later, after she had been stabilized and sent to Sioux City for tests, we discovered Mom had colorectal cancer. Her only chance for survival, and it was no guarantee, was to remove almost her entire colon. She'd have to spend the rest of her life with a colostomy bag.

Mom had known something was seriously wrong. We found out later she had been taking suppositories and laxatives for more than a year, and she had been in almost constant pain. She hadn't wanted anyone to know. For the first time in her life, Mom didn't want to face down her enemy. She said, "I'm not going to have the surgery. I'm tired of fighting."

My sister was distraught. I told her, "Val, this is Mom. Give her time."

Sure enough, five days later Mom said, "I don't want to go this way. Let's have the surgery."

Mom survived the surgery and lived another eight months. They were not easy months. We brought Mom home, and Val and Dad took care of her around the clock. Val was the only one who learned to manage the colostomy bag; even the nurse couldn't change it as well. I came over every night and cooked dinner for them. Difficult times, but also some of the best of my life. Mom and I talked about everything. There was nothing left unsaid. There was no laugh we didn't share. She slipped into a coma near the end, but even then I knew she heard me. She heard all of us. She was never too far away. She died as she had lived, on her own terms, with her family at her side.

In the summer of 2006, a few months after she died, I placed a small statue outside the window of the children's library in my mother's honor. The statue is of a woman holding a book, ready to read to the child clamoring around her. To me, that statue is Mom. She always had something to give.

Chapter 24 ⁓

Dewey's Diet

Dad says Max II, his beloved Himalayan, will outlive him. He finds comfort in that certainty. But for most of us, living with an animal means understanding we will experience our pet's death. Animals are not children; rarely do they outlive us.

I had been mentally preparing for Dewey's death since he was fourteen years old. His colon condition and public living arrangement, according to Dr. Esterly, made it unlikely Dewey would live longer than a dozen years. But Dewey had a rare combination of genetics and attitude. By the time Dewey was seventeen, I had nearly stopped thinking about his death. I accepted it not so much as inevitable but as another milestone down the road. Since I didn't know the location of the marker, or what it would look like when we got there, why spend time worrying about it? That is to say, I enjoyed our days together, and during our evenings apart I looked no further than the next morning.

I realized Dewey was losing his hearing when he stopped responding to the word *bath*. For years, that word had sent him into a scamper. The staff would be talking, and someone would say, "I had to clean my bathtub last night."

Bam, Dewey was gone. Every time.

"That isn't about you, Dewey!"

But he wasn't listening. Say the word *bath*—or *brush* or *comb* or *scissors* or *doctor* or *vet*—and Dewey disappeared. Especially if Kay or I said the dread word. When I was away on library business or out sick, as I often was with my immune system so compromised by surgeries, Kay took care of Dewey. If he needed something, even comfort or love, and I wasn't around, he went to Kay. She may have been distant at first, but after all those years she had become his second mother, the one who loved him but wouldn't tolerate his bad habits. If Kay and I were standing together and even thought the word *water*, Dewey ran.

Then one day someone said *bath* and he didn't run. He still ran when I *thought* bath, but not at the word. So I started to watch him more closely. Sure enough, he had stopped running away every time a truck rumbled by in the alley behind the library. The sound of the back door opening used to send him sprinting to sniff the incoming boxes; now, he wasn't moving at all. He wasn't jumping at sudden loud noises, such as someone setting down a large reference volume too fast, and he wasn't coming as often when patrons called.

That, however, might not have had much to do with hearing. When you get older, the simple things are suddenly not so simple. A touch of arthritis, discomfort in the muscles. You thin out and stiffen up. In both cats and humans, the skin gets less elastic, which means more flaking and irritation and less ability to heal. These are not small things when your job is, essentially, to be petted all day.

Dewey still greeted everyone at the front door. He still searched out laps, but on his own terms. He had arthritis in his back left hip, and jostling him in the wrong place or picking him up the wrong way would cause him to limp away in pain. More and more in the late morning and afternoon he sat on the circulation desk, where he was protected by staff. He was supremely confident in his beauty and popularity; he knew patrons would come to him. He looked so regal, a lion surveying his kingdom. He even sat like a lion, with his paws crossed in front of him and his back legs tucked underneath, a model of dignity and grace.

The staff started quietly suggesting that patrons be gentle with Dewey, more aware of his comfort. Joy, who spent the most time out front with the patrons, became very protective of him. She often brought her nieces and nephews to see Dewey, even on her days off, so she knew how rough people could be. "These days," she would tell the patrons, "Dewey prefers a gentle pat on the head."

Even the elementary school children understood Dewey was an old man now, and they were sensitive to his needs. This was his second generation of Spencer children, the children of the children Dewey had gotten to know as a kitten, so the parents made sure their kids were well behaved. When the children touched him gently, Dewey would lie against their legs or, if they were sitting on the floor, on their laps. But he was more cautious than he used to be, and loud noise or rough petting often drove him away.

"That's all right, Dewey. Whatever you need."

After years of trial and error, we had finally found our finicky cat an acceptable cat bed. It was small, with white fake fur sides and an electric warmer in the bottom. We kept it in front of the wall heater outside my office door. Dewey loved nothing more than lounging in his bed, in the safety of the staff area, with the heating pad turned all the way up. In the winter, when the wall heater was on, he got so warm he had to throw himself over the side and roll around on the floor. His fur was so hot you couldn't even touch it. He would lie on his back for ten minutes with all his legs spread out, venting heat. If a cat could pant, Dewey would have been panting. As soon as he was cool, he climbed back into his bed and started the process all over again.

Heat wasn't Dewey's only indulgence. I may have been a sucker for Dewey's whims, but now our assistant children's librarian, Donna, was spoiling him even more than I did. If Dewey didn't eat his food right away, she heated it in the microwave for him. If he still didn't eat it, she threw it out and opened another can. Donna didn't trust ordinary flavors. Why should Dewey eat gizzards and toes? Donna drove to Milford, fifteen miles away, because a little store there sold exotic cat food. I remember duck. Dewey was fond of that for a week. She tried lamb, too, but as usual nothing stuck for very long. Donna kept trying new flavor after new flavor and new can after new can. Oh, how she loved that cat.

Despite our best efforts, though, Dewey was thinning

down, so at his next checkup Dr. Franck prescribed a series of medicines to fatten him up. That's right, despite the dire health warnings, Dewey had outlasted his old nemesis, Dr. Esterly, who retired at the end of 2002 and donated his practice to a nonprofit animal advocacy group.

Along with the pills, Dr. Franck gave me a pill shooter which, theoretically, shot the pills far enough down Dewey's throat that he couldn't spit them out. But Dewey was smart. He took his pill so calmly I thought, "Good, we made it. That was easy." That's when he snuck behind a shelf somewhere and coughed it back up. I found little white pills all over the library.

I didn't force Dewey's medicine on him. He was eighteen; if he didn't want medicine, he didn't have to take it. Instead, I bought him a container of yogurt and started giving him a lick every day. That opened the floodgates. Kay started giving him bites of cold cuts out of her sandwiches. Joy started sharing her ham sandwich, and pretty soon Dewey was following her to the kitchen whenever he saw her walk through the door with a bag in her hand. One day Sharon left a sandwich unwrapped on her desk. When she came back a minute later, the top slice of bread had been carefully turned over and placed to the side. The bottom slice of bread was sitting exactly where it had been, untouched. But all the meat was gone.

After Thanksgiving of 2005, we discovered Dewey loved turkey, so the staff loaded up on holiday scraps. We tried to freeze them, but he could always tell when the turkey wasn't fresh. Dewey never lost his keen sense of smell. That's one reason I scoffed when Sharon offered Dewey a bite of garlic chicken, her favorite micro-wavable lunch. I told her, "No way Dewey is going to eat garlic."

He ate every bite. Who was this cat? For eighteen years, Dewey ate nothing but specific brands and fla-vors of cat food. Now, it seemed, he'd eat anything.

I thought, "If we can fatten Dewey up on human food, why not? Isn't that better than a pill?"

I bought him braunschweiger, a cold loaf of sliced liver sausage many people around here consider a deli-cacy. Braunschweiger is about 80 percent pure fat. If anything would fatten Dewey up, it was braunschweiger. He wouldn't touch it.

What Dewey really wanted, we discovered acciden-tally, was Arby's Beef 'n Cheddar sandwiches. He gob-bled them down. Inhaled them. He didn't even chew the beef; he just sucked it in. I don't know what was in those sandwiches, but once he started on Arby's Beef 'n Cheddar, Dewey's digestion improved. His constipation decreased dramatically. He started eating two cans of cat food a day, and because the fast food was so salty, he was slurping down a full dish of water as well. He even started using the litter box on his own.

But Dewey didn't have a couple owners, he had hun-dreds, and most of them couldn't see the improvements. All they saw was the cat they loved getting thinner and thinner. Dewey never hesitated to play up his condition. He would sit on the circulation desk and whenever someone approached to pet him, he would whine. They always fell for it.

"What's the matter, Dewey?"

He led them to the entrance to the staff area, where

they could see his food dish. He'd look forlornly at the food, then back at them, and with his big eyes full of sorrow, drop his head.

"Vicki! Dewey's hungry!"

"He has a can of food in the bowl."

"But he doesn't like it."

"That's his second flavor this morning. I threw the first can away an hour ago."

"But he's crying. Look at him. He just flopped down on the floor."

"We can't just give him cans of food all day."

"What about something else?"

"He ate an Arby's sandwich this morning."

"Look at him. He's so thin. You guys have to be feed him more."

"We're taking good care of him."

"But he's so thin. Can't you give him something for me?"

I could, except Dewey did the same thing yesterday. And the day before that. And the day before that. In fact, you're the fifth person he's hit with the starving-cat routine today.

Now, how was I going to tell a patron that? I always gave in, which of course just encouraged more bad behavior. I think Dewey enjoyed the taste of food more when he knew I didn't want to give it to him. Let's call it the taste of victory.

Chapter 25

The Meeting

As Dewey entered old age, the kindness of Spencer Public Library patrons really began to show. Friends and visitors alike were gentler around him. They talked to him more and were attentive to his needs, much as you would be to an older relative at a family reunion. Occasionally someone would comment that he looked weak, or thin, or dirty, but I knew their concern was a manifestation of their love.

"What's wrong with his fur?" was probably the most common question.

"Nothing," I told them. "He's just old."

It's true, Dewey's fur had lost much of its luster. It was no longer radiant orange, but a dull copper. It was also increasingly matted, so much so I couldn't keep up with a simple brushing. I took Dewey to Dr. Franck, who explained that as cats aged, the barbs on their tongues wore down. Even if they licked themselves regularly, they couldn't do an efficient job grooming because there was nothing to separate the fur. Tangles and mats were just another symptom of old age.

"As for these," Dr. Franck said, studying Dewey's clumped back end, "drastic measures are required. I think we better shave."

When she was done, poor Dewey was fuzzy on one end, bare on the other. He looked like he was wearing a big mink coat and no pants. A few members of the staff laughed when they saw him, because it was a hilarious sight, but they didn't laugh long. The humiliation on Dewey's face stopped that. He hated it. Just hated it. He walked away very fast for a few steps, then sat down and tried to hide his rear end. Then he got up, walked quickly away, and sat down again. Start, stop. Start, stop. He finally made it back to his bed, buried his head in his paws, and curled up beneath his favorite toy, Marty Mouse. For days, we found him with his top half sticking out into an aisle and his back end hidden in a bookshelf.

But Dewey's health was no laughing matter. The staff didn't talk about it, but I knew they were worried. They were afraid they would come in one morning and find Dewey dead on the floor. It wasn't his death that worried some of them, I realized, but the thought of having to deal with it themselves. Or even worse, having to make a decision in a health crisis. Between my own health issues and my trips to Des Moines on state library business, I was frequently out of the library. Dewey was my cat, and everyone knew it. The last thing they wanted was to have the life of my cat in their hands.

"Don't worry," I told them. "Just do what you think is best for Dewey. You can't do anything wrong."

I couldn't promise the staff nothing would happen while I was away, but I told them, "I know this cat. I know when he is healthy, a little sick, and really sick. If he's really sick, trust me, he's going to the vet. I'll do whatever it takes."

Besides, Dewey wasn't sick. He still jumped up and down from the circulation desk, so I knew his arthritis wasn't too bad. His digestion was better than ever. And he still loved the company of patrons. But it took patience to care for an elderly cat, and frankly, some of the staff didn't think that was their job. Slowly, as Dewey aged, his support peeled away: first those in town with different agendas; then some of the fence-sitters; then a few patrons who wanted only an attractive, active cat; and finally the staff members who didn't want the burden of geriatric care.

That doesn't mean I wasn't blindsided by the October 2006 library board meeting. I was expecting a typical discussion of the state of the library, but the meeting soon turned into a referendum on Dewey. A patron had mentioned he wasn't looking well. Perhaps, the board suggested, we should get him some medical help?

"At his recent checkup," I told them, "Dr. Franck discovered hyperthyroidism. It's just another symptom of age, like his arthritis, his dry skin, and the black age spots on his lips and gums. Dr. Franck prescribed a medication that, thank goodness, doesn't have to be taken orally. I rub it in his ear. Dewey has really perked up. And don't worry," I reminded them, "we're paying for the medicine with donations and my own money. Not a single penny of city money is ever spent on Dewey's care."

"Is hyperthyroidism serious?"

"Yes, but it's treatable."

"Will this medicine help his fur?"

"Dullness isn't a disease, it's a function of age, like gray hair on a human." They should understand. There wasn't a head in the room without a few gray hairs.

"What about his weight?"

I explained his diet in detail, from the obsessiveness with which Donna and I changed his cat food to the Arby's Beef 'n Cheddar sandwiches.

"But he doesn't look good."

They kept coming back to that. Dewey didn't look good. Dewey was hurting the image of the library. I knew they meant well, that they were interested in finding the best solution for everyone, but I couldn't understand their thinking. It was true, Dewey didn't look as appealing. Everybody ages. Eighty-year-olds don't look like twenty-year-olds, and they shouldn't. We live in a throwaway culture that stashes older people away and tries not to look at them. They have wrinkles. They have age spots. They don't walk well and their hands shake. Their eyes are watery, or they drool when they eat, or they "burp in their pants" too much (Jodi's phrase from when she was two years old). We don't want to see that. Even the accomplished elderly, even the people who gave their whole lives, we want them out of sight and out of mind. But maybe older people, and old cats, have something to teach us, if not about the world, then about ourselves.

"Why don't you take Dewey home to live with you? I know he visits you on holidays."

I had thought of that but dismissed it long ago. Dewey could never be happy living at my house. I was gone too much, between work and meetings. He hated to be alone.

He was a public cat. He needed people around him, he needed the library around him, to be happy.

"We've had complaints, Vicki, don't you understand? Our job is to speak for the citizens of this town."

The board seemed ready to say the town didn't want Dewey anymore. I knew that was ridiculous because I saw the community's love for Dewey every day. I had no doubt the board had received a few complaints, but there had always been complaints. Now, with Dewey not looking his best, the voices were louder. But that didn't mean the town had turned on Dewey. One thing I'd learned over the years was that the people who loved Dewey, who really wanted and needed him, weren't the ones with the loudest voices. They were often the ones with no voices at all.

If this had been the board twenty years ago, I realized, we would never have been able to adopt Dewey. "Thank God," I thought to myself. "Thank you, God, for past boards."

And even if what the board thought was true, even if the majority of the town had turned its back on Dewey, didn't we nonetheless have the duty to stand by him? Even if five people cared, wasn't that enough? Even if nobody cared, the fact remained that Dewey loved the town of Spencer. He would always love Spencer. He needed us. We couldn't just toss him out because looking at him, older and weaker, no longer made us proud.

There was another message from the board, too, and it came through loud and clear: Dewey is not your cat. He's the town's cat. We speak for the town, so it's our decision. We know what's best.

I won't argue one fact. Dewey was Spencer's cat.

Nothing has ever been truer. But he was also my cat. And finally, in the end, Dewey was *a* cat. At that meeting, I realized that in many people's minds, Dewey had gone from being a flesh-and-blood animal with thoughts and feelings, to being a symbol, a metaphor, an object that could be owned. Library board members loved Dewey as a cat—Kathy Greiner, the president, always carried treats in her pocket for Dewey—but they still couldn't separate the animal from the legacy.

And I have to admit, there was another thought going through my mind. "I'm getting older, too. My health isn't the best. Are these people going to throw me out on my ear, too?"

"I know I am close to Dewey," I told the board. "I know I've been through a hard year with the death of my mother and with my health, and that you're trying to protect me. But I don't need protecting." I stopped. That wasn't what I was trying to say at all.

"Maybe you think I love Dewey too much," I told them. "Maybe you think my love clouds my judgment. But trust me. I'll know when it's time. I've had animals all my life. I've put them down. It's hard, but I can do it. The very last thing I want, the very last thing, is for Dewey to suffer."

A board meeting can be a freight train, and this one pushed me off to the side like a cow on the tracks. Someone suggested a committee to make decisions about Dewey's future. I knew the people on that committee would mean well. I knew they would take their duty seriously and do what they thought best. But I couldn't let that happen. I just couldn't.

The board was discussing how many people should

be on this Dewey Death Watch Committee when one member, Sue Hitchcock, spoke up. "This is ridiculous," she said. "I can't believe we're even discussing this. Vicki has been at the library for twenty-five years. She's been with Dewey for nineteen years. She knows what she's doing. We should all trust Vicki's judgment."

Thank God for Sue Hitchcock. As soon as she spoke, the train jumped the tracks and the board backed off. "Yes, yes," they muttered, "you're right . . . too soon, too much . . . if his condition worsens . . ."

I was devastated. It stung me to the heart that these people had even suggested taking Dewey away from me. And they could have done it. They had the power. But they didn't. Somehow, we had won a victory: for Dewey, for the library, for the town. For me.

Chapter 26 ⟶

Dewey's Love

I'll always remember Christmas 2005, the year before that horrible meeting, when Dewey was eighteen. Jodi and Scott stayed at my house. They had
twins now, Nathan and Hannah, a year and a half old.
Mom was still alive, and she put on her best lounging
outfit to watch the twins open presents. Dewey sprawled
on the sofa, pressed against Jodi's hip. It was the end of
one thing, the beginning of the next. But for that week,
we were all together.

Dewey's love for Jodi had never diminished. She was
still his great romantic affair. Whenever he got a chance
that Christmas, Dewey stuck by her side. But with so
many people around, especially the children, and with
so much going on, he was more content than ever to just
watch. He got along well with Scott, not a hint of jealousy. And he loved the twins. I replaced my glass coffee
table with a cushioned ottoman when my grandchildren
were born, and Dewey spent most of Christmas week

sitting on that ottoman. Hannah and Nathan would toddle up and pet him all over. Dewey was cautious around toddlers now. In the library, he slunk away when they tried to approach him. But he sat with the twins, even when they petted him the wrong way and messed up his fur. Hannah kissed him a hundred times a day; Nathan accidentally knocked him on the head. One afternoon, Hannah poked Dewey in the face while trying to pet him. Dewey didn't even react. This was my grandchild, Jodi's child. Dewey loved us, so he loved Hannah, too.

Dewey was so calm that year. That was the biggest difference in old man Dewey. He knew how to avoid trouble. He still attended meetings, but he knew how far to push and which lap to choose. In September 2006, just a few weeks before the board meeting, a program at the library brought in almost a hundred people. I figured Dewey would hide in the staff area, but there he was, mingling as always. He was like a shadow moving among the guests, often unnoticed but somehow there at the end of a patron's hand each time someone reached to pet him. There was a rhythm to his interactions that seemed the most natural and beautiful thing in the world.

After the program, Dewey climbed into his bed above Kay's desk, clearly exhausted. Kay came over and gave him a gentle scratch on the chin. I knew that touch, that quiet look. It was a thank-you, the one you give an old friend or a spouse after you've watched them across a crowded room and realized how wonderful they are, and how lucky you are to have them in your life. I half expected her to say, "That'll do, cat, that'll do," like the farmer in the movie *Babe*, but this time Kay left all the words unsaid.

Two months later, in early November, Dewey's gait became a bit unsteady. He started peeing excessively, sometimes on the paper outside his litter box, which he had never done before. But he wasn't hiding. He was still jumping up and down from the circulation desk. He still interacted with patrons. He didn't seem to be in pain. I called Dr. Franck, and she advised me not to bring him in but to watch him closely.

One morning near the end of the month, Dewey wasn't waving. All those years, and I could count on one hand the number of times Dewey wasn't waving when I arrived in the morning. Instead he was standing at the front door, just waiting for me. I ushered him to the litter box and gave him his can of cat food. He ate a few bites, then walked with me on our morning rounds. I was busy preparing for a trip to Florida—my brother Mike's daughter Natalie was getting married and the whole family was going to be there—so I left Dewey with the staff for the rest of the morning. As always, he came in while I was working to sniff my office vent and make sure I was safe. The older he got, the more he protected the ones he loved.

At nine thirty I went out for Dewey's breakfast of the moment, a Hardee's bacon, egg, and cheese biscuit. When I returned, Dewey didn't come running. I figured the deaf old boy didn't hear the door. I found him sleeping on a chair by the circulation desk, so I swung the bag a few times, floating the smell of eggs his way. He flew out of that chair into my office. I put the egg-and-cheese mush on a paper plate, and he ate three or four bites before curling up on my lap.

At ten thirty, Dewey attended Story Hour. As usual, he greeted every child. An eight-year-old girl was sitting on the floor with her legs crossed, in the position we used to call Indian-style. Dewey curled up on her legs and went to sleep. She petted him, the other children took turns petting him, everyone was happy. After Story Hour, Dewey crawled into his fur-lined bed in front of the heater, which was running full blast, and that's where he was when I left the library at noon. I was going home for lunch, then picking up Dad and driving to Omaha to catch a flight the next morning.

Ten minutes after I got home, the phone rang. It was Jann, one of our clerks. "Dewey's acting funny."

"What do you mean funny?"

"He's crying and walking funny. And he's trying to hide in the cupboards."

"I'll be right down."

Dewey was hiding under a chair. I picked him up, and he was shaking like the morning I found him. His eyes were big, and I could tell he was in pain. I called the veterinary office. Dr. Franck was out, but her husband, Dr. Beall, was in. He said, "Come right down." I wrapped Dewey in his towel. It was a cold day, end of November. Dewey snuggled against me immediately.

By the time we arrived at the vet's office, Dewey was down on the floor of my car by the heater, shaking with fear. I cradled him in my arms and held him against my chest. That's when I noticed poop sticking out of his behind.

What a relief! It wasn't serious. It was constipation.

I told Dr. Beall the problem. He took Dewey into the back room to clean out his colon and intestines. He also washed his back end, so Dewey came back wet and cold. He crawled from Dr. Beall's arms into mine and looked up at me with pleading eyes. *Help me.* I could tell something still wasn't right.

Dr. Beall said, "I can feel a mass. It's not feces."

"What is it?"

"He needs an X-ray."

Ten minutes later, Dr. Beall was back with the results. There was a large tumor in Dewey's stomach, and it was pushing on his kidneys and intestines. That's why he had been peeing more, and it probably accounted for his peeing outside the litter box.

"It wasn't there in September," Dr. Beall said, "which means it's probably an aggressive cancer. But we'd have to do invasive tests to find out for sure."

We stood silently, looking at Dewey. I never suspected the tumor. Never. I knew everything about Dewey, all his thoughts and feelings, but he had kept this one thing hidden from me.

"Is he in pain?"

"Yes, I suspect he is. The mass is growing very fast, so it will only get worse."

"Is there anything you can give him for the pain?"

"No, not really."

I was holding Dewey in my arms, cradling him like a baby. He hadn't let me carry him that way in sixteen years. Now he wasn't even fighting it. He was just looking at me.

"Do you think he's in constant pain?"

"I can't imagine that he's not."

The conversation was crushing me, flattening me out, making me feel drawn, deflated, tired. I couldn't believe what I was hearing. Somehow I had believed Dewey was going to live forever.

I called the library staff and told them Dewey wasn't coming home. Kay was out of town. Joy was off duty. They reached her at Sears, but too late. Several others came down to say their good-byes. Instead of going to Dewey, though, Sharon walked right up and hugged me. Thank you, Sharon, I needed that. Then I hugged Donna and thanked her for loving Dewey so much. Donna was the last to say her good-byes.

Someone said, "I don't know if I want to be here when they put him to sleep."

"That's fine," I said. "I'd rather be alone with him."

Dr. Beall took Dewey into the back room to insert the IV, then brought him back in a fresh blanket and put him in my arms. I talked to Dewey for a few minutes. I told him how much I loved him, how much he meant to me, how much I didn't want him to suffer. I explained what was happening and why. I rewrapped his blanket to make sure he was comfortable. What more could I offer him than comfort? I cradled him in my arms and rocked back and forth from foot to foot, a habit started when he was a kitten. Dr. Beall gave him the first shot, followed closely by the second.

He said, "I'll check for a heartbeat."

I said, "You don't need to. I can see it in his eyes."

Dewey was gone.

Chapter 27

Loving Dewey

I was in Florida for eight days. I didn't read the newspaper. I didn't watch television. I didn't take any phone calls. It was the best possible time to be away because Dewey's death was hard. Very hard. I broke down on the flight from Omaha and cried all the way to Houston. In Florida, I thought often of Dewey, alone, quietly, but also surrounded by the family that had always sustained me.

I had no idea how far word of Dewey's death had spread. The next morning, while I sat crying on an airplane to Houston, the local radio station devoted their morning show to memories of Dewey. The *Sioux City Journal* ran a lengthy story and obituary. I don't know if that was the source, but the AP wire picked up the story and sent it around the world. Within hours, news of Dewey's death appeared on the CBS afternoon newsbreak and on MSNBC. The library started getting calls. If I had been in the library, I would have been stuck an-

swering questions from reporters for days, but nobody
else on staff felt comfortable speaking to the media. The
library secretary, Kim, gave a brief statement, which
ended up in what I now think of as Dewey's public obituary, but that was all. It was enough. Over the next few
days, that obituary ran in more than 270 newspapers.

The response from individuals touched by Dewey
was equally overwhelming. People in town received calls
from friends and relatives all over the country who read
about Dewey's death in the local newspaper or heard it
on a local radio show. One local couple was out of the
country and learned the news from a friend in San Francisco, who read about his passing in the *San Francisco
Chronicle*. Admirers set up a vigil in the library. Local
businesses sent flowers and gifts. Sharon and Tony's
daughter, Emmy, gave me a picture she had drawn of
Dewey. It was two green circles in the middle of the
page with lines sticking out in all directions. It was beautiful, and Emmy beamed as I taped it to my office door.
That picture was the perfect way for both of us to remember him.

Gary Roma, director of the documentary about library cats, wrote me a long letter. It said, in part: "I don't
know if I ever told you, but of all the many library cats
I've met across the country, Dewey Readmore Books
was my favorite. His beauty, charm, and playfulness
were unique."

Tomoko from Japanese Public Television wrote to
tell us Dewey's death had been announced in Japan,
and that many were sad to hear he was gone.

Marti Attoun, who wrote the article for *American Pro-*

file, wrote to say the Dewey story was still her favorite. It had been years, and Marti was now a contributing editor. It seemed so unlikely, given the hundreds of stories she had written, that Marti would remember a cat, much less still think of him fondly. But that was Dewey. He touched people so deeply.

By the time I returned to my office, there were letters and cards stacked four feet high on my desk. I had more than six hundred e-mails about Dewey waiting in my inbox. Many were from people who met him only once but never forgot him. Hundreds of others were from people who never met him. In the month after his death, I received more than a thousand e-mails about Dewey from all around the world. We heard from a soldier in Iraq who had been touched by Dewey's death despite what he saw there every day—or perhaps because of it. We received a letter from a couple in Connecticut whose son was turning eleven; his birthday wish was to release a balloon to heaven in Dewey's honor. We received numerous gifts and donations. A librarian at the Naval History Museum, for instance, donated four books in his memory. She had followed Dewey's story in library publications and read his obituary in the *Washington Post*. Our Web site, www.spencerlibrary.com, went from 25,000 hits a month to 189,922 in December, and the traffic didn't let up for most of the next year.

Many people in town wanted us to hold a memorial service. I didn't want a memorial service, nobody on staff did, but we had to do something. So on a cold Saturday in the middle of December, Dewey's admirers gathered at the library to remember one last time, at least officially, the friend who had had such an impact on their lives. The staff tried to keep it light—I told the story of the bat, Audrey told the story of the lights, Joy remembered the cart rides, Sharon told how Dewey stole the meat out of her sandwich—but despite our best efforts, tears were shed. Two women cried the whole time.

Crews from local television stations were filming the event. It was a nice thought, but the cameras seemed out of place. These were private thoughts among friends; we didn't want to share our words with the world. We also realized, as we stood there together, that words couldn't describe our feelings for Dewey. There was no easy way to say how special he was. We were here; the cameras were here; the world stood still around us. That said more than any words. Finally a local schoolteacher said, "People say what's the big deal, he was just a cat. But that's where they're wrong. Dewey was so much more." Everyone knew exactly what she meant.

My moments with Dewey were more intimate. The staff had cleaned out his bowls and donated his food while I was away, but I had to give away his toys. I had to clean out his shelf: the Vaseline for his hairballs, the brush, the red skein of yarn he had played with all his life. I had to park my car and walk to the library every morning without Dewey waving at me from the front door. When the staff returned to the library after visiting Dewey for the last time, the space heater he had lain in front of every day wasn't working. Dewey had been lying in front of it that very morning, and it had been working fine. It was as if his death had taken away its reason to heat. Can a malfunctioning piece of equipment break your heart? It was six weeks before I could even think about having that heater repaired.

I had Dewey cremated with one of his favorite toys, Marty Mouse, so he wouldn't be alone. The crematorium offered a mahogany box and bronze plaque, no charge, but it didn't seem right to display him. Dewey came back to his library in a plain plastic container inside a blue velvet bag. I put the container on a shelf in my office and went back to work.

A week after his memorial service, I came out of my office a half hour before the library opened, long before any patrons arrived, and told Kay, "It's time."

It was December, another brutally cold Iowa morning. Just like the first morning, and so many in between. It was close to the shortest day of the year, and the sun wasn't yet up. The sky was still deep blue, almost purple, and there was no traffic on the roads. The only sound was the cold wind that had come all the way from the Canadian plains, whipping down the streets and out over the barren cornfields.

We moved some rocks in the little garden out front of the library, looking for a place where the ground wasn't completely frozen. But the whole earth was frosted, and it took a while for Kay to dig the hole. The sun was peeking over the buildings on the far side of the parking lot, throwing the first shadows, by the time I placed the remains of my friend in the ground and said simply, "You're always with us, Dewey. This is your home." Then Kay dropped in the first shovelful of dirt, burying Dewey's ashes forever outside the window of the children's library, at the foot of the beautiful statue of a mother reading a book to her child. Mom's statue. As Kay moved the stones back over Dewey's final resting place, I looked up and saw the rest of the library staff in the window, silently watching us.

Last Thoughts from Iowa

Not much has changed in northwest Iowa since Dewey died. With ethanol being the next big thing, more corn is in the ground than ever before, but there aren't more workers to grow it, just better technology and more machines. And, of course, more land.

In Spencer, the hospital added its first plastic surgeon. Cleber Meyer, now eighty, was voted out of office and went back to his gas station. The new mayor is the husband of Kim Petersen, the library secretary, but he's no more a reader than Cleber was. The Eaton plant on the edge of town, which makes machine parts, moved a shift to Juárez, Mexico. One hundred and twenty jobs lost. But Spencer will survive. We always do.

The library rolls on, cat-free for the first time since Ronald Reagan was president. After Dewey's death, we had almost a hundred offers for new cats. We had offers from as far away as Texas, transportation included. The cats were cute, and most had touching survival stories, but there was no enthusiasm to take one. The library board wisely put a two-year moratorium on cats in the library. They needed time, they said, to think through the issues. I had done all the thinking I needed. You can't bring back the past.

But Dewey's memory will live on, I feel confident of that. Maybe at the library, where his portrait hangs beside the front door above a bronze plaque that tells his story, a gift from one of Dewey's many friends. Maybe in the children who knew him, who will talk about him in decades to come with their own children and grandchildren. Maybe in this book. After all, that's why I'm writing it. For Dewey.

Back in 2000, when Grand Avenue made the National Registry, Spencer commissioned a public art installation to serve as both a statement about our values and an entry point to our historic downtown. Two Chicago-area ceramic tile mosaic artists, Nina Smoot-Cain and John Pitman Weber, spent a year in the area, talking with us, studying our history, and observing our way of life. More than 570 residents, from young children to grandparents, consulted with the artists. The result is a mosaic sculpture called *The Gathering: Of Time, of Land, of Many Hands.*

The Gathering is composed of four decorative pillars and three pictorial walls. The south wall is called "The Story of the Land." It is a farm scene featuring corn and pigs; a woman hanging quilts on a clothesline; and a train. The north wall is "The Story of Outdoor Recreation." It focuses on East and West Lynch parks, our main municipal recreation areas; the fairgrounds on the northwest edge of town; and the lakes. The west wall is "The Story of Spencer." It shows three generations gathering at grandma's house; the town battling the fire; and a woman making a pot, a metaphor for shaping the future. Just slightly to the left of center, in the upper half of the scene, is an orange cat sitting on the open pages of a book. The image is based on artwork submitted by a child.

The story of Spencer. Dewey is a part of it, then, now, and forever. He will live longest, I know, in the collective memory of a town that never forgets where it's been, even as it looks ahead for where it's going.

I told Jodi when Dewey was fourteen, "I don't know if I'll want to keep working at the library after Dewey's gone." It was just a premonition, but now I understand what I meant. For as long as I can remember, when I pulled up every morning the library was alive: with hope, with love, with Dewey waving at me from the front door. Now it's a dead building again. I feel the chill in my bones, even in the summer. Some mornings, I don't want to bother. But then I turn on the lights, and the library flickers to life. The staff files in. The patrons follow: the middle-aged for books, the businessmen for magazines, the teenagers for computers, the children for stories, the elderly for support. The library is alive, and once again I have the best job on earth, at least until I get ready to leave in the evening and there's nobody begging for one more game of hide-and-seek.

A year after Dewey's death, my health finally caught up with me. It was time, I knew, to move on with my life. The library was different without Dewey, and I didn't want my days to end that way: empty, quiet, occasionally lonely. When I saw the book cart go past, the one Dewey used to ride on, it broke my heart. I missed him that much, and not just once in a while, but every day. I decided to retire. It was time. More than 125 people attended my retirement party, including many from out of town I hadn't spoken with in years. Dad read one of his poems; my grandkids sat with me to greet well-wishers; two articles ran in the *Spencer Daily Reporter* thanking me for twenty-five years of service. Like Dewey, I was lucky. I got to leave on my own terms.

Find your place. Be happy with what you have. Treat everyone well. Live a good life. It isn't about material things; it's about love. And you can never anticipate love.

I learned those things from Dewey, of course, but as always, those answers seem too easy. All answers, except that I loved Dewey with all my heart and he loved me in the same way, seem too easy. But let me try.

When I was three years old, Dad owned a John Deere tractor. The tractor had a cultivator on the front, which is a long row of shovel-like blades, six on each side. The blades are raised a few inches off the dirt; you drive the handle forward to put them in the ground, where they chop into the soil, tossing fresh dirt against the corn rows. I was playing in the mud by the front wheel of that tractor one day when Mom's brother came out after lunch, threw the clutch, and started driving. Dad saw what happened and started running, but Mom's brother couldn't hear him. The wheel knocked me down and shoved me into the blades. I was pushed along by the blades, passed from one to the other, until Mom's brother turned the wheel and the inside blade tossed me through the middle chute and left me lying facedown behind the tractor. Dad scooped me up in one motion and ran me back to the porch. He looked me over in amazement, then held me in his arms for the rest of the day, rocking back and forth in our old rocking chair, crying on my shoulder and telling me, "You're all right, you're all right, everything is all right."

Eventually I looked at him and said, "I cut my finger." I showed him the blood. I was bruised, but otherwise, that tiny cut was the only mark.

That's life. We all go through the tractor blades every now and then. We all get bruised, and we all get cut. Sometimes the blades cut deep. The lucky ones come through with a few scratches, a little blood, but even that isn't the most important thing. The most important thing is having someone there to scoop you up, to hold you tight, and to tell you everything is all right.

For years, I thought I had done that for Dewey. I thought that was my story to tell. And I had done that. When Dewey was hurt, cold, and crying, I was there. I held him. I made sure everything was all right.

But that's only a sliver of the truth. The real truth is that for all those years, on the hard days, the good days, and all the unremembered days that make up the pages of the real book of our lives, Dewey was holding me.

He's still holding me now. So thank you, Dewey. Thank you. Wherever you are.

Acknowledgments ⟶

To my agent, Peter McGuigan, for contacting me and believing there was a story to be told about Dewey's life. Thank you, Peter, Hannah Gordon Brown, and everyone at Foundry Literary who worked so tirelessly to make this book bigger than I ever imagined.

To Bret Witter, who not only found my voice, but also became a friend and confidant through this process. Thank you, Bret, for making the book so well written. We were passionate about quality, and I think we achieved it.

To Karen Kosztolnyik, Jamie Raab, and Celia Johnson at Grand Central Publishing for fighting for the book even though they saw only a forty-five-page proposal. They believed in the story before it was even written. Thank you to Matthew Ballast, Harvey-Jane Kowal, Christine Valentine, and everyone at Grand Central: there would be no book without all of you.

To Dick Montgomery for being my lawyer and friend through all the legal "stuff," and to his wife, Mary Jean, for all her support.

To the current and former Spencer Library staff who

supported this project, sat through interviews, believed in me, and cared for Dewey over the years, including Jean Hollis Clark, Kay Larson, Joy DeWall, Sharon Joy, Audrey Wheeler, Cynthia Behrends, Paula Brown, Donna Stanford, Tammi Herbold, Jann Arends, Mary Jo Wingrove, Doris Armstrong, Kari Palm, Sheryl Rose, and Jackie Webster.

To all the other folks who agreed to be interviewed for this book and filled in my memory gaps, including Bob Rose, Kirby Schmidt, Mike Baehr, Jack Manders, Cathy Greiner, Esther Connell, Judy Johnson (both of you!), Marcie Muckey, Pat Jones, Dr. James Esterly, Verlyn Jipson, and Jodi Carlson. And to Louisville Metro Transcription, for transcribing those hundreds of hours of interviews.

To the board members who were in place when the decision was made to adopt Dewey, including Jack Manders, Mike Baehr, Mary Houston, Esther Connell, Bernie Keninger, JoAnn Lawson, Gail Peterson, Lee Lookingbill, and Grace Rindsig. They made a quick decision that would affect the library for years. I always had their full support; they gave me wings to fly.

To the current board members who gave me permission to write this book (on my own time), including Cathy Greiner, Esther Connell, Jim Morony, Sue Hitchcock, Roger Littlefield, Wayne Koppen, and Amanda Hoffman.

To the Board of the Friends Group who were always there when I needed them, especially Sandy Fleck, Marcie Muckey, and Trudy Elbert.

To my family, who helped me with the book and

supported me through the process: Verlyn Jipson; Jodi and Scott Carlson; brother Doug (who edited film of Dewey), Merrillee, Verlyn, James, and Merrill Jipson; brother Mike and Monica Jipson, and daughter, Natalie DeHaven; sister Val and Don Bonney, Andrea, Josh, and Lindsay; and my niece MacKenzie Dunn. To my brothers David and Steve, whose lives were rich but much too short. To my mom and grandma Stephenson, who were strong role models for my life. And, most of all, to my delightful twin grandchildren, who make me laugh when the stress is too much: Hannah and Nathan Carlson.

To my uncle, Duane Jipson, who read everything he could get his hands on (including the encyclopedia) until his death at age ninety-four. His example of love, kindness, gentility, and education touched everyone, and especially me.

To Jim Fanning, former manager of the Montreal Expos baseball team and lifelong friend, for his support during the lean times and for believing that I could accomplish anything.

To Dr. Ron Kolegraff, friend and surgeon, for understanding my emotional needs when no one else could see it or discuss it.

To Treva Johnson, for helping me understand the needs of the disabled in the library long before the ADA Act was passed and for being my colleague on the Spencer ADA Council since 1991.

To Dewey fans, both near and far, for the thousands of letters, e-mails, gifts, and personal visits to see Dewey over the years, especially Harry and Rita Fein, from

New York (who remembered every year for Christmas), Doreen Walker (his first British pen pal), Phyllis Lahti (founder of the Library Cat Society), and Gary Roma (filmmaker and comedian), who all believed in Dewey's magic before he was famous.

To the city of Spencer staff and council who stood up for me and supported the library over the years, especially city council member David Scott, who volunteered his time as Board of the Friends attorney for over twenty-five years and went to bat for me many times. And to Bob Fagen, current city manager, who treated me with respect and understood the significance of this book for Spencer.

To my friends, who always got me through the dark times and laughed with me in the good times, including my Run Away Women friends who consulted on the book: Trudy Henry, Faith Landwer, Barb Feder, Idelle Walton, Rita Mathine, and Pauli Wright. To Bonnie McKewon, friend and colleague, who read an early manuscript and made suggestions; her husband, Ron McKewon, who supported Dewey though his art; Dorothy DeGroot; and my many local friends for keeping me sane.

To my mentor, Dr. Roger Greer, and the professors from Emporia, who gave me the knowledge and tools for a successful career, not just in Spencer but across Iowa and beyond. I still use "Greerisms" in all the classes and workshops I teach.

To Dewey's doctors, Dr. James Esterly, Dr. Sophi Franck, and Dr. Tom Beall, for taking gentle care of him. To "Ashes To Ashes" for donating cremation of Dewey's remains along with his fur basket to keep him warm and Marty Mouse to keep him company. To

Warner Funeral Home, thank you for donating Dewey's memorial stone.

And, finally, to Dewey, my magical little buddy for more than nineteen years. I can still feel the heartstring that connects us, and I will never let go.

Special Thanks to the great Iowa writer Bill Kinsella, whom I had long admired but never met, for his wonderful endorsement and for allowing me to paraphrase from his book *Shoeless Joe* (and the movie based on it, *Field of Dreams*) on page 129. No one will ever express the magic of Iowa any better.

THE
HARROGATE
SECRET

CATHERINE
COOKSON

SUMMIT BOOKS

NEW YORK • LONDON • TORONTO • SYDNEY • TOKYO • SINGAPORE

SUMMIT BOOKS
Simon & Schuster Building
Rockefeller Center
1230 Avenue of the Americas
New York, New York 10020

Copyright © 1988 by Catherine Cookson
All rights reserved
including the right of reproduction
in whole or in part in any form.
SUMMIT BOOKS and colophon are
trademarks of Simon & Schuster Inc.
Designed by Edith Fowler
Manufactured in the United States of America

10 9 8 7 6 5 4 3 2 1
10 9 8 7 6 5 4 3 2 1   (Pbk.)

Library of Congress Cataloging in Publication Data

Cookson, Catherine.
    The Harrogate secret.

    I. Title.
PR6053.0525H35   1988   823'.914   88-2148

ISBN 0-671-65941-3
ISBN 0-671-70520-2   (Pbk.)

Contents

PART ONE

As It Happened
When I Was Ten

1

Robert Musgrave eased himself off the low platform bed set in the alcove and, using his arms, propelled himself backwards across the stone-flagged floor towards the door of the cottage. In doing so he had to pass between the open-hearth fire and the two small children playing on the mat in front of it and the back of his wife who was standing at the table in the middle of the room. When he reached the door he lifted up one arm and pushed the sneck; then with a practised fling he swung his two useless legs to the side in order to allow himself to reach the top step, and there he sat for a moment looking out.

In the fading light he could still make out other cottages dotted here and there on the steep hillside down to the row of dwellings that bordered the shore.

But as clustered as the cottages were on this part of the hillside, Robert often thanked God that he was housed here and not further along the hill in the main town where the principal winding street on the bank of the river ran from Low Lights to the Bull Ring, and from which led numerous sets of steps, some counting up to a hundred and these giving onto the houses on the hill.

Situated as the cottages were here, the wind coming from the river and the German ocean did sweep away the stink; but along there it was so congested with the muck and the human offal lying in the streets that in parts they had to wait for the pigs to swarm in in the mornings to clear it for them.

Something should be done. He had said this for many a year. Cats buried their mess and the scorned pigs chose their places to empty themselves, but human beings seemed to wallow in their own excrement; yet the fine ladies and gentlemen could emerge from their big houses on the top of the hill and step daintily over muck without blinking an eyelid.

"Sitting on your bare backside on a cold step is not going to bring him any quicker; he'll come when he's ready."

He looked back into the room towards his wife. She wasn't looking towards him but was concentrating on the coarse flour and water dough she was kneading on the table.

"He isn't runnin' the night," he said; "he saw the faggot man the day and got no word."

"He could have sculled across the river to South Shields, the tide's low."

"Aye, but for only another half hour or so. That's what's worryin' me."

"Well, it shouldn't. He's been caught afore by it an' he's gone to his gran's. What's different the night? What's the matter with you?"

She turned from the table, dusted her hands on her coarse apron, then went towards the door. She was a big woman all of five foot eight and broad with it, but her width was made up of bone and muscle. Providing for her family since the day, ten years past, they had carried her man in, his legs bloody and dangling, had kept the flesh stripped from her. At times, even now, she could still hear him screaming, not with pain, but at the doctor who had wanted to cut his legs off.

He'd always had a dread of having no feet. In bed on their wedding night he had laughingly told her he had one fear in his life, that he would lose his feet. And on that occasion, such was their enjoyment of each other she had tickled his soles and caused him to squeal.

The bone man from along the coast had pushed the bones back into the torn flesh, the while she held him down and Jimmy Harper from next door poured rum down his gullet. So he had kept his feet and the bones had knitted, but not quite as nature intended: his feet were splayed and his legs useless from the knees down.

As if tending a child, her hand went to his head and stroked the straggling hair from his brow, and he put his own up and laid it on top of hers for a moment, pressing it tight, and his voice was quiet as he asked, "Why do you never seem to worry about our Freddie?"

"Because I know nothin' will ever happen to him."

"Because he's small and slippery?"

"No, no, not that. And he'll grow: he's nearin' the time for growin', they sprout after ten. No, it's because he's got things in his head. He's somehow like me dad used to be, sees things that are comin', and I feel that this'll always help him to keep clear."

Still gazing abroad, Robert smiled quietly to himself. He wanted to answer her: "It didn't stop your dad from being picked up by the press gang," for then she would have likely come back, saying, "No; and it didn't stop him from escaping them, although it took him two years." And she was right about Freddie. He was a lucky lad, picking up a tanner here and there and more at times. And then there was his job at the butcher's from where he often brought home a pile of chitterlings; and he was lucky an' all in that his mother wouldn't let him go down the pit. Aye. Aye; not like John. John was down there now in the dark. My God! if ever there was a hell it was down that pit.

John was twelve now. He had been down since he was eight. But on that first night down he wasn't the only one who had cried, for he himself had lain wide-eyed following every move that would take his lad into the depths. He himself had gone down as a lad of seven, clinging to a man's waist, the man himself clinging to a rope and being lowered into the black hell. When he was fifteen he realised that a man could become depraved doing such work. He hadn't put it under the heading of that word then, he only knew something in himself protested against his body being used so and his mind being sullied.

Then when he was twenty he got his eye on a lass, just caught glimpses of her now and again, a big strapping lass. It was her hips he noticed first. They swung her thick serge skirt from side to side as she walked. She was only fifteen or so but already a woman, and from her hair to the toes of her steel-capped boots she was strong. She was working in the salt pans at the time, but her people were fisher folk from across the water in South Shields. Her name was Jinny Williams. He had courted her and married her and loved her, and she had loved him, and she still did. Strange that, him a useless cripple; yet not quite useless, for hadn't he made all the furniture in this cottage, and wasn't it the best and cleanest comfortable cottage at this end of the hill?

It was she who had got him to leave the pit and go into ship building. They were turning out ships by the dozen on both sides

15

of the river then, and within ten years he had become as good a carpenter as any man who had been apprenticed to it from a bairn. It was during this time he had built the little sculler for John, no bigger than a coracle it was, and it would hold two at a pinch. But it was odd, John never took to it; he didn't care for the river, would rather walk the countryside. No; it was Freddie who, from when he was able to toddle, would tumble into it; and he was sculling like the best of them when he was four, and seemed never to have been out of it since. And it had stood him in good stead. By God! it had.

So when he had woken up to the fact that he would be helpless for the rest of his life and that he couldn't walk nor move from the house unless he was lifted into the bogie and wheeled down to the town, he realised he still had a trade of sorts, he could make things out of wood. But then it didn't take long for him also to realise that there were carpenters in the town, and it was their living, and that they resented a chippie from the boats muzzling in. So he had concentrated his skill on replacing the cheap stuff they had first set up house with.

What was more, he had fathered ten children. Nell, his firstborn, was sixteen now and married these two months. They had lost Mary, Joe, and Harry with the pox. Then had followed John. John was the steady one. Then Nancy had come. Nancy, beautiful, big, dark-haired Nancy, like her mother in everything but her eyes, for she had been stone blind from birth. Yet strangely Nancy had more light about her than any of his brood, and was indeed the happiest of the lot of them. Next came Freddie, Freddie who now at ten years old could be taken for seven or eight, in fact it was his smallness and babyish look that denied all that was in his head and which had saved him so far from the customs men, and the chimney sweeps and such.

Billy had followed Freddie, but he too had died, again with the smallpox. There hadn't been another until Jessie came. He turned his head slightly to the side and looked at his four-year-old fair-haired daughter with a face as plain as a pikestaff. She was playing with his latest effort, Lily, who at two years old was making up for Jessie's plainness, being pretty and curly-haired.

"That's Nancy." Jinny nudged his shoulder with her knee, and they both listened; then they looked towards the steps that

16

led downwards about six feet from the adjoining cottage and slowly through the deepening twilight there emerged onto the rough cinder path that fronted the cottages an eleven-year-old girl.

"You're late, lass."

"I got talkin', Ma."

Robert gave a small laugh now as he said, "You spend your life talkin'."

"And listenin', Da. An' listenin'."

"Aye; aye, you're right there. You've got a pair of ears on you like a cuddy's lugs. I've said it afore and I'll say it again, you should hire them out."

Jinny now backed from the door, saying, "Come on in, both of you; Freddie will be here when he comes, not afore an' not after."

"He hasn't come back yet, Ma?"

"No. And I suppose you haven't seen anything of him the night?"

It didn't seem odd to them that they should ask a blind girl if she had seen anything of her brother for her ears were her eyes and she seemed to observe through them things that escaped the sighted.

"I knew he had gone across the water earlier the day, an' when I got to Nell's she and Joe had just got in and Joe said when he was loading salt on a ship he saw him goin' over. . . . Ma."

"Yes, pet?"

"Nell made me laugh although she was very tired. She'd been wheeling coal all day and feeding the fires. But she told me there'd been a fight atween two women: one was after the other's man, she said, and they rolled into the river. She said, it must have taken some of the steam out of them. . . . Ma"—her voice changed—"she doesn't seem to like workin' there in all that steam."

"No; but who does, pet? There's one good thing about it, though, lass, them that work on the salt rarely get the plague. It's been proved again an' again, so she's lucky in that way. And so's Joe." And now Jinny added on a yell, "You! Jessie; leave Nancy alone; let her get settled. All right, all right, take her stick and put it in the corner, an' mind the ram's head doesn't bite you."

17

The small child laughed, saying now, "Can't bite, Ma, 'tis wood."

"Oh, 'tis amazin' what wood can do. Which reminds me, it's about time we had a light on the subject. Bring a candle, Jessie, and give it to your da."

The child dutifully went to a square painted tin that stood on the end of a piece of furniture doing duty both as a long chest of drawers and as a sideboard and, taking from it a tallow candle, brought it to her father and he, sitting now on the mat to the side of the fireplace, took a spill from the hearth and, handing it to her, said, "Light it an' give it to the candle." And when the child had done this she said, "You want your pipe lit up an' all, Da?"

"No; not the night, lass, not the night."

Not tonight because he had no baccy. Perhaps come the week-end one of his friends would drop in a twist or a small bag of snuff; not that he liked snuff, that usually went across the water to Jinny's mother. But there had been no hand-outs for the last two or three weeks, the customs blokes were on the watch. What must it be like to be hated as that Mr Taggart was. To look at him he seemed a decent enough fella; but he was out to get you, get anybody, one an' all, even the occupant of Storey's Hall over at Low Lights wasn't above suspicion. Wasn't there hell to pay when Taggart appeared at the front door and asked questions.

He turned now and looked at his wife who was saying to Nancy, "Could you eat a griddle?" And his daughter answered with a smile, "Oh, aye, Ma, anytime I could eat a griddle," which prompted him to ask her, "Didn't you get a bite along at Nell's?"

"No, Da, no. 'Cos they were both harassed and had to clean up, and Nell was dead on her feet, she sounded it."

"Can I have a griddle, Ma?"

"No, you can't, our Jessie; you had your supper not an hour gone. Now get off to bed, and take Lily with you. Take her clothes off, all but her last petticoat. An' you do the same. If you get into bed with them on I'll come in there an' pull the lot off you, mind." Jessie laughed with her mother, then went over to her father and, her face almost on a level with his as he sat with his back against the wall, she kissed his stubbly cheek, saying, "Good night, Da."

18

"Good night, pet. Sleep tight, an' mind the bugs don't bite."

The two small children gone from the room, Robert now asked, "Did you hear any crack the day, Nancy?"

"Odds and ends, Da, odds and ends." She cocked her head to the side and added, "Oh, here's John."

Within a few seconds the door opened and there stood her twelve-year-old brother, nothing distinguishing him from a black boy except his eyes and the red gap of his mouth as he opened it, saying wearily, "Hello there."

"Hello, lad," said his father.

"Tired, lad?" asked Jinny.

"Same as usual. It's a nice night though, stars out an' a nip in the air. It's lovely an' cool, the air."

The daily sadness descended on Jinny as she made her way to the fire and lifted from a chain hanging there a round iron pot full of boiling water which she then carried out through a side door into a small lean-to, saying over her shoulder, "Will you have an all-over-one?"

"Aye, Ma; I want it off me back." He now turned and looked down at his father and asked, "What d'you think, Da? It's balderdash, isn't it, them saying it weakens your back to wash it?"

"I agree with you, lad, it's balderdash."

As the young boy passed his sister he asked quietly, "All right, Nancy?"

"Aye, John, fine. You know somethin', John?"

"No, Nancy; what's that?" He was divesting himself of his coat and muffler as he looked down at her, and she said, "Mrs Twaite is gettin' up a concert and its gona be held at The George. She asked me to go and sing."

There were gasps now from her mother and father both exclaiming together, "You never told us!"

"Well, I've just got in, Ma." She was laughing. "And I was keepin' it until Freddie came in to tell you all together."

"What'll they pay you?"

"A shilling at least, Ma."

"My! My!" Her father screwed himself round from the wall and grabbed her hand, saying, "Could be a start, hinny. Could be a real start."

John was now in the scullery where his mother was cooling down the boiling water with a bucket of sea water she had

19

brought in from outside the front door, and as he unloosened his short leather trousers he said to her, "I hear there's a man in Newcastle who trains voices."

"Trains voices! She doesn't need her voice trained; it's as clear as a bell."

"Aye, Ma; but there's different ways of singin' like."

"How d'you know? Who've you been talkin' to?"

"Oh, different ones. We get on talkin' at bait time. You know Mr Knight, Billy Knight, he's in the Methodist Chapel choir, he sings, but he said you can't get anywhere, not proper, unless you're trained. He took lessons when he was a lad, that's of course when his people had a shop in Newcastle. They've come down since that."

"Aye; how the mighty have fallen! Well, get your wash. And there's mutton soup an' some griddles. Then the best thing you can do is to get yourself to bed; no walkin' along the quays or the hills the night."

He had turned his back on her and his voice was soft as he said, "It's the only time I see the sky, Ma, 'cept Sunday."

Her head slightly lowered, she went back into the kitchen. What she would give if she could get that lad out of that pit. She would do anything, anything . . . except whoring.

She had just finished laying five plates around the table when the door opened and there entered a ten-year-old boy. His fair hair was sticking out from both sides of a black greasy peaked cap. He was wearing boots and his legs were bare to the ragged bottom of his calf-length trousers; his short jacket at one time must have been gray.

"As usual, you've turned up like the bad penny." His mother's look was soft, belying the harshness of her words. And he responded brightly, saying, "Aye, like a bad penny, Ma. I passed one the day, foreign it was. Wait till Pratt looks in his till the night."

"Where did you get a bad penny, lad?"

"I found it on the sands just as I got to yon side, Da. I looked down and there it was sticking up. It had a funny head on it. I didn't only find one, I found a bunch of 'em together. Look." He thrust his hand into his trouser pocket and brought out about ten coins, saying, "I'll just have to pass them now and again else somebody'll twig."

In the light from the fire and the tallow candle, Robert

squinted down at the coin he was holding up before his face and after a moment he said, "Bad pennies? These could be Roman coins, lad. It could be a find."

"Oh, well, Da, that makes the offence worse in passing 'em. Anything you find like that you've got to hand over to the authorities in Newcastle. They said so last year when that fella found that mug."

"He's right." Jinny nodded at her husband, thinking, How that boy remembers things, then saying, "Best not traffic with those; put them back where you found them, I'd say."

"I can't do that, Ma, 'cos the tide'll be up by now." He laughed, then said, "Hello there, Nancy"; and even as she was answering, "Hello, Freddie," he was already addressing his mother again: "John in?"

"Aye, he's having his wash."

The small figure now darted to the lean-to scullery and, putting his head round the door, he said in a surprisingly deep voice for one of such slight form and years, "Watcher, big fella. How ya feelin'?"

"As well as can be expected in my condition until I see the doctor, 'cos I've washed me back."

Freddie laughed, and like his voice, the sound didn't match his size or age; and turning again to his father, he said, but softly now, "Did you hear that? He made a joke."

"Aye, I heard." His father grinned back at him, then asked, "What's your news?"

"Aw! Things are movin'. I'll tell you when I've had me supper 'cos me belly thinks me throat's cut."

"Had nothing today, lad?"

"Well, I called at me granny's an' she gave me some broth, but it was so weak I had to help it out of the basin; an' she didn't offer me a bit of bread with it. Eehh! she's a mean scrub. Sorry! Ma. Sorry, Ma."

"You might be ten and consider yourself a very important individual," Jinny said to him, "but to me you're still in knicker-bockers and your ears are askin' for it, understand?"

"As clear as Christchurch bell, Ma. But you must admit your ma's niggly an' more than a bit on the . . ."

"I've told you mind!"

Robert was laughing. Nancy was laughing. Freddie was laughing; it was a happy atmosphere, and Jinny, ladling out the

21

mutton stew, thought as she often did, I've got a lot to thank the Almighty for. . . .

The meal over, the plates washed in another bucket of heated sea water, they were gathered round the fire: Robert in his usual position with his back against the wall, Jinny on a low cracket next to him—she always sat on a low cracket so her breadth and height wouldn't emphasize his position and condition—John sat next to his mother, Nancy next to him, and Freddie at the other side of the fireplace. Impatient for news, Jinny looked towards Freddie, saying, "Well, let's have it. What's happened the day?"

"Well," Freddie drew in a long breath, paused, as a true story-teller would be apt to do, then, addressing his father, said, "There's one thing sure, you won't get any baccy this week-end, nor snuff nor a drop of the hard stuff either."

"They're not runnin'?"

"No, they're not runnin'. But Taggart thinks they are. Somebody's split."

"Any idea who?" John asked.

"Could be one, two, or three, only time'll tell," he said. "You see, Mr Blaze, Mr Johnson, and Alec Crighton were to take a sculler out and pick up some kegs that was dumped on the last run. And also Mr smarty Keelman"—Freddie thumbed towards the wall to the side of him—"he and his mate and their Mick were to make the run down from Newcastle on the full tide later the night. Twas all set. Then I was on the quay and I saw the faggot man. I was expectin' him. An' I followed him to the tavern. He always goes in the best end and stays at least half an hour. But he was out within a few minutes again. He must have just had one drink, an' as he passed me he tossed me the usual penny. 'Faggot-face, you here again?' he said. 'Well, that's the last you'll get for some time. You've got me broke with your beggin'. If you don't work you don't eat.' It was that last bit, if you don't work you don't eat, that told me. And then he laughed and cuffed me ear an' nearly knocked me on me back. And there was Mr Johnson the cobbler and Ned Tiller from the brewery, they laughed as I went away holdin' me ear. It didn't really hurt but I made on."

"Then what did you do, I mean just from that, what did you learn?"

"Well, that the trip was off and I had to let them know, that

22

was, our lot, I mean those down in the shore cottages. He'd likely got word to t'others."

"What about the fella across the river, the one that comes on horseback to the Shields front that you meet at times? They store stuff there, don't they? You've been to his house."

"Oh, they'd never be on to him; he's a big pot, an' he would get to know in some way. If he'd been expecting a run that night he'd have come along through the market an' down to the shore. Anyway, I went over on speck and he wasn't there. If there's anything on he times it for slack tide so I can skip across."

"Skip across!" Jinny shook her head. "One of these days you'll be too late in your skipping in that little shell; you'll be caught."

"Well, Ma, if I do, there'll be lots of others caught at the same time."

"They're not as foolhardy as you leavin' it till the last minute."

"Well, if the tide came on me, Ma, unknowingst like, I'd just use me wings an' fly."

"Don't be too clever, boy."

"I'm not, Ma." Then his tone becoming deep and serious now he said, "I'm never too clever. I work things out, more so now since that day Mr Taggart thought he was bein' funny an' took me down into the cellar of his house an' showed me the neck manacles they tie smugglers to. Then he started to pump me about one an' another and I played dumb, daft like. No, Ma, I never act too clever. But I can be funny in me own home, can't I?"

His mother didn't answer, and a silence seemed to build up until his father said quietly, "Aye lad, you can be funny in your own home. If you can't be funny here where can you be funny?"

"I heard something funny today, Ma. I couldn't understand it."

"What did you hear, hinny?" They were all looking at Nancy now.

"Well, I saw two men. It was just after Mrs Twaite had spoken to me about the singing. They were coming out of the inn. They weren't from around here . . . well, not the usual ones that are on the main street."

"How d'you know that?" John had turned to her.

"Well, by their smell, John . . . you know, I know everybody by their smell."

23

"Well, you know lots of people by their smell, but you can't really know everybody by their smell."

"Well, I know if I haven't smelt anything like them afore, John."

"What did they smell like?"

"Different: not sweaty, not fishy, not from the salt pans, nor from the brewery, nor did they smell of the ships or from the top houses in the town. One smelt of snuff like we take to grandma, but different, a stronger smell; the other one, he smelt of—" She paused, then went on, "It wasn't scent; like onions, but not onions. Anyway, they were both different from what I had smelt afore except that time when the carriage stopped. Do you remember, Ma, when we walked to the highroad that day after we had been through the fields and that carriage stopped and you pulled me back to let the ladies out and pass us? That was a beautiful smell. I liked their smell better than I liked their voices."

"But what did you hear, Nancy? Go on, tell us what you heard?"

She turned her head towards Freddie now and said, "Well, it's to do with a tower, an' strangely, they were talkin' about smells and about scent, and one said to the other, 'They're on the wrong scent, and we're only here to put them off.' They were quite some distance away and I could only catch bits, but it was their smell that caught my fancy, an' that's why I listened. And then one told the other when he had got his order and who had given it to him. He said somethin' about just two hours ago, and he had come pell-mell from the city. And then they said somethin' about the business would be all happenin' across the water in the tower . . . or at the tower. First of all I thought they must be meaning the priory at Tynemouth, but when they said across the water I wondered where the tower was. They moved away then and I just heard one say to the other, 'I could never stand him 'cos he imagines he's a clever . . . ' He used that word, Ma, you know . . . b. 'But he's in for the shock of his life,' he said. Is there a tower across the water, Da?"

"What is it?"

Freddie had jumped to his feet. Looking down on his father, he said, "It must be The Towers she was hearin', Da. That's where he lives. That's where I went, I told you, the big house. I go there with the little parcels. They're special like. But he takes in the big stuff an' all. I'll have to go."

"*Freddie!* Now you can't, not at this time of night."

"I will, Ma, I will. I'll have to get across the river afore the tide turns 'cos remember over a year gone, when things were bad, we were glad of him. He helped me, he started me on the running when there was trouble on the Sunderland side and they couldn't get things through. We would have had nothing. But he set me on, an' now he's in a pickle. If the excise is all at this end he won't know nowt about it. And I told you last time, didn't I, his young wife was expectin' a bairn. It's his second wife, I told you. She was bonny, very bonny."

The urgency in his voice seemed to have got all, except his father, on their feet, and John came with him to the door, saying, "You'll still get across on the slack all right, but it's gettin' back; that little tub would be swamped by the incomin' tide. You couldn't battle against it."

"I won't try; I'll go to me granny's." Freddie looked back to where his mother was standing with her hand on his father's shoulder and addressed them both: "Don't worry," he said; "I'll be all right. I'll be careful. I always am. Really, I always am." Then for a ten-year-old he added words that made them wonder from where he came by his wisdom: "Cos it's daft to be brave," he said, then ran out into the night. But immediately John followed him and, catching up with him half-way down the steps to the shore, he said, "Hold your hand a minute! Look; I'll come along of you."

"Don't talk daft. *We would* be swamped then."

"What if the river scullers are lined up for the night and won't let you beach?"

"Oh, I'll drift down below them, or at worst camp on a sandbank. There's plenty of them."

"Don't be funny, our Freddie, you could be in trouble either way; those river blokes across there are a real rough lot. And, your size won't help you. Anyway, what's this bloke in the big house really like?"

They were running side by side now along by the row of cottages and onto the shore.

"Oh, gentleman like; but funny tempered I'd say. But, as I said, he's not stingy."

"You can't go on like this much longer, our Freddie, you know that; you'll start sproutin' soon. An' you said you didn't want to keep on at the butcher's. I wouldn't neither. I don't like dead meat, not really. What would you like to do if you had your way?"

"Make shoes."

"What!" John eased up in his run, but Freddie kept on.

"That's what I said, make shoes; not just be a cobbler, make shoes. For that you've got to make money though. But if I had money, John, I'd first get you out of the pit. That's what I think about an' all, I'd get you out of that pit if I had the money."

"Aw, lad, you're a funny 'un; but ta all the same for thinkin' that way. It's the air I miss an' the sky. If it wasn't for the folks I wouldn't mind starvin' above ground, anything rather than go down into that bloody hole."

It was Freddie who now paused in his run. He had never heard John swear before. His mother didn't allow swearing in the house, yet he once heard her swear like a fishwife when she was having a row with a woman at the water tap in the centre of the town. But then, John must hear a lot of swearin' workin' with the men down below. He himself could swear roundly, but only when he was outside. His mother's hair would stand on end if she heard him at times. But it was still strange to hear John swear.

They were both breathing heavily when they reached a comparatively empty stretch of the waterfront, and there, bobbing on the water next to a fishing smack, was a small sculler.

"How you going to manage without a light?"

"Put me finger in me eye and make a starlight."

"Don't be so damn funny!"

"Well, look across there! There's lights all along the shore."

"Aye, yes, you can see them but who's gona see you?"

"Aw, John man, you worry too much. And look; I've got to look slippy or I will be in trouble."

Freddie was quickly into the sculler and away; and John could soon hear only the dipping of the oar.

Freddie was well aware of the danger of a fast-running incoming tide as he made for the South shore, and knew how easily he could be dashed against the moored river keels; and so was surprised when a few minutes later he did just this with a bump, and a voice yelled? "What the hell!" Then a light shone down on him and the voice went on, "My God! Where've you come from at this time of night?"

"I was lookin' for Mr Stoddart."

"Billy Stoddart?"

"Aye."

"Well, you're too late, he made the London trip with coal two days gone."

Freddie knew about this but showed great surprise and disappointment in his voice as he cried, "Aw, He lets me tie up me boat to his'n now an' then."

"Your boat!" The man laughed. "But what you over here for at this hour?"

"Me granny's bad; I'm gona stay the night."

"Aw, well, take your monkey nut shell along to the end of the line and tie her up.. I'll see she's all right till the morrow."

"Ta, mister. Ta. I'll see you right."

At this the man let out a bellow of a laugh, saying, "Oh, you will, will you? Well, I don't want coppers mind, a tanner or nowt."

Freddie laughed with the man; then hastily pulled himself along by the scuppers until he came to the end of the line. Here, steps led up to the quay, and just beyond them he tied up his sculler to an iron ring; then stretching, he drew himself back to the steps and scrambled up them.

He now ran like a shadow along the dock side, threaded his way through hovels, crossed the market square, up the bank, past a farm, across two fields; and so to the better part of town.

Even before he reached Westoe village the houses had the appearance of wealth: they were terraced, but they were large with their own iron gates and front gardens.

He stopped and merged into the garden of one when he saw a swinging lantern approaching: a night watchman, carrying a cudgel as well as the lantern, passed by. Through the village the dimly lit houses all suggested quality.

He was beginning to feel tired. It must be twenty minutes since he had crossed the river. Remembering the fields here-abouts must by now have been harvested, he decided to cross them and so skirt Harton hamlet. But oh! how the stubble hurt his feet.

He came out by the coach road and recognised the two big houses, each approached by their drives, but the bulk of each discernible as a dark mass against the night light. Another hundred yards or so further on he came to the gate of The Towers.

He hung on to the bars of the iron gate for a while before thrusting it open; then he really had to grope his way along a verge to keep himself clear of the line of trees that bordered the drive. He had no idea of the layout of the grounds, he only knew that the house itself looked enormous and that there was a tower at each gable end. He had some idea of the size of the rooms because on his second visit he had stood gazing at the two long windows to the right of the front door, and they were lit up to a brilliance such as he had never seen before, and he had reached up and pulled himself onto the balcony that ran under the windows to give himself a better viewing point. He had then seen a lady and gentleman sitting at a table, and there was a lamp at each end and one hanging from the ceiling full of gas mantles.

The master himself had brought him on his first trip. He had pulled him up onto the front of his horse and, like that, had ridden right from Shields. He had brought him a little parcel. The faggot man had strapped it to his body underneath his singlet, and when the gentleman on horseback had asked for it and he had told him where it was, he had laughed and had then hauled him onto the front of his saddle, saying, "Well, little fellow, if you're going to be undressed we'd better do it in private."

That was the first parcel he had carried to him. Previously he had only taken messages from the faggot man to the men in the cottages or down the road at Cullercoats.

But tonight there were no lights on downstairs, not in the front of the house anyway, although a faint light was showing up part of a stairway and another bright light appeared in a window which could have been a bedroom.

He was sweating profusely when he entered the courtyard and made his way to the far end and the kitchen door. Before reaching it, he could hear voices coming from there as if in argument; but when he knocked sharply on the door the voices became still. And it was quite some seconds before it was opened and he looked up into the face of Connie the maid. She was holding a lantern shoulder high and she exclaimed under her breath, "Dear God! What are you here for this night?"

"I . . . I've got a message."

"Who is it?" The man he knew to be Connie's father was now towering over him. "Boy," he said, "what are you after?"

"I have a message for the master."

"A message? Come in. Come in."

Their hands clutching his shoulders, together they almost lifted him into the kitchen.

"What kind of message?" The man was bending over him again.

"I . . . I've got to give it to the master."

"God Almighty! this an' all; an' the night of all nights!"

"Well, Da, you'd better go up and tell him."

"Not me. Not me. The state he's in he's likely to fell me, an' I don't want to see him choke the truth out of her afore the bairn's born."

"You think as he does, Da?"

"Aye, I do. But I don't blame her, for she's had no life: he's past livin' with. Anyway, it was a mistake from the beginning. I said so. But this youngster—" He now turned his attention down on Freddie, saying, "Is it so important? Who's the message from anyway, the same one?"

"Aye, the faggot man." It was easier to say that than try to explain.

The elderly black-coated man turned and looked at his daughter and said, "That's Mr Freeman from Newcastle; he gives him a penny for faggots. Tis important if it's from him. Look; go on up and tell your ma to tell him. He'll listen to her if nobody else."

The young woman hesitated for a moment. She looked at her father, then down on Freddie, and he gazed up at her. He remembered the first time he had looked into her face, and he had wanted to laugh; but then he'd had a strange feeling, a kind of sad feeling for her because her face was pock-marked, and she was cock-eyed an' all. As his da would have said, she had one eye in the pot and t'other up the chimney. Yet her voice was nice and her manner kindly as now she said, "Come on along of me."

"No, God! Don't take him up there with what's goin' on. Are you mad?"

"Well, d'you think he'll leave her and come down here, Da, when he's been out since early mornin' from he knew the Spaniard's ship was in? He couldn't have found him though, else he would have spilled it before now that he murdered him."

Freddie gaped from one to the other. She was actually yelling at her father. She didn't seem a bit afraid of him, although he was a big man. And now she went on, "Two hours he's been up there with her; an' he's like a fiend, he won't leave her be. God help her! Tisn't that he ever cared for her; 'twas her money he was after 'cos, if you ask me, any human feelings he ever had were for Mistress Ellen. What's wrong with him is pride; it's been split open. And again I say I don't blame her. . . . Come on, lad." She held out a hand and pulled Freddie forwards. And now, with not a little apprehension in his eyes he looked back towards the elderly man; but the man flapped his hand towards him as if pushing him on.

The kitchen was long and stone-flagged. The corridor they went into was also stone-flagged, with a number of doors opening off it. She pulled him through one; and now they were in a hall. Although only dimly lit by light from the stairs, he could see the ceiling was beamed. The beams were big and black like those used for the keel of a ship. The bannister to the broad stairs was black and highish; he found it easier to grip the rails as she tugged him upwards. At the top they seemed to be in another hall with the same sort of rails edging it. She was now almost dragging him along another corridor. In the dim light it looked almost as long as three cottages put together. She brought him to a sudden stop as a high scream came from behind one of the doors and for a moment he found himself clinging to the young woman's side, and when he looked up at her her eyes were closed and her face screwed up as his had been. She had her hand round his shoulders now and she pressed him tightly to her, saying, "It's all right. It's all right." Then bending down to him, she whispered, "Don't be frightened. It's the lady of the house; she's havin' a bairn. You understand?"

He nodded but didn't speak. He understood all right. He remembered when Lily was born his mother had yelled out something like that and he had buried his head under the pillow tick. And now he had the urge to bury his head in the big white apron that this maid was wearing. "Stay there," she said now as she pushed him against the wall. "Don't move."

She opened the door which was only a foot away from him and a man's voice roared out of it, crying, "Hold back of me, would you! Well, we'll know, won't we, when you decide to let it come; you can't hold on forever, you loose little whore!"

When the door was banged closed, a woman's voice, almost as loud as the man's but the words thick sounding like those of the voices he was used to, cried, "Let up, Mr Roddy! You'll be sorry for this when you come to yourself."

"Shut your mouth, Betty! I am myself. At this moment I am myself, never more."

There followed a silence. It seemed to go on for a long time but it could only have been a minute before the man's voice came again, yelling, "Bring him in then! Bring him in!"

"*No, no! Not in here, surely!* It isn't seemly. Go out and see the lad."

"What! and miss the coming of the black Spaniard? Bring him in, I said. He won't faint at the sight of naked limbs; he's the scum of the waterfront. Bring him in!"

The door opened once again and the maid, without saying a word, gripped Freddie by the shoulder and pulled him into the room, where he stood within the doorway, his mouth agape at the sight before him.

It was a large bedroom. There was lots of furniture in it, but the main thing was a big four-poster bed, with all its draperies hooked back towards the head of it, so exposing the two bottom poles, the rumpled bedclothes and the woman lying on the high mattress, which was all of four foot or more from the carpeted floor.

The woman's face on the pillow was turned towards him. It was red and running with sweat. Her hair was spread out all around her head; it looked as if the wind had tousled it. The sweat was running down her face, and the old woman who he knew to be the maid's mother was mopping it with a flannel. But of a sudden she put out her hand and pulled the nightdress over the heaving mound of flesh. It didn't cover all the woman's nakedness, her legs were spreadeagled, and if it hadn't been for her face and the expression on it he would have thought she looked awful. He had never seen his mother like that.

He watched the man turn from the bed; and then there he was towering above him, and he had to put his head right back to look up at him.

"*Well! What is it?*"

He found his throat was dry: the explanation why he was there was all in his head but he couldn't get the words out. And when the man bawled, "Come on! Come on! Have you lost your tongue for once?" he stuttered, "Tis . . . 'tis the excise. The . . . they're c . . . comin' the night."

"What d'you mean, they're comin' the night? Have you spoken to Mr Freeman . . . the faggot man?"

He nodded; then swallowed deeply before saying, "He . . . he gave me a message for t'others that meant it was off the night. He . . . he said you would likely know that."

"Yes, yes; of course, I would know that."

"Twas my sis . . . sister."

"*What!*"

"She's . . . she's blind."

The man put his hand up to his head and ran his fingers through his hair, but he said nothing, only stared down at the small boy. And Freddie, his wits returning, went on quickly, "But she makes up for it with sharp ears an' she can tell people by their smell."

Still the man didn't speak, but his eyes grew wider and his expression indicated he didn't know why he was standing here listening to this prattle.

"She heard two strange men talking; they weren't from the town. She knows nearly everybody in the town from where they work 'cos of their smells. And what she heard was that it was all a put-up job that they were there on our side of the river, kind of puttin' everybody off the scent; what they were going to do was raid this end . . . an' you."

The last word was almost whispered.

The man bent down towards him and in a much calmer voice said, "Your sister heard all this? D'you mean to tell me that this kind of thing was discussed openly in the street?"

"Aye; well outside the tavern. She was some distance off; but she's cute, she hears things, an' sees with her ears, an' 'cos she's blind nobody takes much notice of her. Any road, she thought they were talkin' about somebody in a tower an' she was tellin' us the tale after we had our supper, an' I jumped to it, it wasn't a tower it was this house, The Towers, and they're on to you."

"God in heaven!" He straightened up and began to laugh, and the expression on his face changed: he wasn't the same man who had been bawling his head off a few minutes earlier. "So I'm going to have some visitors, am I? But am I the only one?"

"Aye. As far as I could make out."

He turned about now and looked towards the old woman who was still mopping her mistress's brow: "What's in the dining room, Betty?" he said.

Without turning towards him she answered, "A bottle of

rum, the remains of a bottle of whisky, that's if you didn't finish it after your dinner, and a bottle or two of port."

"All labelled, authentic?"

"Aye."

"You're sure?"

Now the old woman did turn towards him and she hissed at him, "Yes! I'm sure. Why didn't you look yersel? I filled the bottles the day afore yesterday. But I haven't done anything about the two kegs that are down the old well, and if it's them fellas, they'll rummage till they find that an' all."

As he stared towards her it came to Freddie it was odd that a servant would talk to a gentleman like that, and he her master. It was like his mother might have done if she was in a paddy, and like the pock-marked woman had done to her da.

He didn't even yell at the young woman, although he spoke swiftly and definitely, saying, "Tell Frank to get them up, *and right away,* and bury them in the midden."

"In the midden?"

"Yes!" His bark was back now. "That's what I said, in the midden and well down. It's not likely they'll look there. As for the rest—" He turned and looked towards the bed and, his voice changing, he added softly, "Even God Himself wouldn't disturb a woman in labour. Would He, dear?" He was addressing his words to his wife now while none too gently thrusting the old woman from her towards the foot of the bed; then bending over the panting, writhing figure, he said, "You have something to tell me, dear?"

The young woman's mouth opened and shut a number of times before she whispered, "Yes; yes, Roderick, I have something to tell you."

But before she could get any further words out her knees came up and she let out another agonizing groan that caused Freddie to turn his face to the wall.

For a moment, both the old woman and the man seemed to have forgotten the boy's presence, for she now shouted at him, "Will you for the love of God! let up on her."

The groans subsiding, the man began again: "You were saying, Mirabelle, you had something to tell me. Come along, my dear, I'm waiting."

"Yes, I have something to tell you Roderick"—but the words were coming out between gasps now—"and it's just this. . . . I

33

hate you now . . . and I've hated you . . . since the first week we were married. You want to know who . . . the father of my child is. Well . . . Roderick, you'll never know, never, never. . . . If it comes out dark or fair you'll still never know because your mother . . . looks like a Spaniard, doesn't she? and the child might . . . hark back to her. I . . . I'll not live once it's . . . it's born because I have no desire to live. But wherever I am I shall . . . think of you sitting . . . in this mausoleum of a house . . . drinking your rum and your port . . . in between sniffing your opium . . . and all the time wondering . . . wondering, how many times we were together. What did we do when we were together . . . he and I? Perhaps you'll wonder if . . . if we did the same as you do when you . . . visit the brothels on the Shields wa-terfront. . . ."

"Don't you dare!" The old woman had thrust him aside. "Lay a hand on her again an' I'll do what I promised you the last time: we'll up, the three of us, and go. I'm an old woman an' me time's runnin' out, like hers is, but I'll tell you this much, I'd open me mouth wide, aye wide, an' you know I've always meant what I've said. It shocks me that I have to say this to you of all people, but I'm doin' it, so move yourself away."

He was glaring at her as if his hand would come out and deal her a blow when the door was thrust open and Connie Wheatley cried, "They're comin' into the yard. There's four of them."

"Did you tell your father? Has he got them up?"

"He's bound to. Oh, he's bound to by now."

He turned and looked almost wildly round the room and, his eyes alighting on Freddie, he said to her, "Get rid of him."

"Where'll I put him?"

She had hold of his collar as she spoke and was pulling him from the room when the man cried, "Hold! Hold a minute! They'll recognise him; like all his kind, a runner is stamped on him."

"There's . . . there's the cubby hole." Her voice sounded as agitated as his own, and when he answered, "No, no; I wouldn't put him in there," she thought: No; he wouldn't put a dog in there, which showed he had some feelings left that weren't buried deep below bitterness and recrimination.

"Under the bed," he said.

"He'll never get under there."

"He will. He's not as thick as two slats. Here!"

Three strides and he had Freddie by the arms, which brought a protest from the boy against he knew not what, crying, "Eeh! no, Mister. Eeh! no."

"Still that tongue of yours! Not a murmur out of you."

The hands now shook him like a rat. "Lie flat. Put your legs out. Do as I say!"

He did as he was bidden. He saw the heavy valance of the bed being lifted up, and then he was being pushed along the carpeted floor and under what he imagined to be a shelf. The next minute he was in total darkness and the voices seemed far away but still audible, as was the scream that brought his eyes tight shut. Then he heard the old woman's voice saying, "That's it, love, that's it. Here it comes. Here it comes."

There followed the sound of a commotion, the vibration of feet thudding on the floor. They came to him as if they were going to walk onto him; then two loud voices seemed to tumble one on top of the other, saying, "I am a customs officer, I have a warrant." That voice trailed away as another, and recognisable to him now, yelled, "What, sir, do you think you're up to? What is this anyway? I'll have the law on you, customs or not. Can you see what's happening here?"

Above him, in the room, the excise man and another man stood open-mouthed looking at the man in his shirt sleeves, his hands covered with blood and the woman on the bed, his wife, giving birth.

The excise man gulped, turned and glanced at his companion, then said, "I'm sorry, sir; but 'tis my duty."

"Then carry on with your bloody duty: search the house, if that's what you've come for, search it from top to bottom, outside too, you're welcome. But let me tell you you haven't heard the last of this, no by God above! you haven't. I'll have that uniform stripped off you if it's the last thing I do, and I'll see you running in your bare pelt."

When there came another cry from the woman on the bed he turned to where the heaving body was pushing the head out into life. Then his gaze swinging back to the men, he said, "Get to hell's flames out of it!" And almost instantly they stepped back into the corridor and the door was closed once more.

He now looked to where old Betty Wheatley was cutting the cord; then he watched her lift the crying blood-smeared mass, cradle it in her arms and wipe its eyes, his own eyes

35

riveted on the child's head and the small ridge of black hair sprouting from it.

"Look, love! Look, love! It's . . . it's all right; it's all over." She was holding out the child now to the mother in the bed, and the young woman went to lift her hand but the effort was seemingly too much. Her lips moved as if asking a question, and, as if she had heard it, Betty said, "Tis a girl; and she is whole and bonny. Sleep, love, sleep."

When she stepped back from the head of the bed and the man went to take her place, she half barred his way and in a low voice and in which was a note of pleading she said, "Not another word, Mister Roddy, please! In God's name! not the night. She's low, she's been low these many weeks. Have you no pity in you? What's done's done."

He turned from her to the bed just as the door opened and Connie Wheatley came in, whispering, "They're ransackin' the house, every nook and cranny."

"Did Frank get the barrels up?"

"Aye; but just in time, for he only just got the muck off him, and the stink. He hadn't time to clean his boots"—she was now addressing her mother—"he dropped them in the rain barrel. He won't be able to use them any more." She now looked at the child in her mother's arms. "What is it, Ma?" she asked.

"It's a little lass."

"Oh, nice."

She now glanced at her master and recognised the expression on his face which spelt trouble; then, glancing at the bed, she exclaimed, "She's bleedin' heavy, Ma!"

"Here! take her." Her mother thrust the child at her. "Clean her up." Then she added, "The doctor should have been here! But he's another one that's likely skittering around burying his kegs in the muck," and she indicated the urgency, saying, "And you tell your da to go for him this minute."

"You'll do no such thing."

"She's got to have attention."

"Attention or no, you won't find him there tonight. He was off to Newcastle earlier on to a meeting, and it's a sure thing that he'll have to be carried back. So get on with it, both of you. And"—his voice dropped—"get rid of that. Understand me? Get rid of it."

"No, by God!"

36

"*Oh, yes by God!* Betty. Walk out, as you say you would, the lot of you, and split until your tongue runs dry, but *that* is not surviving in this house. Either you do it or I'll see to it; but I should imagine you'll be more gentle than me because I've had me answer." He now glanced at the deadly white face on the pillow, then stalked out of the room. And for some moments after the door banged behind him neither of the women moved but listened to his voice bawling at someone on the landing. Then Connie whispered, "He means it, Ma. He would do it in."

"Aye, he means it. And aye, he would do it in. But put it to one side for a minute, on the couch there, and help me to see to her because we've got to get the rest away."

What time they dragged Freddie from under the bed he didn't know for he must have fallen asleep, but his mind took in the voice saying, "Eeh! we forgot all about him. Is he all right?"

"Oh, he's all right, lass; he's a tough 'un, although he looks like a bairn."

"No more than six or seven."

"Well, I should imagine he's twice that, the head he's got on him. He's been a runner for the last two years. They rely on him an' his little tub a lot across the water, just for that reason: like a bairn playin' about. Wake up, lad. Wake up. Get on your feet."

"Poor mite; I'll carry him down."

"Oh, let him walk."

"He's dead asleep, Da."

He felt himself being lifted up into two sturdy arms, and in a short while he knew he was in the kitchen again, and he heard someone say, "He can sleep by the side of the fire with Tinker, she likes company."

That was all he remembered, until the voices came at him again; but then it was daylight. . . .

He had lain for some time between sleep and wakefulness because he felt warm and comfortable. He had his arm around someone, hugging them to him, the pulse beat of their heart was in his hand while his own heartbeat was thumping through his ears. It often did when he lay on his left side. He knew he felt stiff but he was warm, and there was a nice smell in his nose. A voice above him said, "They look canny together. Tinker's

37

never had a child as a mate. I bet he's thinkin', better late than
never."

"You'd better wake him. He'll want to see him shortly if it's
only to give him a tanner."

"Oh, Da! I think last night's bit of work is worth more than
a tanner. He saved his bacon if anybody did. But then, I suppose
he saved the boy's too as well as his own, for who knows but they
would have made for the bed if he hadn't played up as he did;
they've been known to pull beds to bits, them lot. And there was
that poor soul. I'm glad she's out of her misery. She's where God
pleases, but I'm gona miss her. Ma will an' all. She was a sweet
creature."

"Aye, she might have been but she shouldn't have done
what she did: she should have realised that he wasn't the kind of
man to play about with, made a cat's paw out of. An' God only
knows what's gona happen to the bairn. He'll likely smother it
and have it buried with her."

"Oh, no, Da. No."

"Oh aye, aye. I won't say he hasn't his rights. And he's had
them since he was a lad but never got them. Funny that; you
know he hated his father but he's like him in many ways. If
only the mistress hadn't died; she made a different man of
him for a time. But look what happened to their child. He
couldn't stand the sight of him; and he was all of four when she
went. He rarely goes to see him. It's a good job his granny took
him. Anyway, he'd have a better upbringing with her than he
would have here. But you can see, lass, if he turned against the
legal one what care would he have for this one who's not his
own?"

"You can't prove that, Da."

"Oh, you've just got to look at it. Hair like pitch. And look at
the eyes: newborn bairn's eyes are often blue, nearly always so;
but look at hers, browny-black already. Well, God help her, she'll
be happiest alongside her mother. An' she's puny, she wouldn't
last long at any rate."

Freddie was wide awake by this time with his ears stretched.
He heard the kitchen door open and the older woman's voice
came to him, saying, "He wants to see him."

"How is he?"

"Need you ask. Wake the lad."

"Come on. Come on. Get up!"

He opened his eyes, and then pulled his arm from around the dog and stared at it in some amazement, and a gentle voice above him said, "Aye, you've been cuddling a dog all night. Come on, give me your hand an' get on your feet, an' go and put your head under the pump in the yard. Then I'll give you a bite of breakfast afore you go an' see the master."

Blinking his eyes against the strong morning light, Freddie made his way into the yard. Seeing it for the first time in daylight, he was amazed at the size of it. It was mostly bordered by stable doors, two being half open, each with a horse's head nodding out.

When the icy water hit the back of his head he shivered and groaned; but rubbed his face with his hands and squeezed the water from his hair, and felt somewhat better, at least refreshed; then he walked slowly back to the kitchen.

He knew the smell of bacon, but it was always of the fat kind in long strips; but there, on a plate, was two shives of lean bacon, and to the side of them an egg reposed on a slice of fried bread. He had never seen such a breakfast; but strangely he had no appetite for it.

The man said to him, "Well, tuck in, lad. I doubt if you'll see many plates like that."

"I'm . . . I'm not very hungry."

"What!" It was a chorus from the three of them. And the man said, "Not hungry! Across there you must be fed on fish most every day. Well, are you goin' to eat it or not?"

"I'll . . . I'll try."

"He'll try." They nodded from one to the other, and they chorused again, "He'll try."

"My God! the folks, tall an' short, you come across. Well, hurry up an' try"—Betty's voice was hard—" 'cos the master wants to see you an' then you'll be on your way."

He ate one piece of the bacon and half of the fried bread, but he gulped at the drink the young woman placed before him: he had never tasted anything like it. It was a bit scenty and his face crinkled against it, and she, bending down to him, said, "That's tea, China tea. Never had it afore?"

He shook his head.

"It's nice, soothin', make you feel better."

A minute later, Betty said, "If your lordship's finished would you mind comin' along of me?"

"Aw, don't take that attitude, Ma; he's but a bairn."

"And an all too knowin' one if you ask me." And in a lowered voice she said in an aside, "And after last night he knows more than's good for him." . . .

He was in the hall again. In the daylight it looked enormous, yet had dim corners.

They didn't go up the stairs, but behind them and along another corridor.

When the old woman opened a door she stopped just within, and he looked past her into a large room that seemed packed with furniture of all kinds and colours. But immediately she said, "He was here a minute ago. He's likely in the study," and swung him round with her hand on his head now and pressed him forward and further along the corridor. At the end she guided him up four shallow wooden oak steps and onto another landing.

Here she paused at the first door before knocking on it, and when there came a grunt from within the room she opened the door and pressed the boy forward.

The man was sitting in a deep leather chair to the side of a fire that was burning brightly, and the first thing Freddie noticed about it was that it had big lumps of coal on it, roundies, the best, not slack dust like theirs at home.

"Leave him," the man said; "I'll ring for you in a moment."

He was alone with the man now, standing in front of him. He looked different from what he did last night. His face looked different. His voice sounded different. Was he drunk? No; because men like him generally bawled when they were drunk, or angry. But now this man's voice was quiet, oddly quiet.

"You're a smart little fellow, aren't you?"

He gave no answer, for what could he say? He knew he was smart but it didn't do to brag about it.

"What do you think of last night's business?"

"I don't know."

"Oh, come on, come on; you worked out what your blind sister told you. You said she was blind, didn't you?"

"Aye, she is."

"You also said she saw with her ears. Funny expression that."

Again he made no answer.

40

And now the man said, "What would you think if I told you that the message you brought was just another red herring?"

"What d'you mean?"

"I mean, as far as my man Frank can ascertain, someone was playing double and treble games. What would you say about the two men over on the North side being fooled in their turn and the squad on the South side also being fooled? It would seem that somebody apparently gave us away, me and one or two others, but that in turn was another red herring in order to let the Newcastle lot distribute a load of loads. Immediately they could after the tide crossed the bar they went over it with some precious cargo. What would you say to that?"

What would he say? His mind was trying to work it out. Yes, he could be right; but then the faggot man, and Mr Blaze and Johnson and Alec Crighton, they would have known about it, wouldn't they? Perhaps they didn't 'cos they were at loggerheads with the Newcastle lot. He'd heard tell a while ago that there was a man come up from Devon, a place in the West country wherever that was, it must be as far as London town or some foreign territory like that. But this man was well up in the game and clever. It was said he had escaped the excise men and made his way here. . . . He had thought it was just a story.

His head was beginning to swim with his thoughts and the heat of the room and not a little from the stare of the man's eyes on him.

"Well, what have you got to say to that?"

"Some men are clever."

"Huh! Well, that's as good an explanation as any I've heard. Do you think you're clever?"

There it was again. He'd have to answer something.

"I have me wits about me."

The man didn't speak for some seconds, and then he said, and with a change of voice for his words now came slow and deep, "Well, I hope you have enough wits about you to keep a silent tongue in your head or else you could get into dire trouble. You understand me?"

Yes, he understood him, but he didn't say so. And the man went on. "You heard a lot of talk last night and you saw a lot. You know my wife is dead, don't you?"

His mouth fell open. No, he didn't, not really. Yet he had heard them say something in the kitchen, but it hadn't really sunk

41

in because they hadn't used the word dead. But the poor lady was dead, like Billy, his brother two years ago. He had cried when Billy died, because Billy had been like Nancy, gentle and kind.

"And the child was very sickly; it died too." He stopped there, and Freddie watched him turn his head away as he muttered, "But it'll not go along of her; her brat'll be put where it belongs in . . ." His voice trailed away into a growl as Freddie's mind yelled at him, Eeh! Eeh! What was he saying!

The man was talking directly to him again: "Now, you are to forget all you heard or saw last night. Do you hear? Now pay attention to me: if you divulge, I mean, if you talk about it to anyone it will come back to me, and I have ways and means of paying for services done, good or bad. Again, do you understand me?"

Oh yes, he understood him. But in this moment, he had one wish, that he was grown up and big, oh yes, really big, with a big fist that he could bash in between this man's eyes, 'cos he was going to smother his bairn. That's what they had said in the kitchen, and they had been right.

"Hold out your hand."

He held out his hand, and when a coin was put into it the man said, "How much is that?"

He knew what a sixpence was and a bob and half a dollar and a five shilling piece but he had never seen a sovereign before, or was it a half sovereign?

"It's gold, it could be a half sovereign or a sovereign."

"You haven't seen one before?"

"No; least ways not close up."

"What do you mean, not close up?"

"Well, I've seen such goin' over a counter."

"Oh. Well, this is not a sovereign, it is a half sovereign, and that is a lot of money, don't you think?"

"Aye, it is."

"Boy."

"Aye?"

"You say 'sir' when you speak to a gentleman."

There was a pause, and then he said, "Aye, sir."

"What is your Christian name?"

"Freddie."

"Your full name?"

"Musgrave."

42

"Well, Freddie Musgrave, that is the first payment for your silence; but once you open your mouth . . . and you've got to do that just once and I shall know, the payment will be very different. You understand?"

Again those two words; and again he paused in answering because now his heart was beating so quickly it seemed to be sticking in his throat. But he brought out, "Aye, sir," on a sort of gulp. And then the voice came cracking at him, no longer soft: "Where do I store my stuff? Come on, tell me where I store my stuff."

His body began to tremble. If he said he didn't know he would trick him, trip him up in some way. He gulped again, then said in a very small voice, "In the bed underneath."

"Good. You spoke the truth, so now you know. But that's one room my friends didn't search, isn't it? And it will come to some sharp-witted individual later, and likely they will return, but by then they will only find two horse-hair mattresses and a feather tick, because it would be silly to leave the stuff where it is, wouldn't it, Freddie Musgrave?"

"Aye, sir."

"And do you realise, Master Freddie, that we haven't seen the last of each other? You will be paying me further visits now and then. . . . How many are there in your family?"

"Six at home, sir. Nell, the eldest, she's married."

"Your father, what does he do?"

"Nowt, sir; 'cept make bits of furniture for the house. His legs are broken."

"Are you the only breadwinner?"

"No; there's John. He works down the pit. He's older'n me, twelve."

"And the blind girl, how old is she?"

"Eleven, sir."

"Well, Freddie Musgrave, your family seem somewhat in need, and this alone should help you to keep a still tongue, shouldn't it?"

"Aye, sir."

"Here!" His hand had gone into his pocket again, and drawing out a washleather bag he opened it and now thrust another half sovereign into Freddie's hand, saying, "You should now be asking yourself how you are going to account for that money. So how are you going to account for it?"

43

He hesitated a moment before saying, "Payment for warnin' you 'bout the raid, sir."

"Yes; yes, quite good, payment for warning me about the raid. But—" Now the man was leaning forward, his nose almost touching Freddie's as he said, "It wasn't payment for the raid, was it? Answer me!"

"W'well, not quite, sir, but you . . . you'd have likely given me somethin'."

The man fell back into his chair now and, looking up towards the ornamental ceiling, he gave a hollow laugh, saying, "This little fellow will go far. Perhaps, being such a wise owl, he could tell me how one should respond to sympathy in losing your second beautiful wife and her child."

When the man said nothing further but still sat with his eyes fixed on the ceiling, Freddie stood as if frozen to the spot although the sweat was running down from his hair. Then he almost jumped as the man's hand was thrust out towards a side table from which he picked up a long-stemmed pipe and started to draw on it, pulling at it with his breath, but there was no smoke coming from the head of it.

"Go on, get out! . . . *Get out!*"

As Freddie hastily backed from him, he saw that the man was still looking at the ceiling, while still pulling on the pipe, and well before reaching the door he turned and ran; and his hand fumbled with the door handle before he sprang into the passage, looked first one way then the other, before remembering he had come up some steps. And now he was flying across the hall, and when he opened the kitchen door he stood with his back against it and gasped while he looked at the three people further down the room all gazing back at him.

"What is it? What is it, hinny?" The old woman's voice was soft now, and as she came to meet him he ran towards her and leant against her for a moment as he gasped out, "He . . . he was acting funny, frightenin'."

"There's nothin' to be frightened of; he's not well, he's ill, bad you know."

His head was against her waistband, and he found himself looking towards the settle on which was a clothes basket and in it the child. And of a sudden he was running from her towards it. The baby's eyes were open and it was sucking on a linen bag of some sort and its small hand was moving in and out. He turned

44

and, looking from the old man to his daughter, he muttered, "She's not dead! She's not dead!"

"Listen, youngster"—the old man was on his hunkers before him—"the master's likely told you you've got to forget all that's happened here. Now, be a good lad and go home and do as he bid you, forget all about it. Speak to no one. I repeat that, do you here? no one, because he has ways an' means of gettin' back at those who do him down. He can be a good friend an' all, and I should imagine you and your lot over there are in need of a friend. Now think on it. These things happen." And his face now stretching into a smile, he added, jocularly, "There's worse things happen at sea every night, for that matter on the sea front, on both shores."

Freddie turned to the older woman and she nodded at him, saying, quietly, "Do as my husband tells you, lad. And here; I've got a bag of stuff ready for you to take back to your family. There's a ham shank in there an' some butter an' cheese and a fresh loaf, an' odds an' ends. The bag's nearly as big as yersel. My man's got to go an errand into the town, he'll take you on the cart to the shore. I should imagine you can afford a keel boat across the river the day. How much did he give you?"

He seemed to have difficulty in opening his fist because the nails had pressed into the flesh in his fright. And when he exposed the two half sovereigns they all nodded, and the old man said, "Well, that's good pay. I'll say it is. You can't say it isn't. Nor can you say he's not generous to his own. You stick on the right side of him lad, an' he'll see you through. An' your family an' all. So come on now, an' don't look so white about the gills. Everything's gona be all right. But put that lot deep in your pocket an' don't let on about it to no outsider."

In doing as he was bid, he began to walk towards the man, then turned and looked into the wash basket again. The child looked to him like Lily had done only a short while ago when she used to lie in the skip sucking a pap bag, and he asked a question, but in a very low apprehensive voice, "He . . . he won't hurt her, I mean you won't let him, will you?"

There was a pause before both the old woman and the young one said together, "No, no; don't worry. It'll be all right." But as he stared at them he felt sure that neither of them could do anything. "Go on now." The old woman patted him on the head, and when she lifted the bass bag from the table and

45

handed it to him the weight of it almost pulled him down, but he had to force himself to look at her and say, "Ta, missis. Me ma'll say ta an' all."

He saw the old woman bite on her lower lip before saying, "Your ma's got a nice little lad in you. Tell her that from me. Go on now."

At the front door the old man took the bass bag from him and hoisted it up onto the cart, then lifted him up onto the front seat before taking his place and saying, "Gee up! there," to the horse. And so Freddie rode most of the way back home, for Frank Wheatley himself put him in a keel and paid his penny fare and an extra penny to have his little sculler pulled behind. And so he crossed the river on the morning tide, and for the rest of his life he thought of it as the morning after the night when things began to happen to him.

2

He had been landed at the far end of the town and as he wended his way through the long narrow street he was jostled by every kind of inhabitant and vehicle; twice he slipped on some garbage, and the contents of the bag was only saved from spilling by the strings at its top.

It was as he left the town and passed the row of cottages prior to taking the steps that led to home when he saw in the distance two of the excise men. One was Mr Dees who was the Principal Coast Officer, and he was with the Landing and Searching Officer called Robert Leitch. Mr Leitch lived at yon side of the town in a nice house and he seemed a nice enough man because he had spoken to him. But then you didn't get many nice men among the excise.

He had never seen them along this way before, at least not together, and this early. Mr Dees's office was just above the quay and that didn't open for business till ten in the morning.

Now, as if the bag was a featherweight, he sprinted up the steps, then along the path and into the house.

And his entry caused his father to jerk himself from the bed and his mother to rush out of the other room, and it was evident from the expression on her face that she was about to yell at him. But when she spoke her voice was even but very low. "So you've got back," she said.

"Aye, Ma."

He hoisted the bag onto the table, and she approached from the other side and, looking down at it, she said, "And what's that may I ask?"

"Some bits and pieces from the housekeeper over there." He jerked his head back towards the door.

47

"Why? What did you do to earn that?"

"Don't ask the road you know, woman." His da was sitting on the floor near the edge of the table now, and he put his hand out and touched his son's thin shoulder, saying, "You look tired, lad."

His mother came round the table and stood at the other side of him. "I've got some broth, still hot; could you do with a bite?"

"No, Ma, ta. I've . . . I've had me breakfast."

She stared at him, then said, "Well, you may have had it, but you look fagged, boy. Sit down." She pointed to a cracket, but he didn't obey her; instead, he undid the strings on the top of the bass bag and, one after the other, he pulled out the eatables while his parents stared open-eyed at the array.

"By! it looks as if your boat's come in, lad."

Robert placed his forearms on the edge of the table and hoisted himself up a little further. "That must be a pound of butter if it's an ounce. And there's some ham on that shank. My! I've never seen so much stuff all at once for many a long year. They must keep a good table in that kitchen where you spent the night."

He now slid back to the floor. "Did you spend it there? or did you go to your granny's?"

"Don't be daft, man." His wife thrust out her foot towards him. "Would he have brought this lot back if me ma had got her hands on the bag?"

"Aye, you're right there, Jinny, you're right there. Anyway, come and sit down lad and tell us all about it."

As his father propelled himself to his favourite spot at the side of the fireplace to sit with his back against the wall, Freddie seated himself on the cracket; and he drooped his head and looked down at his hands pressed tight between his bare knees before he forced himself to say, "Not much to tell, Da," when all the time he wanted to fling himself, not against his da, but into his mother's arms and howl out all his feelings about what had happened in that house across the water, especially about the poor lady and her bairn.

"Did you get there in time? Did the excise come?"

"Aye, just, Da; just in time. And aye, they came, but they found nowt."

"Was there anythin' to find?"

"Aye, casks of rum down the well; but the master knew

that's where they would likely look and he had his man put them in the midden."

"*In the midden?*"

"Aye. Well, they were in casks, it wouldn't do them any harm."

"And he just had two casks? That's all he had?"

Freddie hesitated: he blinked and wetted his lips. "I think he had other bits and pieces like baccy an' wine an' silks an' stuff, but it was where nobody could find it. . . ." Then he added, "I suppose, 'cos they didn't get anything."

"Did . . . did they see you?"

"No."

"Where were you in all this then?"

Things were getting difficult. He slowly looked from one to the other before answering, "Outside, in . . . in the garden."

"Freddie." His father had hold of his hands now. "You . . . you frightened about something?"

Yes, he was frightened about something. Oh! Lord God, he was. For a moment his da's face seemed to have become another's looking into his, the nose almost touching his and the promise in the eyes of what would happen to him if he talked, at least about. . . . He couldn't even tell himself what the special thing was he must keep silent about, and so he said, "No, Da, except . . . except that I'm tired."

"You didn't get much sleep then?"

"No . . . no, I didn't."

"Well, if that's how you feel you're not doin' any butchering this mornin'." It was his mother speaking now. "You can get yourself to bed for a couple of hours. Tommy Preston called in earlier on. He said Mr Aynsley might take you on half-days 'cos Mrs Bing's takin' their Georgie away. She's sendin' him half-day to the Jubilee School. He was snobbin' boots for Fluts in Bedford Street an' she took him away from there, you remember? No prospects for her son, she said, in snobbin' boots. He hadn't been there but a couple of years, an' she expected Mr Flut to have put him on to ladies' slippers, silk lined at that." She laughed. "Anyway, you seem to get on if you're a Methodist. But lad, there's a full half-day for you ready an' waitin' if you want it. . . . Do you want it?"

He stared up into his mother's face for a moment before saying softly, "I'm not taken with butchery, Ma, never was. I . . . I wouldn't mind goin' into boots an' snobbin'."

49

His father pulled him round towards him again. "But there's nothin' in it, lad," he said; "they tell me the town's full of boot an' shoe makers these days. You trip over them wherever you go. They even beat the butchers, an' they run the shipowners neck and neck. And that's saying something."

"Eeh!" his mother now put in, "My gall rises when I pass the Dock Inn or the Duke of Bedford, or one or other of them bars that swarm the town an' see them comin' out with their peaked caps an' their brass buttons an' their bellies pokin' their trousers ready to burst. And the air of them. My God! I don't know about the Duke of Bedford, you'd think they were all descended from the Duke of Wellington."

Robert laughed now, saying, "Aw, lass, they're not all alike. There's good an' bad. . . ."

"Few and far atween with that lot, an' what they make on the side in the bottom of their holds. Why doesn't the excise collar them?"

"They do, lass, they do. They all have to take their turn. What d'you say, boy?" He pushed Freddie gently, expecting his son to laugh. But when there was no response except an almost blank stare from this lad whom he imagined was so full of spirit that nothing could get him down, he said gently, "Go and rest yersel, lad. Go on. And thank you for bringin' this grub. We'll have a beanfeast the night. Go on now."

Without hesitation Freddie went into the other room. There was no one occupying any of the three shake-downs on the floor. Nancy, he knew, would be on the shore pushing the bogie which held Lily and the drift wood Jessie was picking up. He went to the bed farthest from the door and which he shared with John and, sitting down on its edge, he pulled off his boots and his coat but kept on his breeches; then he crept under the patchwork pad and buried his head in the striped pillow tick.

It was only then that he remembered he hadn't mentioned the small fortune that reposed in the pocket in the lining of his trousers, and as his hand instinctively felt for the coins he wondered why he hadn't handed them straight to his mother. There must be a reason; he didn't forget things, at least where money was concerned. There must be a reason, and deep down he knew that part of the reason was fear, fear of not being able to keep his mouth shut, because in his ma's and da's eyes that lot of food on the table out there should have been payment enough for any night's work. They would reckon he had done something big or even something bad to be paid a whole sovereign, when John worked six days down the pit for four shillings and he himself only got a shilling a week for sorting out bloody entrails. The thought of such work, as usual, upset him; and yet he was always thankful that the animal had been killed before he got there. Even so, the flesh was still warm, especially the heart. And his ma wanted him to work the full half-day there. Just because he might then be paid one an' six a week.

Of a sudden he felt sick. He didn't want to go back to the butcher's shop. For a moment he had the wild idea he could run away to sea and that would solve all problems. Mr Gallagher could hardly do anything to him then, could he? if he was at sea. But that would mean he would have to go off to Newcastle, and who would sign him on at ten years old especially when he only looked eight?

It was funny, but he didn't feel ten years old. In fact, he felt older than Mick Harper up the street, and he was fourteen; certainly older than Ernie Blaze or Tom Crighton, an' they were over twelve. Two of them worked in the brewery and one went out fishing, deep sea, but they talked daft, well not exactly daft, silly though. But even that wasn't the right word to describe the difference between him and them. The only thing he knew was that they didn't think about things like he did. They were slow on the uptake. Aye yes, that was it, they were slow on the uptake.

But what was he going to do about the money? How many one and sixpences were there in twenty shillings? He reckoned on his fingers: thirteen and a bit. He could stay away from the butcher's for thirteen weeks and still give his mother his pay. . . . He discarded the idea, it was too complicated. What would he do when he wasn't at the butcher's? And Tommy Preston would certainly be here the first day he didn't put in an appearance. . . . It was a daft idea.

He could save the money. But only rich people saved, and Methodists. Well most of them. The Prestons were Methodists. His mother always reckoned that Mr Preston was a warm man on the side 'cos he neither drank nor smoked so he must have money.

But where could he save? . . . He could hide it. Where? There was no place in the house or out of it.

Maggie Hewitt. Eeh! but his ma didn't like Maggie Hewitt 'cos she made money out of lending it. But some liked her: the men from the boats who wanted to change their money did. And another thing, Maggie Hewitt liked him. She always joked with him when they met on the quay. She would pull his hair or his ear and call him funny names. Jack-the-giant-killer, she said he was, or Fearless Freddie.

Fearless! She didn't know. Nobody knew. Of a sudden he wanted to cry, but he knew he mustn't 'cos that would bring his ma in, and he hadn't cried since Billy died. He jumped from the bed, dragged on his boots and coat, then went into the kitchen. The door was open and his da was sitting on the front step and he looked at him in surprise.

"Where's me Ma?" he asked.

"She's gone to the pipe for some water."

If his ma had gone to the stand pipe in the main street for some clean water that would mean she wouldn't be back for an hour, 'cos that was her treat for the day when she met up with the other women and they jabbered, argued, and even fought. It was a known thing that the men kept clear when the women were round the stand pipe. Men who had been foolhardy enough to try to enter their conclave had come away with broken heads and faces. So he said to his father, "I can't sleep, Da; and . . . and I'm not goin' to the shop this mornin'; I'm gona take a walk."

"Somethin' troublin' you, lad? There is, isn't there?" Robert's arm went out in a curve inviting his son to come into the comfort of it, but Freddie sidled past him, saying, "I'll be all right, Da; I'll just walk it off."

As he ran along the path towards the steps his father called after him, "Look up Nancy an' the bairns; help them with the wood. That's a good lad."

When he reached the shore he turned in the opposite direction from where he knew his sisters would be gathering and hurried towards the main quay. There would be bustle there, men milling about, and boats that had managed to avoid the sandbanks on the way down from Newcastle waiting hopefully to put out to sea; others unloading some of their cargo in order to lighten the load to help them up the river to Newcastle to clear their cargo and pay their dues to that hated city. But his mind's eye would always follow these boats leaving the river on their hazardous journeys across the Black Middens that claimed so many ships and lives, and out into the German Ocean.

He stood on the quay looking at the Africaine. She was quite a big ship and new, a three-hundred tonner. She had been built in Jarrow, and was owned by the Coxon company who had their office along the quay there. His eyes travelled beyond the ship to another lying at anchor. She was a whopper that one, a five-hundred tonner likely. She was a Newcastle one. Nobody liked the Newcastle boats; they always tended to be better and bigger than anybody else's along the river. For himself he fancied the smaller ones, like the Anna, the North Shields Anna. There were lots of boats called Anne and Anna, some from Newcastle, some from South Shields, and there were two from here; all with the same name, but belonging to different owners. What would it be like to own a boat? He'd rather own a boot shop.

The smells on the waterfront stung his nostrils: tar, fish, hides, baccy, wood. The wood came from the prop boats. He liked the smell of these. The props came from Norway. What was Norway like? Was it full of big men, like the ones who docked here with fair hair and ruddy faces? He knew one thing, they were nearly always big drinkers and big fighters, very pally and nice when they were sober but they raised hell outside the bars, especially the night before they sailed. Would he like to be a sailor? No, he didn't think so now. Anyway, he had been through that.

"And where is Jack-the-giant-killer off to this morning?"

He came to himself as if from a daydream and blinked at the woman who was now walking at his side.

"Nowhere, Miss Hewitt," he said.

"Shouldn't you be at Mr Aynsley's?"

How did she know he worked for Aynsley?

"Ah, you're wondering how I know you work at the butcher's? For the simple reason, young man, that I deal with Mr Aynsley and I've seen you through in the back shop, your grubby little hands tearing at the entrails. How many hours do you work?"

"Three a day."

"For how much?"

"A shilling a week."

"Eighteen hours for one shilling . . . twelve pence. What's twelve into eighteen?"

He tried to work it out but couldn't. "I don't know," he said.

"You don't know, and you can't read or write, but you think you're a big fellow, don't you?"

53

He slanted his glance at her. What was she up to?

"Did you enjoy your trip across the water last night? You were late going and early coming back."

He actually stopped and gazed at her. How did she know? She could have seen him coming back; but who could have seen him going?

"How do I know? I know lots of things, young fellow-me-lad, that would surprise you. Well, what did you do across there?"

"I minded me own business." It came out before he could check it; and her reply was a short laugh and a thrust from her hand and, "You cheeky monkey!"

The push she gave him brought him against a stack of barrels and although they shook just the slightest a voice bawled, "What the hell do you think you're up to! Tryin' to climb on top?"

The man had come from behind the pile, his glare fixed on Freddie, but his tone changed immediately when he saw the woman, and his voice was a greeting, saying "Oh, hello there, Maggie."

She didn't answer him but, looking at Freddie, she said, "Come on you."

He felt embarrassed and slightly defiant. He wanted to say, "I'm goin' back," but then he had thought about her earlier on, hadn't he? and the fortune in his pocket. So, apparently obediently, he walked by her side.

"Your father's a cripple, isn't he?"

He looked up at her but didn't answer. She wasn't very big, not like his mother. He reckoned she was just over five feet; and although she wasn't dressed ordinary 'cos she was wearing a black straw hat, she wasn't turned out like the ladies from yon end of the town. Her skirt was grey but it wasn't very full, and she had a three quarter length coat on. It was tight into her waist. She was skinny. He said, "You seem to know a lot, don't you?"

"Don't be cheeky, young man. And I could say the same to you, and to my mind too much for your own good."

He had heard those words before. When he shivered visibly, she said, "You cold?" her tone expressing surprise, and he answered, "Aye, a bit."

"Well, you must be in for something because it isn't cold this morning. What did you do last night?"

He jerked his head and looked at her in some alarm, and

she said, "Oh, it's all right, it's all right. You went across to Gallagher's, but it was all a set-up job. You should have been over here; there was some fun. I don't know who Robert Dees hates most, your lot or those two from Newcastle."

She had said, your lot; she must know about Mister Blaze and the rest.

"Damn and blast it!" She stepped quickly to the side, shaking the excrement from her foot, and she glared at him as she said, "Do you know what I'd like to bet, and I wouldn't lose on it, this is the filthiest town in the country. They're sitting on their bloody committees debating whether they should have a tunnel or a bridge across the bloody river that will vie with anything in Newcastle, while the pigs are still running the streets, instead of sweepers. By God! I'll do something about this, I will! I will!" and she stepped briskly towards some rotting hay lying against a coil of chains and, swishing her foot, she cleaned the mess from it. "You know something, boy? Pigs are cleaner than people."

She hurried on, picking her way now until they left the quay past the row of one roomed cottages that looked like hovels and which also came in for her disdain as she thumbed towards them, saying, "You know nothing about statistics, boy, but you'll know that practically every working man's house in this town and along the coast contains only one room."

"We have two."

She turned her head and looked down on him. "You're lucky then."

"And the other cottages in our row have two."

"You're all very lucky then." She bounced her head with each word, and they walked on again, up a cindery bank now and onto a narrow road. And as he continued to walk by her side he wondered why he was staying with her. Yet he knew why. But they'd soon be out in the country.

They walked on in silence for some way until she said, "What are your plans for this morning, young sir, may I ask?"

She seemed to be laughing at him now, but his answer brought her to a halt when he said, "To see you, to talk to you."

"Really? You mean our meeting was not unintentional or accidental?"

He didn't quite get the gist of her words but his answer was, "Well, I thought about you when I was lying in bed."

The laugh she let out was, strangely, a nice laugh: it was

55

high and sort of tinkling, different altogether from her face that looked leathery and old, older than his mother's.

"So you had been thinking of me in bed? Well! Well! all I can say to you is that your appearance is very deceptive and that you are starting early on a downward trail."

He couldn't follow her now, but he said, "I want to talk to you about money."

"Ah!" Her mouth opened wide. "So now we know . . . money. You want a loan?"

"No."

"*No?*"

"I want you to keep some money for me."

She remained silent staring down at him. Then she said, "You want to do business? Well, if that's the case, let us go on and quickly."

They walked on. She didn't speak any more until she turned from the road onto a bridle path. And as he walked up it slightly behind her, he wondered why he had never been along this way before. But then he very rarely left the town, there was never any time, except on a Sunday. And he always had a long sleep on a Sunday and afterwards he would do whatever John wanted to do.

His open mouth showed surprise when her hand guided him through a white painted gate, then up the green path towards a house with green shutters. It was a real house, like those on the top of the bank in the town. He took in immediately it had actually eight windows; no . . . nine, there was one in the roof. The heavy door, he noticed, was of black oak, and when she inserted a big key into the lock and turned it and there was no grating sound, he knew it must have been well oiled. And now he was as surprised as he had been when he first stood in the hall of The Towers: this one was smaller, but as grand; well, not grand but better in a way, interesting. His eyes took in the wheels of two ships hanging on the wall right opposite the door and in between them a painting of a sailing ship, full blown. It was so real he could even imagine the wind in the sails.

She had taken off her hat and coat and was saying, "Come along," as she pushed him gently in the back and through one of a number of doors that went off the hall, and into a room that looked like one of the ship's offices along the quay, only a bit more comfortable. She pointed to a leather chair, saying, "Sit down. Would you like a drink?"

"No, no; ta . . . thanks."

"Like something to eat?"

"No; no thanks."

"You want to get down to business, is that it?"

He said nothing; and so she walked over to the chair behind an oak desk placed in front of the window, and having sat down, she leaned forward with her forearms on the desk and said, "Well now, if it's business you want to talk about, let's talk business."

He stood up, put his hand down inside his breeches and into the lining pocket and pulled out a piece of rag and, placing it on the desk, he unfolded it and exposed the two half sovereigns.

She now leant further forward and looked at them. She seemed to look at them for a long time before she raised her head and asked, "What had you to do to get that amount?"

He could have answered simply, "Keep me mouth shut," but he said nothing, just stared at her.

And now she asked, "Did you get more than this?"

He shook his head.

"Then why didn't you give it to your mother? You're in straits along there, aren't you? She has her hands full, so I understand. Your father being like he is, and with a blind daughter, she could do with this."

"I know."

"Then why in the name of the Almighty! haven't you given it to her?"

"Cos . . . 'cos it would make her worry; and she would ask the same questions as you, what did I get it for?"

"Then I ask again, what did you get it for? Did you do something bad?"

"*No.*" His voice was loud now, almost a yell. "No, I didn't!"

"All right. All right. Don't blow your cap off. Well now, we've got to talk, you and me, haven't we? Why have you come to me? I could give you away, you know I could, couldn't I?"

"Aye, you could . . . suppose."

"But you don't think I will?"

"No."

"You're a funny one. Frank said you had a head on your shoulders that would fit your granny."

Who was Frank? And he wasn't pleased at being associated with his granny because she was a crabby old scut. She didn't like him and he didn't like her.

57

"What do you want me to do with your money?"

"Keep it for me till I want it. I'll pay you."

She chuckled now, saying, "If I keep your money, laddie, it's me that will be paying you. Have you heard of anything like interest?"

"No. I just thought you charged."

"Well, for your information"—her face was now grim, as was her voice—"I am no money lender, I am not a penny in the shilling woman. So you understand what I mean?"

Yes, he understood her all right now, 'cos some of the old wives charged a penny a week for lending you a shilling, so his da said. And he had thought she was one of them.

Her voice still grim, she said, "I don't deal in pennies, cents or sous, I'm what you call a commission agent for various things ... miscellaneous. A commission agent you could say without a licence, for I am not registered in Newcastle, and I'm a thorn in the flesh of many males in this town, those who consider women fit only for bed and breeding."

She was talking angrily now, walking about the room, and it wasn't as if she was addressing him: "They don't know the difference between an American and a Spanish dollar, although it's only a penny at the present time, four and tuppence to four and threepence." She now stopped in her walking and stabbed her finger at him; then went on, "In one day I can deal with riels, eight to the dollar, sixpence h'penny at best, or a gold rupee. And you know how much a gold rupee can bring? The last one I had through my hands brought twenty eight and ninepence. And why am I talking to you, telling you this?" She stopped in front of him again. "Because if you understand half of what I've said I could be in the soup. Your sideline is being a runner, my main sideline is exchanging money, but not ripping the poor sods off like Johnson and Rickmore up in the city or Tate along in the town there." She bent over him, her hands on her hips, her body leaning forward. "Now you know my secret, tell me yours."

What secret? He didn't understand anything she had been saying except that she changed the sailors money. Well, lots of people did that, so he understood. There was an office along the quay. And they could get it changed in the Shipping Company too. So he didn't really know what she was at; but he reckoned she was sly. Even so he felt tempted to tell her exactly what had happened. He didn't really know why except he was sure that he could trust her, she wouldn't give him away.

He recalled how whenever he'd heard her name mentioned it was always associated with . . . what was the word? Not fear, no; he supposed it was what his ma called respect. She was always saying, you can respect this one or that one, or on the other hand, this one or that one breeds no respect. But still he daren't, for the life of him, tell everything, so he said, "I . . . I warned the master that the excise were on to him, and . . . and he was glad I did."

"As far as I can gather you've warned others that the excise were on to them, but did they give you a sovereign?"

"No."

"What did they give you?"

"Some baccy for me da and a draw off of rum."

"No white powder for your da?"

He screwed up his eyes at her. "White powder? No."

"Well"—she straightened up—"that would likely do him more good than the rum, help him to blot out life. Still, every man to his taste. You take the powder across the river though, don't you?"

"I don't take no powder across the river. What kind of powder?"

He watched her face soften. She came towards him and put her hand on his head, and her smile was sweet and her voice soft as she said, "No matter what they say you're still just ten, and one of these days that little shell of yours will be taken out on the tide if you're not careful. . . .Well, I'm going to have a drink of cocoa. You like cocoa?"

"Never had it."

"Aw, well, we'll have to see if we can tempt your pallet, and also with a raisin bun. But first of all let us decide on our business association. You have, young man, this day, pledged with me two half sovereigns which I'm to keep for you for an unknown time. That's right, isn't it?" His head bobbed again. "Well, as long as the sovereigns remain with me you will receive some interest. Usually interest is paid every six months, or once a year. Now at two and a half per cent you will be entitled to sixpence at the end of the year and I will be entitled to say, well, a penny of that sixpence for looking after it for you. You see what I mean?"

His eyes flicked from her to a side table on which there were a number of photographs, then to the desk, then to the fireplace to the right of him where a wood fire was still smouldering, and then, looking at her, he said, "The penny would be your cut?"

He saw her close her eyes, put her lips tight together, and swallow before answering: "Right, partner. Right."

She was laughing at him again. He knew this, and he smiled at her. But the stiff expression returned to her countenance again as she said, "Of course, that's if you leave your money for a year. Are you going to?"

"I don't know. If . . . if things get bad I might have to take a bit out at a time; or if I decide to leave the butcher's, 'cos I don't like it there, I might take me wage out."

"Oh"—her face stretched—"I can see this is going to be a different proposition. Still it is my job to face difficulties. Well now, sit where you are"—she pointed at him—"and don't touch a thing on my desk. You understand?"

He had the desire to answer her back but he didn't. And when she had left the room he let out a long breath and sank into the soft leather of the chair for a moment, telling himself that all this business was nearly as queer as last night, only not so frightening. She was a funny card, but he liked her. She was cute in a kind of way. His mother would have said she was as fly as a box of monkeys.

He turned his head to look at the paintings on the wall opposite the window and desk. One seemed to be of the same ship as in the hall, only smaller; and to one side of it, there was a painting of a sailor with a beard and brass buttons, with a young lass by his side; and to the other, a painting of a young clean-shaven sailor, also with brass buttons and the same lass by his side. He looked at them for a long time trying to work out who they were. Likely her da and her ma. Her ma looked bonny. He got up and walked over to look at them more closely when the door was pushed open abruptly and she came in carrying a tray and on it were two steaming mugs and a plate of buns. She paused a moment watching him as he looked, startled, back at her as though he had been caught out, and he stammered, "I . . . I . . . I was only . . . look . . . lookin'."

"Well, I won't charge you for looking," she said and walked over to her desk.

He followed her, and as she placed the tray down he, seeming to have regained his usual composure, nodded backwards and said, "They're nice. Is that your ma and da?"

"No, young sir, that isn't me ma and da. That is my father and me."

His mouth dropped slightly open as he looked from her weather-beaten face to the pretty girl. And when she said, "Oh, yes, yes, I have changed. Thirty years and salt spray and wind and—" She stopped, swung round and picked up a mug of cocoa and, handing it to him, she said, "Taste that and see if you like it."

He tasted the thick brown stuff. It was hot and sweet and the only thing he could couple the taste with was cinder toffee. "Tis nice," he said.

"I'm pleased you like it." Then she said, "Try a bun and see if you like that too."

As he took a bun she walked back to the paintings, to the one of the girl and the young man. And she stared at it for a moment before, pointing now to the ship, she said, "That was my father's boat."

Her eyes were fixed tightly on the painting as she went on quietly now, "She went down on the Black Middens and he with it, and Sam too." She turned towards him. "That is Sam." She pointed to the young man. She didn't go on to explain who Sam was but said, "We lived on The Lawe, you know, across the water in Shields. I was born there, almost within sight of the Middens." She placed the photograph slowly back on the table, then returned to her desk.

Having taken a long drink from the mug, she suddenly leaned towards him and, wagging her finger in his face, said, "Never go to sea. Do anything: clean guts in the back of a butcher's shop, swill middens, anything, but don't go to sea. Of all the treacherous bitches in the world, she's the biggest, for she takes men from their wives and grooms from their brides; she deprives children of fathers; and even when she's kind she cripples men and makes women old before their time. Don't ever go to sea, boy."

The next moment she was out of the room and he was left alone, a half-eaten bun in one hand, a half-full mug of cocoa in the other, staring towards the door. Was she potty? Bats? Up the lum? Well, there was something the matter with her. He looked at the bun. It was a nice bun. He'd never tasted one like it. And this cocoa was nice an' all, warming. But he'd better go.

It had been a funny morning . . . it had been a funny night. Everything had been funny since he crossed the river last night.

But here she was, coming back into the room. And her voice was soft again as she said, "I got a bit carried away, didn't I, about the sea? But I don't often have visitors, especially in this room. In fact, I don't do business here at all. My office is on the quay, you know. Well, I call it my office but it's known as Maggie Hewitt's house, isn't it, because there's no brass-plated plaque outside. Anyway, finish your cocoa and your bun and then we'll put our business in writing, eh?"

"I . . . I can't write."

"I didn't expect you could, but I can. And if you can't write you can't read, I suppose. Is that it?"

"No; I can't read."

"Well, there's a school of sorts in the town; why don't you go there instead of skittering up and down the quays? What do you get for your skittering anyway?"

"Oh, sometimes a bit of fruit, an orange or some lemons, or when they're revictualin' I get the old stuff."

"Is that as far as you think, getting the garbage from the boats?"

"It . . . it helps at home."

"Aye, it might. But what when you grow up? And you'll be grown up, you know; you won't always remain that size. What are you going to do then?"

"I would like to go in for a shoe shop. Well, I mean, not a shoe shop, just make shoes."

She nodded at him now, saying, "Well, there should be money in that, but not in this town. They're falling over each other here."

"That's what me da says."

"Then you have discussed your future?"

"Well, I've told them I don't want the butchers."

"If that's the case, then there's hope for you." She turned to the desk, pulled a book towards her, flicked over a number of leaves, then dipped a quill pen into an ink well and began to write. She hadn't sat down but was bending over the desk; and now she turned her head and said, "See what I've written here?" He went round the desk and looked on the page and saw some squiggles and she said, "It says, 'Deposited with me on the first of September, eighteen forty-three.'" Then stopping and turning her head towards him, she said, "I'm dating it from the first: I'm being kind to you," before going on, "'the sum of two half

62

sovereigns to be invested at two and a half per cent per annum. Interest to be half-yearly if so required. Signed this day, Margaret Hewitt, spinster, and Freddie Musgrave.'"

"It should be Frederick."

She glared sharply at him and started writing again, then said, "'Frederick Musgrave.' Here"—she handed the pen to him—"put a cross there where I'm pointing to."

His hand shaking, he made a cross. She now took a rocker blotter and dried the ink before, pointing to the writing again, she said, "You have this day, Frederick Musgrave, done your first business deal. And I don't think it'll be the last one. What do you say?"

"I . . . I don't think I'll get any more sovereigns."

"Oh"—she wagged her head—"you never know. And Frederick"—she stressed his name as she brought her face down to his—"you haven't hoodwinked me. Get that into your head. Do you hear? You haven't hoodwinked me this morning. Because you didn't get those sovereigns for carrying a message to Mr Gallagher, not just for carrying a message; but you'll tell me some day. Oh yes you will, you'll tell me some day. Or perhaps I'll be able to tell you before you tell me. What do you think of that?"

What he thought was, she would never be able to tell him what had happened last night or what had happened this morning, 'cos not even the staff knew what the master had said to him, although they knew what he intended to do with the bairn. Oh, that poor bairn.

At the door she said, "Go on now; and if I were you I'd make up my mind quickly between the butcher's and the boots', because, let me tell you, you'll come to no good running the quay all day. You might be too young to be picked up by the press gang but there are other ways to disappear, laddie. So get yourself into a settled job. Do you hear me?"

"Yes, miss."

"And one last thing: if you get worried about anything, anything at all, just make your way here or to the house on the quay. I'm either in one place or the other, except on a Thursday afternoon and a Saturday morning when I'm in Newcastle."

"Thanks, miss. Aye, I will. And ta for the cocoa an' . . . an' for puttin' me name in your book."

Her face relaxed and she smiled now and, her voice low again, she said, "Go on with you. You'll do. . . ."

Before descending the cinder hill towards the beach he stood still for a moment and looked along the river as far as he could see both ways. It seemed packed with boats, large ones and small ones. In the far distance he made out a keelman sculling coal from the staithes to a boat in the middle of the river. It was one of those too big to come inshore the way the tide was at present. And from where he stood he could see over the other end of the town and the steam rising from the salt pans. And the noise of the town and the river merged and rose to him, and it was like the sound of bees swarming, punctuated every now and again by the banging of hammers in rhythmic flow as if from a forge. And a voice, rising above the rest and conveying to him that it would be carrying an oath from someone on the quay to someone on board ship, or the other way round.

It was said there were well over eight thousand people in the town. How many was eight thousand? He could count up to a hundred and that was a fair amount, but he couldn't visualise eight thousand.

What was he going to do now? Go to the butcher's and get his lugs clipped and his backside kicked, or go and see if he could be set on in a boot shop? But that would mean a full day, six days a week from seven in the morning till six at night, and then if he was lucky. And it would be mostly cobbling. Oh, he'd better go home first and talk it over with his da. But he wouldn't go the way of the quayside, or by the market and the main street, he would skirt the town 'cos it wasn't so mucky on the outskirts. But why was he bothering about it being mucky? It had never struck him until she had mentioned it. He could see her angrily wiping the muck from her boot. Aw, he was thinkin' daft. He would go the way he always went.

And so he ran down the hill and along the road to the quay. There was a fruit boat in at one place and he picked up a partly squashed orange that had got wedged between two crates, and as he did so there was a shout from the deck of the ship, and he looked up and saw two oranges come flying towards him. He managed to catch one and quickly retrieved the other; then turning, his face bright, he shouted, "Ta, mister," and the orange thrower laughed and answered in a foreign language. Minutes later he had reached the end of the quay where it merged into the beach when he saw Mr Tommy Johnson coming round from behind his boat. He was humping a creel of herring

64

and he called to him, "Hi! there, Freddie," then waved him forward.

He hesitated a moment before approaching him because he knew there would be more questions. But when he reached the fisherman all Tommy said was, "Take them to your ma," and handed him four big herring on a hook. Then he added, "Tell your da I'll be popping in to see him later. Understand?"

Yes, he understood. "Ta, Mr Johnson. Ta." As he turned away and climbed to the road above the beach, he thought, That's funny, Mr Johnson rarely came empty-handed to see his da, so there must have been a run of some kind last night; or perhaps Mr Johnson was just bringing something from his own store. And he likely did have a store because he was a sober man was Mr Johnson; after a run he didn't get totally bottled like the rest.

Before he reached the house he knew they had company, and when he entered the room he stood in amazement looking at his granny. His granny never came across the water, she was frightened to be in a sculler or the ferry, but there she was, and a strange lass with her. His mother said, "Look what the wind's blown in. And this is your cousin Lizzie from Darlington."

He was looking at a young lass. She had a face like a full moon, or more like a turnip lantern that the lads made when they wanted a bit of carry on at night to scare folks. But the face that he was looking at wouldn't scare anyone, he thought it was too dull. And she was nursing a bundle on her knee. He didn't know what made him step forward and look at the baby without giving a greeting to his granny or this new cousin. The thing was swaddled up to the eyes and it stank of pee. Last night's baby had looked clean and bonny this morning. What he could see of this one's face was red and puffed; it looked dull like its mother.

"Not a word of greeting; we mightn't be here."

He turned and looked at his grandmother, then said, "Hello, Granny."

"Oh, he's seen me and he's just asked how I am an' how I managed to get across that flaming river; and would I like some of those herrin' he's holdin' to take back home with me, and one of the oranges an' all."

As he handed the fish to his mother, he said, "Mr Johnson gave me these, Ma, and"—he glanced now at his father sitting against the wall—"he said he'd be along later to see you, Da."

"Oh, that's nice. That's nice."

65

"You haven't been to the shop then?" His mother spoke directly to him for the first time, and he shook his head and said, "No, Ma. I . . . I wasn't feelin' like it."

"My God! in heaven, did you ever hear anythin' like that?"

All eyes were on his grandmother now. She, like her daughter, was a tall woman, but that, apparently, was the only resemblance between them. She was wearing a black skirt and a blue striped blouse. He could see it through her open knee length bead cape that matched her bonnet. Besides her voice, her presence seemed to fill the room. His mother was now saying to her, "Will you have a drop of broth, Ma?"

"Broth it is. Well, I could have got that at home, but beggars can't be choosers."

He looked at his mother and she looked at him and he smiled inwardly at the thought that she wasn't bringing out the ham shank, nor the butter and cheese and white bread. "Who gave you the oranges?" she said, and held her hand out for the fruit that was lying along the crook of his arm.

"A fella on a boat." But he didn't offer them to her; instead he said, "I'm keepin' these for the bairns, Ma."

"Oh, aye, aye." As his mother nodded to him her mother, addressing her granddaughter, said, "Did y'hear that? He's keepin' the fruit for the bairns, no, can he, Ma? or, we'll share, Ma." The old woman now looked towards her son-in-law, saying, "Who's boss in this house anyway?"

And his father infuriated her more when he answered, "Oh, he is, has been this long while."

"It's no joke, but would seem so," she said.

His father winked at him and the look in his eyes said, Come on, laugh at her; but he couldn't laugh at his granny; her joking was always pointed and hurtful for somebody. And he turned and walked from the room now and into the bedroom, and there, lifting the lid of a wooden trunk that held their clothes and was set between the girls' beds, he put the two whole oranges in the corner. Then closing the lid again he laid the squashed one on the top and sat down beside it.

He hadn't been sitting long before his mother came into the room and, closing the door quietly after her, she went to the small window and pulled the curtain a little to the side to let more light in. Then coming to him, she bent over him, saying, "You all right now?"

66

"Aye, Ma."

"Really? Better than you were?"

"Aye, Ma."

She now put her hand on his shoulder and in a conspiratorial voice murmured, "I'm not fetchin' out that food while they are here no matter how long they stay. What d'you say?"

He smiled back at her, saying, "You're right, Ma."

"We'll have a do when they're gone, eh? By the way, she's just lost her husband . . . Lizzie. She's come to live with your granny, and the bairn's only six weeks. It won't last if you ask me; 'cos there's trussin' and trussin' an' bindin' an' bindin'. I wouldn't like to give a guess when she last changed it. She looks a lazy little bitch to me. Anyway, come on and be pleasant. It was nice of Mr Johnson to give you the fish. And you say he's comin'?"

"Aye, Ma."

"And there wasn't a run last night?"

"No, Ma."

"Well, he must have something. It'll please your da. Come on now."

"I will in a minute, Ma."

She straightened up; then stood looking down on him for a moment before going out. And he sat on, thinking. He thought about Miss Hewitt—he no longer said Maggie in his mind—and her house and the way she talked. His thinking seemed concerned only with the way she talked and what she talked about. She was clever was Miss Hewitt. By! yes, he would say she was clever . . . and different, different from them out there.

He didn't question whether he was including his mother and father in "them out there."

3

Three weeks later Miss Hewitt came to the house. She came because she hadn't seen Freddie on the quay for more than a week.

Jinny had been about to leave the house; she had got set on at the Rope Works half day, one o'clock till seven; but when the knock came on the door and she opened it and was confronted by a slight-figured neatly, even smartly dressed, woman whom she and everybody in the town knew as Maggie Hewitt, sometimes prefixed with miss, her jaw dropped.

"Mrs Musgrave?"

"Aye, that's me."

"May I come in?"

Jinny glanced back into the room where Robert was sitting on the floor, a bundle of shavings to his side as he whittled away at the leg of a chair. He'd had a stroke of luck. Buckhams, who had the shop in Saddle Street, had given him an order for three chairs. It was the first time for years it had happened. Lily was sitting on the mat playing with her clouty doll, and Freddie was in bed in the other room. But what did this one want?

She soon said what she wanted once she had stepped into the room. "I . . . I haven't seen your son for some days. Has . . . has he gone away?"

"No. No, ma'am; he's . . . he's been sick."

"Sick? Ill? What has been wrong?"

"It was his stomach, ma'am. But he's on the mend now." She nodded towards the bedroom. "He'll be up and about in a day or two."

The two women stared at each other for a moment: Jinny trying to weigh up this woman who spent her time on the waterfront doing business with men and who spoke like a lady and

68

almost dressed as one, except that her clothes were plain, no frills or laces. But what did she want with her lad? She had never heard Freddie mention the woman's name. She saw her looking now towards Robert, and Robert was saying, "Good day to you, ma'am."

"Good day, Mr Musgrave. I see you know how to carve."

"I'm a carpenter, ma'am. Twas my trade; still is."

"Did you make this furniture?" Miss Hewitt looked around the room at the table, the chairs, the small sideboard, the carved wooden mantelpiece upon which were four brass candlesticks and all shining, and apparently not used for the purpose for which they were made for there was a tin candle holder at each end of the shelf. There was no sign of a lamp in the room; they must still depend on candles.

"Will you take a seat?" Jinny pulled the chair from under the table, and as she did so Lily rose from the mat and stumbled towards her, only to be checked by her mother, saying, "Play with your doll, Lily; that's a good lass." And obediently the child returned to the mat.

"I meant to come and see you before this, at least after I'd found out if your son was agreeable to my proposition."

After I'd found out if your son was agreeable to my proposition. Jinny threaded the words through her mind. Whatever it was this woman was proposing she was going to talk to Freddie about it first. But she listened to her as she went on: "You see, I need a gardener and someone who can do odd jobs," she was saying. "I have two acres of land on the outskirts of the town and it is very badly overgrown. It hasn't been seen to for more than a year. The man who attended to it died and I've never bothered engaging anyone since. But I understood your son was looking for new employment and I wondered if you would be agreeable to his taking on the position?"

"Gardener?" It was Robert speaking. "He knows nowt about gardenin', miss. Doubt if he's ever been in one; not many gardens round here."

"I'm well aware of that, Mr Musgrave. But there are gardens round about, and there's only one gardener in the town, that is Mr Blyton of Union Street, and he is fully occupied."

"I don't know whether he'd take to it, ma'am." Jinny's voice was stiff. "He's been used to the shore and the quay-front all his life. Boats are more in his line."

"Perhaps, perhaps. But if he was willing, would you agree to his taking on the position? I can offer him at the beginning three shillings a week together with his food. The hours would be eight till six in the summer and nine till four in the winter. And, as I've indicated, his wage will rise according to his capacity for the work."

According to his capacity for the work. What was surprising Jinny as much as anything was the way this one talked. She had heard she could swear like a trooper and handle men no matter what their class or size. But what was she saying? Three shillings a week and his food and a rise if he was worth it. And he'd be worth it because he'd put his heart into any job he was doing, even the butchery. That's why they wanted him round there. And that's why that pig of a man had given him that lump of meat; he was never the one to give lumps of meat away. And it had been rotten. She knew when she was cooking it it was rotten. They'd all had diarrhoea for days, but it had hit Freddie worst of all. Eeh, dear God! She thought she had lost him, yes she did. That morning around three o'clock she thought she had lost him, and if he had gone the spark would have gone out of her life. She had weathered Robert and his useless legs; she had weathered Mary, Joe, and Harry going; and she had just about weathered Billy dying, after getting him up to eight years old, too; but if Freddie had gone, oh no, she couldn't have stood that. And here was this woman offering him a position as a gardener. Funny that, to think of Freddie being a gardener when his main object in life was to be a cobbler. No; not a cobbler, a shoe maker.

"Do you think I could see him for a moment?"

Jinny paused, then said, "Well, yes. And he's not 'fectious."

"Oh, that wouldn't trouble me if he were infectious; I've got a leather hide that germs can't penetrate." She smiled from one to the other; and Robert smiled back at her, but Jinny didn't smile, she led the way into the bedroom, saying, "You've got a visitor."

Freddie was lying propped up against two bare pillow ticks, and at the sight of Miss Hewitt he pulled himself up straight for a moment from the pillows before sinking back, and he looked from the visitor to his mother who was saying to Miss Hewitt, "I'll bring you a chair."

He continued to stare at the woman standing at the foot of the shaky down. She looked tall from this angle, and it was as if she had gone back into one of the dreams he had been having about her, the latest only last night when she had been captain of that big sailing ship. He had watched her take it up the river. He had stood to her side as she turned the wheel, and the sails had billowed, and the shanty man had sung as they rounded the sandbanks. But there she was, and his mother was placing a chair for her, saying, "I meself have got to leave, ma'am; I'm due at me work."

"Oh, are you working?"

"Yes, at the ropery."

"Oh, yes, yes. Well, undoubtedly, we'll be seeing more of each other in the future, Mrs Musgrave, at least I hope so."

There she was smiling again, but his mother gave her no return smile or answer but turned about and went out; and they were left together, and Miss Hewitt did her best not to wrinkle her nose against the smell in the room. It wasn't the stench as in some houses she had been in, but it certainly reeked of humanity in all its processes.

"How are you?"

"All right."

"I didn't know you had been ill."

"It wasn't the plague or anythin'."

"No, so I understand. What caused it, do you know?"

"Aye, rotten meat."

She clicked her tongue, then said, "I've been looking out for you."

"Aye?"

"I want to offer you a position."

"Me? Runnin' for you?"

"No, not running for me. I don't need that kind of a runner. Anyway, once what they call The Free Trade Bill gets passed that'll put a stop to your running. There'll be no need for it. Yet"—she shook her head—"there are those who do it for the excitement, like Peter Morley. You remember him?"

Yes; he remembered Peter Morley. They caught him 'cos he had been too cocksure liftin' a cask from the river in the early dawn. A daft thing to do. He'd been manacled by the neck in the cellar of the customs house. They kept him there for a week before they took him to Newcastle. He was in the House of Correction now, and lucky to be there some said; a year or so back and it could have been Australia.

71

She was saying, "How would you like to be my gardener, and see to my glass house and maintenance about the house itself?"

He jerked in the bed. "Me? Gardener. I couldn't be a gardener, I know nowt about plants and things."

"I suppose you can use a shovel and dig?"

"Aye."

"Well, that would be your first job, clearing the vegetable garden that is all over-run and the brushwood from the grounds. And by the time you have finished that you will have learned that the first stages in gardening are digging, weeding, and sweating; knowledge will follow . . . three shillings a week, your food and moderate hours. What about it?"

As he stared at her the butcher's shop receded into the past, but the boot shop did not follow immediately. He saw the plate glass window: just such a one as he had seen in Newcastle, the only time he had been there. And behind were rows and rows of beautiful shoes and boots and gaiters, and leggings, and the colours rose from black to all shades of brown. There were even a pair of white doeskin slippers, at the very front, made to fit a bairn.

She could see his mind working, weighing up the pros and cons of the proffered situation.

"I can't start till next week," he said; "me legs are rocky."

She looked at him for almost thirty seconds before she said, "That'll be all right. Leave it longer if you must. The weeds have stopped growing anyway, and so you can work in the conservatory to begin with."

"In the what?"

"The glass house. Didn't you notice it? It begins at the side of the house and runs its full length and has doors into the sitting room and dining room. Oh, of course"—she nodded now and her smile widened—"you came on business that day, business only."

This caused him to look towards the door and he wagged his hand at her, whispering now, "They don't know I went along to you."

Her voice was as low as his. "They don't?" she said.

"No."

She drew in a short breath before saying, "Of course you're right. I'm very dim about some things. You couldn't tell them."

She wasn't dim, she could never be dim, but she had thought he must have mentioned her in some way to his ma and da.

"You wouldn't have a job for two of us, would you?"

The look on her face expressed surprise and slight indignation. "What!" she said. "Two of you? What do you mean?"

"Me brother John. He works down the pit, I told you, but he'd give one eye and a thumb to be out of it. He rarely sees daylight he says, 'cept Sundays, and then he's so tired he sleeps half the time."

"Well, I'm afraid I can do nothing for your brother"—she paused—"as yet." Now she gave a sort of chuckle and, leaning forward, she said mischievously, "You're sure there's no other member of the family you want to put into business?"

Although he knew she was joking he answered her seriously, saying, "No. Our Nell's married and set, and Nancy's goin' on the concerts again, singin'. She got two shillings last time and she's singin' in the Methodist Chapel come Sunday. She won't get paid for that though."

"No, I'm sure she won't get paid for that. She's the blind one, isn't she?"

"Aye. And Jessie's only four, but works for her keep; she hauls more wood up than many twice her size."

He saw her body shaking and when she said, "As yet the baby is unemployed," his face went into a wide grin as he said, "Aye, you could say that."

She stood up now, saying, "Well, that's settled. You can start on Monday if you're able; if you're not I shall understand." She put a hand out as if to touch his head, then drew it back; and she had reached the door when he stopped her by saying, "I . . . I can still do me runnin' at night." It was both a statement and a question, and she looked at him across the dim room for a moment, her face straight now as she said, "I'd rather you didn't."

"I want to. I . . . I mus. . . ."

She'd had the latch in her hand but she didn't open the door, she kept it pressed closed as she said softly, "You were going to say, you must. Does that mean someone's got something on you? You've done something?"

"No, no; I haven't." There was a hiss in his voice. "I didn't mean nowt; I just meant I want to do it."

She looked away towards the small window where the piece

73

of curtain obscured most of the light and she said slowly, "Well, if you want to do it, you must do it, but not in my time." And on this she went out.

If he wanted to do it he must do it. He didn't want to do it, not any more. It had somehow been fun up till a few weeks ago. And from what his da said there had been no run since then, well, not from this side, at least round about. But then nobody knew what went on across at South Shields or up the river. They said the Newcastle lot were well organised; and of course they would be 'cos all the boats had to dock there first. But what had she meant about this free trade?

A few minutes later his father propelled himself into the room and straight to the foot of the shaky down; and he leant his arms on it and looked at his son as he said, "Well, lad, it seems you're set for life. But who would have thought it? A gardener. With all the industry an' jobs that's goin' on in this town and along the river, you've got to be set for a gardener. There's breweries, and boat builders, and bakers, and booksellers, and butchers, that's just going through the B's. And there's clogmakers, and coopers, and couriers, and joiners, and nailmakers, and painters, and plumbers, not to mention the pawnbrokers. God above! I could go on with blacksmiths, bottle makers, and that's not touchin' on half. Everything to support birth, life an' death is created in this town. But have we heard of a gardener? No."

"There is, Da, there's one."

"Aye, that's what she said an' all. I didn't tell her he wasn't my idea of a gardener, more like a grave digger, he sees to the grass. Well, what d'you think of the idea?"

"I said I would do it, Da."

"Aye; an' you're right to say that. You won't get another chance of a full time job an' your grub an' three shillings a week. Aye, I bet John wishes he had the chance. But he'll be glad for you. He's been worried about you. There's one thing your ma an' me's certain about, you'll not go butcherin' again."

"D'you like her, Da?"

"Who? Maggie Hewitt, or Miss Hewitt as she's called to her face? Well, now you've asked me a question. It's hard to say if you like or dislike her. They say she's as sharp as a ferret about business, an' she's never been known to give much away. She does a lot of work on the side, I understand, for foreigners an' their money, and she's liked among that lot because she doesn't rip 'em off. They tell me she comes from a seafaring family. Her da was a big nob at one time, used to race in sail, captained a big schooner. It went down. Her and her mother used to live in a house outside of town. She still lives there, I hear, but spends most of her time in the front. Queer card; not quite what you'd call a lady but not quite anything else either. Anyway, you can but try workin' for her. And I'll tell you somethin', lad. If I can get a few more orders like the one I've got, an' you bring your three shillings a week home, with John's pay and the odd shilling or two Nancy brings in, we'll be in clover, an' your mother won't need to go to the ropes, for that's a hellish job that. Backwards and forwards up that hill, the blood runnin' from the hands in the winter pullin', pullin', pullin'. I'll be satisfied if we can get her out of that. . . . She's a good woman is your mother, Freddie. Always remember that."

He didn't say, "I know, Da" or "I will, Da," but he looked at his father; and with a nod, Robert twisted around and eased himself through the door and into the kitchen again.

His da had just said they'd be in clover. He looked round the room, but he was seeing the house with the green shutters: no wind would get through them; the sea wouldn't shake its foundations; the putrid smell that rose from the streets wouldn't have impregnated its walls.

There were different beds of clover.

PART TWO

As It Happened
When I Was Twelve

1

"Read that."

"All of it?"

"Yes. Yes, all of it."

"I don't know whether I can or not."

"You won't know until you try."

Freddie took up a small sheet of newspaper and, holding it well away from his face, he began to read:

FIVE GUINEAS REWARD

Whereas Sunday Morning last about Three o'clock, Three or Four Men landed from a Sculler Boat, at the Quay a little above the Custom House Quay; quarrelled with and ill-used the Waterman; pulled down a Coal House belonging to Mr Horner and also Water Spouts belonging to Mr Horner and Mr Tyzack; and com . . . mitted various other Dep . . . red . . . ations to the Terror of the neighbour . . . hood, whose Windows were ass . . . as . . . sailed with Stones.

A REWARD of TWO GUINEAS will be paid by the said MR HORNER and MR TYZACK and a further REWARD of THREE GUINEAS by the NORTH SHIELDS and TYNEMOUTH ASSO . . . CI . . . ATION for prose . . . cuting FELONS, to any PERSON, or PERSONS who shall give such in . . . for . . . mation as may lead to the Con . . . viction of the Offender, or Offenders.

NORTH SHIELDS

26th November, 1817.

"Not bad. But what do you notice about that piece?"

"It happened years ago, and it was far too much money for the reward. The coal house and windows wouldn't have cost half that much to put up again."

"That isn't the point. What else did you notice?"

"Nowt."

"Can't you say nothing instead of nowt?"

"Everybody says nowt."

"Everybody doesn't say nowt. And what do you notice about that piece, I've asked you?"

"Just what I said."

"Did you notice that a lot of the words began with capital letters not just the paragraphs or the beginning of the sentence?"

"No."

"No, I suppose not." She sighed. "Well, for your further information Master Frederick Musgrave, every noun in that piece began with a capital letter. And a noun happens to be the name of anything."

Freddie stared at her in some bewilderment. She was always bewildering him. He had been working for her now for over eighteen months but never a day passed but she seemed to spring something new on him, and not always pleasant either. He had never wanted to learn to read; write his name, aye, but you could get the gist of all you wanted to know by just listening to other people. But then on the other hand he must give her her due because he had felt different since he could read a bit. And then he had gained a sort of prestige in the house because, at home at night, he could read snatches of paper writing to them. His da was tickled to death. And Nancy loved listening, but his ma wasn't pleased about it, he knew that. His ma hadn't taken to Miss: she hadn't a good word for her even when he brought the big bag of buns back on a Saturday night. The Miss made the buns herself; she was a dab hand at cooking. Oh aye, he'd say she was; he had never tasted food like what she put on the table. Of course, give his ma her due, as a rule she only had the neck end of mutton or tripe and chitterlings to deal with and bran flour for the bread. It was good wholesome food, he admitted, but it wasn't like the stuff the Miss dished up: a pudding made with white flour, milk and eggs, it melted in your mouth; and roast beef with gravy that you could suck up like soup. But still, at first, he didn't enjoy his meals very much 'cos she was always at him about how he was eatin' it. Apparently you didn't eat with your mouth open nor wipe your mouth with the back of your hand. As for your nose, he'd wished many a time in those first weeks that he hadn't got one. And then there was washing. She was worse than his ma about washing. His ma always made them dip their hands in the bucket before they came to the table, but the Miss made him scrub his nails. Still you had to take the good with the bad, and in the main it was good here. Oh aye, it was very good. He had to stop talking about it to John though, because John was a bit green. Anyway, it looked as if John would soon be seeing a lot of daylight, because there was a big strike about to break. Pitmen were always striking, it seemed; if it wasn't about one thing it was about another. It used to be about money, but now it was about conditions. Well, it was to be expected 'cos look what happened in the last disaster. There were a lot of fatherless bairns in the town now, many of them in the poor house. And only this week three young lads went to the House of Correction for stealing.

"I saw you talking to Mr Freeman yesterday. What did he want?"

He didn't raise his head as he said, "Just passin' the time of day."

"Don't try to hoodwink me, Freddie Musgrave; remember who you are talking to. There's a run on, isn't there? But talking of runs, don't forget what happened last month to the Newcastle fellows they picked up; they're well and truly along the line now, aren't they? They won't come ashore for sometime again, their bellies strapped tight with silk and such. Idiots they were, braving the daylight! And was it worth it for a dozen or so yards of lace! Yes, one had lace and the other silk." Her voice changing, she said, "You know what will happen, don't you, if you are caught anywhere near anyone if they've got the stuff on them? It will be no use saying you don't know anything about it, because those excise fellows are no fools: they've been picked for their job, they keep their eyes open. And let me tell you, they know that you're used. I've tried in my own way to put it about that that episode in your life is past. You're in a good job now and you're learning your letters and if you behave yourself you've got a good future afront of you." She put out her hand now and caught his and there was a plea in her voice as she said,

"Tell me, Freddie, now tell me the truth, just answer yes or no. Has Freeman got something on you?"

He could look her straight in the eye and say, "No."

She let go of his hand and straightened up; then, in a characteristic manner, her body jerked forward and again she had hold of his hand, demanding now, "Then who is it? You're frightened of somebody, I know that. I've known it from the day you brought your half sovereigns to me. Is it Mr Gallagher?"

He couldn't answer, but in returning her stare his throat contracted and he had to gulp at his spittle. And when she said, "Ah! Ah! I knew there was something. And it happened that night, didn't it? You were away all that night. It happened then?"

"No. No." He was shaking his head.

"Don't lie to me, boy." Her voice changed again, becoming soft and pleading now: "Trust me," she said. "You know you can trust me, you know that. I'm your friend, your good, good friend. I want to see you get on and . . . and I don't want to see anything happen to you. Mr Gallagher is a queer customer, not for him just French wines and a cask now and again, he goes in for bigger stuff, or I could say smaller stuff. Look! Tell me what you know about it."

He could again say honestly to her now, "I . . . I don't know anything, miss, I don't honest, not about what he goes in for. All he had that night I was there was two barrels down the well, an' I told you his man stuck them in the midden. I don't know anything else that he gets."

She sat back from the desk and her voice held a weary sound to it now as she said, "Well, if it isn't that, what is it, boy? there's something, isn't there?"

"Yes, miss."

"Ah, well, that is an admission. At last we're getting somewhere."

"No, miss, we're not, 'cos I can't tell you, but . . . but I will some day."

"Why some day? Why not now?"

Why did he answer her with the next words?

"I want to grow up a bit, miss."

Her face screwed up at him and the lines from her eyes to the top of her ears formed deep furrows, and she repeated quietly, "You want to grow up a bit, what do you mean?"

He didn't know exactly what he meant except that he

82

wanted to live, and he felt that he wouldn't live long if he talked about Mr Gallagher killin' his bairn. It wouldn't be like murdering a grown up or anything like that, but it would still be the killing of somebody and if that didn't mean hanging it meant gaol. And a man like Mr Gallagher would, as he had promised, pay anybody in full who would be the cause of his being found out. He looked at her face. It looked sad, worried, and it came to him that he liked her so much he would do anything so that she needn't worry; he sensed that she was a lonely woman. She had lost her father and the young man in the photo. He knew that he liked her, too, as much as he did his ma but in a different way, a sort of wider way although he couldn't explain the feeling that prompted the thought wider. But the next minute he was standing and bending forward across the desk towards her, saying, "Don't worry any more. I'll promise you something. I have to run this one message an' that'll be the last. I'll tell him."

She didn't smile as she often did when she was pleased, but her face seemed to relax and she said, "Thank you, Freddie; but couldn't you get out of doing this last run? You know, I told you about the free trade coming. . . ."

"No, not very easily," he cut in on her words, his own tumbling over each other. "I don't know where the faggot, I mean Mr Freeman lives; and anyway, it's too late now to even try to find out."

"You're crossing the river?"

"Aye."

"To Mr Gallagher's?"

He looked downwards, then muttered, "Aye."

From under his lowered gaze he watched her rise from the chair, move round the desk, and as she passed him on her way towards the door, she said, "Come on; let's have a bite, and then you can go home."

As he followed her across the hall towards the kitchen she asked, without turning round, "Do your parents know where you're going tonight?"

"No, not yet."

"You must tell them."

"Aye. Aye, I will."

"What are you taking across?"

They were in the kitchen now and she had gone towards the

83

fireplace that had an iron oven at one side and a boiler at the other and, before opening the oven door, she took down a towel from a brass rail running under the mantelshelf and, unhooking the iron latch of the oven, she took from it a large pie dish. This she set on the table, replaced the towel on the rod, took two plates that were lying on the top of the steel and brass fender and returned to the table, placing a plate at each side of it before she said, "Well, what are you carrying?"

"I don't know. Tis the truth, I don't know. I've got to see Mr ... well, somebody at this end of the Low Lights later on."

"Sit down." He took his seat at the table and watched her cut the pie crust, then ladle out chunks of steak and kidney and gravy on to his plate. But after she had passed it to him he did not begin until she had served her own portion which was not half the size of his. When she was seated she nodded to him, and he began to eat. Some times, when she was in good humour, she would say the funny grace. He had repeated it to his da, and it made him roar with laughter for it went:

> Meat and grains,
> Water and wine,
> Hold your hand, stomach,
> And it will be thine.

His da often said, "Hold your hand there," when he meant "Wait a minute," so the rhyme was understandable. She always said it in a funny voice. And then during a meal she often talked about places that she had been to, like France and Italy, and three times to Norway. She liked Norway. She had once said to him, "We'll go there one day. We'll get on a boat and we'll hie for the fiords." He had said, "What are fiords?" And she had told him.

It had been like a story, and he had described this, too, to them back home that night sitting round the fire. . . . He only wished his ma would like her. He didn't know why she hadn't taken to her, 'cos his da spoke well of her, and Nancy's opinion was she had a good smell; strong and clean, was how she described her. And she was right, she was strong and she was clean and she had a good smell.

He finished the meal with cheese and bread. There was still half the pie left. He wondered if she would give it to him to take home. After the meal she washed up the dishes in the wooden sink next to the fireplace in hot soapy water—she didn't use soda—and he had to dry the dishes. At first he hadn't liked that; it was only women who dried dishes. He had never told his da or any of them at home that he had dried dishes, for in a way it would have taken some of the highlights out of his position.

When he was ready to go she walked to the gate with him, and there she said, "The tide'll be over the bank about ten. What time are you going?"

"I don't know for sure. I'll be knockin' about from dark."

"You can't knock about without people seeing you, and you know who I mean."

"I can. I'm good at hidin'."

"You might have been, but you're not as small as you were. You're sprouting."

"Aye," he said; "I am, but . . . but I'll be all right. I'll see you in the mornin', an' I'll be on time." He now did an odd thing, at least he thought so, for he put his hand out and touched hers. It was the first gesture he had ever dared to make to her, not that he hadn't felt inclined to do so before this moment. Her other hand came on the top of his and pressed it tight and she said, "I'm worried for you."

"I'll be all right. I know I will." He grinned, adding, "I'm lucky. Didn't you give me a job and learn me to read and write a bit; I'm lucky I tell you."

She said nothing more but pushed him from her, and he went down the road feeling very odd as if he didn't want to leave her.

But he hadn't gone more than twenty yards or so when he heard her voice calling, "Freddie! Freddie! Wait a minute."

She came running towards him panting, "Listen!" she said rapidly. "If you promise to stick to your reading and writing and learn your figures I'll take you into the office and your brother can have your job. What do you say?"

"Eeh! you would?"

"Yes, I would; but it will mean you spending most of your evenings for some months to come sticking to your books."

"I'll do it. I'll do it. And I can tell him?"

"Yes, yes, you may tell him. But it all depends on you."

"Oh, ta. Ta, miss. Eeh! What did I tell you, miss, I'm lucky. We're all lucky."

He turned from her and raced along the pathway. He ran until he reached the top of the cinder bank. He ran the whole length of the Low Lights, then along the shore, past the row of cottages, up the steps, along the pathway and into the house. And, standing gasping, he looked around him.

They were all there. His ma and da; Nell who came in to do shoppin' because it was Friday night, and with the sweat still on her hair from the salt pans; John who was home early because the strike had started; Nancy, bright-faced, smiling kindly as usual; plain little Jessie; and Lily. They were all there and all had their eyes on him. It was his da who said, "What's up, lad? You look as if you've lost a tanner and found a sovereign?"

"As good as, Da, as good as." He went straight up to John now, saying, "You always said you wanted to get out of the pit, didn't you?"

"What you at? I'm out of the pit, we're on strike."

"But for good, I mean, for good."

"What d'you mean?" John's voice was dull; his whole attitude was dull.

"Well"—he turned now and looked at his da and then at his ma and he kept his eyes on her as he said, "The miss just said if I stick to me books and learn to reckon an' write I can go into her office and she'll give John here me job."

There was silence in the room for a moment, then a complete clamour.

"Eeh! God above! that is news. I've just said to John there, 'Don't worry, lad, when a door closes another one opens.'"

"How wonderful, John! You've always wanted to work in the open air. Remember the Methodist minister last Sunday night, God always answers prayers."

John didn't reply to Nancy but, looking at his small brother, he said, "You know what you are, you're a marler."

"Aye, I suppose I am a bit of a marler. I said to the miss I'm lucky. Don't you think I'm lucky, Ma?"

They all turned excitedly and looked at Jinny for her confirmation, but her reply came out flatly: "There's luck and luck," she said; "some kinds of luck has got to be paid for."

"Aw! woman, what d'you mean by that? Don't be a wet blanket. It's the best news that's come into this house for years. First, the youngster here being started with a woman like Miss Hewitt." Freddie had noted for some time that his employer was no longer addressed as Maggie. And his da went on, "And now the promise of gettin' John out of that hell-hole. Aw! lass, what's the matter with you? Be happy for them."

"Do you think she wants a housekeeper?" It was Nell now laughingly asking the question, and Freddie answered, "It's a pity, Nell, but I doubt it. I can't do anythin' for you in that line 'cos she's a good cook. She makes. . . ." His voice trailed off because his mother had turned her back on them and was now walking into the bedroom. John had nudged Freddie with his elbow, then jerked his head in the direction his ma had taken. And Freddie slowly left them and followed her.

She was standing near the window looking out into the deepening twilight, and he tugged her skirt, saying, "What is it, Ma? I've upset you, but I didn't mean to. All I want to do is to please you, to ease things. Why . . . why don't you cotton on to me workin' for the miss?"

She turned and looked down on him, then quickly she dropped on to her hunkers and, putting her arms about him, she pulled him into her embrace.

Never in his whole life, even when he was small, could he remember her hugging him like this. Her body was shaking. And when he looked into her face he saw that her eyes were moist and her voice was thick as she said, "I'm a silly woman. I . . . I suppose I'm jealous; I don't want to lose you."

"What! Ma. You lose me? Aw, don't be daft, Ma; you couldn't lose me if you tried."

"You seem to like her very much."

He paused for a moment before he said, "She's very lonely, Ma. Her da was drownded and the young man she was goin' to marry was drownded in the same boat along of him. She yells and shouts on the quay and bosses people about and even some of the men are frightened of her, but she's not like that, she's got nobody and she's old."

She took her fingers and combed his hair with them back from his brow, smiling now as she said, "She's not old. Am I old?"

"No; not really."

"Not really?"

"Well, I mean . . . you know what I mean. But she's a lot older than you."

"She isn't, she can't be fifty."

87

"Well, that's old, Ma."

"Yes, I suppose it is, to a twelve-year-old that's old."

"Ma."

"Yes, son?"

"Try to like her, will you, 'cos she needs people to like her. I don't think anybody visits there at all. Well, nobody comes in the daytime except to deliver the groceries an' that. An' you know somethin', Ma?" He hunched his shoulders. "Peabody tried to sting her on one of the bills. They charged her tuppence a pound extra for the butter. But she was on to them. She wrote them a letter saying she was going to move her custom. And you know, she deals with Aynsley. Well, he got it in the neck an' all 'cos she paid for the best stewing steak and they sent her tough meat. She kept it till the next day and when the lad came she sent it back with another letter. There's no flies on her, Ma. You know something? I . . . I didn't know whether I'd like her at first when I went there. I even thought I'd go back to the butcher's."

"You never did!"

"Oh, aye, I did, 'cos she didn't only make me wash me hands, she made me scrub them."

"Right too."

"And you know something else she made me do and she still makes me do it? I don't like it but I've got to do it. You won't laugh, Ma, will you?"

"No, I won't laugh."

He knew that he had her smiling already. And so he played on it, and he wagged his head a bit and looked downwards before he said, "She makes me dry up the dishes."

He lifted his head. Her face was stretching. She said, "Never! Dry up the dishes? She made you dry up the dishes? I've never been able to make you dry up the dishes."

"I know, and . . . an' I refused at first."

"You didn't!"

"I did."

"What did you say?"

He looked away, then bit on his lip before he answered her. "Well, she put it like this, Ma. If I didn't help to dry up the dishes she wouldn't wash me plate and each day she'd put the same food on it until I decided that I would do me share of the chores. That's what she calls them, the chores."

"She's a funny woman."

"Aye, Ma, she is; but . . . but she's kind an' she's . . . well, I don't know a word for it except sort of lost like."

She was holding his face between her two big rough hands now and her voice was a whisper as she said, "I love all me bairns, but you were always special. But mind"—her voice and expression changed—"I'll break your neck if you ever take advantage of what I'm sayin', or repeat it, d'you hear, Freddie Musgrave?"

"Aye. Aye, I hear Mrs Musgrave."

They fell together for a moment and if he could have expressed his feelings in words he would have said he was experiencing a moment of ecstasy.

A moment later she opened the door into the kitchen and pushed him in, saying loudly now, "This one's gettin' too big for his boots; he's tryin' to run this family. He's just told me it's about time I packed up; I'm about ready for me chair at the side of the fireplace."

There was laughter in the kitchen; everybody seemed happy. And so it remained until eight o'clock, when the two children were in bed and the candles were lit and his ma and da and brother and sister were preparing to sit round the fire and listen to his crack, for then he surprised them by saying, "I've got to go out, but I won't be long."

His father pulled himself on to the mat in order to be nearer to him and, putting out his hand and gripping his shoulder, he said, "I thought you were finished with that?"

"This'll be the last time, Da, the very last time."

"Is it the faggot man?"

He looked at his mother. "Aye, Ma."

"Something big?"

"I don't think so, just an errand."

"I don't like it, lad."

He was looking at his father again. "It'll be all right, Da. I'll be back straightaway, 'cos I'll have to make use of the slack tide. . . . Ta-ra!"

The farewell was divided among them all, but as he went out of the door he was aware that no one moved to see him off, and, too, that there was no warning from his mother to be careful, nor did John say he'd come with him to look at the full moon, 'cos it would be that tonight.

He did not make his way straight down to the quay; there was plenty of time. His usual procedure before going on a run was to mingle with one or another set of lads, for he knew most of those that frequented the quayside in their spare time which was mostly late at night. One of the things they got up to was teasing Granny Brimstone's dog. It was chained up, and the lads would throw bones out of its reach and the poor thing would go wild, and the old woman would come out screaming blue murder at them.

If there was plenty of time he might join those who were doing the tin walk along the fancy houses at the top of the hill. The tin walk was exactly what it said, two holes were bored in the tin, some ropes slotted through and you stood on them pulling the ropes tight to keep them on your feet; then you clattered up a street. When there was a dozen or so of you and you walked on the flags, like some of the houses had up there for paving stones, the clatter that twenty odd tins made, especially if they did a sort of jig, was quite something. He had once had a chamber pot emptied over his head, and so he tended to avoid the tin walk, if possible. But it was well to be seen playing about; and then it was easy to slip away to the appointed place.

But what was the appointed place the night? He didn't know. He only knew he'd have to be near Northumberland's wharf. Some people called it Hall's wharf because it was owned by a woman. She was the wharfinger. He had never before been told to stick near this particular wharf; and so he decided to stay a good way off and keep an eye on it. There were men still working on the quay and their flares and lanterns would show up anyone coming along.

He took a position in the shadow of a bloater smoking hut, and, his hands in his breeches pocket, he leant against the tarred wood and prepared himself to wait. He guessed he wouldn't be contacted for another half hour because the water was not quite slack yet, and they knew he couldn't cross on a running tide. So when a voice came to the side of him, saying, "You're in good time, that's right," he would have sprung up from the shadow, except for the hand gripping his shoulder. He had recognised the voice as that of the faggot man, but when he turned to look at him he appeared different. He knew him as the gent who always rode into town on horseback and was always well dressed in knee breeches and polished leather gaiters. But here, he could just make out a man looking like any other workman along the quay, even to his cap which was pulled down over his brow almost to his eyes. But he could see his eyes all right because they seemed to glint.

"Now listen to me, little 'un, and this is important. You scoot across now. Now! you understand?"

Before the man got any further Freddie said, "I can't. Why, I can't! River's still runnin'. It'd take me out to sea."

The next minute he felt himself being shaken almost like a terrier shakes a rat, his teeth seeming to come free in his head.

"Listen to me! things are not as they appear tonight, quiet like. There'll be a lot of movement once the tide has covered the bar. Now it's your business to get across before that. Understand? It's important, very important that you do. Is that clear?"

Freddie made no answer, for the man was now holding something before his face. It was a packet not more than three inches long and an inch or so wide, and it seemed to be wrapped in some shiny material, too shiny for calf's skin.

"You have a pocket, haven't you, inside your breeks?"

"Aye."

"Well, let me see you put it in."

He undid the buckle of his narrow belt, unbuttoned the flap; then, taking the small parcel from the man's hand, he pushed it down inside his trousers.

"How deep is your pocket?"

"Deep enough."

"Is there a button on it?"

"N'no; but I've n'never lost n'nowt yet from it." He couldn't stop stammering; he sensed something different; he was frightened.

"Well, you can pray to God that you don't lose this. Now listen. When you climb the other side, don't take your usual route up through the town. That's the way you usually go, isn't it?"

"Aye; m'most times."

"Well, not tonight; for as soon as you reach the top bank turn to your right. There's a row of boathouses along there and the road leads up to Cookson's Wharf. Now, you'll see a man on horseback; more likely he'll be standing by his horse. You know who it is, don't you?"

He said nothing.

"Well, you'll give him the package. . . . That's all. It's as easy as that."

He dared to say now, "Well, if it's as easy as that why don't you take it across, or one of your men?"

"Do you want your ears rung or your lip busted just for a start?"

For all the man's big talk, Freddie realised it wasn't this man he was afraid of: he seemed no different at this moment from any man, any workman in the town, and so he said, "What do I get for it?"

The man thrust his hand into his pocket and placed a coin on Freddie's outstretched palm. And now as he peered at it, Freddie said, "This is only a tanner; I never get less than a bob. Now you know that, even half a dollar."

"Well, that's all you're getting now, at least from me, because you'll be well paid at the other end. Now, scat!"

"If I go now I'll get wet, sodden; an' I'll likely drift."

"I'll be watching you, and I'll give you one minute to reach the quay and if you're not in that skip of yours by then I'll come down there and hold you under just long enough for you to get wet all over. Now what d'you say?"

He said nothing but he walked away from the man, he didn't run, he just walked. Inside he was now feeling defiant. He had the strange wish that the miss would suddenly appear on the shore and say, "That's enough. You're not going."

When he climbed into his sculler and pushed off into the river he noticed, in the moonlight, there was another but bigger sculler bobbing in the water further along the beach and two or three men standing on the shore. They seemed to be messing about with nets, and his mind asked him why they should want nets in a little sculler like that? Of a sudden the night became dark, the pale moon was obscured by a black cloud and for a moment he seemed lost as to his direction; and when his paddle hit a mound of sand he really experienced a surge of fear. He could evade the sandbanks by daylight but in the blackness it was a different thing, especially if you didn't carry a lantern. Swinging his thin body from side to side, he paddled furiously towards where he could make out the lights on the South shore.

The moon suddenly escaping from the black cloud, he saw he was more than half-way across; he also heard above the rush of the water a muffled shout. He turned his head and looked back; and, there, he made out two men in a sculler and they were rowing furiously, and like the rush of the outflowing tide over the sandbanks it came to him why.

The swell now lifted him to the outer row of hiring keels and he grabbed at them and pulled himself along to the steps, and a ring where he could tie up. Only habit made certain his sculler was secure before he scrambled up onto the dockside; but he didn't hesitate once his feet touched it and, following the faggot man's directions, he ran as fast as his gasping breath would allow past the boathouses and towards the figure of the man and the bulk of the horse standing waiting for him.

He almost threw himself against Roderick Gallagher's legs, spluttering, "They're comin'! they know. Two in a boat just ahind me."

As he pointed along the dark road the man swung himself up into the saddle and seemingly in one movement he gripped the back of Freddie's coat, and the boy thought he was going to choke as his narrow collar clamped tight around his windpipe. Then his body jerked and it seemed that he would be bounced from the horse's back onto the road; but the man's arm came about him and his voice yelled in his ear, "Straddle your legs and hold on to the pommel." He leant forward and gripped something. It was handfuls of horsehair.

All the bones in his body appeared to be rattling. It was like a continuation of when the faggot man had shaken him. He didn't know which part of the town they were riding through because the moon had gone in again. But when it reappeared, he had time to realise they were just passing out of Westoe; then that they weren't taking the usual road to his house. He was aware, too, of the man cursing before drawing the horse to a skidding stop to listen. He too listened; but for some seconds he could only hear the gasping of his own breath; but then, like the man, he made out the sound of horses hooves in the distance. . . . Yet those men in the sculler didn't have horses.

He noted that they were now going along a narrow path one side of which was covered with brushwood and thicket. The next second he was gasping and he thrust out his hands in protest as the man gripped his collar again, crying, "I'll come back for you. Lie low!" and he knew he was actually flying through the air and into blackness. But for how long he wouldn't have known.

When he came round he lay still listening, thinking he

would hear the riders passing. He was lying on his side and wondered why the moonlight was dappled on his hands; then realised he was lying amidst greenery.

Slowly he put his hand out and felt down the length of his body. Part of it was lying on soft ground, but the side of his leg was against a stone, and when he touched it he winced. Oh God, what if it was broken. He immediately conjured up a picture of his father dragging himself from the low bed, and with it his foot jerked and he let out a slow, slow breath. Next he felt his face. The side of it seemed wet. He brought his hand before his eyes and shivered as he saw blood on it. Tentatively now, he felt the back of his head: his hair there was wet too, sticky. . . . He'd cracked his head. That man could have killed him. Perhaps that's what he'd wanted to do. But he groped in his mind for something. Then he remembered: he said he was coming back for him. And yes, of course he would come back for him because he still had the parcel on him. The thought brought his hand down his trousers and into the pocket. "Eeh!" The exclamation was loud. It was busted.

Slowly he pulled the packet out of his pocket, and as his fingers came in contact with the loose powder the word "Eeh!" escaped him again, and, pulling himself into a sitting position, he looked at it.

The wrapping, whatever it was made of, was split. The inner wrapping which he saw was silk, that too was split. But what he noticed rightaway was there were two separate little packages: besides the one with white powder there was one holding brown powder. He moved his finger in the white powder and was amazed to feel pieces of glass. Dusting the powder slightly aside he saw the pieces of glass. And when he did the same with the brown powder, the pieces of glass he saw were red.

At first he thought of them as glass because his mind wasn't working properly. But of a sudden it seemed to spring back to life and he thought, God Almighty! These are jewels.

He knew traffic went on in jewellery, but he understood it was just the Newcastle lot who got up to that lark because it was so dangerous. Ten years or more you could get, he understood, if these were found on you. And this is what he had been carrying! He had thought it was just powder which was really a drug. Why people risked their necks for drugs he couldn't understand because you could go to the dispensary in the town and buy all kinds of drugs and have them made up into medicine. They were all arrayed in coloured bottles around the shop. Some of the bottles were more than a foot high and quite bonny. The lids were like helmets with points on. But this man's powder had been just a sort of package for stones, like these. Eeh! Dear God! He wished he would come and take them and let him get back home.

He was feeling dizzy again. He'd better wrap these up as best he could and put them back in his pocket.

He had just accomplished this when a bout of tiredness, as he thought of it, overtook him, and as the moon disappeared once more he slipped back into sleep. . . .

When he next woke he was so stiff he could hardly move. His head was aching and his hip was sore. With an effort he pulled himself to his feet. His head was just above the brushwood in which he had been lying and there, just a few feet away was a narrow road. He turned about, to see that the brushwood stretched away into the distance to some houses and his muzzy thinking told him to make for them. But when he attempted to walk he almost cried out with the pain in his hip, and so, dropping on to his knees, he crawled further into the brushwood.

He had gone about ten yards when he was brought to a surprising halt, for there before him was a shallow gully with a rivulet of water running along it. As if he were in a desert and had found water he slipped down the side of the gulley and, kneeling down, he splashed his face and hair with the water. And as he did so his tongue lapped it, and it tasted cool and fresh. He guessed it was from a spring.

The blood cleared from his hair, his fingers searched for a cut, but he could feel only grazed skin, and he wondered why, if that was the cause, he should be feeling as odd as he was?

You could take your trousers off and look at your leg.

As if obeying a voice that sounded like that of the miss he first took off his boots, then carefully slipped off his trousers, lifted up the tail of his rough shirt and saw that his leg was whole but black and blue from the hip down to the side of the knee.

He was lucky, he told himself, he had just hit the side of that stone. If he had landed full on it he could have broken his hip, or his back. The thought made him shudder: he was always careful about his legs, fearful lest he got a knock. That's why he

95

rarely went barefooted if he could help it; Sandy Ramshaw had lost a foot after he had trodden on a broken bottle.

As he lowered his bruised leg into the water he gave a sigh as if of pleasure, but he crawled up onto the bank again and, bare from the waist down, he lay there until the sun dried his skin; then he put his trousers on and, lying flat on his back, he looked up into the sky. He wasn't hungry, he was just tired; but he mustn't go to sleep again. If only that man would come and take his package, he could then get home. There came into his mind a picture of home; but again it wasn't the kitchen with his father sitting propped up against the wall and Lily and Jessie on the mat, his mother at the table and Nancy sitting beside their father making bobbing lace, while John, worn out with work, dozed in the chair; no; it was the kitchen with the iron range and the table with the white cloth on it and the delph rack holding all the blue china, and the brass helmet coal scuttle that stood between the fender and the sink, and the pump that splashed water into the sink. The last picture in his mind was of the miss cutting the crust of the meat pie last night. . . .

What was the matter with him? He blinked his eyes and stared up into the darkening sky. It was just a minute since that he had been looking up and the sun had been on his face. He couldn't have been asleep all this time. What was the matter with him? Had something gone wrong in his head? He pulled his stiff slight frame upwards. Had the man been looking for him? Eeh! he'd have to get up and get to the house before it got too dark and he wouldn't be able to see his way out of this.

When he got to his feet he buttoned his jacket up because now he was feeling chilly; then he put his hand to his head as though to straighten his cap, and remembered feeling his head and finding the blood. He hadn't the cap. Then he remembered the stone. He must have left it there.

Standing up now, he limped his way back through the brushwood to where he could see the road. And he congratulated himself on his sense of direction because there was the stone and the place where he had lain, and he knew it to be the same place because there was some blood on the stone. That must have come off his hand. But his cap wasn't lying anywhere about. Somebody had got his cap.

He stepped onto the road and as he did so he told himself that he didn't know where this led to, so the best thing to do was to go back to where it branched off and take the road he knew. This he did; and he met no one, not on this branch which wasn't much more than a path, nor on the road that led to The Towers.

He went up the drive, past the front of the house and into the courtyard.

When he knocked on the kitchen door it was opened by the maid he remembered from time back with the pock marks and the wobbly eye and what she said was, "My God, it's you. Come on! Come on! Come on away in!" She pulled him into the kitchen and, looking towards her mother, she cried, "He's here!"

Betty Wheatley stared at him for a moment, then as if he had just left the house earlier on that day or perhaps the day before, she said, "Where on earth have you been, lad?"

"I hit me head. I must have fell asleep. He . . . he threw me into a thicket."

"Did anybody see you come? What I mean is, did you see anybody on the road?"

"No, not a soul. I was in a sort of field. I didn't know me way from there and so I came onto the proper road."

Betty turned to her daughter, saying, "Go and tell your da to tell him."

"Me da's had enough of him for one day; I'll take him in. Anyway, Da's on the look out: you never know when we'll have another visit, they won't let up. As me da says, they've got their teeth in now and they won't let go. Where's it all gona end?"

She didn't wait for an answer but, grabbing Freddie's sleeve, she said, "Come along with you!" then, "What's the matter? You've hurt your leg?"

"Aye. When he tossed me I fell onto a stone."

"It's a wonder you didn't break your neck."

He followed her across the hall and up a corridor; but before she reached the end of it she stopped and, turning, whispered, "Don't aggravate him by answering back. If I remember owt about you, you've got a ready tongue an' it won't have bettered with time. Now do as I say an' don't answer him back."

He didn't want to answer him or anybody else back; he just wanted to hand over the parcel and get himself away from this house and everybody in it.

Connie didn't knock on the door but pushed it open, saying loudly, "He's here!"

Roderick Gallagher sprang up from the chair he had been sitting in and in his haste he almost toppled over a table on which there was a decanter, a glass, and a long pipe and two blue stone jars.

Steadying the table with one hand, he watched Freddie limp towards him. And when the boy stopped by a chair at the other side of the fireplace he spoke, saying below his breath but almost in a growl, "Where the hell do you think you've been?"

"I . . . I was lying in the thicket."

"Don't tell me bloody lies. I went to the thicket. What's this!" He bent over, reached out and picked up the cap from the hearth. "I was about to burn it. You forgot it, didn't you?"

"I kept fallin' asleep an' . . . and I felt funny. I was gona try to reach a house, so I crept back an' . . . and I came to a stream, a little stream, and I bathed me head an' me leg." Now his voice dared to rise a little as he said, "You could have knocked me out; you did for a time. I hit some stones when I fell and after that I . . . I kept fallin' asleep. Me leg's all black an' blue, an' me head's cut." He pointed first to his side and then to his head.

"Where's the package you were given?"

"It's in me pocket here."

"Well, let me have it. Come here!"

Freddie took two steps towards the man, undid his belt and the flap of his trousers, and as he put his hand down to his pocket he said, "It got bust on the stone when I fell."

"Bust? What do you mean, bust?"

"Well, it split."

"And it spilt?"

"Oh, no, no; it just split. I put me hand in to see if it was all right and I felt it split."

He drew out the package and placed it on the outstretched palm; then he watched the man look at it for a moment before moving his fingers in the white powder, and then in the brown. "You knew what you were carrying, did you?"

He told himself he had to be careful here, so he said, "Aye, powder, a kind of drug. I've carried it for you afore."

"Have you looked into this powder?"

Freddie looked towards the palm now and shook his head, saying, "No; I told you I was too tired to bother. As long as it was all right and the powder hadn't spilt. I was careful when I pulled it out and put it back again."

98

He now looked towards the fire. The room was very hot; he felt he could fall asleep again at any minute. He said, "Please . . . please can I sit down?"

He shrank back a little as the hands came out towards him, and felt surprise as he was lifted from the floor and placed in the big leather chair. Then a glass was being held to his mouth and the man was saying, "Drink that. Sup it all up."

He knew what rum tasted like, and ale, he'd had drops on the sly, but this was different, and when he screwed his face up and coughed the man said, "It's a pity, but you'll never acquire a taste for fine French brandy."

He sipped at the glass again. He liked it, and it seemed to take the tiredness away.

The man was sitting opposite to him now and he was saying, "You kept your word. Do you remember the last conversation we had in this room?"

"Yes, sir." He remembered that too: he had always to address him as sir.

"This is the first time we've met since that night; there's been a go-between at other times, hasn't there?"

When he didn't answer the man said, "Too many cooks spoil the broth, and go-betweens get greedy. You were never greedy. What did Freeman give you?"

"Sixpence."

The man put back his head and looked up towards the ceiling saying, "Good God!" and the gesture brought back the time when he had watched him do that before. Then he was looking at him again and saying in quite an ordinary tone, "I hate that fellow, you know. I hate meanness, but I'll fix him before he's finished. He's got enough stored away to fill Jingling Geordie's Hole. You know the hole?"

"Yes, the one above the short sands, near the castle. They say the Romans made it."

"They say more than their prayers and they whistle them; they've got no authority for that, no more than they have for the subterranean passage that was supposed to run from there under the Tyne all the way to Jarrow so that the monks could trot through to visit their kin on the other side. But anyway, who knows, they were merely men with men's wants and women are always ready and waiting; no need for enticing. How old are you now, boy?"

"Twelve, sir."

"Oh well, it'll soon be on you."

He didn't know what would soon be on him, but again he was feeling sleepy and the man's voice became a drone in his ears. He was talking about the money that was being spent on Lord Collingwood's monument that was to be erected next year. Something about it standing on a fifty foot pedestal. Now he was on about the black middens below the Spanish Battery. Now he was talking about South Shields and the hard sands.

His eyes were closing and he seemed to be on the point of sleep with the voice saying, "That bloody lot in Newcastle sucking the river dry. But their time's running out, did they but know it."

Then he was shot into wakefulness by the bursting open of the door and Mrs Wheatley's voice crying, "Frank's just signalled. They're here again."

He was dragged from the chair as the man swung him round towards the woman, saying harshly, "Get rid of him."

"Where? But where?"

"Anywhere."

"That's a daft answer."

"Yes, I suppose it is, but where?" The man was now beating his fist against his brow. "He can't go outside: he's been concussed; he'll fall asleep in the yard. Put him in the cupboard in the kitchen."

"Oh, talk sense!"

Fancy her talking like that to him. But she still went on: "The cupboard in the kitchen after they prised the floorboards up in the attic!"

"The attic." He was wagging his finger wildly at her now. "The cubby hole."

He wasn't fully awake but wide enough to listen and to see a look almost of fear on the woman's face as she stammered now, saying, "You've always said. . . ."

"Yes, I know: I wouldn't put a dog in there. But woman! what'll happen if they come in and find him?" And saying this, he thrust his fist now into Freddie's chest, causing the boy to stumble against the edge of the chair and to sit down; but only momentarily before he was whipped up again.

"Put him in there; it's the only place. God, damn it! he'll be the death of me yet, this one. Take him, quick!"

Holding a candle in one hand, the woman was now dragging him along the corridor with the other; then up the stairs; across the wide landing; up another flight and onto a bare landing; and from there into a carpetless room.

In the flickering light of the candle he saw that the room, except for a few trunks, was entirely bare. There was an iron fireplace built into one wall with a high grate and a small mantelshelf above it, and there was a window to the side. But there was only one other door in the room, and this she wrenched open and thrust him into what he imagined must be a broom cupboard. The miss had a cupboard like this where she kept her brooms, buckets and cleaning things. And there was a brush in here and a bucket and what looked like rough dish clothes hanging from a peg.

Holding the candle high, she put her free arm upwards and pressed her hand against the low ceiling. And now his eyes nearly popped out of his head as the whole wall of the cupboard slid away and there showed up before him a weird room. Even in the poor light of the candle he knew it was weird. But what was more weird still was the movement in the far corner of it.

He was shaking visibly as he watched her pressing something in what looked like a mattress stuck to the wall while the door slid into position again.

When, his voice a whimper now, he said, "Missis," she said, "It's all right, lad, it's all right. You'll come to no harm in here. And she won't hurt you, poor mite."

His eyes were stretched wide, his mouth agape as he stared in amazement down on the child sitting on what looked like a half single mattress in the narrow slit of, he couldn't call it a room, just this place.

Again the woman was speaking to him. She had her arm round his shoulder and she was pointing to the child, saying, "You remember the baby? He . . . he wanted to do away with it. Well, he . . . he thinks it's gone, but . . . but we couldn't. Connie defied him on the side like. He doesn't know she's here. He'd murder the lot of us if he did. We're at our wits end. We don't know what to do with her. It's keepin' her clean an' fed, that's the trouble."

He muttered now, "What's . . . what's this place?"

"It's what we call the cubby hole. He's frightened of it, the master; he'll never come near it. You see he used to be pushed in here when he was a young lad. I think it's gone a long way to make him turn out as he has. It was his father. You see, his grandfather built this place specially, I mean the whole house, he was a master builder, and he built this special room on with his own hands so he could put his wife in when she had one of her turns. He wouldn't have her put away to an asylum. You see there's no sound can get out; these are all hair mattresses." She put her hand out and tapped the padded wall. "An' behind them is another layer of padding. The grandmother didn't last all that long but I think the master's father was given a taste of this room himself; then he passed it on to his son. Give the master his due, he always said he wouldn't put a dog in here. So the child's been safe so far. But God only knows what would happen if he found out. I tell you he'd murder the lot of us, 'cos he still has nightmares about her, the mother. You remember? He can't get over the fact that she made a cuckold of him."

His breath was catching in his throat. He was still staring at the child who looked like an inanimate doll except for the rapid blinking of her eyelids in the candlelight.

"Is . . . is she left in the dark?"

"God forgive us! Aye. We've got to leave her in the dark most of the time. We can only take her out when we know that the road'll be clear for a few hours."

"Tis terrible. Tis cruel." His voice was high.

"I know that, lad. I know that, but what would you have us do? Bury her as he ordered? When Frank refused to do it he was for taking her down to the river himself, but Connie stepped in. She would bury her, she said. And that's what she did, supposedly. Oh, what a to-do it was, but our Connie's got more spunk than her da. But as I said, she's grown, and what we're gona do with her now, God alone knows. Anyway, this time I'll leave the candle for I must go down else that lot'll be trying to find me."

"How . . . how long will you be?"

"Not long. He'll want you downstairs and out as soon as the coast's clear."

"How d'you . . . how d'you get out without anybody seein' you?"

She pointed to the top of the padded wall to the side of the door, and she said, "When anybody puts their foot on the outside landing that gives a tinkle. As for air, up there." She pointed to the high padded ceiling. "There's a vent that lets into the chimney, and it's a tall one, and if any noise got through it just sounded like the rooks in the trees beyond."

"He thought of everything, that man, didn't he? But what use was a bell inside here?"

"Well, I understand that the sound stopped her thrashing about, at least so I was told; it sort of calmed her for a little while. But it wasn't all that effective because he told me"—she now thumbed towards the floor—"that he saw his grandfather come out at one time with his ear almost hanging off. Oh, he's to be pitied, for the only pleasure he seems to get in life now is cheating the customs. I daren't think of the times he's risked his neck. But they'll have him one of these days. An' you, lad, have nearly been the means of it. An' here's another time."

"If they catch you going out what'll you say?"

"Once I'm in the cupboard I can hear a mouse on those stairs, and if they were to come into the room then I'm at the old trunk in the corner taking out some of the mistress's clothes for cutting up. But don't worry about me, lad, only sit quiet, talk to her. She understands. She can say some words."

"What . . . what d'you call her?"

"Belle. Just Belle."

As she pressed the spring in the mattress he turned in panic to her, saying, "You'll come . . . you'll come back quick, won't you. Eeh! Look, I . . . I can't stay in here."

"Now, now, lad; steady on. Of course I'll come back, but if I didn't, laddie, all you've got to do is to press the spring and the door will open. So there's nothin' to worry about. But talk to the bairn, comfort her, 'cos she's not barmy or daft."

Nevertheless, in spite of her words he almost yelled out when he watched the panel glide back as if it was on oiled hinges, then slip into place again and causing the candle light to flutter just the slightest.

He stood as if transfixed staring down at the child; then he looked about him. He hadn't far to look. The place was about eight feet long and five feet wide. The only articles in it were the mattress, an enamel chamber pot, a bucket and a tiny low table on which the candlestick rested.

His nose was wrinkled against the smell, but the air though heavy was breathable. He looked around the mattress-padded walls and, reaching out, he tried to put his fingers in between two of them, but they were so firmly packed he doubted he could insert even a finger nail. Then he looked at the thing in the corner again. He couldn't yet put the name child to it. There were two dark blots in a small round face, the whiteness emphasised by the blackness of the hair surrounding it. The child was sitting motionless like a dummy; the black orbs seemed fixed on him. She had said, comfort it. How? How was he to comfort it? He was afraid of it, scared to touch it: as yet it still wasn't really a bairn, even though his mind told him it was the baby who had been lying in the wash basket the morning he had left this house all that time ago. But he still couldn't move towards it.

Then the child made a sound. It wasn't like ma or da but more like caw, like the sound a seagull made. Then she said it again, loud and clear this time; and now he recognised it as Con. The servant's name was Connie.

When she held out her arms he very slowly dropped onto his knees by the side of the mattress pad, and the next minute he found himself hugged to the small body. At first the feeling made him shudder; then to save them both falling sideways he put one arm about her while supporting himself against the floor with the other. Now the small face was close to his, the tongue on his cheek as if kissing it or sucking at it. He heard himself say, "There, there. There, there." Then like a small animal burrowing into the flesh of its mother she snuggled her head into his neck and put her thin legs around the side of his waist, and then she became utterly quiet.

Oh, Ma. Ma. He found himself repeating the cry in his mind. He wished he was home: he wanted his ma to put her arms about him, as she had done in the bedroom last night. Running was one thing; he wasn't really afeared of running, it was exciting in a way; but . . . but this was different, he was afeared now. And this poor bairn. How long would they be able to keep it in this place? It would go mad here, like the woman who was its great-grandmother. It wasn't right. No it wasn't. He should be brought up before the justices. But . . . but then he didn't know anything about it; he thought it was dead. Well, it would have been better dead. But what when he found out, would he still kill it?

What was he to do?

Mind his own business.

He couldn't mind his own business; he wouldn't be able to sleep at night for thinking of this bairn in here.

He looked towards the candle. It was half down. He wished she would hurry up and get back. Yet she said he could get out when he wanted. Well, he wanted to now, the sooner the better. He went to unloosen the child's arms from around his neck but it clung to him. He had a picture of the day when the men had flung the cat over the dockside with a piece of wood attached to its neck so it wouldn't drown straightaway. He could see its claws coming up and grappling with the wood which pressed it under the water. The men had laughed; all but Joe Armstrong, and he had knocked Bill Storridge into the water in the battle royal that followed. And Bill Storridge couldn't swim. But he had been the one who had thrown the cat in. Joe Armstrong had hauled the cat out but wouldn't give a hand to Bill Storridge, and Bill Storridge's blokes had fought Joe Armstrong's. They were always two warring factions working at either end of the quay, hitting out whenever they came together, mostly in the bars.

She was like the cat, she was still clinging tightly to him. But she was no weight; Lily, he imagined, could make four of her. He pulled himself to his feet, asking how long he had been in here. Well, he had been in here for as long as it took a candle to nearly burn itself out, and he just couldn't be in here in the dark.

Oh no, by God! not that. Oh no! not in this place in the dark because he, too, would start yelling out. And anyway in black dark he would go round in circles and he wouldn't find that spring.

He made for it, reached up and, his fingers on it, he hesitated and looked back towards the low table and the candle about to gutter. Then screwing up his eyes, he pushed his finger on the button. When the mattress slid quietly past him, he remained standing where he was for a moment. His first reaction was to tear the child from him and push it back into the room, but he couldn't do it, he couldn't push it back into the blackness where it must have lived for most of its life.

He was in the cupboard now, and he didn't stop to put up his hand and press the door back but thrust open the cupboard door and stepped into the comparative light from the starlit sky coming through the one small window in the room.

He stood gasping and hardly able to breathe for the child's

boney arms were constricting his gullet. Its face was still hidden in his shoulder, but he said to it, "It's all right. It's all right," and it was as if he was comforting himself for being out of that hole. Eeh! Dear God! He couldn't believe this was happening to him. They wouldn't believe it at home; they would say he was stretching it. But when they saw the bairn.... He almost sprang from the room onto the landing. What was he talkin' about? It was them downstairs that would have to have the bairn. And he would tell them they hadn't to put it back in that hole else he would split on them. Aye, he would. By God! he would an' all.

He had the opportunity of telling them this in the next minute or so when he stepped off the bottom stair into the hall for, there, Betty Wheatley and Connie were both hurrying from the kitchen doorway, and they both stopped dead in their tracks when they saw him. But before he could speak Betty had reacted and rushed forward, crying, "You should have left her there, lad. What's up with you? He could be in at any minute. Oh God! in heaven, what now? Here, give it to me!"

When she went to pull the child from Freddie's arms the baby gave a high piercing cry, and Connie, putting her hand across her mouth, said, "Eeh! Ma! God Almighty! Did you hear that? That's the first time she's yelped out. Ma! Ma!" Connie was pulling at her mother's arm now. "It could be a way, a way out. Let him take her. She'd ... she'd be safe across there an' lost among the lot of them. We could send somethin' now and again."

"No, no; you can't; me ma's got a job to keep goin' as it is." He was yelling now.

"Well, don't let's stand here. If he bursts in that door we'll all be done for." Betty was pushing him now none too gently through the green baized door, along the corridor and into the kitchen now where her husband exclaimed on an oath, "Christ Almighty! Are you mad, woman? Why did you let him?"

"I didn't let him. Where is he?"

"He's ... he's ridden over to Doctor Black's, likely to see what's happened there. But he expects to go visiting somewhere else because he told me to get the cart ready. I've got Prince in the shafts."

"Where's he for?"

"You ask me. I don't know. But wherever it is it's too far to

106

take Jumbo because he's been riding him on and off all day. But what's up with you woman? Do you want us all murdered?"

"I've thought of somethin'. Let the lad take it across the water."

"Don't be so soft." There was scorn in his voice. "How is a lad like that to account for a bairn in arms? The authorities would be on to it."

"Not if he took it into his house. They all live like rats."

"No, we don't. We don't live like no rats."

"All right, all right, you don't live like rats; but you're huddled together in one room."

"We're not, we have two."

"Oh well, you have two. How many are there of you in the two?"

"Seven."

"Well, then, one more won't make any difference, will it?"

"Shut up, Ma. Go softly. Look, lad." Connie was bending down to him now. "If you could take her across with you, your mother, being a wise woman, would find some excuse to give the neighbours for it being there; an' I'd come across every week, I promise, an' bring you a shilling or so and a bag of food to help for her keep. It'll more than help for her keep what I'd bring you."

"You know what?" He looked from one to the other as he seemed to get worked up; then he stammered, "Yo . . . yo . . . you're awful, the lot of you, keepin' a bairn up . . . up in a mad room."

"Better than havin' it buried alive or drowned in a sack," Frank Wheatley now growled at him.

"Shh!" Connie held up her hand. "Did I hear the front door?"

They listened; then Betty said, "He wouldn't come in the front door, he'd come into the yard with the horse, wouldn't he? And oh, for God's sake! shut her up; I haven't heard her cry like that afore." Betty was pointing to the child now whose head was raised from Freddie's shoulder. But lifting her hands, Connie commanded silence when she hissed, "Shh! I tell you there's someone in the hall."

"Well, go and see." Her father thumbed towards the far door; and she moved immediately, only to stop at the far side of the table within arm's reach of her mother; and now they both stared at their master standing within the doorway.

Freddie too was staring at the man, and for a moment he wanted to throw the child from him. Then he found his arms tightening about it. The child of a sudden had stopped crying; it too seemed to be looking at the man advancing down the room.

Roderick Gallagher stopped within two arm's length of his housekeeper and his maid, and he looked between them to where the little runner stood with a child in his arms. The child was pale-skinned with great dark eyes and black hair. It didn't seem to have grown or changed since the morning he threw it at his man and told him to bury it. He recalled that Frank had said, "Why not just smother it and bury it alongside its mother." But no; even dead, he wasn't going to afford her that comfort. But when his man had said, "But you have no bairn to bury with her, master," he had told him that he had already thought of that: there were ways and means of obtaining a dead child from the workhouse or hospital under the guise of dissection. Anyway even if Doctor Black had been in at the birth he wouldn't, three days later, have noticed anything.

"You bloody lot of twisters!"

As Gallagher sprang forward, Connie thrust an arm back to the table and, grabbing up a long wooden rolling pin, she brought it in a swinging arched movement towards him. Fortunately for her it missed his head and struck him on the shoulder, causing him to stagger sideways for a moment. He was screaming now like a madman, and so was Betty Wheatley yelling at her husband: "Get them away!" She yelled to him, "Use the cart. Get them away!"

As Frank grabbed Freddie by the coat collar and almost lifted him from the floor, he saw the two women fling themselves onto the man. Then, in the next second, it seemed he too was being flung into the cart, and as he fell on his side the child let out a startled cry. The next thing he experienced was being tossed from one side of the cart to the other while aiming to protect the child with one arm and trying to find something to hang on to with the other hand.

He knew when they had left the country road and taken the broader way into South Shields, for he wasn't being tossed about so much. When they passed an inn he saw in the light from the lanterns that the child had its eyes wide open and its mouth was agape, but that it was no longer crying. It was still gripping him tightly, and every now and again he had to loosen its hands from the collar of his coat.

They were in the town now and he pulled himself up by the iron frame of the seat and yelled at the man, "Where are you goin'?"

And Frank turned his head and yelled back, "Where d'you think? To drop you nearest the river, then to make myself scarce or I'll be done for the night."

"I . . . I don't think I'll . . . I'll be able to get across. The tide'll be high about now."

"That'll be your look out."

"No, it isn't, mister. She's not my look out . . . this 'un I mean."

"Well, if you don't want to see her end up in the river you'd better let her hang onto you. And as my lass said, you won't lose by it. Although what'll happen now since he's found out God alone knows. Here's one though that's not waitin' to see. So prepare yourself, laddie, I'm goin' to dump you along the quay here."

"But . . . but the bairn, mister, what'll I say to people?"

The horse had pulled to a stop now and Frank Wheatley called over his shoulder, "Say it's your sister's like: you're mindin' her bairn. It's your sister's. Well, here we are; I daren't go any further. I'm goin' to drop you now and leave this lot at the ostler's. It's where he usually leaves it. He'll call for it the morrow; but he won't find me there, no, by God! Anyway, I've had enough, years of it. So come on, get down, an' look slippy."

Easing himself to the end of the cart, Freddie dropped to the ground; but he had hardly time to relinquish his hold on the iron rail when he heard, "Gee up! there." And by the dim front lamps of the cart he saw it disappear into the distance.

He stood for a moment peering about him. He knew where he was all right, but he'd have to walk some way to get to his sculler, and from what he could see of the river below the dock wall the tide was rising high.

Two figures passed him but took no notice of him or of what he was carrying. A group of youngsters came racing from a side alley; they were having some sport. There were lasses among them, but they took no notice of him either. There were shouts from the river from where a boat was likely being coaled.

Then he saw a dim shape coming towards him. It was a woman; and he thought his mind was going a bit funny again because he seemed to recognise her walk. And as she came nearer he saw she was carrying a lantern in one hand and a cudgel in the other, and he thought. . . . But no; it was only a night-watchman. He hadn't got over the knock on his head. And that must be true because he was feeling tired again. Then the figure stopped in front of him and raised the lantern and said, *"In the name of God!* And"—there was a pause—*"What have you got there?"*

"Oh, Miss, Miss, am I glad to see you. Oh, it's been awful, it has. You wouldn't believe, Miss. You were right. Aye, you were right. I should've told you. You were right. This is it."

"This is what, Freddie? This is a child. Whose child is it?"

"It's his an' the one he was gona dump that night a long time ago when I couldn't tell you."

He saw that her face was all screwed up, and she said, "Oh! boy. Oh! boy. Well, we'll hear all about it when we get to yon side. But, oh my goodness! you've had us all worried. Your people are distracted. You know that? Quite distracted. You've got to stop this."

"Oh, Miss, 'tis stopped, all stopped. But . . . but I'd better get across home 'cos I feel he's after us."

"Who? Gallagher?"

"Aye. Aye; he went mad when he found it was alive."

She was hurrying him forward along the dockside now. "What do you mean, when he thought it was alive? Did he think it was dead?"

"Aye; I've told you. Oh . . . oh dear me, Miss, I'm tired. I fell an' I've been tired since. I don't know how I've kept awake all this time. I think it was the cart rumblin' that kept me. . . ."

"Shh! What's that?" She had pulled him close to her. "That's a horse coming, galloping. Who'd come galloping along the quay at this time of night? My God! It could be an' all, it could be him. Come on! We can run for it. I've got a sculler farther along. Come on! Come on!"

They were on the long shore now and it seemed deserted, but there was no doubt who the man dismounting from a horse on the bank behind them was.

"Give me the child!" she cried as she ran; then immediately contradicted herself, saying, "No, no! You go on."

It was then the voice hailed them, shouting, "Hold there! Hold!"

She swung the lantern up and it showed the tall figure coming down the bank, his high boots sending up sprays of sand while one raised hand brandished his horse-whip.

He was within an arm's length of them now when he stopped and, bending forward, peered at the figure who, likewise, had a raised arm. And as if in surprise he muttered, "Maggie Hewitt?"

"Yes, Maggie Hewitt."

"What have you got to do with this? I want that boy and the child."

"Well, you're not getting the boy, or the child."

"Don't try to stop me, woman! That's my child."

"For how long? Till you throttle it?"

"What d'you mean?"

"You know what I mean. Your child was buried with your wife. Everyone knows that. Now get back or else you'll wish you had."

"Woman! don't try to thwart me or you'll find yourself in the river. I warn you."

She now made a backward movement with one foot, saying quickly, "Go on! Go on, Freddie. Go on over; the sculler's just along there."

But the boy didn't move. Whether it was he was petrified of the man or he didn't want to leave her, he wouldn't know; but he stood there, the child clinging to him and a portion of his mind aware that it was once again wetting and that urine was running up his sleeve.

When he saw the whip miss Maggie's head he did move, and that was forward, only to be stopped almost in his stride by a cry from the man as Maggie's cudgel caught him in the middle. The next moment his mouth sprang agape when, as the man's body seemed to tumble forward, Maggie delivered another blow which caught him on the back of the head. And there he was now doubled in two lying at the water's edge.

He watched her, in amazement now, raise the lantern and peer back towards the dock, then up the river. There were still voices coming from the loading boat and there were voices and figures moving along the far shore.

The next moment she had turned and thrust the lantern, then the cudgel, into his free hand and, without saying a further word, she now bent forward and began to roll the recumbent body further into the water. Then she was in the water herself urging the bulk forward; and only when the water reached almost up to her thighs and had blown her skirt into a bell did she stop.

In the flickering light from the lantern he saw the huddled shape sink beneath the water, and he stood in petrified stiffness looking to where her dark shape was bending down as if she was gazing at the incoming tide. Of a sudden he felt funny again: he wanted to go to sleep just where he stood with the water now creeping over his ankles.

He wasn't aware that she had turned towards him until he felt a hand on him, and then he experienced bodily relief when she took the child from him, gasping as she did so, "On! . . . Go on!" He went on splashing through the water, the swinging lantern casting weird shadows before him.

When they reached the boat he saw that she had put the child inside her coat, and now she ordered tersely, "Row!"

"I can't use two oars."

"Nobody's asking you to. Give one here!"

A wind had risen and with the uneven rowing the boat rocked, and when she cried at him, "Steady!" he said nothing; he was tired, frightened, even petrified: she had killed him; perhaps not at first, but she had made sure by drowning him.

"Put out the light."

"What?"

"I said, put out the light. Quick!"

Gathering breath, he blew into the top of the lantern that rested between his feet. And when presently she said, "We'll run in here, but be quiet," he thought he knew the shore even in the dark, but apparently he didn't know it as well as she did.

She didn't take the first path up the bank leading to the Low Lights but kept on. He knew she was holding the child in the crook of one arm while still gripping the cudgel because she was guiding him very firmly with it pressed against his shoulder.

Lights showing ahead pointed out that they were nearing the quay where the work was still going on; but before they reached it he was twisted around to climb some slimy steps jutting out from a wall. There was no rail and as he neared the top he fell onto his hands and knees, and her voice hissed at him, "You're all right. Stand up!"

They were now in a labyrinth of short streets where the lights from windows told him that they were nearing the top of the hill. She was walking slower now and she had taken her hand from him; but she still did not speak; neither did he, for all he wanted to do was to drop down and sleep.

At times he knew he was walking with his eyes closed, but when some time later—he had no account of how long, whether it was five, ten, or fifteen minutes—she pushed him through the gate and up the drive, he couldn't believe that he was home. And in relief he did think of it as home at this moment.

"You're all right. You're all right." Her voice was floating about him.

"I'm . . . I'm very tired."

"Yes, yes, I know you are, lad. Have . . . have you been hurt?"

He was aware that she was stripping his clothes off him and he said, "When he threw me off the horse I hit a stone, or a rock." And at this she said, "Aha!"

He opened his eyes and was amazed to see she hadn't a skirt on, or boots, or stockings, she was standing in her petticoat and bodice. What was the matter with him? Oh, he was just tired. But the bairn?

He said now, "Where's the bairn?"

"Don't worry, don't worry, she's all right, she's all right. Go to sleep."

"You killed him."

"Yes, I killed him. You wouldn't like to have seen me go to the House of Correction would you for bodily assault, while you were doing time there, too, for kidnapping? And he would have had us both. Oh, yes; Roderick Gallagher would indeed have had us both, because how could we prove that he intended to murder his child? His servants? Servants can be bought off. Oh yes; money talks loudly. And he was powerful in his own way, was Gallagher. Very powerful. We'll talk more in the morning. Go to sleep."

And he went to sleep.

When he next awoke he was to look up into his mother's face. She was bending over him and stroking the hair from his brow, and he said, "Ma. Am I home?"

"Aye, lad." She nodded. "You're home."

He looked beyond her to a bedrail and beyond that to a mirror attached to a piece of furniture. They hadn't anything like that in the bedroom. He was at Miss Maggie's. When he went to pull himself up his mother's hand stayed him as she said, "Lie still now. Lie still."

"Ma."

"Aye, lad?"

"There's a bairn."

"It's all right. It's all right. You can talk in a little while."

His eyes were wide open now. He stared at his mother, then asked, "How did you get here?"

"On me feet."

"Oh, Ma, don't be funny, 'tis serious."

"I know 'tis serious, lad. By the way, did someone hit you?"

"No, no, Ma. When he threw me off the horse I fell against a stone and after that I kept fallin' asleep. Where's ... where's the bairn, Ma?" He again attempted to rise, and again she pushed him back, saying quietly, "She's all right. She's been fed and she's asleep. And clean for once in her life, poor bairn, at least as clean as we can get her at the moment until her scabs heal; she must have sat in wet for God knows how long. They should be gibbeted that lot."

"They ... they saved her Ma, and ... and had to hide her. Where's miss?"

"I'm here."

The last time he had seen her she seemed to be almost naked. Now she was in a grey dress with rows of buttons down the front. Her hair was combed back, making her face look more weatherbeaten still.

She came round to the other side of the bed and sat down, and said quietly, "You hungry?"

"No; but ... but I'd like a drink."

"I'll get it." His mother got up and left the room, and, his eyes widening, he looked towards the door through which she had just gone, saying, "She knows where to go?"

"Oh, yes, yes; she's grown up enough to find her way to the kitchen."

"Who ... who brought her?"

"I did."

"Oh."

She moved up the bed closer to him now and, putting her hand against his cheek, she turned his head right round towards her as she said softly, "Now listen. Can you remember what happened on the shore last night?"

He looked away from her up to the white ceiling, then down to the flowered wallpaper, and then into her face again before saying, "Aye, everything."

"Well now, listen very carefully. *Not to your mother,* nor to another soul must you describe what happened. We know nothing about a man who tried to take the child from us. You understand? You can tell your mother . . . and me everything that happened until I met you on the dockside. From then, we just got into the boat, crossed the river and came here. Now this is *important, Freddie. Do you hear?* Because he'll be found later, and . . . and there'll be bruises on him, and"—her voice dropped to a mere whisper as she went on—"you wouldn't like to see me swing by the neck, would you?"

"Oh, Miss."

"Now"—she was wagging her finger at him—"your mother too must be given to understand not to mention a word of what you tell her because people would put two and two together if the whole story came out. I think those across the water that kept the child alive, they'll keep their mouths shut too, at this stage. Anyway, I'm going to get in touch with one of them. But listen, and carefully, the child is the *daughter* of my *cousin* who *died.* You understand?"

After a moment he brought his chin into his chest by way of confirmation, then said, "She is the *daughter* of your *cousin* who died." Then in a normal tone, he said, "How you goin' to bring that about? Everybody knows. . . ."

"Everybody knows what? That I haven't got a cousin? I have got a cousin, two cousins: one's in London and one's in Darlington. But it's all worked out. I'm going to take a few trips, and one day very soon, and it will have to be very soon, within the next week or so, I'll come back with the bairn in me arms. It'll have to be at night, because china dolls don't cry. Do you follow me?"

He didn't, not quite, not about the china dolls because his head was muzzy, but what he said was, "You mean to let her live with you? We won't have to take her?"

"Don't you think your mother's got enough to look after? And why shouldn't I take her? It's about time I took on some responsibility. I've had it too easy, don't you think?"

He knew she expected him to give no answer, but, a faint smile on his lips, he said, "Aye; aye, I think you have." She slapped his face gently with her finger tips, saying, "Concussion hasn't dulled your wits."

"What d'you mean, concush. . . ?"

"That's what you've got, that's what's making you sleepy. You'll be like this for a couple of days yet. And you're very tired too, in any case."

"But . . . but who's goin' to look after the bairn? If I'm goin' to do the garden an' things, I couldn't."

"Of course you couldn't. Who'd expect you to look after a bairn?"

"I used to look after our Lily."

"Well, your mother's going to look after . . . my bairn."

"She is? Me ma? She's workin' on the ropes half day; an' then there's me da."

"Shut up and go to sleep again, at least after you've had something to drink. Your mother's taken on a new job: she's working for me now, here. And close your mouth, you're nothing to look at at any time but with it open you look like a gargoyle."

"A what?"

"A gargoyle. Which reminds me, you're going to school."

"No, by God! I'm. . . ."

"And we'll have no more by God!s either. You're going to school, at least part of the day."

"I'm not though."

"You are though."

She rose from the bed as his mother came into the room and, speaking to her across the distance, she said, "He's so pleased he's going to school and stop being an ignorant little lout."

"You were goin' to larn me."

"I haven't the time now. And anyway, it's not larn. And that's just by the way; there'll be lots of by the ways for you, young man. . . . Sit yourself down, Jinny, for I must be off for a while or else those cutthroats down on the quay will have collared half my business."

116

He took the mug of cocoa from his mother and gulped at it; then he looked at the two women, sitting one at each side of the bed, at the big boney bulky form of his ma and the thin narrowness of the woman whom at this moment he knew he liked as much as he did his ma, but who last night had murdered a man, and it hadn't seemed to have affected her, for she was still acting the same.

He didn't know, but his mother knew that Miss Maggie Hewitt had spewed her heart up in the closet after she had come for her early this morning.

2

A fortnight had passed and tongues were wagging along the quay. Did you ever know such a thing? Maggie Hewitt had adopted a bairn. A cousin of hers had died and left it to her. She didn't seem over pleased about it; you couldn't get a civil word out of her at times. And it must be telling on her for she looked peaky. Well, it was to be understood, wasn't it? because she'd had to spend out, and who had she spent out on? The Musgrave family. Taking on big Jinny as a part-time housekeeper, and the little 'un's brother as a gardener, and he himself, it was said, was going to school. Oh, they'd believe that when it happened because that would be like tying an eel up with silk ribbon. And then what would the gang do for a runner. It was also said there was one place he wouldn't run to any more, and that was across the water. Funny business that, for a man like Gallagher to be found in the river and been bashed about an' all, neck broken with a heavy instrument. So the coroner had said. He was missing for five days. The first inkling of his being missing was when his man came looking for him. He had been gone twenty-four hours. Twas then they knew who owned the horse that had been picked up at yon end of the sands. His man had said his master had ridden out to meet some friends. But the question now was: who were the friends? And the customs had been interested too. But there was nothing found on the body. It was understood he had a son by his first wife who would come into the estate; but the boy was only ten years old and had been living in the care of his maternal grandmother.

Freddie himself had had a visit from two customs officials. One was from the excise office in Saville Street, a Mr Thomas Brayhay. It was the place where you went for permits. This man had asked him what he was doing on the river in the dark on a certain night and he had answered glibly he was going across to see his granny who had took bad; his ma couldn't go 'cos she had to see to his da and the bairns.

Was it not that he went to meet a certain gentleman with a message?

No, no. Anyway, he didn't run messages any more for anybody, the fish men or the butcher, 'cos he was going to have a half-time job in Miss Hewitt's office and go to school.

But the man had then wanted to know why he went across the river in a little sculler when the tide was going down; and, too, had he not heard someone calling on him to stop?

No, it was a windy night, if he remembered rightly, he had said.

Miss Maggie had come on the scene and she had laid about the customs man with her tongue and said in future she would be responsible for anything that the boy did and that they had to come to her. And the conversation had ended funnily because the man had smiled at Miss Hewitt, and had said, "Oh! Maggie, Maggie." And she had turned a funny colour and wagged her head, then showed him out.

Then another man had come across from South Shields and when he had asked the same questions he had answered in the same way, except he added, his granny hadn't been well and he had stayed with her 'cos she had nobody to look after her since her granddaughter had gone back to Darlington. Fortunately his granny had been primed with half a dollar and had kept to the same story. But it had given her something of a hold over his ma which he didn't like. But the excise man from the permit office had been the worst. He was still the worst, for he had collared him only yesterday and said, didn't he think it was funny that his mother should be walking the waterfront enquiring of the boatmen if any of them had seen him the day following the night he went across the river if she had sent him to his granny's. And the only way out of it was to cheek the man, and he said, Oh, his ma had funny turns, sort of fits and starts, which had brought the man's hand out at him; but he had dodged it.

When later, he had told the miss about it she had said, "Don't try to be a clever clout with that lot. If they question you just say you know nowt or keep dumb, act stupid. They can't have much on you then. But there's one thing, they're not going to let this drop. They know there was something big afoot that night and they're going to find out what it was." It was then she had looked at him and said again, "Have you any idea at all what he did with the bag?"

And he had repeated for the countless time, "No; I've told you. The last I saw of it was when the woman came in the room and gave the alarm. And the main thing that stuck in me mind after that was that awful room an' the bairn.

Three odd things then happened before this chapter on Freddie's life closed. The miss came to him and said, "They've gone." And for a moment he didn't know to whom she was referring and he said, "Who's gone?"

"The staff. The lot from The Towers. I . . . I made enquiries. It appears they all got the push. There's an old lady in charge now, with a young boy, Gallagher's son, and she brought her own staff with her. And she must be a woman of some substance because there's eleven of them and two carriages. And she's having the whole place torn apart and redone. I don't suppose you'd have an idea where those three went, would you?"

He had just shaken his head and felt sorry for them, for they'd be out of work. From what he could gather, too, they had been with the family from before the time *that man* was born. . . .

But what had happened to that lot was made clear when one morning, as he was about to go down the garden the gate opened and the muffled figure of a woman entered. As he went towards her he gave a slight gasp when he recognised the pock-marked face. It seemed to be even more disfigured, although it was shaded with a deep brimmed bonnet and the collar of her cloak covered her chin.

"Hello there, lad," she said.

"Eeh! it's you. I thought you had gone."

"On the point of. On the point of."

"You all got the push?"

"Aye; we all got the push."

"Twasn't fair."

"Oh, don't worry, we're all right. How's the bairn?"

He looked back towards the house and said, "She's lovely now."

The woman's lids shaded her eyes and her head drooped before she acknowledged quietly, "She was in a state, I know, but we couldn't do anything about it. I used to rub her with lard, but it was the mess an' the wet. And there were days when he was in the house and we daren't go up because he was restless, you know goin' from one place to the other. And if he'd seen us up on that floor where none of us ever really went 'cos there was no need, just to sweep the cobwebs away now and again, he would have twigged and he would have murdered us. Instead he was . . . well, somebody must have done for him, mustn't they?"

He made no answer to this, and she said, "We all wondered how you got across. We didn't know what had happened, only that you must have reached home and taken the bairn with you. We thought your mother had it, that was, up till yesterday. When me da came across the water he went in a bar and heard bits and pieces, and he put two and two together. Why . . . why did the woman take her? I mean the owner of this place?"

"Oh"—he hesitated—" 'cos I suppose she's lonely. An' . . . and I work for her, an' you see it was her who helped me across the water that night. She happened to be just comin' back from some place over there. And I had to tell her . . . well a bit, not everythin'," he lied, "about the bairn that nobody wanted. An' it just went on from there."

"I . . . I couldn't see her, could I, the bairn?"

"Eeh! no. I don't think it would be wise. Me ma's in there; she might go for you, 'cos it was in a state, its backside an' that."

Her head was bobbing now as she said, "I just thought. Anyway, we're off. We're goin' off to Scotland the morrow."

"You lookin' for work?"

She gave a deep laugh now, saying, "No, laddie, we're not lookin' for work. I can say this to you 'cos you've got a big head on those little shoulders, we won't need to look for work. You see we'd worked for that family . . . well, me da had from he was a lad, and me ma, she started when she was five, and I was born there, and we stuck by him through thick and thin. There was a time when things were thin afore he married . . . well, the bairn's mother. And she had a bit. Oh aye, I'd say she had more than a tidy bit and he got the lot. That's all he married her for, the money. Yet she was bonny, beautiful, and the nicest lass you'd care to meet. But I think any good that was in him was buried with his first wife. Yet, he couldn't bear to look at her child after she went. Now isn't that funny? But good days or bad he never gave us a penny piece over our wages, an' they weren't big I can tell you; three shillings a week I was gettin', me ma five, and me da eight, never a penny more. And so when he didn't turn up . . . well I ask you! What would you have done? He had a few hidey holes he thought nobody knew anything about. He thought he was the cutest thing on two legs. Of course, mind, when the old girl took over she found quite a bit in the safe, as well as his first wife's jewellery, and his second wife's an' all, at least most of it." Her eyes widened under her bonnet as she bent towards him now, whispering, "What I really came across for was to see your ma, 'cos I thought the bairn was with her, you see, an' to make it all right that she wouldn't be out of pocket for some time. But I can see the bairn's in clover, and if your ma's lookin' after her she'll be all right an' all. But anyway—" She now put her hand into a pocket and pulled out a purse. It was chamois leather and was very like the one's he had seen her master use. She drew out a half sovereign and handed it towards him, saying, "That's for yourself 'cos you're a good lad."

He gave her no thanks but looked at the money in the palm of his hand, and he had the strange desire to hand it back to her and say, "I don't want that, that's his." But she was saying now, "I don't suppose we'll ever meet again 'cos Scotland's a long way off, at least where we're goin'. So ta-ra! lad. It's been a strange do, hasn't it?"

"Yes. Aye, it has."

She backed from him towards the gate, and now he felt forced to say, "Good luck to you."

"Thank you, lad. We've already got it. God looks after his own. An' good luck to you. He'll see to you an' all. As I said to me ma, you'll do things, go places, be somebody. It's in your face. Ta-ra!"

"Ta-ra!"

He'd do things, go places, be somebody.

Would he?

The second thing took place the next morning. It was the day on which he was about to attend half-day school. His mother had given him a clean pair of trousers, saying, "Put them on. And there's a clean shirt as well. And put some blackin' on your boots mind. Anyway, I'll be over there later to see that you do."

When he reached the house Maggie said to him, "You can stop helping John from now on. Anyway, he's better on his own. He's been at it for the past hour; I think he'd work all night if he had a light. You're coming down to the office with me. You're starting school today and a morning at my place will show what it will lead to if you can take it into that thick skull of yours." She had smiled at him; then, looking at the parcel he had unwrapped, she said, "Oh! clean trousers and shirt. Go and put them on now, so you'll be ready."

The trousers he had on were the same as those he had worn on the night he had crossed the river carrying the little parcel in the inside pocket. He couldn't remember when he had first started to wear them or when he hadn't worn them, they seemed stiff with glar, but he considered they were still all right for gardening work. As he took them off he looked at them and thought, I've got a feelin' in me bones that I'll never don you again. And then, as if putting his hand into the inner pocket for the last time, he groped with it, only to bring it out sharply as if he had been stung under the fingernail. It seemed, he thought, as if there was a pin in there or something. There was a seam in the bottom of the pocket and it felt thick with fluff on both sides. So again he put his hand into the pocket and now gently scraped his fingernail along one side of the seam; and there he felt the sharp thing again. Now he used two fingers to scrape along the seam until he felt the prick, then pulled out fluff mixed up with black dust which he put on the table. Gently now he blew at the dust until what looked like a piece of glass was left.

He thrust his hand quickly back into the pocket, and again his fingers travelled along the seam, and again they found something sharp. Once more he was blowing at the dust and revealing something red, red glass this time. For the third time and at a pace now, both fingers were raking along the seam, and for the third time he brought out a piece of glass. Now he turned his trousers inside out and tried to turn the pocket inside out, but this was impossible. So once more he scraped wildly with his fingernails. But there were no more pieces of glass to add to the one red and two white pieces of glass that seemed to be dancing on the table in the sunlight. But they weren't pieces of glass, he knew that; they were what must have fallen out of that package when his side hit the stone. Eeh! Eeh! dear God. What if they

123

were. . . ! But they were. Where was the miss? He looked round the room wildly as if to conjure her up.

"*Miss! Miss!*" He was out in the hall now and running towards the kitchen.

"What is it? What's the matter?"

"Come. Come an' look at this." For a moment he didn't realise that he was almost naked and that his middle was covered only by his shirt tail.

She followed him into the small back bedroom, and there he pointed to the table with the three pieces of glass on it.

She stood looking down at them but didn't touch them; and then, turning her head slowly, she said in a very stern voice, "Where did you get these?"

He now pointed to his trousers lying on the floor and, picking them up, he tried to explain to her that they had got into the fluff, but his words were coming out in a stuttering gasp.

"Sit down. Sit down." She pushed him onto the side of the bed. And now she picked up the stones and examined them, saying, "You know what these are, don't you?"

"Aye. What I had in the parcel for him."

"Huh! Huh!" She began to laugh. First, it was only her shoulders that shook, then her whole body and her head seemed to bob with laughter, and then it burst from her mouth and she laughed until the tears ran down her face. Of a sudden she threw her arms around him and hugged him. And when her laughter subsided it was she who now stuttered, "Y'Y'Your interest will certainly go up with these, boy. Oh certainly."

"I can keep them?"

"What else. What else. But keep them is the word, and for a long time, years in fact. They won't depreciate in value. Am I to be your banker again?"

His mouth now went into a wide grin; then he said, "We'll have to discuss it, won't we?"

Her hand did not go out and clip his ear, but her voice was soft as she said, "Oh! Freddie; this could be the rock on which to build your life."

He looked from her to the stones. That young woman Connie had said he'd do things, go places, be somebody. And now Miss had said these could be the rock on which he could build his life. Funny the things people said.

*   *   *

The third thing worried him a bit.

Mike Harper said to him: "Why did you leave your sculler across the river an' come over with Maggie Hewitt in hers? You didn't think you were spotted, but you were."

He didn't relay this conversation to the miss, for he felt she would worry on the side; already she had been sick a number of times over the past weeks. Cheery all day when folks were about, but he'd heard her vomit at night, from what was his bedroom now, at least it was for two or three nights a week when his mother had told him to stay to help the miss with the bairn when it was fractious and couldn't sleep and cried. At such times he would walk the floor with it and hum to it. It seemed to soothe it. It was then he had heard her vomiting.

His answer to Mike Harper had been, he had met up with the miss and she had asked him to take an oar for the tide was running fast and she didn't think she was up to getting across herself. So now he knew. And did that satisfy him?

And Mike Harper had said, no, it didn't, and that he thought he was a clever clogs, but he'd be caught out one day and he'd be there to see it.

Freddie wasn't to know, of course, that Mike's prophecy, too, would come true.

PART THREE

As It Happened
When I Was a Man

1

"Ben Hutton is going to swallow his spittle and choke himself when he gets this account. I can hear him yelling now: 'Ninepence in the pound tax! I won't pay it. I won't pay it.' " Freddie was leaning across the desk addressing Maggie who was sitting deep in a leather chair, her feet on the fender, soles upturned towards the roaring fire, and a glass of steaming liquid in one hand, and he went on, "Remember in fifty-five when Gladstone put it up to one and tuppence? Eeh! He danced, didn't he? Actually left the floor in the office. Remember Andy Stevens was clerk then, and he burst out laughing and Ben Hutton brought him one across the lug and knocked him off his high seat?"

"Yes, and you, big fella, said, we'll have none of that. And you nearly lost us Hutton's contract."

"You know something, Maggie"—Freddie now sat back in his chair—"I've often wondered about his giving us the contract. His business now is big enough to take on two or three clerks."

"Well, if he did that he'd have to pay two or three clerks, wouldn't he? And you know, when they first started they did all their own summing up between them, him and his fat bejewelled Bessie. Oh, how that woman gets on my nerves! And there's another thing." Maggie now pulled her feet from the fender and placed her glass on the side table before swivelling round and pointing her finger at him. "You know as well as I do he doesn't declare half, and I've told you you should probe into it a bit further and let him know that you know. I don't forget the dirty work he did at the new election of councillors sometime before then, in forty-nine; he tried for the Tynemouth Ward when Solomon Mease got it, and Spencer got in for here. Old Tyzack got in too. Remember old Tyzack?" As she leaned back in the

chair again he looked at her, as he often did, in genuine
amazement. She had a wonderful mind and a wonderful memory. She could pinpoint people and dates back to those days
when, as a girl, she lived on the Lawe in South Shields. At times
he asked himself what he would have done without her, and
what would he do without her were she to go. She had a pain
now and again in her chest that worried him seemingly more
than it did her. He had stopped asking himself why he loved her
more than anyone in his world; yes, even Belle. But then, that
was a different thing, a different feeling. Belle was a sprite, a joy,
something as light as air, yet as dark as bog oak; but Maggie . . .
Maggie was a rock. She was a mind that instilled itself into you,
and she certainly had instilled her mind into him. It all went back
to that night when they had come across the river, he, she, and
Belle. Yet all she had put into his mind had not given him the
power to put words to the feeling he had for her, which wasn't
like the feeling he had for his mother. He felt guilty in knowing
that that feeling for his mother was a faint shadow compared to
the way he thought of Maggie Hewitt. It could have been the
feelings of the son for the mother, yet it wasn't. It could have
been those of a man for his wife. Yes; yes, it could, but it wasn't.
It could have been for a teacher, a wise teacher, a stern, grim one
at times, but nevertheless kind and wise teacher. No, no; he
couldn't put words to the feeling he had for the woman sitting in
that chair. He only knew he wanted to hug her to him. He had
done it twice. The last time had been on New Year's morning,
and he felt he must never do it again because the result of it then
had been her going into her room and crying so bitterly that he
could hear her through the locked door. This woman with her
weatherbeaten face and her skinny body which he knew would
harbour everlastingly the girl who had never been given the
opportunity to become a real woman, was someone he loved and
loved so much that he was daily fearful of losing her.

He said now, "Belle finishes school tomorrow. What are you
going to do with her?"

"What d'you think? Put her in a cage on show?"

"You could do; it would be the safest because you've got a
problem on your hands. I suppose you've thought about that."

"Yes, Mr Musgrave, I've thought about it. And so have you,
haven't you?" She cast a sidelong knowing glance at him, and he
shrugged his shoulders before he said, "Naturally."

"Well, would you mind sharing your thoughts with me?"

He picked up a mass of scattered papers, then tapped the bottoms on the desk to bring them into order, after which he laid them on the leather bordered blotting pad before going round the desk and seating himself in a chair to the other side of the hearth from her. "Finish that hot drink," he said.

"Never mind the hot drink, answer my question."

"Well"—he pursed his lips—"she's got to be told sometime, but when, that's one problem; how, is another problem. And, as you've already found out, she has a lively enquiring mind, and so doubtless she will want to go across the water not only to see the house but also her half-brother so called. And that, Maggie, is as far as my thoughts go on the subject; except that I can't see any need for bringing the matter up unless something untoward happens, and my mind doesn't give me a picture of anything so untoward that would make you tell her that you are in no way related to her, that she is not the daughter of your cousin but that, nevertheless, you love her like you would your own daughter; in fact, the moment you first saw her she became the focal point of your life and everyone else was excluded."

He stopped here, and they looked at each other for some seconds before she said quietly, "You fishing?"

"Fishing? What would I hope to catch?"

"Well, talking of catching, I'm going to ask you again, what are you going to do about May? Now, now! don't get up, and don't evade the question." Her hand was wagging towards him. "You know how I feel about May, always have done, but you should do the right thing, either marry her or give her up. It's five years now you've been dangling with her, and a little bird tells me she gets very nasty at times."

"Your little bird wants its beak slapped, if not glued up."

"You can't stop people talking, Freddie." Her voice was quiet now. "I said when you became engaged to her, such as it is without a ring, she wasn't for you; you've moved out of her world; you've risen and you're going on rising. Now there is a vacancy coming up in the Tynemouth Council shortly, but can you imagine her acting as the wife of a councillor?"

He was on his feet now looking down at her, his face grim. "Maggie, this is one thing I'll make me own mind up about. She's a good lass; she has her faults, haven't we all? But she's no more dying for marriage than I am."

"Oh! don't talk so bloody soft." She had sprung out of the chair, almost upsetting the little table on which was the tray and the empty glass. "She's been ready for marriage since she was fourteen, that one, when she was skitting up the alleys after you. She took up with two or three others, as you know, to try to draw you on and got a name for herself, so much so that nobody would touch her, not for a wife, that is. Then, God knows why, because I don't, you take up with her when you could have had the pick of most of the town."

His voice was unusually calm as he said, "Pick of most of the town? Don't talk rubbish, Maggie! It's only over the last few years that even you have been considered fit to sail through the brass-studded doors of the huh! so-called gentry up the bank. As for me, all your training and polishing couldn't get *me* in. It was only as my sister's escort when she was singing at one of their soirées that I got past the door."

"All right, all right, that may be so"—her voice too was quiet now—"but things have changed over the last three years, and they'll go on changing rapidly from now on, and it's up to you to take advantage of it. You've got a head on your shoulders, you're well read. I'll say you're better read than any other man in this town, or up the river to Newcastle. And who knows more than you of what actually goes on in Parliament today. Half of them don't know the name of the Prime Minister. Palmerston, they'll say, who's he? Even those who are paying taxes through Gladstone wouldn't know he's the Chancellor of the Exchequer. So now I'm coming out in the open, Freddie, and I'll say this once and for all, you marry May and you might as well go back to the time you were a runner. I hate to put it so bluntly, but there it is. What is more she doesn't like me and I don't like her, we both know where we stand, and you're in the middle." As she turned and went towards the door he said quietly, "Maggie, I'm sorry; but I can't see a way out."

"Then I'm sorry too, lad." She had the door handle in her hand when she paused and looked over her shoulder at him and said, "By the way, don't hurry back here the night, I'm all right on me own."

"I'll be back," he said.

"Please yourself."

He turned now and put his two hands on the mantelshelf and looked into the mirror above it. The light from the lamp behind him made his grey eyes look dark and his thick fair hair that fell below his ears take on a brown reddish tint. His full large mouth was set tight and his chin appeared knobbled with the thoughts passing through his mind.

She had said he might as well go back to being a runner. Had he ever been a little runner, a tiny mite of a thing? His mother said he was still a mite at fourteen. But after he had got up after that long spell in bed with fever, he had seemed to sprout like a bean pole and remain as thin as a bean pole. He couldn't recall when he had stopped growing. But there was a time, he remembered, when he feared he would grow too tall. It wouldn't have mattered so much, he had told himself, if he had grown broad with it, but his growing had come to a halt when he was just about six foot tall.

It wasn't until he was twenty that he realized that clerking all day and learning most nights didn't give a man strength to combat the quay prowlers, or even to row up to Newcastle in a sculler, so he had done something about it. When he started to run the hills first thing in the morning Maggie said he would kill himself by getting another fever. And when he took up Swedish drill exercises she said he was mad. But that was nothing to the opinion she expressed when he joined a boxing club, but not in the town or across the water in South Shields, no, in Newcastle. And what a waste she had said, and still said, because it hadn't put an ounce of flesh on him, muscles yes, here and there, but you couldn't really notice them.

He stepped back from the fireplace and stood gazing down into the fire for a moment before turning about and going upstairs and into his own room ... his own room because for years now he had spent more time in it than he had done in his own home. Which fact caused his mother to show her spleen at times, although she had everything to thank Maggie for, such as a better house. It had three rooms and a separate kitchen, besides which it had a patch of garden with a workshop at the bottom of it in which his father spent most of his days. There was only Nancy at home now, for John had been married these six years. He was a father of twin boys and had a position as an under-gardener in an estate outside Westoe Village across the water. Jessie, now twenty-three, had been in service in Durham since she was fifteen. She was with a good family and they were kind to her. She had though, at least so he felt, cut away from her own family for there were times when she didn't come home on her leave days.

Lily had died at four years old, another victim of the fever.

The move from Grub Street to Bing Cottage had taken place only a matter of weeks following his mother's position of part-time housekeeper to Miss Hewitt, and it had caused a bit of a sensation. As his mother said, she'd have to live it down because no longer did she go to the centre of the town to the main tap to get her water, for there was a tap laid on near the house. She really did miss her daily trot with the bucket and her conflab with the women of the town, but because apparently she had gone up in the world she had lost a lot of her old friends. The bitterest against them had been their neighbours, the Harper family, that was until Freddie took up with May and then everybody seemed to be happy, for a short time at least.

Freddie now got into a Melton cloth great-coat, then took from a cupboard a high-topped hat and a pair of calf-skin gloves, and went downstairs.

When he opened the front door, he did not immediately go out but, donning his hat and stuffing the gloves into his pocket, he took up a taper from the jar that stood beside the oil lamp on a marble topped table to the side of the door. And he lit it, shielded the flame with his hand, went out onto the step, lit first the wall-lamp, then, bending down, he set flame to the wick of the glass-covered lantern standing on the side of the step. This done, he blew out the taper, returned it to the jar, put on his gloves, went out and closed the door and, picking up the lantern, he walked down the path, out of the gate and onto the road. It was necessary to have a lantern for this end of the town because it was not yet, as was the main thoroughfare, lit by gas.

It was a routine he had followed literally hundreds of times over the past winters and he looked upon it as all part of his life with Maggie. Since that day she had sent him to school, except for the time he spent in bed with the fever, he had been with her every day of the year, Sundays included; and he had slept in her house until now it was his home more so than Bing Cottage. Oh, yes, much more so, although he would never dare to voice it.

He did not, as once had been his custom when he reached the end of the narrow road, drop down over the cinder bank and make his way past the Low Lights along the quays, then up the steps to home. But now he turned abruptly left, went up another bank and crossed the old coach road that led to Newcastle and out to an open piece of countryside on which were scattered a number of houses now distinguishable by the diffused light from behind curtained windows.

Within minutes he was going up a short garden; but before he reached the door it opened and there silhouetted against the light stood Nancy.

"Where you off to?" he said.

For answer she said, "Oh, hello there, Freddie. You're late. I've been waiting for you. I'm going along to see Jessie."

"Jessie, is it?" he said. "And what about Rob?"

"Oh, Freddie, don't be silly."

"All right I'm silly. You're going to see Jessie, but give Rob my regards; he'll likely be on the look out for you."

"What's kept you? I've wanted to talk to you about tomorrow. You know we'll have to leave here at six o'clock sharp. You'll bring Belle?"

"That's if she wants to come."

"Of course she'll want to come. Stuck in a girls' school all this time, she'll be like a bird let out of a cage."

He made no answer to this, but he thought, Yes. Yes, perhaps you're right, Nancy. She will act like a bird let out of a cage. And she'll be more than frustrated, having been kept at that school for another year when she had hoped Maggie would let her leave when she was sixteen.

"Come in or stay out, but close the door; the wind's raisin' your mother's skirts." They both laughed at their father's voice; then he said, "Don't worry; I'll be here at half past five. Go on; but mind how you go."

Her voice sinking to a whisper, she said, "It's you who had better take that warnin', our Freddie. May's been round an' she didn't sound pleasant. She expected you to be here an hour ago. I told her you were likely staying on with Miss Hewitt because she wasn't very well. But then I think I said the wrong thing there. Anyway, I wouldn't dither in the house too long. Bye."

"Bye, Nancy."

He stepped straight into the living room and closed the door behind him. His father was sitting in a low hide-padded chair to the side of a roaring fire. He looked comfortable but old. His

135

mother too was sitting beside the fire, but further back from it, and she was busily turning the heel of a sock. Glancing up at her tall son, she said, "You've got here then?"

"Now don't you start. Let me get in, and my coat off." He had already taken his hat off.

"I wouldn't bother if I were you, lad."

"What d'you mean, Da?"

"May's not long gone."

"So I understand. Nancy told me. But why all the fuss; I never keep to time, not strictly speaking."

"Well, apparently you should. An' you know you disappointed her on Sunday."

"Well, what did you expect me to do, Da? Leave Maggie on her own and her almost coughing her guts out?"

"She should see about that chest of hers."

"Well, she's like you, Da, she's mutton-headed and stubborn and she doesn't like doctors. So you've got that much in common."

"How was she when you left her?"

He turned to his mother now. "Not too bad, except her temper was a little frayed."

"What about?"

"Oh, this and that and the other. You know her."

"Is she looking forward to tomorrow and having Miss Belle on her hands from now on?"

"Well, she's looking forward to having her home. But what d'you mean by, on her hands? I would say there's what is known as an inference in your tone."

"You can leave your book learnin' outside the door, lad; you know what I mean. That lass is goin' to prove a handful. And Miss Maggie is goin' to find herself gettin' tired with her about the place day after day. It was all right when she came home for holidays. She got everybody tuned up, as our Nancy would say, and hit the high notes, but you can't go on livin' on the top of high notes. And have you thought about her future an' what's gona happen if she wants to get married or such?"

"No, I haven't, Ma. Anyway, it's got nothing to do with me."

His tone was more than testy; and his mother now brought the three needles of the heel into line, stuck the fourth needle through the leg, then placed the sock on her lap before saying, "Got nothin' to do with you, you say? You turning stupid all of a sudden? Why, in my eyes you could have almost fathered her. All right, all right, I said almost. That's a funny thing to say but that's how I see it: from what went on she wouldn't have survived very much longer if you hadn't lifted her that night. I can still see the sight her poor little body was in. And what you seem to forget, lad—" And now, lowering her voice and inclining her head deeply towards him, she said, "You're the only one who knows the true facts of her beginning. What Miss Maggie an' me knows was just hearsay but you were there from the time she was born. And you might have forgotten some things but it's my bet that one day, an' not too far into the future either, you'll likely be called on to remember because you'll be the only one who can. Those three servants have disappeared as if from the face of the earth. You said the daughter came and had a word with you; well, that's over fourteen years gone to my reckoning. I also reckon that because they were makin' for Scotland they had greased their palms afore they left the house an' God knows to what extent. They said Scotland, but likely enough to take them across the water out of the country to Canada or the Americas. So when you stand there, lad, an' say her life has nothin' to do with you, I say think again."

"You finished, Ma?"

"Yes, for the present."

"Ta . . . thanks, and looking back over the last hour or so I seem to have run the gauntlet in one way or another; and so now I think I'll go and find a little solace in the Harper family."

A smothered laugh from his father brought him around to ask, "You find that funny, Da?"

"Aye, lad; aye, I find it funny after the way May went out of that door a while ago. Aye, I do, I find it funny."

"Ah well, forewarned is forearmed, Da, so here I go." He now picked up his hat, bent over his mother and flicked his thumb against her cheekbone, then said, "I'll give you all the news of the battle in the mornin', Ma; that's if you arrive on time because I'll be setting off for Newcastle shortly after eight."

She made no reply, just slanted her glance sideways at him, but his father, still laughing, said, "Good-night, lad. Mind how you go. Swing your lantern well 'cos someone was attacked by a footpad the night afore last up your way. Time they had lights up there."

"All right, Da, I'll swing it, and I'll swing it off their heads if the opportunity arises."

Going out the door he called loudly, "Good-night to you, Mrs Musgrave," and his father's high laughter followed him.

But once on the road again he didn't bother swinging his lantern wide but walked slowly and steadily towards James Harper's house.

The Harpers too had moved from the row but not into such a salubrious part of the town as his parents. In fact it was a house merely higher up the same hill, still with two rooms but with an attic now and a washhouse. James Harper was still a keelman and his son Michael, now a tough loud-mouthed stubbily built man, was his partner. Michael had been married these past ten years and had added to his family each year, and all miraculously had survived in a two-roomed shanty lower down the hill. So there remained at home only May.

May had started work at eight years old as a part-time maid and washerwoman, but at sixteen she had graduated to shop assistant in Dixon's the fruiterers in Union Street. This elevation had naturally caused her to have ideas about her station in life. At the time she considered herself on an equal footing with Freddie Musgrave, because what was he after all but a little tin clerk in Maggie Hewitt's house office on the quay?

It took some years and some thinking before it was forced home to her that if Freddie Musgrave didn't think he had become too good for her, Miss Maggie Hewitt did and that she had stuffed him with education to point out the difference.

Freddie was well aware of all this and in a way he was sorry for May: she had waited for him when he didn't want her to wait. In those far gone early days he had avoided her. He had laughed at his father's chipping: "May'll net you yet, lad, you'll see." And always his answer had been, "Not if I've got me eyes open, Da, and me fins flapping."

How had he become entangled with her? How had the word marriage been approached? Oh, he knew how he had become entangled with her. It was that night when the sap was rising in him. No; it had been rising in him for some long time and she was there ready and willing, and by Harry she had been willing. He had felt scared for weeks afterwards in case she should come to him and say, "I'm goin' to have a bairn." And that was something very odd, she had never fallen with a bairn. Of course he hadn't given her much chance this past year or so.

When he thought about it, he could say to himself he had been lucky. Many a fella being as free as he had been and her as willing would have been tied for life. . . . What was he thinking about? He was goin' to be tied for life to her; he was goin' to marry her, wasn't he?

Oh God! no. The thought brought him to a dead stop. He was standing at the foot of the steps leading up the hill, the lantern hung still but slack in his hand. His teeth ground together, his chest became tight within. In the light from the lantern he could see the steam from his breath dispersing like a silver spray into the blackness now.

How could he get out of it? Could he tell her straight . . . but tactfully? Oh, God Almighty! there was no tactful way to tell a woman that she wasn't wanted any more, particularly if she had been used and had been promised for five years. But that was it, he couldn't recall any promise, any talk of marriage, except from her. It was at that New Year's do when they were having a party and Jimmy Blaze had opened up a full barrel of rum he'd had put by for years and everybody was merry, very merry. They toasted everything and everyone, and one of the toasts had come from May. Lifting her mug up she had said, "Here's to Freddie and me, we are gona be married." And they had all slapped him on the back. He might not have remembered but the accompanying comments surfaced the next day: "Glad to see, lad, you're stickin' to your own," and, "That Maggie Hewitt hasn't turned you into a proper upstart yet," and, "You've got a fine lass in May, made for each other you are."

When, a few minutes later, he knocked on May's door it was she herself who opened it with the greeting, "So, you've got here then." In a way, she sounded like his mother or his wife, but she wasn't his mother or his wife; and looking at her round high-coloured face with its peevish expression which he had come to recognise spelt trouble ahead his mind said, And she never will be.

"Yes, I've got here in the flesh."

"Been very busy I suppose?"

"Yes, as you say, May, I've been very busy."

"You're always very busy, if you ask me."

He looked around the dull kitchen. There was a brass

fender in front of the fire, but it wasn't shining. The wooden table top had never seen sand and salt for many a day, nor had the clippy mats that covered the floor been shaken for sometime either. And it offended his taste to see pieces of food sticking to the black rags that went to make the mat that was set alongside the table.

"Are you alone?" he said.

"Not quite; me ma's in bed, an' me da's gone to bring our Mick."

"What for? Is your ma worse?"

"No, me ma isn't worse, but me da thinks it's about time we had a talk, an' our Mick an' all."

"Have a talk? Your da and your Mick, and me, about what?"

"Oh, don't play the innocent. You know what about. It's five years now since I've been promised, an' I want to be married. You know I do."

He stared at her before saying flatly, "Well, what if I don't want to be married, May?"

"Oh, don't you come that with me. You're gona marry me, or else."

"Yes? Or else what?"

"Well, me da an' our Mick'll tell you. Aye, they will. I've kept them back till now. But the morrow that one'll be back in Miss Maggie's fancy house, the one you're never out of, an' I know what happened last time when she was on holiday. I hardly saw hilt or hair of you an' I'm not goin' to put up with it again because now I understand she's home for good. With the airs an' graces she puts on you would think she was the Duke of Northumberland's daughter instead of some homeless waif that Maggie Hewitt took under her wing. And that's another thing, whether you know it or not, she's supposed to be the daughter of Miss Hewitt's cousin. Well me da was talkin' to a man some time gone by who knew her and her da and the family, an' he couldn't remember her havin' a live cousin. Her mother was an orphan, but her father had one brother, and he had two daughters and they were the same age as Maggie Hewitt but they died in their teens, both were hit with the cholera. He said he helped to bury them. So you explain that if you can."

He shook his head, saying, "I can't; but perhaps if you had a word with Miss Hewitt herself she would explain it. All I know is that Belle is the daughter of Miss Hewitt's cousin, and if you ask me I can't think that Miss Hewitt, being who she is, would take on anybody else's child. Can you?"

"Funny things happen. Me da says lots of funny things happened along this coast years back, an' that's one of them, that Belle."

"Well, as I said, you'd better talk to Miss Hewitt about it. But with regard to us, May. . . ."

"Aye, with regard to us, what about it?"

He stared at her. What could he say? In this moment I dislike you . . . I'm sorry for you but I dislike you? And: Yes, I've used you but you've wanted to be used, not only wanted but you've almost eaten me alive at times; and I've sickened myself when I've touched you? Could he say that?

What he said was and quietly, "May, I don't think we'd make a go of it. I must face up to it. Quite candidly it isn't because I don't want to marry you, it's because I don't want to marry anybody. I'm . . . well, you could say I'm not the marrying kind."

"Oh my God!" She was moving her head slowly from side to side now while keeping her eyes on him. "You know what I could do to you this minute, Freddie Musgrave? I could stick a knife into you. By God! I could. But I'll leave that to me da and our Mick. When they've finished with you you'll wish you'd never been born, I can tell you that. You're a dirty rotten sod! You're a bloody upstart, a dirty big-headed nowt. . . ."

"May! May!"

She turned her head in the direction of the bedroom, shouting now, "Shut up! Mother."

He was about to turn from her and go towards the door when she almost sprang across the room and, standing with her back tight against the door, she said, "Oh, no, you don't! You dirty bugger you! You'll stay there if I have to claw you to bits until they come in. An' I hope they've had a drink on the way 'cos then they'll be able to use their feet better on you."

"I don't want to manhandle you, May, but get away from that door."

"You try it, big fella. You try it."

He looked behind him: one door led into the bedroom and another into the washhouse.

She realised his intention before he could make a move and she screamed at him, "You try that way an' I promise you I'll do me best to tear you to shreds. You know me strength, don't you. You've had a taste of it in other ways, haven't you?"

There was the sound of footsteps outside and the next minute she was pushed forward as the door opened, and there entered her father and brother.

They were small and thick-set men and although they were muscular due to the type of work on the keel they were both bloated with their beer drinking. James Harper's protruding stomach gave him the appearance of being almost as broad as he was long, and his son was almost a replica.

They were both looking at him now, and it was Mick who, looking at his sister, said, "Been havin' a chat like, eh May?"

For answer she said, "The dirty bugger says it's all off. He says he's not the marryin' kind."

"Oh, he does, does he?" The words were ominous.

"Look, lad," said James Harper; "let's talk this over, eh? What d'you say? You've been welcome in this house for years; we want no bad feelin'. You're gona marry me lass, aren't you?"

"No, Mr Harper, I'm not going to marry your lass; and I've just told her. And if you think your bashing and kicking"—he glanced towards Mick—"will make any difference, you're wrong. And I'd just like to tell you that when there's any bashing and kicking to be done I can do me share."

"You can?" James Harper's lower jaw jutted out, and in the short silence that followed Freddie heard the grinding of his teeth; then with an almost lightning jump he missed the blow that had been aimed for his face.

When next Mick made to come for him his father yelled, "One at a time! lad. One at a time! I'll leave some for you; just let me deal with the pink-livered lily." And his hobnailed boot came out and contacted the side of Freddie's knee and sent him stumbling towards the table, which in preventing his falling also enabled him to spring around and almost in the same action to deliver his fist between James Harper's eyes. The elderly man stumbled backwards, his two forearms across his face now. But his son had already taken his place and was pounding at Freddie's body; and Freddie, in turn, was lashing out at him. For a moment they were locked together until the toe-plate of Mick's boot tore down the length of Freddie's shin. Perhaps it was the agony of the flesh being ripped from the bone that brought his own knee up and into the man's groin with such force that sent him reeling back.

Freddie's vision was now partly blurred with the blood running into one eye from a tear in his brow, but out of the other he could see the two men lined up against the door, with May to one side of them. Not only was she screaming but her mother's voice had joined hers, for the elderly woman, looking like a witch, had appeared in the bedroom doorway.

Freddie was aware that the two men together could do for him, then dump him in the river. Such things had been done before, and the fear of this caused him to bend swiftly and grab at a two foot iron poker leaning against a fire blazer to the side of the grate. And now brandishing it, he cried, "Open that door because if you don't I'll brain the first one that comes near me. You're out to do me, well, it's the same from this side. And I might not only finish one but the two of you."

There was a silence in the kitchen for a matter of seconds, yet it was a silence full of hissing breath.

"Let him be!"

No one took notice of the voice from the bedroom door until it came again, screaming now, "Let the bugger be! He's not worth it. If he maims you that's your job gone."

Again there was the silence, until once more the woman screamed: "Our May, you stupid bitch! Get them from the door. D'you hear me? Get them from the door."

He watched May glare at her mother; then, reaching out a hand she grabbed her father's arm and without a word pulled him to the side. Now there was only Mick left, and it was his mother's voice that moved him: "Have I got to come across there and shift you?" she yelled. "Let him out! There'll come other times. Let him out!"

As if pressing against a force Mick Harper stumbled sideways and joined his father. And now, slowly, Freddie, sidestepping and his eyes riveted on them, made towards the door, with the iron poker held ready to strike.

When he opened the door he did not immediately step outside, but he thrust it wide because he knew that once he made a step through it they would bang it on him and likely knock him flying again. Before going through it, he shouted, "Move to the table!"

And he watched them, like wounded animals ready to spring, slowly make a move towards the table. But not May, until he said, "You an' all!"

Her head moved as though this was more than she could bear; but then she joined her father and brother. And when he had them in full vision he stumbled backwards onto the stone slab, then reached forward and pulled the door closed with a bang, and seemingly all in the same motion grabbed up the lantern and broke into a staggering run.

He had no fear of their following him now for he guessed they were in as bad a condition as himself; and he knew he was in a pretty bad state and must get home.

On the way down the slippery stone steps toward the quay he stumbled once and only just saved himself from an uncontrolled hurling to the bottom by grabbing at the broken balustrade to the side. He lay over it gasping. He had instinctively managed to hang on to the lantern, which he now placed on the step, then sat down and let his head droop forward between his knees for a moment to get rid of the faintness that was overtaking him.

The blood was still running down his face and he was aware that his mouth was stiffening and also that there was something wrong with his leg; and this for a moment filled him with fear, the old fear of anything happening to his feet.

He'd have to get home. But which home? His mother would look after him, yes; but not the way Maggie would; nor had she the facilities. And what was more, Belle would be home tomorrow and if she knew he was ill she'd be along to the house, and would stick around. And his mother wouldn't like that.

He pulled himself to his feet and stumbled down the rest of the steps and made his way slowly and erratically, which brought occasional and ribald comments from passersby, to the house he really thought of as home. . . .

After he had pulled at the bell and the front door was opened by Maggie, he literally fell into her arms. And as she gasped, "Oh, my God! What's happened, man?" she lowered him onto the carpet while reaching hastily out and picking up the lantern that had fallen from his hand and was now lying on its side, its oil spilling and aggravating the flame.

A minute later, the door closed, she helped him to his feet

and into the sitting room and, peering at him now, she again said, "Oh my God!"

"Mag . . . Maggie."

"Yes, lad, yes, what is it?"

"Give . . . give me a drink, will you?"

She seemed to fly out of the room and fly back again; and then she was holding a glass of raw spirit to his lips; but in his efforts to gulp at it, half of it ran down his chin.

"Let's get your things off. Come on, get up."

She had to help him to his feet, then lead him into his room; and there he dropped as he was onto the bed and made no protest as, for the first time in his life, she undressed him.

It was when she finally pulled off his trousers and his small clothes and saw the sight of his shin from the knee to the top of his foot that she brought her lips tight together for a moment before saying, "Well, the buggers did a good job on you here. Who was it, a mob?"

His lips scarcely moved as he muttered, "My in-laws to be."

"Oh, now . . . now I understand. . . . It's over then?"

"Aye. . . . Aye, you could . . . say . . . it's over."

"Well, my God! they've made you pay for it. You could have them jailed for this." She straightened up for a moment, then said, "I should get the doctor."

"Maggie."

"Yes, lad?"

"Just . . . just wash my leg will you? The rest will be all right. Just wash my leg."

"I'll do that. I'll do that." Her voice was soft; it was as if she knew of his fear.

While she washed his leg he had to make a great effort not to scream, and all the while he thought of his father and what he must have gone through when they were trying to push the bones back. . . .

When he went to sleep, he had no idea, but he faintly remembered waking up several times, once thinking he had died and was in hell, another time there was a young girl bathing his head and he knew her to be Maggie, but she was only seventeen; another time he was aware that it was Maggie as she was.

When he finally awoke it was to see his mother standing at one side of the bed, but he couldn't see who was at the other because his eye was bunged up. And when he tried to turn his head he thought his neck was broken. Then Maggie's voice came at him, saying, "Here's Doctor Villiers."

"Well, well! I thought the Crimean War was over."

The jovial tone irritated him. He felt ill. What was wrong? He tried to recall what had happened to him, and for a moment he had the queer feeling that he was lying in some shrubbery and he'd hit his head upon a stone. But . . . but that was years ago.

The voices were talking across him now. "It must have just happened after he'd left our house, Doctor."

"You should have come for me last night, Maggie."

"How could I? I couldn't leave him in this state and he was raving half the night."

The doctor's hands were moving over him now, and no one spoke for a time until he said, "I would say this is a case for the Justices. You could put those two Harpers along the line and right into the House of Correction for a time."

"No, no." His voice sounded like a croak to himself. "Tis over, finished."

"Well, that's up to you, but during the time you got this I hope you left a little impression on them."

He said nothing, but he knew he had left a little impression on them for he could recall the pain in his knuckles as they landed between the dark baggy eyes.

Gradually he became aware that every inch of his body was paining, but his main concern was still his leg.

"My leg, Doctor."

"Oh, it's nasty but it's clean, stripped to the bone in parts. It must have been some iron toecap to rip through your trousers and take the flesh off and that deep. But don't worry, it'll be all right. It remains to be seen if you've got good healing flesh. And by the look on your face I can see you will be on liquids for a few days. Well, there's nothing so sustaining as gruel and rum, and hot milk and whisky for a change. You won't come to much harm if you keep to that diet. Now I don't need to tell you to lie still, do I? But I may pop in later; if not, I'll see you tomorrow. You've got two good nurses here so you needn't worry. But the next time you want to finish a courtship I would think about doing it in a different way, if I were you."

Laughing at his own joke, he went out, and Maggie followed

him. He was left with his mother, and what she said to him was, "Well, the finishing of that courtship could have finished you. You've had a lucky escape; and it's a wonder you got clear of those two. But anyway, you're free. You can thank God for that. You're free."

He was free. He was free. For a moment he could feel no pain, no stiffness, no ache, no thumping in his head. He was free from May. . . .

He went to sleep again, only, later, to wake with a start thinking, I've got to go and collect Belle. And then there's tonight. Who'll take Nancy?

He opened his eyes. There was no one in the room, and when he tried to raise himself the pain in his body was so excruciating that he fell back on the pillow, groaning aloud.

The door opened and Maggie came in. She was dressed for outdoors, and, on seeing her thus, he attempted to speak but his mouth refused to open and the sound that came from his throat could have issued from the far end of a tunnel.

"Belle."

"Don't worry yourself about Belle. I'm all ready for the road, can't you see? in my best bib and tucker. All you've got to do is to lie quiet and do what your mother tells you. We should be back middle of the afternoon." And then she smiled before adding, "Goodbye peaceful and quiet house. . . . How you feeling?"

Again the tunnel sound as he emitted, "Terrible."

She bent over him: "It'll pass," she said softly. "But oh, I'd like to have those two up before the Justices. Anyway, I'm going down to open up first and I'll tell Andy to keep his ears open and find out if they've managed to get to their keel this morning."

When he attempted to speak she caught the word, "Fleet," and she said, "Don't worry about the fleet; Roy will see to our interests in that line. Anyway, there's a glut of fish at present and you know what that means, poor returns. But we'll survive, won't we?" She grinned at him. "You have nothing to worry about, not any more, only"—she straightened up—"to prepare to protect yourself from the flying angel that'll be here in a few hours."

He couldn't smile; he could make no response either with his face or his voice, but he managed slowly to lift his hand towards her. Then he lay thinking.

She had said we'd survive. That indeed was a joke. She

always said we, and so included him when talking of business. She had her fingers in so many pies that if half of them sank she'd still swim. The half share in three fishing boats was just one of them, a minor one. Yet he himself owned nothing. Well, he didn't expect to. She paid him a spanking wage, and over the years she had sold the diamonds and the ruby for him and even the Roman coins that had reposed in a tin on the mantelpiece for years. And so now it could be said he was a man of property; and as such, although his property reposed in the bank, he was entitled to vote. But then hadn't he been eligible to vote for a long time, since he first had ten pounds; any man with more than ten pounds could vote.

He touched his swollen and battered face. Would he ever get his looks back? he wondered. He wasn't vain but he was naturally pleased that he was pleasant to look at. He had been called handsome once or twice, but that was soft-soaping him. But he had been lucky in the last pox epidemic that he hadn't been touched, as many had in the town.

His mother's coming into the room broke into his thoughts and he beckoned her and croaked, "Nancy."

"Yes; what about her?"

"The night?"

"Oh, don't you worry about the night, she'll find somebody to take her; there's always Rob; so settle yourself."

There was nothing he could do but settle himself.

He slept fitfully all morning; then when at mid-day his mother had spooned gruel and rum into his mouth he had the desire to heave it up, but his ribs didn't seem to be capable of the effort. And when she went to spoon liquid from a bottle he flung his arm wide and, enduring the pain of opening his mouth, he brought out, "No laudanum. No, Ma; no laudanum," nodding his head in emphasis, and Jinny, tipping the spoon back to the neck of the bottle, said, "Well, if you enjoy the pain, carry on; you'll have plenty of it in the next few days."

The lamp was lit and the fire was burning brightly in the small iron grate when he heard the commotion in the hall and her voice. It was different from any voice he had ever heard: it held no trace of the Northern accent; in fact, at times some of her words sounded as if she was a foreigner speaking English. He had always loved her voice. He had always loved her. She had been his little sister for years; but then, as Maggie had pointed out, he could have been her father, so attached had she become to him.

It was more than two months since he had last seen her, and he realised then that she was no longer a little girl. What would she look like now?

He saw what she looked like when the door was thrust open and there appeared a slim young woman, five foot six in height or thereabouts with alabaster skin in which was set two oval shaped eye sockets each filled with a dark shining glow, a nose that just missed being large and a mouth that was large, and the whole topped by a mass of raven black hair that fell straight from the crown of her head onto her shoulders.

She had stopped just within the doorway for a second, but now she skipped across the room to come to a halt at the side of the bed; and, her hands going out, she caught his, saying, "Oh! Freddie, Freddie, what have they done to you? Your face. Your poor face."

"Don't slaver over him; he's had enough of it, he's enjoying it."

Maggie's voice brought the young girl's head sharply round and she said, "Oh, Aunt Maggie, he looks dreadful, shocking. Will it ever come right again?"

For answer Freddie pulled his hands away from hers and croaked at her, "What if it doesn't?"

"Well, in that case you'll have to wear a mask." Her voice was as chirpy as Maggie's now."

"You've . . . you've grown."

"Yes, I know I have. I'm an old lady, as Miss Rington pointed out to me before I left: 'You have now entered your eighteenth year,' she said; 'try to act accordingly, Mirabelle.' But you know what Madam Evette said?" She hunched her shoulders now and glanced at Maggie and pursed her lips before saying, " 'Live, laugh, and love, child, so that when you are old you will have at least your memories to keep you warm.' "

"If you ask me she wanted her lugs smacking, that one, a flighty piece if ever I saw one. Frenchie all over."

"What are you talking about, Aunt Maggie? You once said she was the only one that had any life in her in the whole school."

"Well, you know me, I talk through the fat of me neck sometimes. Anyway, leave him alone now and come and get your

149

meal. Jinny's waiting to get away; she's been here long enough the day."

She took hold of Belle's arm and turned her from the bed, saying now to Freddie, "You can take heart: neither of your friends got to their keel today. I called in at the office on my way back. Andy tells me it's the talk of the quay. You won't recall anything, but there were lots of eyes watching you stagger out of that door last night and there had been lots of ears listening in to the commotion that took place when Freddie Musgrave chucked May Harper."

Belle now tugged herself from Maggie's hold and, turning to the bed, she said, "Oh, I was so pleased to hear that. You should have—chucked her—years ago. I never liked her and I know she loved me."

Her hand came out swiftly to pat his face. But she checked it, and, her face now hanging over his, she said softly, "Oh, it's wonderful, Freddie, to be back. I'm never going to leave home again, or this wonderful house, or. . . ."

"You'll leave it in a minute for I'll swipe you so hard that you'll find yourself sliding off the face of the earth and leaving all your mush talk behind. Come on with you."

For answer, the young girl turned and flung her arms about Maggie and, kissing her boldly on the mouth, she cried, "You know what you are, Miss Margaret Hewitt, you're a bossy old crab, but"—her voice dropped—"I love you." Then glancing over her shoulder, she looked towards Freddie and added, "And I love you."

She could say nothing more before Maggie pulled her, laughing, from the room, and Freddie lay staring towards the door. "I love you," she had said. But what did that mean? That she looked upon him as her brother, even her father?

Look!—A voice was yelling loudly in his head—You've just got out of one tangle, and barely with your life. You are her brother, her loving brother. Get that into your napper. What place you take in her life from now on will be seeing to her future. . . .

Later on, when Maggie came to bid him good night, she sat on the side of the bed and said, "Well, what d'you think of the finished article?"

"She's grown."

150

"Is that all, grown? You should have been on Newcastle station. She had them goggle-eyed, especially when she pushed her bonnet back. She hates bonnets. I'll have to get her a hat and a pile of new clothes; the things she's got will soon be up to her calves. But on that station their eyes were sticking out like pike shanks."

She smiled softly now as she added, "We're going to have trouble ahead. They'll be beating a path to the door, so we'll have to be careful in our selection."

He drew in a painful breath before he spoke from the side of his mouth, saying, "I think you'd better face up to the fact that the selection won't lie with us. She's headstrong, she'll do the choosing."

"Well, she'll be guided; and anyway, she's got a head on her shoulders; she'll pick right."

As if to change the subject he said, "How did you find things up there? Any change?"

With an impatient movement she rose from the bed, saying, "That's a daft question with the boats stuck in the river like frozen dummies."

"I meant, have they got the big steamer free yet?"

"No; and not likely to, although there's a steam tug at her. Eeh! that river. You've never seen anything like it. You know something? Before long there'll not be a pennorth of trade on this side, or yon, I'm telling you. Most of them are going into Sunderland, and no wonder, them advertising deep water there. Men are fools, fighting against each other like children. They thought when Newcastle lost the charter the sandbanks would disappear overnight, just melt away and leave free passage. And what's happened? There they are, boats stuck in the river for months on end. And you know what? They're starting to unload part of the cargoes across the water in Shields in order to lighten the boats so they can get up the river. Did you ever hear anything like it? No wonder that inspector said last year it's the worst river in the country. They're all for dredgers now when they should have been using them ten or fifteen years ago. Oh, it gets me mad. Even a little sculler couldn't get up there on low tide now. By the way, I saw a lad in yours yesterday. He was skimming across at slack tide. It's amazing how that little thing's lasted. Well, here I am off to me bed. Is there anything more you want?"

"Just a new face and a new body."

"Well, yes, it would be an improvement." She grinned at him; and he flapped his hand at her; then she went out.

He lay thinking, not about her or Belle, but about the little sculler, for it was that that had started it all. If his da had never built it for John and he himself hadn't toddled into it from he could walk, he wouldn't be lying here now in this house at this minute. No, he wouldn't; he would have been married to May for sure.

2

It was four days later. He was up now but he hadn't yet been out of the house. He was at his desk in the study going over the rents that had become due from Maggie's property. And over the years, this had spread far and wide up the river, from a row of one-roomed hovels in the town here, to three terraced houses in Newcastle to mention but a few.

She was a shrewd business woman, was Maggie, with an eye for a bargain, and she seemed to have the knack of buying at the right time as well as selling when the market was favourable. And besides the half share in the fishing boats she had financed a number of small shops. Even so, all this was only part of the business. Most of her money came in from the interest on loans; and she could have had twice as much business in this way because she didn't skin people like the banks did. She was chary though, and picked her customers where she willed.

She had never dealt in a penny a week or a month for a shilling loan; this she considered daylight robbery; but she had advanced ordinary sailors money, until they could get signed on a boat, and often she would promise to keep their families going when they were beginning on a long voyage and when the half-pay note they left was so meagre that it wouldn't supply a grown family with bread, let alone meat.

So she had a good name on the waterfront and was respected; but at the same time she was also feared and envied and resented, for was she not a woman in a man's world. There were a few such about, though in different capacities, up and down the river, and there was a natural dread in many male quarters that their numbers could grow.

"We are off then." Maggie appeared in the doorway. "I can

see I'm going to get some work done these days gallivanting about the place."

"Isn't there anything in the shops here that would suit her?"

"Don't be silly. Do the so-called ladies patronise the local shops? And me ladyship here knows what she wants. Listen to her."

He listened. She was singing, and his face broke into a twisted smile as he said, "Her musical voice won't get her very far."

Maggie laughed, saying, "No, she's no Nancy. What d'you think about letting her go tonight?"

"Well, it's seemingly all arranged, isn't it, with Mr and Mrs Twaite?"

"You wouldn't risk going like you are?"

"Don't be daft, Maggie; one look at me and they'd have me thrown out."

The sound of singing came nearer and then it flooded the office. It certainly wasn't musical, but then it wasn't unpleasant.

"What's that you're jabbering?"

She approached the desk, saying, "It's a little French song about two birds: one sits on the nest and one goes off gathering food; then a big crow comes and takes the poor little mother bird, and when the father bird comes back he finds his wife gone and his chicks dying. It's very, very sad."

"Get yourself away."

She reached out across the desk towards his cheek, saying, "The colour's changing. It's yellowish now; in another six months you should be all right."

He picked up a paperweight and pretended to throw it, but she didn't move. Straightening up and in a haughty tone, she said, "You cannot intimidate me. I am a young woman of fashion, at least I shall be in a short while when Auntie Maggie empties her purse." She glanced over her shoulder. "But recalling what my dear headmistress used to say, 'The world is your oyster, girls, but you've got to learn how to open the shell' . . ."

"Get out!"

"Yes; let's get out. And my purse strings, my dear girl, are tight; and that's how they're going to remain. Come on."

Her hand near her cheek, Belle now wagged her fingers at Freddie; then skipped from the room.

And he sat looking at the ledger for some minutes before he picked up the quill again.

A short while later his mother entered, carrying a cup of tea on a tray and, laying it on the corner of the desk, she sat herself on the chair to the side of it, saying, "It's a pity you can't go along with them the night; it's goin' to be a big thing for Nancy. Second time in a week at the same place. She must have gone over well."

"Naturally, she would. What is she going to sing?"

"Aw. 'Molly Bawn,' 'Comin' Through the Rye,' 'The Keel Row.' They always ask for these. Then, of course, the usual local ones, the favourites that they can all join in. You've never been in that place, have you?"

"No I haven't; in fact, I've never heard of it before. Cora's: it sounds like a ladies tea room."

"Oh, from what Mrs Twaite said, it's far from that. But there's no strong liquor sold; coffee mostly, but you can have tea. It's the food though that's the attraction, an' the entertainment. But the food sounds plain to me: potato hash and rabbit pie, and for their pudding, plum duff with honey; and then she has what they call savouries, bacon pancakes, which is just a slice of bacon rolled up inside a pancake. But they seem to have taken on. They've been there nearly a year. And Mrs Twaite said the customers all seem to be respectable, good class ones, nothing rowdy. Well, she wouldn't take Nancy to anything rowdy, would she?"

"I don't know." He laughed gently now. "If she thought there might be a bigger cut in it, who knows?"

"Well, she's got to charge for the travelling and her time, hasn't she? And I don't begrudge her what she gets because she's put Nancy on her feet. Without her, Nancy wouldn't be where she is the day."

"No, that's right. That's right."

"What's the matter?"

"What d'you mean, what's the matter?"

"You seem down in the mouth."

"Well, Ma"—he sat back in his chair, his two hands resting on the desk—"look at me. How d'you expect me to act? I'm still aching from head to foot."

There was a moment's silence before she said, "Belle's grown into a bonny lass."

He turned a sharp glance on her. "Yes, she has," he said.

"An' she's nice with it. In spite of that smart school learnin', she's ordinary like. Well, not ordinary, but you know what I mean."

"Yes, Ma; I know what you mean."

And yes, he did know what his mother meant. His mother was a very discerning woman.

"Well, I'd better be gettin' on; this won't get me work done. By the way"—she turned about—"our Nell's threatened to leave him."

"Not again!"

"Aye. He's never sober. He's got in with that lot on the quay. And there's a couple of hussies down there that would strip off for a tallow candle. They live in one of those filthy lodgin' houses, sleepin' twelve to a room an' the pee runnin' out of the door. They raided one the day afore yesterda', I hear, and one of the polis spewed with the smell inside. And Nell's got her suspicions he's been with one of 'em. Well, she knows for a fact, so she means it this time."

"Well, as bad as the lasses might be they'd have to be badly in need of a man to take up with Joe."

"Oh, some women would take a clothes prop with trousers on. Anyway, she says she's gona move, to Gateshead of all places, across the river and right up yon side . . . it's opposite Newcastle."

His pain-racked body shook now as he muttered, "Ma, yes, Gateshead's opposite Newcastle."

"Oh!"—she was indignant—"what you laughin' at? Everybody isn't as travelled as you, smart arse."

When the door closed after her none too gently he stopped chuckling to himself and repeated, "Not so travelled as you." And where had he travelled to? Newcastle mostly; no, he'd been as far as Durham.

Travelled! she had said. It was pitiful in a way how the lack of education stunted the mind. *God* that did sound pompous, and against his own mother.

"Tell me how I really look, Freddie?"

"I've just told you, Nancy, you look beautiful, really, really, beautiful. I've never seen you in a dress like that before and it . . . what is the word? Enhances. Yes, it enhances you. But you were beautiful before you put it on."

"Oh, Freddie." She put out a hand towards him. "You were always kind."

"I'm not being kind; don't be so daft, you're a beautiful woman. But that dress. . . . Velvet. I suppose you'd call it plum?"

156

"The lady in the shop called it pale magenta."

"Oh, that's what it is? Anyway in local jargon, you're a bonny lass. Yes, I'd say, a real bonny lass."

"I wish you were coming, Freddie. I always feel . . . well, different when you're with me. And it's such a nice place."

"What kind of place, a cross between The George and the Methodist Chapel?"

"Dead in the middle, I'd say. The voices are different, the smells are different. Oh, they are not smells, they are scents."

He laughed. "Mixing with the smell of the tatie hash? And tell me, do they go on eating while you are singing?"

"Strangely, no, Freddie. I . . . I do wish you'd come and see the place for yourself. Anyway, you will soon and then you'll get rid of this feeling against it."

"I haven't any feeling against it. How could I?" His voice sounded indignant.

"Well, you seem to scoff at it."

"Oh, it's the name, Cora's; it sounds utterly female."

"Well, it's owned by a female; at least the family run it."

The door opened and Belle came in. Freddie didn't speak, he just looked at the figure walking slowly towards him; it was Nancy who said, "Oh, you smell beautiful, Belle."

Belle made no reply to this, but she looked at Freddie who had risen from the chair and it was a long moment before she said, "Well?"

He swallowed, then said, "Aye, well. So this is what the money's gone on! Is . . . is that what is called a dance frock?"

"No." She shook her head. "Just . . . oh, I suppose a party frock. But Nancy tells me they clear a space on the floor on a Saturday night and they waltz—" She now bent slightly towards him as she ended, "Decorously."

"And what colour might you call it?"

"I might call it forget-me-not blue, and I might inform you that the material is chiffon on top of silk. And my cloak is of a similar shade but in velvet, and at the present moment Aunt Maggie and Jinny are attaching a hood to it because I'm not going to wear a hat, and I couldn't possibly go out without a covering to my head, could I?"

"You're being saucy."

She stared at him, then said quietly, "You haven't said yet if you like it or what I look like."

How could he say what she looked like? For the very sight of her was bringing heat to his body which a large hot rum had never accomplished. Of a sudden he had the urge to dash upstairs and change and say, To hell! with how I look, because once she was let out in public looking like that she'd be eaten alive. She didn't look as if she belonged to this earth. That would never be made apparent to anyone until she spoke and they discovered she had a mind of her own. He forced himself to say, "It looks bonny. You both make a bonny pair."

She turned now to Nancy, saying, "Do you hear that, Nancy? We both make a bonny pair. What does that word convey to you? A new Easter frock, or a clean pinny? Couldn't he say, we are two beautifully dressed women, charming, fascinating, full of female wiles? Anything but not just bonny."

Nancy's laugh rang out. "Oh, Belle, don't tease him, you know he thinks you look wonderful."

"How can you tell that, Nancy?"

Belle's voice was quiet now, a solid note of enquiry in it. And Nancy, after a moment, answered, "Oh I can always tell."

A voice from the doorway now interrupted, saying, "Are you two ready? Mr and Mrs Twaite are here."

Nancy moved towards the voice and so to the door, but Belle remained standing looking at Freddie. And now she said softly, "Your face isn't too bad, you could have come."

"I will next time."

"That's a promise?"

"Yes, that's a promise."

"I'll see you in the morning then."

"You'll see me later on tonight. I'll be here when you get back."

Without further words she turned from him and went from the room, and he sat down again by the fire. And when Maggie came in a few minutes later, she began abruptly, "We'd better get more steak on that face of yours and pull it together quickly, because if that one hasn't an escort soon I'll have to see about engaging the militia." Then sitting opposite to him, she sat quiet for a moment before asking, "Did you ever see anyone so beautiful in your life?"

And he answered simply, "No; I never have, Maggie. I never have."

3

A week later, on a Tuesday, he made his way by train to Newcastle. His visits to Newcastle he always found interesting; and this morning's was no exception for in the first class compartment there was a man who told him he was due to appear at the Court of Conscience in the Guildhall, and, as everybody knew, this court was held for debts under forty shillings, yet this man was travelling first class, and he had wanted to ask him why he could afford to travel thus if he was in debt for under forty shillings. But he refrained, for "mind your own business" was part of his motto.

In the city, he would make for the quayside, not to do business at the Harbour Master's Office or the Town Dues Office, or yet at the Assay, but, as he put it, to have a crack here and there and pick up bits of information that might assist Maggie in her next deal.

Then he liked walking the main streets: to stop at the Theatre Royal in Grey street, and then the Assembly and News Rooms in Westgate Road. He had dropped in there once or twice; you could learn a lot if you had time to stay; as you could in the Central Exchange and News Rooms in Grey Street. Oh, he could spend a day, a week, even as much as a month in the city and not get tired of the sights and sounds. As for the churches, God in heaven! they were spewed all over the place. A close second was the Baptist Chapels, then the Methodists, and places that housed denominations he had never heard of before. But there was only one Catholic Church in the city, that was in Clayton Street. He remembered old Mr McNeil as far back as twenty years ago: he used to walk from North Shields right out here on a Sunday morning just to go to Mass. Everybody thought he was strange. Well, weren't all Catholics strange; and in his case it was proved so when he left a decent job and moved to Newcastle and to a starvation wage so that he could be near his church. Religion was a funny thing. He was glad he had nothing to do with it.

But today he wasn't here specifically to roam the quayside, nor to satisfy his desire to know more of the city and what it held; he was here to find the whereabouts of the eating house called Cora's. And he found it. It was tucked away in a side street not a stone's throw from Grey Street. The street was narrow but it would take a carriage. There was a swinging sign above a half bottled-glass door, and it said simply, "Cora's Coffee House." A big bottled-glass window to the left side of the door prevented outsiders from seeing in, but which evidently let in a great deal of light, as he saw when he opened the door and stepped into a long room.

He stood for a moment looking about him. Half of the room, he saw, was taken up with tables of various sizes, some to hold twelve, others simply for two people. It was only half past twelve in the day but most of the tables were occupied. There was a quiet buzz of conversation, threaded here and there with laughter.

He walked down an aisle between the tables and when he saw a small and unoccupied table he sat down at it. He was now at the end of the dining area. In front of him was an open space that took up the width of the room and was about twelve feet deep. This, he imagined, was the floor on which Belle had joined in the dance with the man who had requested the pleasure of her company, and to whom, as the Twaites said, they gave their permission because he was a gentleman, one of a small company dining at a nearby table, all of whom had clapped long and loudly when Nancy had sung. Behind the space was a narrow stage, in the corner of which was a pianoforte, and beyond this was what looked like a small glass-partitioned office. The door to the side of it apparently led into the kitchen quarters, for from it now there emerged a waitress carrying a tray on which were three plates of steaming food. Behind her came a youngish man, he too was carrying a tray and on it two brown jugs of steaming coffee, and as he passed close to him he could see that it held four colourful mugs and a bowl of brown sugar too.

Slowly he turned his head and took in more closely the other occupants of the room. They were mostly men of a business type by their dress. The few women present seemed to be in a family group.

The waitress came up to him now, saying politely, "Yes, sir, and what can I serve you?"

"Well, what have you got?"

"Tis hot-pot the day or rabbit pie. Now that's got a very nice crust. But if you want something cold and light there is pork brawn with red cabbage and new bread. That's very tasty." She nodded at him.

Pork brawn, red cabbage, and new bread. He'd never heard of such a mixture, but he'd try anything for a first time. So he said, "I think I'll have the cold."

"You'll like that, sir, I think . . . an' coffee?"

"Yes; coffee please."

Within the next twenty minutes or so and during which he ate and enjoyed the strange meal, a number of people passed up and down the long room making their way to and from the glass office from where he caught glimpses of a face that looked plastered with powder; at least that's what it looked like from this distance. It wasn't until some minutes later that he went to the partition and had a clearer view of the face through the glass that he drew in a sharp breath as the person spoke, asking, "Did you enjoy your meal, sir?"

His mouth opened twice before he answered, "Yes. Yes, thank you."

"That'll be one and fourpence, sir."

He now placed one and six on the narrow mahogany counter, then pushed it through the arched aperture in the glass towards her. And when he said hesitantly, "That'll be all right," she said, "Oh, thank you, sir. I hope you come again."

He made no answer to this but just inclined his head towards her while his eyes took in once again the heavily powdered face.

Out in the street he walked slowly. It couldn't be, but it was. She hadn't recognised him. Well, would she? How many years ago was it since she clapped eyes on him, fourteen? fifteen? Yes, it must be fifteen. He had been a scrap of a thing, and look at him now. But she hadn't changed, not really. Well, she couldn't change her face, no powder could hide all those pock marks. And then there was the eye dropping into the corner.

How strange. Yes indeed how strange that she would own such a place as that. But did she own it? Yes, he imagined she did. But where would they get the money to start a place...?

Don't be an idiot, he was yelling at himself. Think back to the day when you last saw her in the garden. And what had she said? "Oh, don't worry; we're all right. And he thought he was clever with his hidey-holes."

They had likely left just enough to satisfy the old lady who came to take over.

Well. Well. Well. Cora's Coffee Shop. And her name was Connie. Should he tell Maggie? No; at least not yet because she would be made to wonder why not one of the three of them had come over to North Shields to see how the child was faring. But then hadn't they gone to Scotland? Yes, but according to Nancy they had been open about a year here. And there was something else to worry about. Belle had been there and she would likely want to go again. Yet, it wasn't likely if they hadn't kept track of her, that they would recognise her. But should it come to their ears that Maggie Hewitt was her aunt, they wouldn't have to even put two and two together.

But then what could they do? What would they want to do? They hadn't done anything so far, and there was one thing sure, they wouldn't want their own affairs to be looked into too closely, because where could three such people get enough money to start a business in Scotland and then take such a place in the centre of the city where rents were high. And they would be high for a place like that. Then they would have to have a licence for their entertainment side of it. Yes, where would they have got the money?

Well, the only thing he would have to see to now was that Belle didn't go back there again.

It was as he was making his way through yet another side street that would bring him out into Northumberland Street that he saw ahead of him a man coming out of a jeweller's shop. It was, you could say, a small insignificant shop which had no fine display of expensive rings, bracelets, and necklaces, no gentlemen's watches and chains or ladies fobs, but it seemed to deal mostly with the mending of old clocks, an assortment of which was displayed in its narrow window.

Freddie had become acquainted with the shop some years ago through Maggie, for she had not been above acting as go-between for a little merchandise brought into port by some sailor. But, as she admitted herself, she had never really dealt with anything big until she took the two diamonds and the ruby to Mr Taylor. And that was only five years ago when their value had trebled, for up till then they had lain in her wall safe between the years eighteen forty-six and eighteen fifty-five.

Maggie had seen she was given a good price for those three bits of glass, even though, as she had said at the time, it was nothing to what Mr Taylor would have got when he deposited them in London. Yet she liked Mr Taylor, and so did he. As far as his underground trade went he was fair.

How Mr Taylor had escaped the law over all these years, Freddie told himself, he would never know, unless he had a friend up in the High Court. And that could well be possible. Oh, yes, yes, quite possible. As he was sure had Mr Larry Freeman who was now walking ahead of him and who no longer galloped about on his horse but drove in a fine carriage and pair between his equally fine house on the outskirts of Newcastle and his office where he transacted most of his business.

But now, seeing him come out of Mr Taylor's jeweller's shop, it was apparent to Freddie that he still had his hand in the old games.

Freeman had evidently seen him, for he stopped and, when Freddie came abreast of him, he greeted him in a manner that was both condescending and jocular.

"Well, well! Who do we have here on this fine day? It isn't Freddie Musgrave. It must be all of six months since I saw you. I believe you're still sprouting."

Freddie forced back words his irritation was prompting him to utter. By now he should have become used to this form of address, for such it had been over the years. What he did say, with a smile and which flumoxed Mr Freeman not a little, was, "The day, Mr Freeman, when you address me as man to man I shall know then that you have reached maturity, as I myself did as far back as when I was fourteen."

It was as if a dark shadow had passed over Larry Freeman's face. And, aiming now to come back with a retort to equal the young snipe's, as he thought of him, he said, "As a dirty little runner you were always nimble on your feet, and now seemingly the quality has gone to your tongue, which is a much more dangerous place to harbour a talent."

"Quite right. Oh, you are quite right, Mr Freeman. As is a fact that when one person knows so much about the other it is advisable for both to be civil. What d'you say?"

The joviality went out of his tone now as he added, "And to remember, Mr Freeman, that I was a child when I was connected with your racket, and that I was used by elders. But since I was taken under the wing of Miss Maggie Hewitt, I was, as the preachers would say, saved, and have since lived a blameless life, a state which can't be claimed by everyone." A slight mocking note had returned to his tone, and with the merest lift of his tall hat he left the older man glaring after him.

He made his way now down an alley leading to the main thoroughfare, but when he reached it he found that he was shaking slightly. It wasn't exactly with fear, but he had to admit to a certain apprehension. It was rarely he came in contact with the man, but when he did he remembered Maggie's warning to play dumb with him, because she saw him as a dangerous fellow, but today he had forgotten her warning. And recalling it, he knew he had been stupid in rising to the man's bait. Where there had before been merely condescension on Freeman's part, now there would be the desire to get even and to bring him low in some way. He knew the type: there were many Freemans kicking about, and back in the home town too. Oh yes, he was reminded time and time again that he had come up from being a bare-arsed quay brat.

It wasn't a good day, he decided. That business of finding out who owned Cora's made him ask himself, if Connie Wheatley found out who Belle really was, would she keep her tongue quiet? He didn't know, he just didn't know. And then there was this encounter with Freeman. No, it hasn't been a good day; and being such he should be looking forward to getting home to Maggie and Belle. And he was . . . to Maggie yes, but not to Belle.

4

He was rather late in getting back for he had walked slowly from the station to the house, wondering whether he should tell Maggie about the identification of the owner of the Coffee House. But the choice was settled for him once he entered the house because not only was Belle in high spirits but Maggie too seemed to be quietly pleased about something, for she did nothing to quell Belle's exuberance as she rushed to him, crying, "Where do you think you've been all day, Mr Frederick Musgrave, leaving two lone, helpless females to wander the waterfront where anything can happen, as you've told me time and time again, especially to young ladies who will be so foolish as to wear skirts that only reach to the top of their boots?"

"What's this? What's this?" He took off his hat and coat and hung them in the cupboard in the hall, then followed both her and Maggie into the sitting room.

"Have you had a nice day, or should I say, a successful one?" It was Maggie looking at him now as he sat himself down in a chair by the fire. And in a flat voice he said, "Yes. Yes, miss, I've had what you'd call a moderately successful day business-wise, nothing though to make me jump about and act like a hill goat while the mother goat looks on approvingly." He looked from one to the other. "Well now, I'm just bursting to know what's happened to brighten your day."

"Nothing much." Belle had taken a seat opposite him and she shrugged her slim shoulders now as she said quietly, "But it's been a very pleasant day, hasn't it, Aunt Maggie?"

"Yes; yes, you could say it's been a very pleasant day."

"For all concerned?" He again cast his glance between them

165

and they looked at each other now and laughed as they said together, "For all concerned."

"We've been in pleasant company; that is up till now." Belle made a prim face at him. And when he made no response, Maggie, her voice returning to normal, said, "Go and put the kettle on, Belle, that's a good lass."

It was noticeable to them both that Belle hesitated for more than a moment before obeying. And when the door had closed on her, Freddie, looking at Maggie, said, "Well, tell me. What's all this about?"

"Nothing really; yet it could be something. It's like this. You know the man who asked her to dance at that Coffee House? Well, there he was in town today. They recognised each other, and I must say, Freddie, he's a gentleman. Well, of course, I'm going by his manner, his speech, and his attitude. He asked if he could walk with us, and he came down to the quay. Well, I wasn't going to the office and leave her with him, so the three of us walked further along and we chatted. He seemed to know quite a bit about shipping, but from the Newcastle end, and he was as worked up about the river as any of us. Apparently he has a small house in Newcastle and another in the country somewhere. Well, the top and bottom of it is I could see she was happy and a bit smitten. And who wouldn't be, because he was quite charming. But as I said, I wasn't leaving her with him; and apparently he didn't want me to, and so when he asked if we would join him in a glass of wine, there we were, sipping wine together in the best hotel in town. Following this, we said goodbye, he with the hope that we would meet again. Well, Belle and I went down to the office, and she stayed with me and seemed to be very interested in all that went on. And it must have been about half past three when I left Andy to finish up, and we made for the town again, because she had decided there was a hat in Franklyns that she would like. So there we were and there he was again coming towards us as before. There was nothing planned; we all laughed. It happened that he was on his way to the station, but he said the trains run every half hour so would we like to have a cup of tea with him. Well—" She made a small movement with her head and her voice was low and sad as she went on, "I could see she was happy. And she's on eighteen, Freddie, and youth goes so quickly, so I couldn't put a spoke in. If he hadn't been so nice and of the class he is I likely would have. But you know what I want for her, and you know what she's entitled to." The last words were stressed. "The top and the bottom of it was, we had tea, and he asked us to a musical evening in Newcastle. Really, as you know, under these circumstances he was asking her but he couldn't have her without me, but he's a very, very pleasant sort of fellow. So there it is."

Freddie stared at her in not a little astonishment. If the man had been interested in her herself she couldn't have seemed more pleased. He said flatly, "What's his name?"

"Marcel . . . Baxter, that's how I think it's pronounced. It sounded French to me, and there could be a little of the foreigner in him. Anyway—" She reached out and put her hand on his knee, saying now, "Be happy for her, Freddie. He mightn't be the one, he could just be passing through sort of, but he's a good start. After mixing with someone like him she won't pick lower."

"*Maggie!* You've had enough experience to know that a smooth tongue and a velvet jacket doesn't go to make the man."

"Oh, I know, I know, nobody better. And don't you forget"—her voice was harsh now—"it was me that taught you to distinguish between the gold and the dross."

After a strain-filled moment, he said, "How old is he, a young boy?"

"*Oh, no, no.*" She shook her head. "I would say he's your age. Well, perhaps a little younger."

"I hope you know what you're letting her in for."

"Well, she's got to be let in for something before much longer. You know that, don't you?"

"Yes, yes, I know that. But whoever she marries will have to be put in the picture. Have you thought of that?"

"Yes, I'm well aware of that. And don't shout at me. Anyway, here she comes. And for goodness sake take that look off your face and"—she was hissing now—"face up to facts, she sees you as a brother. Face up to it, man."

As Belle entered the room he rose, saying, "I'm going to have a wash."

Belle, now looking at Maggie, asked, "What's the matter with him?"

"Oh, don't take any notice; he's at sixes and sevens with himself."

"Aunt Maggie"—she bent towards her—"is there something

167

wrong with him? I mean, he hasn't been the same since I came home. Well, not since he was knocked about that night. Do you think he regrets breaking it off with May?"

"*Oh, no.* I should say not. I think he's been trying to break away for some long time before now."

"I get upset when he acts like this, because he wasn't pleased about my enjoying that evening with Nancy, just because I danced with that man."

She laughed now, adding, "Why did I say, that man?" And her smile widened and her voice softened as she went on, "He is nice, isn't he, Aunt Maggie? Different."

"Yes, he's nice and he's different, but you'll meet a lot of nice and different men before you're much older, so don't get too excited about this one. But I admit, he's quite good to start on."

"Oh, Aunt Maggie, good to start on! What do you think they're going to do, line up for me to choose from?"

Her voice serious now, Maggie said, "Yes, yes, girl, be patient and they'll line up for you to choose from."

"I . . . I don't like to think that way, Aunt Maggie."

Maggie looked up into the serious face, "Well," she said, "it shows that you're not a flibbertigibbet. But all I say is don't set your heart on the first man that's nice to you."

"I won't." She bent and put her arms around Maggie's neck. "But he was nice, and so amusing and entertaining." Then mischievously she added, "Are you looking forward to going to the concert, the musical evening with him, Miss Hewitt?"

"Yes, I am. But you never know, I might have a cold that night and neither of us will be able to go."

"Oh, you wouldn't, Aunt Maggie, would you?"

"You never know. Anyway, just remember this"—she put out her hand and stroked the pale cheek—"whatever I do for you it will be done for the best."

5

It was almost two months later when Freddie met the "gentleman," and emotions in the house had been alternating between very high and very low throughout that period. But the height and the depth were experienced during the morning of the day in early December when the gentleman was to come to tea. Maggie had decided it was time they returned his hospitality for, since they had first met him, he had accompanied them to two concerts and an exhibition. But on that day instead of the gentleman turning up for tea he sent a messenger with a letter, not for Belle, but for Maggie. The letter had expressed his apologies and his keen disappointment at not being able to keep the appointment, explaining that he had been called away on business and that he would contact them when he returned. Would she please convey his deep regret to Miss Belle for the loss of her company. He remained, her faithful servant, Marcel Birkstead. The writing was small and neat.

Freddie had repeated the name aloud after Maggie had handed him the letter; he looked at her and said, "You said his name was Baxter."

And she had answered, "Well, it's pronounced like that."

"It reads like Birk . . . stead, to me." And he had added, "Where have I heard that name before? We have no one on the books of that name, have we?"

"No, but we've got a couple of Baxters."

"But this isn't Baxter," he had insisted.

Belle's reaction had been one of keen disappointment. And when she had said to Maggie, "He could have stated when we could expect him back," Freddie had turned on her sharply, saying, "Has it reached that stage where he's got to be account-

169

able for his actions to you?" And to his amazement she had cried at him, "Yes! Yes, it has"; then rushed from the room. And he had looked at Maggie and said, "Well now, what about that? You've never indicated that things have gone as far as this."

And she had replied simply, "Because I didn't think they had. In fact, there's been times of late when I thought she was going off him, especially last week after he had cut into her telling of an incident at school rather sharply."

"You didn't see him last week. At least I wasn't told of it."

"No; you weren't told of it"—her tone had been harsh—"because I didn't want to go through another black period when you never open your mouth until you're forced to. And let me tell you, your mother's noticed it too, and Nancy." Then, her tone changing, she had said in a voice a little above a whisper, "Look, Freddie; you've got to let her go," and on this he had turned on her and yelled, "Why? Tell me why." And she had hissed back at him, "Because as I've told you she doesn't think of you in that way, and if you brought such feelings as you harbour into the open nothing would be the same between you ever again. She'd even become afraid of you. I know. I'm sure of it. You're like her father. What I mean is, you've taken the place of him over the years."

"Ten years older and like her father."

"Ten years can appear like fifty to a girl of eighteen. *Thirty* is old. I know myself how I thought of age at that stage of my life. But that's beside the point." She had paused as though thinking back; then she had ended, "What is the point, and you must get it into your head, is that she'll never think of you but in the light of some sort of a parent." . . .

Christmas had not been very gay. He had accompanied the two of them to the Coffee House because Nancy was singing there again, and only Nancy had seemed to enjoy the evening. But then she had reasons of her own for her added happiness, for a young man, also from North Shields, had come to hear her sing. She had known him for sometime: he had often spoken to her in the town. From the beginning she had liked his smell, his voice, and his hand on her arm as he had guided her across the road, which, of course, was quite unnecessary as she knew her way.

At first this acquaintance with the young man had caused laughter in the house especially from her father; but now both he and Jinny were very concerned for he was a customs officer and, as such, was considered an enemy of the people, especially of Robert's mates, who still at times kept him supplied with a decent drink and baccy. As Jinny had said to Freddie, it couldn't have been worse if she had taken a fancy to a policeman.

The meeting happened on the third Saturday in January when the sky was low and the air was so cutting it penetrated the thickest of clothes, and the general opinion of the weather was that they were in for it. There had been a slight fall of snow earlier in the month but nothing that could stop traffic. But on this day the sky was laden and everyone knew that the snow was coming and that it would be heavy.

There was a blazing fire burning in the sitting room. Maggie had acquired what was called a Chesterfield. The couch was set opposite the fire and Belle was curled up in one corner of it, reading, while Maggie sat in the other crocheting a shawl. She liked crocheting, and Saturday and Sunday afternoons were the only daytime hours she allowed herself to relax in this way. She closed the Quay Office at one o'clock on a Saturday which caused a certain amount of upset in other offices on the quay in which the clerks had to work till five o'clock.

Jinny now appeared at the door. She was holding a large bass bag. "I'm off now, miss," she said. "An' I hope I'll be able to find me way back on Monday. If not the big fellow there"—she nodded towards Freddie, sitting in the leather chair—"better come and dig me out."

"Now have you got everything you want?"

"Yes, thank you, miss. With this lot I could last out a week if we were snowed up." She jerked the bag in her hand; then said, "Well, so long now"; and added, "By! you all look nice and comfortable there."

Freddie rose from the chair and was about to make a remark when the sound of the front door bell ringing brought their eyes questioning each other.

It was Maggie who said, "Who can this be? Tis neither the butcher, the baker, nor the candlestick maker on a Saturday afternoon."

"Tis likely the Duke of Northumberland."

Maggie thrust out her hand towards Belle, saying, "Could be at that, miss. You never know."

Belle was smiling back at her as she said, "No, you never

know; but there are some people who wouldn't be impressed."

"I'll answer it." Freddie was following his mother out of the room, and when she crossed the hall to leave by the back door, he checked her, saying, "Come out this way"; and she laughed into his face. "Why not? Why not indeed?" she said.

When he opened the door they both stared at the man standing on the step. But before he was able to speak Jinny sidled past them, saying, "Well, see you on Monday, lad."

The two men stared at each other, the visitor looking as surprised as Freddie but not so straight-faced. "Yes? What can I do for you?"

"I . . . I have called to see the Miss Hewitts. My name is Marcel Birkstead."

He did pronounce it like Baxter, only drawn out.

Freddie glanced towards the sitting room door before he said, "Come in."

"It looks as if we might have snow." He was offering his high hat to Freddie now.

"I'll take your coat."

"Oh, thank you. Thank you."

Freddie could already see what had got the women, both of them: there was a quiet courteous charm about the fellow. But he was asking himself, and loudly, where he had seen him before; he could swear he had met up with him somewhere.

He now walked towards the sitting room door and, thrusting it open, he said, "You have a visitor."

Both Maggie and Belle were on their feet now, and Freddie could have described Maggie's face as a beam, she was smiling so widely, but not so Belle. Belle's manner, he was surprised to observe, was what could be described as decorous, quietly decorous.

"Good afternoon, Mr Baxter," she said.

"Good afternoon, Miss Belle; and you, Miss Maggie. I'm sorry if I'm intruding."

"You're not intruding, man, sit down. Sit down." Maggie indicated a chair, and once he was seated she began, "You got your business over then?"

"It wasn't quite all business; I . . . I was rather unwell for a time, caught a bit of fever."

"Oh, I'm sorry to hear that. And yes, I can see that, you still look peaked. Well now, what would you like to drink? Something to warm you on this cold day? I could offer you tea, or something very much stronger and hotter."

He smiled widely now, saying, "Tea will be excellent. I'm very partial to tea."

"Well, tea it shall be; and I'll go and make it."

"You'll do no such thing; I'll see to it."

Maggie turned on Freddie now, saying, "And you'll do no such thing. Sit yourself down there. Anyway, you've never made a decent cup of tea in your life."

She laughed, and the visitor laughed, and Belle smiled; but Freddie, sitting down on the corner of the couch, looked at the visitor who was now looking at Belle and explaining that he had been as far as Harrogate over the past weeks.

Where had he seen him before? He was a man of more than medium height, not quite as tall as himself, but much broader. He had deep blue eyes and thick fair hair that framed his longish face; his mouth was wide and full-lipped; his skin at the present moment, pale. He had very expressive hands. He seemed to talk with them, which to Freddie's mind bore out the idea that he could be partly foreign as his Christian name suggested, because the few Frenchmen he had come across always seemed to be waving their hands or their arms around. His voice was pleasant, what he supposed Belle would call cultured.

But where had he seen him before? He had come across him somewhere; he could swear on it.

The man was addressing him now: "I was saying to Miss Belle that there is to be a Grand Ball at the Assembly Rooms in the city. It would complete a foursome if you would join us, Mr Musgrave."

Freddie looked from one to the other. He had missed what had gone before, but Belle must have already accepted his invitation. He replied coolly, "I'm afraid I'm no hand with my feet, so to speak; I've never had time for dancing."

"Don't be silly, Freddie; you've danced here in this very room. On New Year's morning you jigged."

"I don't think they would appreciate our jigging at the Assembly Rooms, Belle. However, we'll see."

"Will one of you gentlemen kindly take this tray from me?"

Maggie had pushed the door open with her buttocks, and when they both sprang forward it was the visitor who reached her first; and she said, "Thank you. Thank you."

173

There was a silver tea service on the tray and the best china.

The tray set on the table, Maggie began to pour out, saying as she did so, "You take lemon with your tea, don't you, Mr Baxter?"

"Yes. How good of you to remember."

"Well, it isn't everybody who has such tastes. Here, Belle, pass that to Mr Baxter. Freddie, you'll have milk as usual?" She cast what could have been a naughty glance towards Freddie, and he nonplussed her for a moment by saying, "No, I'll take it straight."

"Oh, you'll take it straight. Very well, very well."

The conversation turned to the weather: the snow being imminent; how long it might last; whether it would go on for weeks as it had done in past years; would the ice in the river hold up the shipping more than the sandbanks have done? And this went on until Freddie asked a straight question: "What is your trade, Mr Baxter, or should I say, profession?"

"Oh—" The man shrugged one shoulder now and, picking up his cup again from the small side table, he looked at it before he said, "I don't think I can lay claim to either. I was left at school too long, and then I went to University, but didn't shine there and I came down before I should. I then had what they called scarlet fever, which laid me low for a time; since then I have dabbled a little in this and that, buying property mostly. My grandmother owns mills and warehouses in the city; and so now and again I might supervise a cargo coming in or going out. Which reminds me, speaking of my grandmother, she has expressed a wish to meet you all."

He included Freddie in his glance. "And so when the weather is a little more clement, fit for travelling, especially for crossing the river, I would like you all to come to tea one day."

"Your house is at yon side of the river? I thought it was in the country."

"Yes; yes, it's what you call the country. It's well past the outskirts of the town and the villages. It was, at first . . . well, just an ordinary country house with a minimum of land, but over the years my grandmother, who is a real innovator, has extended the property, and the land. Oh yes, certainly the land. She loves land, more so than I do, I'm afraid. Now we have nearly fifty acres whereas in the beginning it was about six. How much land she would have acquired had she always lived there I can't imagine; but she only took over when my father died. I was ten at the time, and The Towers in those days seemed a gaunt, dull. . . ."

Freddie had sprung to his feet. What he would have done next he didn't know because he was seeing a man sitting in front of him, his nose almost touching his, and saying, "You are to forget what you heard and saw last night. If you divulge . . . I mean, if you talk about it to anyone it will come back to me and I have ways and means of paying for services done, good and bad. You understand me?"

But the vision of the man was swept from his mind when he heard the clatter of Maggie's teacup dropping onto the saucer and her squeal when the tea spilled over her lap.

"What is it, Auntie? What is it?"

Belle had her arms around Maggie's shoulders, and when Maggie muttered something about feeling faint Freddie pushed Belle aside and, bending down, he almost lifted Maggie from the couch and led her from the room, shouting over his shoulder to Belle as he did so, "Come along! Belle, and see to her."

Belle turned a startled and apologetic glance on the man who had been in her mind every day for weeks now, and she said, "I'm sorry."

"Please, please, don't be. I'll take my departure; and I'll call again, if I may?"

"Oh yes, please do." She was backing from him, and he, walking towards her, asked softly, "You would like me to?"

She nodded twice, then gulped before answering, "Yes. Yes, I would like you to." Then she turned and ran from the room. . . .

Maggie was in her bedroom sitting by the side of the window and Freddie was bending over her, saying, "Drink this. Drink it all up."

As Maggie took the glass from his hand, Belle said, "What is it, Aunt Maggie? that pain again?"

Maggie nodded just the slightest, but Belle said, "Then we must call the doctor." And she looked up at Freddie. "Call him at once."

"Be quiet!"

"What did you say?"

"I said, be quiet. She doesn't need a doctor, not at the moment."

"Well, if she doesn't need a doctor now I wouldn't like to see her when she does."

"Belle." Maggie's voice was soft. "It's as Freddie says, I don't need a doctor at the moment. Now be a good lass: go and set the table for dinner; I know Jinny left a pie in the oven, see if it's done, will you? And you could put the vegetables on."

"You want to get rid of me, don't you?" The young girl's face was stiff, as was her body. "There's something here I don't understand. I'm not a child any longer, and I feel there's an explanation."

"By God! there's an explanation, girl, and when you get it you won't like it. Go and do as Maggie says."

Perhaps more so than the words the fierceness in his face and tone made her shrink back from him. Then the tears spurting from her eyes, she turned and ran from the room.

"Oh, my God!" Maggie put up her hand and lifted the hair back from her brow. "What lies before us, lad? I knew it would come sometime, but not like this. And she's gone on him, deep, and he on her. And he's a nice enough fella. You could see for yourself."

"Anything that's sprung from Gallagher can't be nice, Maggie. I felt something the moment I saw him. I knew . . . I knew I had seen him before; I'd had that face close to mine. He's a spitting image of his father, almost like a twin only a bit younger. Well, there's one thing sure, she'll have to be told, and right from the beginning."

"No, Freddie. How can we do it!"

"How can we not do it, Maggie?"

"Yes, you're right, how can we not do it? But—" She pulled herself further back into the chair and somewhat eagerly now, she said, "You did mention, if you remember, that there was some question of her mother having gone a bit astray with a sea captain or somebody. If that was the case. . . ."

"Don't lay any stock on that, Maggie. The woman, as I recall, was raving at the time, in the throes of labour, and she likely wanted to get the better of him. And who wouldn't! because he was a beast of a fella, frightening. Those three who looked after the house only stayed on because they were on a good thing, as regards food and pay, and both of these were hard to come by in those days. And by the way, Maggie, there's more you should know. I've kept it back from you to save your peace of mind, but that Cora's Coffee House is owned by one of them, if not the three of them. Connie, as I told you, the daughter, is the cashier. She didn't recognise me but I recognised her in spite of the flour on her face. As I told you, she's covered with the pox and has a deep caste in her eye. And I'd like to bet my life now, she knows who he is because if I recall the resemblance, it's nearly sure she would. And it's almost certain she's found out who Belle is an' all. Oh aye. She came here, as I told you, surprised that it was you who had taken the bairn and not me ma; but, if me guess is right, she's thinking it's best to keep a still tongue in her head because they didn't get the Coffee House on the savings of three servants. You can bet your life on that."

"Well, trouble always comes in three's they say, that's the second. What'll be the third?"

"I can tell you that right now, Maggie. He'll have to be told an' all."

"*Oh, dear God!* Oh, I'm sorry to the heart for that, Freddie, for as much as you say he's like his father, to my mind it might only be in his looks, 'cos I admit, I took to him and can understand Belle's feelings."

"Funny you can understand hers but you can't understand mine, Maggie." It was a quiet statement, and she looked up at him sadly for a moment before she replied, "Yes; yes, I can, Freddie, but as I've told you before, I know her feelings and they don't lie in your direction, not that way ... not the way you would want. And, as God's my judge, I'm sorry at this moment it's so."

He turned from her and stood looking down the room for a long moment before he said, "Well, we can't let her go on in this fashion; we'd better get it over with." He turned to her again. "It's too cold for you to sit in here. Come on back into the sitting room." Slowly she rose from the chair and dispiritedly said, "Yes, we'll go into the sitting room and there take the sparkle out of a young lass's life, because let's face it, once she's got knowledge of her beginnings and such as they were, she'll never be the same again."

6

It was seven o'clock the same evening. The snow had begun to fall. The two lamps with their pink glass frames were filling the room with a warm glow while the fire was burning and crackling brightly. The atmosphere emanated warmth and comfort, but not one of them felt it in any way.

Maggie and Freddie were sitting on the couch now, but Belle sat apart, not in one of the easy chairs set each side of the fireplace, but in a straight-backed chair set a good yard from that end of the couch where Freddie was seated. Her skin had lost its warm tint and even in the glow from the lamp shades it even looked pasty white; and this had the effect of making her eyes look larger still, giving the illusion that they were set deep back in the sockets, and all was emphasized by the black abundance of her hair.

She had sat without speaking for the past half hour: that was when Freddie had stopped talking and Maggie had taken up the story of the night she had brought her across the water. Neither of them, however, as arranged, had made any allusion to what had happened to the man who had pursued them. In fact, they had not mentioned being pursued. But Maggie had gone on to relate that the next day Roderick Gallagher had been missing, and that when, eventually, his body had turned up in the river, it was evident he had been attacked. And at that point Maggie had added, "You need never feel sorry for him, my dear; he wasn't a good man."

It was at that point Belle had spoken when she said quietly, "But he was my father."

Maggie and Freddie had exchanged a quick glance, and it was Maggie who said, "Well, yes, I suppose so." And Belle had raised her voice and cried, "Why do you say, suppose so? He was or he wasn't. Is there something else you are keeping back from me?" to which Maggie had given the non-committal answer: "I wasn't there the night you were born, and you must realise that Freddie here was a little lad." And to this Belle had cried, "Well! for a little lad he seems to have had a very good memory," and then sat without speaking further for almost half an hour until Maggie pleaded: "Say something, dear, please. We . . . we did everything for the best to save you pain."

Such had been Belle's tone that Maggie now expected the girl to retort in anger, but what she said now, and in a quiet tone while looking at Freddie, was, "Is that why I'm afraid of the dark, because I was kept in that room?"

He stretched out and unwound her clasped stiff fingers and just as quietly, and softly, he answered, "Yes, dear, that is the reason. It . . . it was a dreadful place. Even now when I remember it at night, and though the time I was in there was short, I know how riddled I was with fright."

"But why should he want to kill me if I was his own child?"

Freddie swallowed deeply before he said, "He was a jealous man. From what I can gather he imagined your mother might have been . . . well, associating with someone else. You understand?"

"Yes, yes, Freddie, I understand." She withdrew her hands from his and her body moved in the chair as if she was about to rise; but she remained seated and, looking across at Maggie now, she said, "You seemed to hesitate when you were about to confirm that he was my father, why? I can't see that a man would want to kill his child if it was his child. Could . . . could my father have been someone else?"

"I don't know, dear. I don't want to sully the name of your mother."

"Hell! Hell!"

They were both startled. The young girl they looked upon as being incapable of any coarseness was standing glaring at them and swearing at them. And she went on, "Does it matter what my mother did as long as that man doesn't prove to be my father? She could be a whore. . . ."

"We'll have none of that! Now calm yourself down." Maggie too was on her feet, but Freddie remained seated, his head bowed. He knew what was inspiring her to wish to prove that

there was no blood relationship between her and Marcel Birkstead, a name he had no right to use for his name was Gallagher.

"Anyway"—Maggie was shouting now—"there's nothing you can do about it. There's no way you can prove you are or you aren't that man's daughter. But as things stand, you are and that makes our visitor today your half-brother."

"*He's not. He's not.* There's no resemblance. He is very fair and I'm very dark. . . . Was my mother dark?" She was addressing Freddie now. "You saw her on the bed, you said. Was she dark?"

"I cannot recall what she looked like, only that she was a very ill woman."

"If you were there all the time as you say you were and pushed under the bed, you must have heard her say something."

Yes, he had heard her say something, but he couldn't remember her words, only the impression that Gallagher was trying to get a confession out of her that he had not fathered her child. Even now, when the memory was dim in his mind, he knew deep within him that Gallagher had not been the father of the child, the proof of which lay in his determination to get rid of it. So why couldn't he now stand up, put his arms about her and comfort her, saying, "You are not Gallagher's daughter. There is no blood relationship between you and Marcel Birkstead or Gallagher or whatever. So don't look like that, don't change!" But she was already changed. She would never be the same again. His Belle, Maggie's Belle, was gone. In her place was an angry young woman.

She brought his head sharply up as she said, "That woman Wheatley, who owns the Coffee House, you said she was the maid, she could know something. She was bound to know if my mother was meeting another man. I'll go and ask her."

"*You'll do no such thing, girl.*" Maggie was now standing in front of her. "I've looked after you all these years. I've brought you up as your mother might have, in fact, better, because you have been happy in this house and you would have never known happiness in that place across the water, because that man was bad, evil. Now, go to bed. We will talk more tomorrow when we are all in a calmer frame of mind. But remember this"—her hands went out and clutched the thin arms—"I want your happiness. I've always wanted your happiness. So has Freddie. I've always thought about you as my daughter, a daughter I was deprived of having because the man I was going to marry was drowned and my father along of him. For years I was lost. I led a lonely life, and then Freddie came onto my horizon and he altered it. And when he brought you into it, and you've got him to thank for saving your life, don't forget that, girl, always remember that. But when he brought you into my life my existence changed: I became a different woman. I've got that to thank you for too. But at the same time you've got a lot to thank me for . . . and Freddie. Oh, definitely Freddie."

She now watched the face before her crumple, the lips quiver, the eyelids blink, and when a sob burst from her Maggie drew her tightly into her embrace. And her own eyes were wet and her voice had a break in it as she comforted her: "There now. There now. It'll work out. We will do all we can to find out the truth."

Belle slowly withdrew herself from Maggie's embrace and, gulping in her throat, said quietly, "Will he have to be told?"

Maggie turned and looked at Freddie, and they both waited for his answer. And then it came: "Yes, he'll have to be told. Whichever way it works out he'll have to be told."

7

The trains were running on the Sunday but not as frequently as the week-day half hour periods. Freddie boarded one at ten o'clock on the Sunday morning. It was snowing heavily when he alighted at Newcastle. There were no cabs for hire as the horses were finding it difficult to keep their footing on the hilly streets. So it was near eleven o'clock when he reached the Coffee House. It was closed, as he had expected it to be on a Sunday. But he went down an alley-way and knocked on a side door for he had been given to understand that the owners lived upstairs.

He had to rap hard a number of times before it was opened, and there stood a man, old and bent with a shrivelled face and who had no connection in his mind with the driver who had dropped him on the waterfront all those years ago.

He said, "Mr Wheatley?"

"Aye; what d'you want? This is Sunday, we're not open."

"I know that but can I have a word with you and Connie?"

"Who are you?"

"You wouldn't remember me, it's a long time ago: the twelve year old lad you drove one night down to the Shields dockside and dropped him off the cart."

The man took two steps back from him, then muttered something that was like, "God Almighty!" He then pulled the door wider and made a motion with his hand and Freddie stepped into a passageway, and when the door was closed he followed the man up some narrow stairs and onto a landing. It was dimly lit by a small window at the far end, but his feet told him he was walking on carpet. Then he watched the old man thrust open the door and he followed him. It was quite a large room and very comfortably furnished. He saw at once an old woman sitting in a chair by the fire. She had her legs stretched out on a stool and her feet looked swollen. And at the other side of the room and rising from behind what looked like a small mahogany desk was Connie, almost as he remembered her, for she had no flour or powder on her face today: the pocks were evident as was the eye. She came forward slowly, saying, "Good morning, sir."

"Tis no sir," her father was bawling now. "Can't you see who it is! Well, who he says he is, the nipper . . . the runner."

"Eeh! Dear God." The woman in the chair had pulled herself more upright, and she now peered towards Freddie, saying, "I'd never have believed it. You looked stuck there as a little lad, no promise of sprouting. Eeh! I wouldn't have believed it."

He said politely, "How are you, Mrs Wheatley?"

"As you see me, lad, as you see me. Dropsy I've got, so they say. That's what the good God gives you for working hard all your life. Well, I never expected to see you again. Yet why not? Why not? But we haven't been here all that long."

Connie was standing close to him now, looking up into his face.

"You came in a while back," she said, "didn't you?"

"Yes, Connie, I did."

"Funny, I had no inkling, yet there was something about you made me uneasy I remember."

"You needn't be uneasy through me."

"What you after?" It was the man speaking again, and Connie, turning on him sharply, said, "Let him get in first, Da, and then he'll tell us what he's after. Sit yourself down and shut your mouth."

"You'll tell me to do that once too often, you will, you'll see."

"Sit down, Frank." This came from his wife, and the old man sat down in a rocking chair to the side of the fire. And now Connie, indicating a large comfortable leather chair, said to Freddie, "Take a seat."

When he was seated he looked at Connie again, saying, "I got a bit of a start when I recognised you; I never expected to see you at this end again."

"We never really expected to be here."

She had now sat down to the side of her mother and she laid her hand on her mother's where it was resting on the arm of the

chair as she went on, "It was the cold. Ma couldn't stand it. We
think we're badly off here but it's nothing to what it's like in
Scotland. We stuck it for as long as we could. And then there
were the people. We didn't get on: they seemed to speak a
different language. Well they do, don't they?" She gave a small
laugh; and after a short pause she said, "How are you faring?"
but didn't wait for an answer and added, "Well, I heard you were
still with that Miss Hewitt and doing well. But I've never probed,
although Ma here wanted me to go down to North Shields and
see how . . . well, you know, the little miss was faring. But there
never seemed to be time as I have it all on me own hands, I
mean, downstairs, and when you're startin' a business like this
you've got to keep behind people; nobody works like yourself.
You've got to keep your eyes open, although they're a decent lot;
you can't trust anybody these days. We had one in the beginning
who used to bring her family in for meals, an odd one here an'
there, an' slip them plates. Oh, you've got to be on the lookout.
And another thing why we don't hear much is, we keep ourselves
to ourselves."

"Speak for yourself." It was her father again. "I get about
now and then an' I hear things, an' I know a thing or two an' all."

Both his wife and daughter ignored him; and it was Connie
who asked quietly, "How is she?"

"Well, you've seen her at least twice in your eating house."

"I have?"

"Yes. She accompanied my sister, the blind girl who sings."

"Never! Never that one, the one with eyes as dark as sloes
who comes with the blind girl? I thought their name was
Twaite."

"No; Mrs Twaite does the arranging for Nancy. She's my
sister; Mrs Twaite is no relation."

"She's a beautiful girl, your sister, and has a lovely voice. But
the other, to think. . . . And I remember seeing her dance once
with—" She stopped and slowly her hand went to her mouth and
pressed her cheeks tightly inwards. Now she rose to her feet and
looked down at her mother, and then at Freddie before she said,
"Oh my! Oh my! For such a thing to happen, because do you
know who she was dancin' with?"

He evidently surprised her by saying, "Yes; yes I know.
That's why I'm here."

"You know about him . . . I mean, who he is, the Mister

Birkstead, as he calls himself, when it should be Gallagher? He's taken his granny's name. I recognised him the first day he stepped in the door. And when I heard his name I knew it was his granny's. I can see her standing now in the hall, her nose turned up in distaste, saying, 'This place has been neglected.' Then looking at me and saying, 'I'm not really blaming you. It was impossible for one person to keep this house clean, but I won't require you or your mother's services in the future. I am bringing my own staff.' That was Mrs Birkstead. . . . And then there he was that day—I saw him from the office as he came in—he was with two other men and they ordered rabbit pie. I couldn't take me eyes off him; it was as if I was looking at the old master like he used to be when I was a young girl. And I used to think he was handsome in those days, and kindly. He was kindly, wasn't he, Ma?"

"Oh, aye; in his young days he was kindly enough, except at times when his temper got the better of him. That's when he took to the powder to calm him down, I think. But he changed altogether after the first one died. Oh, I'll say. And he married the second one just in time else he wouldn't have had a roof over his head, up to his eyes in gambling debts he was. . . . Would you like a drink, lad? Well, I shouldn't call you lad anymore should I? because you're a well set-up man now. We've got a good port. It comes from the right place. My! I never knew there were so many underhanded dealings went on until we moved to this city."

"Shut your mouth, woman."

"And you shut yours." She now pointed at her husband. "And use your napper, have some sense, 'cos if anybody knows about underhand dealings it's this young man here. He was the best runner the river ever had 'cos the ones that came before him would have bought you at the fore end of a boat and sold you at the aft. Anyway, what about a drink?" When she inclined her head towards Freddie, he said quietly, "No thank you. I take very little, and never any this early in the day."

"Chapel are you?"

He laughed now. "No, no, Mrs Wheatley, not me, never Chapel."

"What have you come for anyway?"

He looked towards the old man but didn't answer him; instead, turning to Connie, he said, "They've become attached,

185

not knowing who they were exactly, it just happened. He called yesterday and I almost recognised him right away. As you said, he's like his father. He came with the intention of asking Miss Hewitt and"—he paused—"Belle to tea. It was then he mentioned his grandmother and that house. I'd understood, and so had Miss Hewitt, that he lived mostly in Newcastle. He seems to have a house here too. Well, she had to be told, we couldn't let it go on. Naturally, she was very upset. I told her everything she should know about the night of her birth and what her supposed father intended to do with her. And it was this word supposed that aroused her curiosity and the fact that there was something odd about a situation where a man would want to kill his own daughter. I had to indicate then that there might be a doubt as to her parentage. But of course there is no way of proving that now, at least I have no way of proving it, but I wondered if any of you"—he cast his glance over them—"could confirm that she wasn't Gallagher's daughter, or on the other hand that she was? I've thought about it a lot and it's probable that she was and that the man was mad jealous of a young and beautiful wife who dared to smile on another man. It happens."

They all sat in silence now, and when he said, "Well?" Frank Wheatley cried, "Well, what d'you want us to do? Look! We want nowt to do with this business. We want to be left alone. We mind our own business, always have, kept ourselves to ourselves. So you can go out the same way that you came in."

"Da, if you don't shut up you know what'll happen, don't you?" Connie nodded slowly at her father and he stared back at her for a moment before looking away and growling something under his breath.

Connie now turned to her mother and said one word, "Ma."

And Mrs Wheatley, addressing herself to her daughter, said, "Well, almost her last words to me were, 'Hang on to it, Betty, for there might come a time when it'll need proof of its true identity,' or words of that kind was what she said. So go and get it."

Connie now turned and went to a bureau in the corner of the room. She pulled open a drawer and seemed to press something; then to his amazement he saw the top of the bureau rise to reveal a six inch high cupboard with a small alcove at each side. He now watched her press what he now supposed must be a button inside the right side alcove, and the small door of the

186

little cupboard sprang open. From where he was standing he only had a glimpse of the contents but his impression was there were two small chamois leather bags lying on the floor of the cupboard, and stuck at the back was a letter. Quickly she picked up the letter between her finger and thumb as if it was something hot. Then she closed the door, pressed the top of the cupboard down until it once more formed a level shelf on the top of the bureau.

Bringing the letter to her mother, she put it into her outstretched hand. He saw that the flap was open; whatever was in it was certainly no secret to those present. When Mrs Wheatley handed him the envelope, he mouthed the words, "Thank you," but no sound came out. Then he was reading simple words on a single sheet of paper. He noticed that there was a crest embossed at the top of the page and an address in fancy writing.

> I, Mirabelle Gallagher, am about to give birth to a child and I wish to state truthfully that my husband is not the father of this child. The father is one Captain Jose Fordyce. He is of Spanish extraction on his mother's side. But I lay no claim to him as he is a married man with a family and his ship is registered in Spain. He was honest with me and I with him. I am leaving this letter with my faithful servant Betty Wheatley in the hope that she will at some stage give it to the child in order that it should know that in no way is it a part of that demon, the man who is called my husband Roderick Gallagher.
>
> I place myself in God's hands.

Slowly he folded up the single sheet and replaced it in the envelope and handed it back to the old woman, but found he was unable to speak; when he could he looked at Connie and said, "You know, if you don't mind I'll have that drink now."

Quietly Connie stood up and went straight from the room; and after a moment her father pulled himself up from his chair and followed her, banging the door shut as he went out.

"Sit down here, lad." Betty Wheatley indicated the chair that Connie had sat in earlier; and as he lowered himself down into it she pointed to the door, saying, "There's a changed man for you if ever there was one. Some men can stand having money like they can stand drinks, others haven't the stomach for it. We had a little windfall you know, and it went to his head." She glanced knowingly sideways at him, then went on, "If it had been beer he could have managed it, but it was rum. And if you want to slide to hell quickly the best way to do it is on rum, constant like. But Connie keeps him in his place. You know something? He's frightened of her. Not of me mind, not of me, but she's threatened to throw him out time and again. But then she can't, can she? If one goes, we all go. But our time is runnin' out anyway. Connie will be all right, she'll always make a livin'. She's got a head on her shoulders for business so she's set. Aye, lad—" She smiled at him a weary smile as she ended, "We had a little windfall one day. Have you ever had a windfall?"

He smiled gently at her as he said, "Yes, I've had two. The first one was a handful of Roman coins I found in the sand."

She laughed out loud now. "I bet that's when you were a little nipper runnin' the sculler," she said.

"Yes, it was."

She laid her head back on the padded top of the chair and was silent for a moment; then she said, "All that happened such a long time ago. It seems two lifetimes ago. Yet how long is it?"

"Fifteen years."

"Just fifteen years. . . . What you goin' to do about the letter then?"

"I'll tell her."

"And him? Are you goin' to put it all to him?"

"I suppose so, but between you and me, if you want the truth, I'd rather nothing happened between them. The fact is, no matter how nice he looks, how charming he appears he's still that man's son."

"Aye, well. But you cannot put the blame on the children for the sins of the fathers. This fellow must have been brought up by his granny. Now his father didn't have a time like that. In fact, there's something to be said for his side 'cos his old man in his turn gave him hell. I told you once didn't I, how he was pushed in that room. . . . I wonder if they still kept it?"

"I doubt it. I understood from what he had said yesterday the house had been practically rebuilt from the inside by the old lady. . . . Mrs Wheatley," he said.

"Aye? What is it?"

"Do you think you could trust me with that letter?"

She looked at the letter that she was still holding in one

hand, and she sighed as she said, "Well, that's what she said, didn't she? She said, if the time ever came when I thought the child should know from where it sprang, I had to show it the letter. So there you are, lad. Take it to her. But you know something? It's lucky ... it's lucky it's still here, 'cos both of them, both Connie and him"—she nodded towards the door— "plagued me to put it in the fire in those early days when the bairn was upstairs because in one of his rages he was not above ransacking every place in the house. And, as Frank was always saying, if he got an inkling he would tear our quarters apart. But then, as I said, who was goin' to give him the inkling? Yet many's the time I was tempted to do just what they said and burn the thing. But when he didn't come back that next day, nor the next, nor the next, and his horse was found by itself and he hadn't been to the ostler's, well, we knew that wasn't like him, and we knew we were for the road in any case, so we made our plans. And it was a good job we did 'cos it was just two days after he was found that there she was, his mother-in-law, as I told you, and among the odds and ends," she stressed the last three words, "we took away with us I fetched the letter, and it lay in the tin trunk for years up in Scotland quite undisturbed and at times forgotten during the three moves we made. Then when we came here Connie bought that bureau because of its secret drawer, and she put it in there."

Connie now entered the room. She was carrying a tray with three mugs on it, steam rising from each, and her mother, looking at it, said, "Where's he then?"

"He's gone out."

"Has he anything on him?"

"Enough ... enough to get him a pint, no more. Don't worry," she said as she handed her mother a steaming mug; "he'll be back, 'cos it'd freeze you out there."

When she herself sat down she looked from Freddie to her mother and back to him again, and she said, "Ain't life funny. Who'd ever think that one day we'd be sittin' here talkin' like this and that the whole thing that had happened all those years gone is about to come to light."

"Come to light?" Mrs Wheatley was sitting up straight now. "You're not goin' to bring all this to light, are you?" She was looking at Freddie, her face and voice expressing her anxiety. And he answered her: "Not if I can help it, oh no! so don't worry." He tapped the pocket of his jacket now, saying, "I always believe in letting sleeping dogs lie."

"Aye, but this one seems to have one eye open," Connie said. "The fellow mightn't see it like you or us."

"If he wants to marry her"—he drew in a long slow breath—"and I suppose he does if his attention is anything to go by, then he'd want the business kept as quiet as anyone. I should think more so, because although he mightn't have seen much of his father he won't relish his being exposed as the man he was. Anyway—" He now lifted his mug and drained it; then putting it back on the tray, he said, "If you don't mind I'll be making a move because the way it's coming down I think I'm going to have a job to get from the station to the house."

He stood up; then bending over Mrs Wheatley, he took her hand and said, "Thank you for your help. Thank you very much." And she answered, "That's all right, lad. Will you pop in when you're this way again an' let us know how things have turned out?"

He hesitated a moment, then said, "Yes. Yes, I will"; and turning to Connie, he added, "You've got a good business going downstairs. Who does the cooking?"

"I do most of it, but I've got two good lasses in the kitchen. They're learnin' my ways."

"I'm glad things are going right for you."

"Well, as I see it, in this life you've only got yourself to blame if they don't. It's hard goin' at times but if you work at it you'll get there."

"Ah, shut up! lass." They both turned sharply and looked at the woman in the chair. She was sitting bolt upright now and pointing to her legs. "Work hard, you said, and you'll get there. What good did hard work ever do for us? Slaved we did from morn till night an' for what? Don't talk rubbish, lass. What you need in this life is luck and opportunity and money an' to hell with hard work. That's what I say."

As she lay back in her chair seemingly exhausted, they went out of the room together and on the landing Connie said, "She gets bitter at times, 'cos now, when she could be takin' it easy, she's troubled with the water and there seems no cure for it. Doctors or herbalists all say the same, take the medicine. But the swelling goes on. I can understand her being bitter. And she's right, you know"—she nodded her head—"you do need luck, and more so opportunities."

On the dim landing they held each other's gaze for a moment before she turned sharply about, went down the stairs, and opened the door for him. Then saying abruptly, "Mind how you go," she let him out into the street; and as he was about to turn and say a final word of farewell, the door closed.

He remained standing where he was for a few seconds, the snow falling gently on him, and he thought, poor woman. And pity for her enveloped him as it had done when he first saw her face.

Now, as he made his way through the thickening snow under foot and the struggling traffic towards the Central Station, he was lifted back to the night when as a lad he had gone across the river in the little sculler and had felt that his life was changing and that things were about to happen to him. . . .

As he opened the door the house greeted him with warmth and the smell of roasting meat. He had shaken the snow off himself outside, but as he stood now divesting himself of his coat both Maggie and Belle appeared from the kitchen. And as Maggie, ever the housewife, said, "Don't let that drip on the floor! Give it me here. You look frozen. You've been some time. What happened?" he replied quietly, "Give me a chance to get in and I might tell you."

Belle was looking at him intently. She had a white apron over her dress, and she undid the straps and rolled it up on her way into the sitting room, her Ladies' School training acting unconsciously telling her that a lady, even of a small establishment, must not enter her sitting or drawing room attired in an apron.

She dropped the rolled bundle onto the couch, then turned and, going close to him now, she gripped the round collar of his jacket, saying, "Freddie, listen to me for a moment before you start. I . . . I don't know what *you're* going to say but this is what *I* want to say. I want to thank you for all you have done for me. In the first shock I could only think of myself and what this discovery meant to my future, but now I realise that I could have been brought up under such conditions I can't bear to imagine had you not risked your life in trying to save me."

When her arms came round his neck and her head rested on his shoulder he stiffened for a moment. It wasn't the first time she had hugged him. Like a child, she was always free with her embraces; but this was different. His arms went about her and for a moment he was holding a woman, and he pressed her to him and when she raised her head and looked up into his face he had to use all his willpower not to let his mouth fall on hers. But when her lips touched his cheek and seemed to linger there, he pushed her hastily from him, and as he did so Maggie entered the room, saving him from making some verbal response.

"Well, let's hear it," Maggie said as she took a seat to the side of the fire.

Belle had hold of his hand now and they both sat down together on the couch.

He began simply: "It's all right; there was a letter left. Mrs Wheatley's hung on to it all these years. Your mother"—he turned now and looked at Belle—"made a statement in it which clarifies things once and for all." He now pulled the letter from the inner pocket of his jacket, but he hesitated on whom to hand it to first. So, to get out of this little dilemma, he said, "I'll read it."

And he read it. And when he had finished he handed the sheet of paper to Belle, and she looked down at it for a moment. Then her fingers moved round the perimeter of it as if feeling the texture as one would of velvet or silk: he realised that this was the only material connection she had with her mother; her mother had handled that paper the day she was born.

Maggie broke into the girl's inmost thoughts when she said hoarsely, "Well, that's settled then; at least at this end. But what now? Do you make things clear to him?" She looked from one to the other; and it was Belle who answered hastily, "Oh, no! No; there's no need is there? I'm your niece, Aunt Maggie, and you'll always be Aunt Maggie to me, in fact, the mother I never knew."

"Hold your hand a minute." Freddie was pointing a wagging finger from one to the other now. "There's three other people that know. Two of them I could trust . . . well, a bit; but the third, Mr Wheatley, I wouldn't trust him as far as I could toss him. And he's got a drink habit and he gets about. He's just got to let his tongue go loose once and that would be that. No, I think the man should be told, that's if"—and now his voice took on a harder note—"he shows his real intentions. Up till now he's given no indication that he wants to—" he paused, shrugged his shoulders as he paused, then finished, "to marry you."

He was looking at her but she turned her head away, saying, "No, but . . . but I like him." She looked from one to the other now, a shy almost embarrassed expression in her eyes. "And I—" she swallowed before finishing, "I get the impression that he likes me."

"Oh, there's no doubt about that." Freddie was on his feet now, his voice loud, aggressive. "All the lads on the quay like you. As Maggie here said when she brought you from school, the eyes were popping out like pipe shanks on Newcastle Central Station. Oh, yes, quite a number of people like you; but there's degrees in liking. At first I liked May, but what did it come to? Dislike, even worse, and we weren't married. Feelings change." He was nodding slowly at Belle now. "Believe me, dear, feelings change. There's a great deal of difference between liking and loving."

"But of course it's better if you like the one you love." They both turned and looked at Maggie now, and she raised her eyebrows, saying, "That's true. I must admit it's better to start with liking because if you're fool enough to fall head over heels in love at first sight that has the habit of blinding you to liking. And there's many a lass woke up one morning to find that the last thing she feels for a man is liking. But, Freddie's right in many ways, lass. Anyway, the dinner'll be kizzened up to cork so let's eat, because, as I see it, whichever way it goes we'll all need sustenance to face the future."

8

The snow became thicker under foot; then it froze and for a fortnight most traffic was brought to a standstill. People had to be dug out of houses, horses out of snow drifts, and here and there in the country there were tales of people actually starving to death. These might have just been tales, but when a shepherd was found frozen to death in a ditch and another man found dead, together with his horse, people said they had known nothing like it in the last thirty years.

Yet the feeling of affection between liking and loving was proved when the great thaw set in and rivulets up in the hills became streams and streams became rivers and the Tyne swept away low bridges. It was really feared it was going to be another big flood. But in spite of this there came a knock on the door at eleven o'clock on the Saturday morning. And when Jinny opened it there stood facing her the man, in high boots and leggings and a three quarter length coat, the tails of which were dripping water. And she greeted him with, "By! you're wet, sir."

"I am a bit. May I come in?"

"Oh aye. But miss is out and so is Freddie. Miss Belle's in, though."

"It's Miss Belle I've come to see."

"Eeh! Well, you'd better take that coat off and let me dry it by the kitchen fire. But I'll go now and tell her, she's in her room, if you'd like to go into the sitting room, sir, and wait."

"Thank you, but I'm afraid my boots are rather. . . ."

"Oh, don't worry about your boots, sir. These floors are used to all kinds of feet tramping over them."

Jinny hurried up the stairs and, knocking on Belle's door, she said, "Miss! Miss!"

"Yes, Jinny?" Belle appeared at the door.

"Didn't you hear the front door bell go?"

"No. Someone called?"

"Aye, somebody's called, an' they want to see you. So straighten your hair, it's all tousled."

As Belle dashed back into the room and grabbed up a comb from the dressing table she called to Jinny, "Who is it, on a day like this?"

"Aye, that's what I said to meself when I saw him."

Belle was on the landing now and she stared at Jinny for a moment, but neither of them spoke except that Jinny inclined her head forward.

Belle did not hurry down the stairs, she walked down slowly and as slowly across the hall and into the sitting room.

He had been standing with his back to the fire. His legs were steaming. But now he came hurriedly forward, saying, "I'm sorry if I've called at the wrong time."

"How . . . but how did you make it through all the slush and the. . . ?"

"Oh, the trains continue to run and the roads are running too"—he smiled now—"some in two feet of water, I'm afraid."

"You're very wet."

She looked at his still steaming leggings.

"Oh, that's nothing; they'll soon dry. I'm used to being wet anyway, very often through to the skin when out riding."

"Oh, well; won't you be seated?"

He sat in the chair she indicated to the side of the fire; then she took her seat on the couch; and for a moment there was silence between them until he said, "I hope the news is that Miss Hewitt is better."

"Aunt Maggie? Oh, yes, yes; it was just a short spasm. She has a pain in her side at times and . . . and on that day it was a rather severe attack."

Again there was silence; then she was startled by his rising swiftly and seating himself beside her. Then taking her hand, he said, "I've missed seeing you. It . . . it seems like years."

She forced herself to smile and say, "It's only a little over a fortnight," while remembering there was a time not long ago when he hadn't bothered to see her for weeks. But he was away on business then; yet still, there was pen and paper. But why was she questioning herself: he was here beside her, close, and looking into her face, and her heart was racing because she felt he was about to say something that she longed to hear. But she knew he mustn't utter those words until he had been put in the picture of their relationship . . . or their non-relationship.

When she in turn now sprang up quickly, he gazed up at her in some amazement, saying, "What is it? You're . . . you're not pleased to see me? I . . . I thought."

"Yes. I mean, I am pleased to see you, but before you say anything . . . I mean. Oh, what do I mean!" She put her hand to her brow and swung round. And now he was at her side, his hands holding her arms and he was saying, "Yes, Belle; what do you mean? You know what I'm going to say."

"Well, you mustn't say it." She almost thrust him off. "Not yet, not yet. You must talk to Freddie."

"Why should I talk to Freddie? He . . . he has no jurisdiction over you. He's no relation as far as I can understand."

"No, he is no relation"—her words were spaced—"and neither is the woman I call Aunt Maggie."

His brows drew together and a look of bewilderment came on his face. "What are you trying to tell me, something about your parentage? My dear"—he put his hand out towards her again, in a gentle gesture now—"wherever you came from makes no difference to me. You are what you are as I see you: someone beautiful and good, so lovely I can't get you out of my mind."

"Please Mr. . . ."

"I am Marcel, my grandmother and close friends call me Mark."

Her head was bowed now as she said softly, "Please bear with me. There are things you should know, *that you must know.* I . . . I can't tell you, but Freddie can."

"Freddie? Then he *is* some sort of relation?"

"No, no. As I said, he's no relation, but . . . but he knows all about me, much more so than Aunt Maggie." Her voice was a mere whisper now. "Will . . . will you please say no more at the moment until you have talked with him . . . with them both? Please!" She was looking at him again.

"Yes; as you wish. But I repeat, nothing that he has to tell me about you can make the slightest difference to my feelings."

She said now, "Do sit down again. And may I get you a cup of tea?"

He did not give her a direct answer, but surprised her by

putting his hand to his head and running his fingers through his hair and laughing silently before saying, "We could be enacting a play. You playing the little lady to a T, as you were no doubt trained at school, not refusing the suitor yet not accepting him, but offering him tea. . . . Oh! Belle." She was forced to smile, but it was a weak gesture, as she said, "Yes; that's what it might appear like, but to me it is no play unless you look upon the play as a tragedy."

"What!" The laughter died in him, then he added words that could have been a question or a statement: "As serious as that?"

"Yes, as serious as that."

"If that is so, please don't distress yourself any further. I will wait and talk to . . . your Freddie who seems to be such an important factor in your life. When may I expect him in?"

"Any moment. They only expected to be gone an hour because there won't be much business contracted on the water-front today, except that of sweeping out the flood. If you'll excuse me, please, I'll get you that cup of tea."

He said nothing but stood up as she went to leave the room.

It was as she was crossing the hall that she heard the commotion outside the front door and then Maggie's voice saying, "Never again! I don't go down there until the sun is splitting the trees." The door burst open and they both came in shaking themselves, only to stop in the process and look at her, and she, in a dumb show, pointed to the sitting room; then hastily approaching them she whispered, "He's . . . he's here."

"He? You mean?"

She nodded, and Maggie said, "How has he made it in this? It's like Noah's Ark out there."

"He was very wet."

Freddie had said nothing so far; he had taken off his coat and boots and was now holding his hand out for Maggie's boots, and for her coat too. But now he said, "You go on in, I'll be there in a minute."

"I can't go in," Maggie said, "not like this in me stockinged feet," only to be told, "He hasn't come here to look at your feet. Go on in."

"Get my slippers, girl, the pair in the office."

Belle ran past Freddie, and he slowly made his way to the kitchen carrying the wet clothes, but Maggie turned about and went into her sitting room, saying loudly as she entered, "I'm in my stockinged feet; I'm a sight but I'm not making any excuses. I'm lucky to be alive. We've had to practically swim along the front. How are you?"

"Very well, Miss Hewitt, very well. It's a dreadful day. It's been a dreadful two weeks. You were very brave to go out in it."

"And you"—she turned and looked at him as she seated herself by the fire and held her feet out to the blaze—"are very foolish to risk the journey from Newcastle. They tell me the river's up to the arches there."

"Well not quite but it's pretty bad. I think it reached its highest in the night."

"Have you had a drink of any sort?"

"No. Belle . . . was about to make one."

"Oh, well, sit yourself down, don't stand about."

He smiled at her words, a rather sad quiet smile, and when she said, "What's amusing you?" he answered, "You sound exactly like my grandmother; she still treats me as if I were ten; I must have warm underwear; I mustn't go out without a coat in certain weathers; I must take a potion of medicine once a week."

Maggie smiled now, saying, "She sounds like a sensible woman, your grandmother."

"She is"—his voice was quiet—"a very sensible and wonderful woman."

"It's good to hear someone speak well of a relative. Ah"—she turned—"here's the family en masse."

Jinny had entered the room carrying a tray holding cups and saucers and a plate of scones, while behind her Freddie carried another tray bearing the silver tea pot. Belle followed, and she closed the door behind her. But their greeting by Maggie, looking from one tray to the other, was, "We haven't reached the time for afternoon tea yet. Why all the palaver? A cup of coffee I should imagine would have been more suitable."

"I asked if . . . I suggested tea, Aunt Maggie."

"Oh, well, if you suggested tea this is the right way to serve tea, I suppose. Thank you, Jinny."

Jinny said nothing, but her face expressed her thoughts and her voice would indeed have been loud if she had given vent to them.

The noon tea party was a very strained affair, so much so that Belle, of a sudden turning to Freddie, said, "Mr Birkstead has called to . . . to, I think"—she drew in a long shuddering breath—"put a proposition to me, but I told him that first of all he must listen to you and"—she now looked at Maggie—"and to you, Aunt Maggie. So . . . so I will leave you to . . . to tell him all you know about . . . me." And looking at Freddie again, she said, "You may add to it my gratitude for the goodness and kindness I've received from you all these years."

To say that the three people she hurriedly left were embarrassed would be to put it mildly; but at the moment the least so was the visitor. That was until Freddie, looking at the man whom he wanted to dislike but found he couldn't, not wholeheartedly anyway, said, "I can put it all in a nutshell to begin with by saying that but for her mother having an affair on the side with a sea captain, you and she could be half brother and sister."

Freddie watched a look of incredulity pass over the man's face, and when he added, "I was in the bedroom the night she was born and heard your father trying to prise the truth out of his wife and also, when the child came into life, ordering it to be destroyed."

"*What! What are you saying?* What is this all about anyway?"

"Well, sir, I would take that seat again because there's a lot more you haven't heard yet, and it's somewhat of a long and detailed story. So if you please, will you be seated."

The man sat, and for the next fifteen minutes he listened to the details which began with a little boy used as a runner because he had a little sculler boat.

The room was hot, they were all sweating, the visitor most of all, and when he spoke his voice was thin with almost a snarl to it as he said, "You've made my father out to be a scoundrel."

"Well, that's how I saw him, and that's what he really was, although the servants seemed to think that circumstances had made him like that, because his father had given him a hell of a time when bringing him up. Anyway, hasn't your grandmother ever indicated what kind of a man her daughter married?"

"Not to that extent. Hot-tempered, taciturn, but not a potential murderer, or a receiver of stolen goods—" He paused now and his head swung from one side to the other before he said, "and an opium addict. That's what you make him out to be. And now you tell me his servants own the Coffee House. How is it that servants such as they must have been, of the lowest order, come to own a place like that?"

"I don't know anything about that. They had a little saved up, I suppose, and they started in a small way in Scotland. Most businesses start in small ways."

"And his death? Was nothing ever discovered about his death?"

Both Maggie and Freddie resisted an exchange of glances; they looked ahead for some seconds, but when Maggie was about to speak Freddie put it, "He seemed to have been attacked, likely for what he had on him that night. That's all that was known."

"My God! He in his turn must have been murdered then?"

"I know nothing about that part of it. Anyway, you must have enquired before, or been told how your father came to die. You weren't such a small child then; you were ten when you moved into The Towers, weren't you?"

"Yes. I understood he had an accident and was drowned. The matter was not discussed after. I knew that my grandmother had no love for him so she didn't talk of him. The only thing she did tell me was that he loved my mother dearly and was a changed man after she died."

"Yes, he certainly was, and this was demonstrated in the way he treated his second wife, who, by what I was given to understand those years ago, was a beautiful young girl and rich, and he married her not for her beauty but for her money."

"I don't see how she could have brought him much money when he only kept three servants in that big house."

"Again I understand he had kept more, but they didn't stay. Those three were faithful to him, as they had been to his father before him. Servants, sir, are human beings: there's some things they'll stand and some things they won't."

"I'm well aware of that, sir."

"Please. Please." Maggie closed her eyes and lay back in the chair. "Don't let us get on to the merits of servants. The question now is, has all this altered your intentions towards Belle? Don't say yes or nay." She thrust out her arm and held up her hand in a warning gesture. "Give yourself time. It would please us both if you would go now without seeing her and think about it, and take into account that if the relationship or the non-relationship was to leak out, and you never know because there's three other people in this secret, and as you've just stated they were common

200

servants, there could be a scandal even if that letter there"—she pointed to the letter lying on the table to her side—"was produced. There's no way of proving that it was written by Belle's mother. There's only Freddie's word of what he witnessed that night and why the man, your father, would want to get rid of the child, and why those servants risked their necks to keep her alive in what must have been that mad woman's hole up in the attic." Maggie's head went back now because he had sprung to his feet again, and it was evident he was finding it difficult to speak. And when he did his voice was low: "I will do as you suggest," he said; "I . . . I shall think about this. But one way or another, you, I mean, Belle, will hear from me. You can understand this has been more than a shock, it's been a . . . devastating. . . ."

Realising the difficulty the man was in, Maggie rose too and she said quietly, "You're right, and whatever you decide we shall understand." She cast a glance towards Freddie, but he said nothing; instead, he hurried from the room and went into the kitchen and collected the man's coat and hat. But in the hall, as he passed them to him, he said, "If you care, I'll see you to the station, the roads are still very precarious."

"Thank you; but I managed to get here alone, I'll manage to find my way back." He inclined his head towards Freddie, then turned to the door, and on Freddie's opening it he stepped out without further words. He had given Maggie no formal goodbye, but they stayed and watched him splash down the path towards the gate. Then they closed the door and what Maggie said was, "Pray God he finds it too much to stomach, because I fear there is another side to him. I expected him to be shocked, but not to look and speak as he did."

9

Three days later a letter arrived by hand. The bearer said he would wait for an answer. Jinny took the letter into the kitchen where Belle was trying her hand at pastry making. When Belle opened it she saw four words written in a small scrawly hand: Will you marry me?

She put her hand to her throat, an action which caused Jinny to ask, "Bad news, lass?" She shook her head; then hurried from the kitchen and into the sitting room, and took from the bureau drawer a sheet of paper on which she wrote one word: Yes. She folded it up, put it in an envelope which she sealed; then went to the door where the messenger was still waiting and handed him the envelope and a shilling, for which he thanked her gratefully.

When the hall door was closed she leant her head back against it and her mouth was wide open; and it was like this that Jinny saw her and said, "What is it, lass?"

Smiling now, she said simply, "I'm going to be married, Jinny." And what Jinny said was, "Well, all I can say is, that's quick work," before turning about and returning to the kitchen. . . .

Maggie and Freddie came in for their dinner at quarter past twelve, and immediately they could see from her face that something had happened, for she met them in the hall and before they had time to take off their clothes she said, "I've . . . I've had a letter from him."

They both stared at her, and it was Freddie who said, "Aye? Well, what had he to say?"

"Come into the sitting room for a minute, will you?" she said, and there was an appeal in the way she looked at them. And when they were in the room she said, "It couldn't have been more brief," and handed the letter to Maggie; and she, after the glance that was all it needed, said as she passed it to Freddie, "Well, there's truth in that."

And he, after reading, retained it in his hand as he looked at Belle and said, "No word of affection, nothing to say he cares for you."

"Oh, Freddie! What's the matter with you. I know he cares for me."

"And you care for him? Enough to marry him?"

"Yes; yes, I do."

"And I suppose you've told him so?"

"Yes, I have." Now her tone was sharp. "I . . . I should have imagined that you would be happy for me that someone like that should . . . should want to marry me."

"Don't be daft, girl!" It was a yell. "Half the country would want to marry you if they knew you were available. What's the matter with you? Don't you know yourself? Don't you look in the mirror? Jumping at the first chance that's offered, and to him of all people, the son of his father!"

He turned about and stamped from the room, leaving Maggie to go to Belle where she was standing with her head bowed, the tears running down her cheeks, and to say, "It's because he's concerned for you, like I am. And it's true, you know, lass, we know nothing about this fellow, only that he's the son of his father. And God in heaven! we both know a lot about his father."

She turned away as if she had said too much; and she knew she had indeed said too much, for now she was thinking, I wasn't supposed to have met the man. But anyway, the girl was in such a state that that slip wouldn't be questioned, at least, please God, it wouldn't for her mind wouldn't be able to stand that business coming into the open at this stage: murder was murder, whichever way it took a life. Self defence would be no excuse. And she had paid for her deed, she had paid in nightmares, if in no other way. By God she had.

She said now, "Come on and have your dinner; at least I want mine, I'm starving. And don't worry, everything will pan out; Freddie will come round. You've only got to remember it's you and your happiness he's thinking of."

The meal was eaten mostly in silence, and when later

Freddie went into the kitchen his mother remarked caustically, "That was a merry meal," and when he didn't answer she went on washing the dishes and talking to him, saying, "Well, it would be best if you put a good face on it. If she wants to marry him she'll have him. I don't know the in's and out's of it, I haven't been told, but I think there's somethin' fishy going on. I'm not one to pry; I can wait until I'm put in the picture. I think you could have trusted me though 'cos over all these years I've never told your da the rights and wrongs of this affair."

"All right, Ma, later. We'll have a talk later. But at the moment I'm worried. I'll tell you that, I'm just worried."

"And a bit more."

As he was leaving the kitchen he turned and looked at her, but stilled the retort on his lips.

Yes, and a bit more, as she said, for the fact was he was burnt up inside with jealousy of the man. Yet that was not all: there was a fear in him concerning the fellow. Perhaps it was because he couldn't get it out of his head that the man was the son of his father.

And he had another niggling little worry on his mind. He'd had a message passed on to him this morning from Mr Taylor the jeweller. Apparently Andy Stevens went up to Newcastle yesterday on an errand for Maggie and while there had called into the jeweller's to see if his watch had been repaired, and Mr Taylor had said to him, "Would you ask Mr Musgrave to call in and see me as soon as he can?" Now why should the jeweller want to see him? He himself had never done any business with Mr Taylor, but Maggie had. As yet he hadn't said anything to Maggie. It had been a busy morning and he'd thought it might be better left till dinner time when they were up home.

He went back into the sitting room now and said to her, "I'm going up to town."

"Why? Andy did all the necessary up there."

"It's got nothing to do with that deal at all. If you want to know, Mr Taylor gave Andy a message when he called to pick up his watch. He wants to see me. Now why should Mr Taylor want to see me?"

Maggie didn't reply for some seconds, and then she repeated, "Yes, that's a question, why should he want to see you? You've had no dealings with him, have you?"

"No, but you have."

"Yes; yes, bits of odds and ends for the sailors. And there were the stones remember. But that's the only thing we would have to worry about. I've had watches mended and I've bought silver from him now and then, such as the tea service. I suppose I've been a good customer over the years; why didn't he ask for me?"

"Well, I won't know, will I, till I see him."

"No; and the quicker you see him the better I'll feel. Oh it's that kind of a day. But hurry back, for there's a lot of discussion to be done. Yet I can't see that any of it is going to alter how she feels, and what I feel in my bones is, she'll go through with it. So you, lad, might as well make up your mind to it."

As before, he gave her no answer, but went out.

Newcastle was a-bustle and everything looked grey and dull. The river had gone down but debris lined the banks. Warehouses had been swamped and were thick with mucky slush.

When he entered Mr Taylor's shop he sniffed; the atmosphere seemed thick. A gas jet was spluttering and an elderly man, standing below it, was bending over some article on the counter. He had a black eyeglass pressed close to one eye and he was talking to a customer, saying, "Very nice workings, beautifully done. But of course age tells. I'll do the best I can with it."

The customer said, "When will it be ready?"

"Oh, it could be two weeks, three; I have a number in and there's only myself now. I've lost my assistant. He was a promising young man but he had trouble with his chest and it took him off."

"Oh," said the customer; then turned and walked out.

Mr Taylor now peered at Freddie, saying, "Ah, I know you better than you know me . . . Maggie's boy."

"Yes, you could say that, Maggie's boy."

"It's nice to see you. Well—" the old man jerked his head back on his shoulders, saying, "There's no customer in sight, if you'd like to step into the back shop with me." He now lifted up the flap in the counter and allowed Freddie to pass him; then he replaced the flap gently as if any untoward noise it might make should disturb the clocks. Then he led the way behind the curved counter and through a door to a room into which the atmosphere of the shop seemed to have penetrated. The only furniture it held, besides countless clocks of all shapes and sizes, was an old battered table, very much like a butcher's block, and a high stool and a chair.

He now offered Freddie the chair by pointing to it, then hoisted himself up on to the high stool and, leaning his bent body so that his elbow could rest on the block, he peered at Freddie through the dim light afforded by a window that hadn't been cleaned for some long time and, coming straight to the point, he said, "Do you know a man called Freeman?"

After a slight hesitation Freddie said, "Yes; yes, indeed, I know a man called Freeman."

"Well, somehow I thought you would. Have you ever had any private dealings with him?"

"No; no private dealings. Perhaps, if you know Freeman, you will know from him that I was a runner when the smuggling was at its height on the coast. I was very small for my age then and had a little sculler and so, in the main, could cross the river without comment. I was"—he paused—"always on the way to me granny's." There was a touch of humour in these last words, and the jeweller took them up, saying, "Well, it's good to have a destination to make for. Now may I ask if you knew what you were carrying across the river at times? As you will gather, there's a purpose in my asking these questions."

"Yes, I can gather that, and except for once, I wasn't aware of what I was carrying. But then, I carried very little, my job was to run messages."

"Yes, I can gather that, too, but at one time you must have carried a precious cargo. You know what I mean?"

Freddie remained quiet and the jeweller went on, "Maggie brought me three stones some time ago, and she got a good price for them. I'm always fair and I admit I got a good price for them too. Now no one knew about that transaction only you, Maggie, and me, at least that is what I thought till recently when I had a visit from Mr Freeman. Between you and me, young man, I've never cared for Larry Freeman. I'm of the opinion that money is badly divided in this world and if you can sort it out a bit all to the good, but some people get greedy and he's one of the greediest men I know. And he's got fingers in many pies, not only in Newcastle but up in the big city too. And that is where the exchanges are made . . . well, with the special pieces of glass." It looked as if he was endeavouring to straighten his bent back and he looked towards the dull window as he went on, "It's always been a mystery to me why women and men go mad about such pieces. Anyway, he wanted to know if you had been in here and passed on some stones to me. Now, I said, lots of people had been in here and passed on stones to me, besides other things, as he was well aware, and, as I didn't keep any record, I couldn't remember if you had or not; that in fact, I was sure you hadn't. Then he said, if you hadn't been in had Maggie Hewitt? Now I had to lie very glibly at this, and I repeated again I had no memory of Miss Hewitt bringing any stones to me, but I did know that she was a very good customer for my silver both new and second-hand and that I had sold her two of the best grandfather clocks in the county. Well, from the conversation that ensued I gathered that the stones in question had reached a certain person in London—amazing how news travels—and that this person felt that these pieces were part of a consignment that should have reached him many years ago via Mr Larry Freeman and then a Mr Gallagher, the man that you used to take messages to. Isn't that so?"

Freddie's throat was dry, and not just from the atmosphere of the shop. He said flatly, "Yes, he was the man I took messages to."

"Well, the two diamonds and the ruby that landed eventually in a certain house in London was but a small part of a larger package which has never been seen since. Now, recollecting all that happened, when this man Gallagher was found in the river there were no such stones on him. Apparently he had been attacked and someone had stripped him before throwing him in the water. Now, although he didn't say outright, Mr Larry Freeman has worked it out that you, as a nipper, but not such a nipper because you were twelve years old at the time, was the last person likely to see him alive other than his servants, of which there were three. Is that correct?"

"You're correct about the servants, but I needn't have been the last person to see him alive because I delivered my message that night and that was that."

"Well, apparently by someone else's statement it wasn't. One of those servants is an old drunk, the father of a woman who has taken a Coffee House here. She's a very disfigured creature, one that can't be missed. Anyway, having been given some cheap liquor this man tells Freeman a very strange tale, quite unbelievable, which Freeman says he discounts, about a child whom his master means to kill and doesn't, and the servants hide it in a room, and you come along and you rescue the child; and Mr Gallagher chases you and this man who was the servant right down to Shields waterfront. And there the servant leaves you knowing that his master is hot on your heels. Now, I think as Freeman, that that's all fantastic rubbish, but what Freeman doesn't consider rubbish is the possibility that Gallagher met up with you. And although you were only a nipper you were wiry and quick on your feet and, to use his words, you could have felled him with a stone or anything else, stripped him of what he had in his pockets, then pushed him in the river. The three stones that arrived in London were part of the haul and that it's more than likely you've hung on to the rest."

"Oh, my God!" Freddie got to his feet. "Do you think if I'd had a haul such as I carried that night, and it was a big haul because the package broke and the three stones that Maggie brought you had fallen into the seam of my trouser pocket, do you think if I'd hung on to the rest I'd still be here? It must have been a big fortune and I would have made a small fortune out of it and you a comparatively large one before it reached London."

"Well, Mr Musgrave, I thought it better to put you in the picture as to what is taking place and for you to be on your guard from now on. Between us both, Freeman is a nasty piece of work, but like other lots of nasty pieces of work he is high up in several quarters in the city. Nobody really knows what he's worth. But I know he stacks a lot of his money abroad, perhaps for a rainy day when things become too hot for him, as it generally does for his ilk." He too rose from his seat now, adding in a sad tone, "The smuggling and the running, the narrow squeaks through the customs and the excise men, the bargaining that took place in this very room, mostly in the dead of night, all lent excitement to life. And there was honour among thieves in those days, and everyone got their fair share of what they managed to haul. But all that is past now, gone like so many other good things. Do you know something, young man? I am glad I am old. Ah, there's the bell, another customer, so I'll say good day, Mr Musgrave. I hope I've been of a little help to you."

"Thank you. Thank you, Mr Taylor, you have." He did not add, "And an added source of worry with regard to things to come, as if I hadn't enough." . . .

Maggie was perturbed at his news, but one thing she said and with which he agreed was that Freeman would bring nothing into the open: he himself stood to lose too much to risk exposure; everything that followed from now on would be underhand.

Here Maggie was mistaken.

The following day Freddie made another journey to Newcastle, this time to the cafe. He went straight up to the counter. Connie was behind it. She didn't seem surprised to see him, and he began without any preamble: "Your father's opening his mouth, do you know that? There could be trouble all round." And to this she answered, "My mother died the day afore yesterday. They're burying her the morrow. And me da broke into the cash box upstairs and has gone on the spree. D'you think I'm worried about anything more that can happen? My mother was more than a mother, she was my friend, the only one I had."

He said, "I'm sorry. I'm very sorry, Connie."

"So am I," she said, "and for meself now."

He had to move to the side to allow a customer to pay for his meal, and he stood for a moment longer looking at her through the blurred glass; then he turned and went out.

When he reached home it was to find that Maggie had had a bout of that pain, and so severe had it been she had had to be helped up from the office. Belle had put her to bed and sent for the doctor.

He had met the doctor in the hall, and had asked straightaway, "What is it? What is really wrong with her?"

Shrugging his shoulders, the doctor had merely answered, "Well, it's the old stomach trouble gathering momentum."

He had wanted to say, "What d'you mean by that?" but that apparently was as far as the doctor wished to prognosticate for he was on his way to the front door. And when a moment later he had stood by Maggie's bedside and asked, "What's all this about then?" her reply had been even more noncommittal: "Oh, I'm sick of work, at least for this week; I've decided to put me feet up properly this time," she said.

"And not afore time, I should say." He looked across at Belle standing at the other side of the bed and said, "When did this happen?"

And she replied, "Shortly after you left. She tried to stop me sending for the doctor."

"Well, what has he done?" Maggie looked from one to the other. "Written out a prescription for the apothecary. It must be something nasty for he usually does his own dispensing. I'll get a bill for that all right. You could have gone down there and got me usual bottle for a shilling, but I'll bet he'll charge five bob if a penny."

"Shut up! and rest yourself." He bent over her and smoothed her hair from her brow; then casting a glance at Belle, he said, "Is there anything hot going? I'm chilled to the bone."

"Oh yes. Yes, Freddie, I'll get you a drink."

As she hurried from the room he pulled up a chair in order to sit closer to the bed, and when she said, "Did you see her? How did it go? What happened?" he said, "Oh, I'll tell you later. It's nothing to worry about. But about this pain, Maggie. Was it all that bad?"

"Bad enough."

"What is it. D'you know? Is there a name to it?"

"Well, I would give it the name of cramp, to be kind, like, you know, you get in the calves of your legs. But I suppose them doctors have a name for it. The guts get twisted or something, spasms. We all have spasms of one thing or another. She's in a spasm." She motioned with her head towards the door. "In spite of her worry over me she can't keep it hidden, it's shining out of her. Freddie"—she gripped his hand—"try to be happy for her, be gentle with her. Married or not, she's going to need a friend through life, and you should be that one. At the bottom of me I'm worried about her."

He wanted to reply, "And you're not the only one"; instead he said, "Don't worry about it. As to my attitude: knowing how I feel, you couldn't expect me to react in any other way, at least not at the moment. But—" He pressed her hand against his chest, saying, "It's you that's on my mind, not her. Now . . . now listen to me. You've got to take care of yourself, so be a good lass and stay there for a week."

"Oh my God! no. I'd go mad lying in bed for a week. Look, lad, this thing just comes in spasms. I might go days, weeks, even months and not have another."

"You haven't had days, weeks, or months between the last . . . spasms, as you call them; you had more than a touch of one three days ago."

Her voice was very low and soft as she said, "Lad, we've all got to go sometime or other."

"Don't say that." He thrust her hand from him. "Don't talk like that, Maggie. Don't scare the wits out of me. What would I do without you?"

"Oh, oh, come on, come on, man; everybody can be done without. There never was a good but there's a better."

"Don't talk such bloody rot." He was actually gasping now, and again he grabbed her hand and, his face coming close down to hers, he said, "Maggie, for God's sake don't leave me. I can do without Belle because I've got to, but I couldn't do without you, because I know. . . ."

"Now! now! stop it."

"I won't stop it, I've got to say this. I've never said it to you afore: I've got a feeling for you that I can't explain even to myself, from the first time you took me under your wing. I don't think of you as another mother, Maggie. I can't, as I said, put a name to how I think of you. Perhaps if you had been a bit younger and I a bit older, even twenty years between us wouldn't have made any difference. I . . . I love you, Maggie. And . . . and this is the first time I've ever said that to a woman. I never said it to May, and I've never said it to Belle, but I say it to you." His head now dropped onto her chest and her hands came on it, but she was unable to make any comment on his words, either derisory or otherwise, for at this moment the pain in her heart was obliterating the growling pain in her stomach. But after a moment, when she raised his wet face up to hers, she said, "Then take comfort, Freddie, because I too couldn't put a name to the feelings I have for you."

He now went to take her face between his hands when the door opened, and this caused him to rise abruptly and, with his back towards Belle now, he muttered to Maggie, "See you later."

She made no response, and he went out. In the hall, he hesitated whether to go upstairs or into the kitchen; but he knew that if he went to his room he might break down altogether, and he had an afternoon's work to face and people to meet.

His mother was in the kitchen and she cast a quick glance at him but said nothing, not until he asked a question: "What is really wrong with Maggie, Ma, do you know?"

"Well, I can't put a medical name to it," she said, "but it's either what you call a tumour or an abscess in her guts, and it's been growing this long while."

"Is there any cure?"

"No, as far as I know there isn't."

He swung round from her and went to the window and looked out onto the courtyard, and Jinny, from where she stood at the table, said, "It's no use lettin' go like that. You must have guessed she's been bad for a long time, and time's runnin' out now."

Swinging about, he cried, "Don't say that, Ma! Don't say it!"

"And don't you shout at me, lad. You asked a question and I answered it." And her lips trembled slightly as she said, "I hope when my time comes you show as much concern, but I doubt it, aye I doubt if you will."

There it was, the old jealousy that he had thought dead this many a year, but it still festered. His voice just a mutter now, he said, "She's been good to me, Ma. She's been good to all of us."

"There's nobody sayin' nay to that. But what you seem to forget, lad, and often, is that I'm still your mother. I may be a servant in this house but I have me pride an' I can tell you this for nowt, you've hurt it many a time. I like the miss; at least half the time, but the other half . . . I hate her for havin' taken you from me."

"You're wrong there, Ma; she hasn't taken me from you, you're still me mother."

"Aye, I might be in name but not in affection. Oh, lad, don't start givin' me any of your high flowing explanations. There's somethin' atween you two, and has been for years, that shut me out." She turned round now, took up a teatowel and, stretching the hem between her fingers and thumbs, she shook it out straight before hanging it on the rod above the fire, when she said, "By the way, I have a message for you from our Nancy. She wants a word with you. I think you had better call in home on your way down. It seems important enough to me for you to take the trouble to call in home."

The angry retort that was on his tongue was quelled, and he marched from the room, all the while heavy with guilt now because he knew that everything she had said was true even to the last remark concerning his spare visits home.

When he was dressed for the road he looked in on Maggie again, saying briskly now, "Do what you're told and stay put." Then turning to Belle, he said, "See that she doesn't move out of there, will you?"

"Don't worry; I'll see to her."

Maggie watched him all the time, and as he made for the door she said quietly, "Wrap up well; it's biting."

Wrap up well; it's biting. No frost or icy wind could make him feel colder than he was already inside. And when he reached the house—he didn't now think of it as home—he found Nancy alone in the kitchen-cum-sitting room.

"Where's da?" he said.

"He's having a lie down." She indicated the bedroom door as if she could see it. "His legs have been worrying him of late."

"You wanted to see me, Nancy?"

"Yes." She walked towards the fireplace which was farthest from the bedroom door and there, her voice low, she said, "You know I've been seeing John Pratt, and I don't care what the neighbours or people think. Do you?"

"What d'you mean?"

"Just what I say, Freddie. D'you care what people think?"

"No, not much."

"That's just as well, because they criticise you for making a new home and neglecting your old one."

"That isn't fair, Nancy."

"Nothing is very fair, I find, Freddie. For instance, I've never thought it unfair that I was blind up till recently, when a man told me I was beautiful and asked me to marry him and I refused."

"Why?" His tone changed. "Why on earth have you refused him? Because he's in the customs?"

"No, of course not." Her voice was scornful; and as he stared at her he couldn't believe this was Nancy who was talking, sweet, quiet, placid Nancy, everyone's comforter. But this is what love did to one, opened one's eyes so to speak; and it was a poor simile but it had opened hers. He put out his hands and drew her to him, and she didn't resist his embrace. And when he said, "You are beautiful, Nancy; and if this man loves you you must take him. Do you care for him?"

After a short silence she said, "Yes. Yes, I do. All the things about him that I sense I like, much more than like."

"Well, what has stopped you? What made you say no?"

"Da's upset because of what his cronies might think. As he said, I was bringing a spy into their midst. To hear him talk you would think the smuggling was an everyday affair. He lives in the past."

"I'll soon settle da in that quarter; you leave that to me." He shook her now gently, saying, "When are you seein' this fellow next?"

"I hope tomorrow. He's taking me into Newcastle. I have an appointment."

"Tell him you've changed your mind. Now promise me? Because he sounds a decent bloke. I've only caught a glimpse of him. There's still so many of them around the town and along the front, it's practically as bad as Newcastle, but I could pick him out. Medium height, isn't he? Sandy haired, brown eyed. Of course you wouldn't know all those particulars."

"I do, and what's more, why I wanted to see you was to give you a message from him."

"*A message* to me from *him?*"

"Just that. Apparently there's something afoot. He couldn't explain what, but there are enquiries being made, especially on the river and even in the city. He says you must have an enemy or two. It's something connected with what happened years ago when you used to be a runner. Although how they can hold you responsible for anything that happened then I don't know, because you were just a tiny little chap. But he pointed out that you were twelve years old or thereabouts and, as he said, they used to transport lads for stealing a loaf, never mind valuables. Did you steal any valuables, Freddie?"

"No, I didn't, Nancy, and you can tell him that. I have never stolen anything in me life, except giblets from the butchers, and bits of fruit when I could."

"Well, what do you think they are getting at? Why are they suspicious? Can you guess why anybody should want to cause trouble?"

"Oh, yes, yes Nancy, I can guess. I can pinpoint the very person; so don't worry, I'll deal with this. But you give Mr Pratt my thanks and tell him I appreciate the gesture he's made. Apart from all that, though, you take back that no. Now will you?"

"I'll think about it, Freddie."

214

"You'll not think about it any more, you'll do it. If you don't
I'll go to him and tell him how you feel. Nancy"—he gripped her
arms—"you must get away from here. Now don't think I'm actin'
the upstart, but ma and da are used to this, they were bred to be
used to this kind of life. As long as they've got their belly full and
a good fire and something to drink they won't worry, but you . . .
you are made for better things. Your voice could carry you far if
you had somebody behind you, and this fella could be the very
start you're lookin' for. Now think on it, because what's the
alternative? You'll end up like Maggie, lonely inside and lost.
And you couldn't stand life with one of the lads from around
here. They're good chaps, many of them, but coarse grained. By
the way, did your friend give you any indication of how this
matter had started? I mean people, somebody put on to me?"

"Oh"—she nodded quickly now—"I think it was an anonymous letter sent to the headquarters in Newcastle first. I sort of
gathered that."

"Huh!" He gave a short laugh. "There's two can play at that
game. But I don't need to write my information down, I can
speak it. Anyway, thanks, love. I must be off now." He bent and
kissed her, saying, "Do as I tell you now. Get your life sorted out
and think of yourself for once. I'll look after the both of them
here; you need never worry about that."

"Thanks, Freddie."

"Ta-ra."

"Ta-ra, Freddie."

Anonymous letter. Of course Freeman wouldn't want to
become implicated, would he? Well, by God! he would show him.
He would go up to Newcastle now, and damn the business.

He burst into the office, startling Andy Stevens and the new
clerk having a quiet smoke in short pipes, their coat tails lifted up
to warm their backsides at the small fire in the office grate, and
he bawled at them, "Miss Hewitt's away sick but I'm in good
health and there's a line of clerks wanting jobs up in the city.
Think on it when next you want to warm your backsides at two
o'clock in the afternoon." But then, his voice dropping, he said,
"I'm surprised at you, Andy."

"We were both froze, Mr Musgrave."

"You've never complained about being frozen before. And I
ask you, what would it have looked like if a customer had popped
in, eh? Now don't let me have to warn you again on this. I'm

215

surprised at you, I am that. As for you, Hooper: you learn and you learn quickly or you go. And now I want a message taken to a Captain Hannan. Tell him I can't come aboard at three as I said, but I'll see him in the morning when they dock again."

"Yes, Mr Musgrave."

He went out, and as he marched along the quay and up through the town to the station his thinking calmed somewhat and he thought he had perhaps been a bit high-handed, because it was the first time he had seen Andy slacking like that and taking advantage. But why had he taken advantage? Simply because he knew Maggie was out of the way. Well then, in future he would have to learn who was boss, wouldn't he? And it came to him that it might take hard work and acting high-handedly on his part to convince them, whereas Maggie had just to appear at the end of the quay and they seemed to smell her presence and would be hard at it when she entered the office. Oh, but what did it matter? What mattered now was the meeting with Freeman. But where would he find him at this time of day? In his office? In which office? He had his fingers in so many pies. If it took till midnight, though, he would find him.

But he didn't have to wait till midnight, he found him in the first building he entered.

There was a brass plate outside the highly polished door which read: Freeman & Son: Builders & Contractors. There was a reception desk in the hall and the hall floor was tiled in a special pattern of a star with beams radiating from it. The young man behind the counter raised his head from a ledger and asked politely, "What can I do for you, sir?"

"I wish to speak to Mr Freeman."

"May I ask if you have an appointment, sir?"

"No, I haven't; but will you tell him that Frederick Musgrave would like a word with him."

The man stood up, saying now, "Mr Frederick Musgrave. I'll see if Mr Freeman is in."

"Do that."

He stood looking about him, particularly at the woodwork. It was all mahogany doors, window frames, and skirting boards. The man was away four minutes, so did the brass clock on the wall in between two doors tell him. And then there he was saying, "Mr Freeman will see you now. Will you come this way, please?"

216

He was ushered into an office that made Maggie's quay room appear like a slum in comparison. The swift impression was the continuation of the mahogany and the sumptuous brown upholstered leather chairs.

Freeman was standing by the side of his desk as the man announced him, saying, "Mr Frederick Musgrave, sir."

Not until the door closed did Larry Freeman speak, and then he said, "By! you've got me puzzled, and I'm asking myself the question, why should he want to come and see me? He's never done this before unless he wants to tell me something I've been trying to find out for years."

"Don't take me for a fool, Mr Freeman, and don't act the innocent bystander. You know why I'm here."

"I do?" Freeman now walked from the desk towards the marble-tiled fireplace and there, stooping down, he picked up the tongs and took a piece of coal from a highly polished brass bucket standing to the side of the equally highly polished brass fender. And having placed it on the fire, he repeated this four times. Then straightening up, he dusted his hands and, his voice changing, he said, "What you after? But before you start, don't think, young man, you can blackmail me in any way. You were a sly little nipper and I don't suppose that mind of yours has improved. No, it certainly hasn't. You're known as a sharp business man on the quay—Maggie trained you well in that—but don't think you'll use your expertise on me because. . . ."

"Would you like to be quiet for a moment."

Freeman now brought his teeth tightly together, and he remained quiet as Freddie said, "You're putting up a very good show, but let me tell you this, Mr Freeman. You can send your anonymous written letters to the customs or the police or who you like, but they won't carry the weight of a feather to what will happen to you when I open *my* mouth. Not only what I know from when I was a runner but from what I've learned since and. . . ."

Freeman was now glaring at Freddie, and he brought the words out slowly, saying, "What the hell! are you talking about. Anonymous letters? I've written no anonymous letters. That's not my way. What's all this?"

Freddie was nonplussed for a moment; and it was some seconds before he could speak, when he said, "I've been given the tip that the customs are on to me for something that happened years ago and it could only be connected with you and the running across the river, and I thought that. . . ."

"Then your thinking proves that you're not as smart as I imagined you were, or as you think you are. What the hell! would I be doing in writing an anonymous letter to give you away when the first thing you would do, as you've just said, is open your mouth wide. And who would come off worse in the deal, eh? A bit of a lad, as you were then, you would get all the sympathy, and me . . . the bad man using you. . . . Don't be so bloody dim, man. Who knows what happened that night anyway?"

"No one knows, except Gallagher's three servants who now run Cora's Coffee House, and the mother died the day before yesterday. But the father's a drunk and he. . . ."

"Oh, I know all about the father"—Freeman brought his hand across his face in an impatient movement—"and I've got a version of what happened that night, if you can believe it. But the old fellow's half barmy and most of it was fancy, and I wouldn't think that old sop would be capable of writing a letter. He could though get somebody to write it for him. But why should he eh? Why should he? And it wouldn't be his daughter because she keeps a tight rein on him. But there's a point. Where did that lot get the money to set up a place like that Coffee House? There's a lot of questions to be asked here, and one I've been wanting to ask you too, for years: what did you do with the rest of the stones?"

"What d'you mean, what did I do with the rest of the stones? I never saw the stones."

"Now look, don't try to hoodwink me. Maggie sold three of those stones to old Taylor. It's funny how things come about. They can lie dormant for years and then just a word and a door opens. I was in London not long ago seeing a friend of mine, in fact he was the friend who was waiting for that consignment that you took across the river that night. It was a very precious consignment that, and this man knows a lot about stones and their quality. I do a bit myself, but I'm a child compared to him. Well, he recognised the ruby; it happened to be one of a set of six; and the diamonds were all out of a special tiara. Do you know what a tiara is?" Freddie remained silent, but his lips curled slightly. "Well, these three stones had come to him through Taylor. He has a great respect for Mr Taylor and Mr

Taylor hinted that they had come to him through a lady, a lady of North Shields who was a very sharp business woman. So what did I do but put two and two together. So I ask *you* now, *you* who were the last person likely to see those stones, what about them, I mean the rest of them?"

For answer Freddie took two steps towards a chair, then said, "May I sit down?"

With an exaggerated wave of his hand, Freeman answered, "By all means. By all means."

"Then I advise you to do the same, because I am going to tell you a tale that is perfectly true. Yet you may not believe half of it. But before I start you can give up any hope of seeing the rest of those stones, as you call them, through me, as I don't know what happened to them."

Freeman was now sitting opposite to him, his body pushed well back in the big leather chair, his hands resting on the padded arms. And now Freddie said, "I'm only telling you this now because I believe you when you say you didn't write that letter."

And so he started, from that night when he reached the Shields side of the river and was picked up by Gallagher, then thrown into the scrub field. He told all that transpired even to the finding of the child. He even went back to the day when it was born. But he finished his tale when Maggie met him on the front and bustled him into the boat.

It was a good minute before Freeman spoke, his head was making small movements as he said, "The old bloke wasn't lying then, it wasn't drunken fantasy. But . . . but he said Gallagher was after you that night. . . . Didn't you see him?"

Freddie's reply was quick and sharp. "No. No."

Freeman drew himself up in the chair and, leaning forward, he said, "And that Spanish-looking girl, Maggie's niece, she's Gallagher's daughter?"

"No, no; as I said, she's not. She's the daughter of a sea captain."

"Oh, aye. Yes, yes. Well now, would you believe that? . . . But haven't you left yourself open telling me all this? What would Maggie say?"

"Under the circumstances she would have done the same as me. The fact that you didn't write that letter proves somebody else did, and apparently they're not only on to me but also on to

219

those I was mixed up with as a boy. So, have you any ideas?"

Freeman thought for a moment; then he said, "Your one-time friend, Harper. You don't throw a lass over and get off with a black eye and bruised ribs. The bully boy Mick came to me and told me that, years ago, on the night Gallagher went missing, his dad saw you and Maggie leaving a sculler, and Maggie was hugging a pile of stuff to her. And what he suggests now is that it was very profitable stuff."

"It was the child."

"Yes, I can believe that now. But to return to this letter business. I'll admit I'm more troubled now than when you first entered the room, because I could have dealt with you and the blackmail I thought you were hatching. Strange, isn't it, that we now find ourselves on the same side as we were years ago, in fact, before Maggie took you under her wing?"

Freddie did not speak his thoughts on this matter, but he said, "What evidence d'you think they'll need before they attempt to pick me up?"

"Oh, it would have to be pretty strong. Of course, if they have knowledge of the transaction of the stones it could be any time, because, like me, they'll think if you had three, then you had the lot, but unlike me, they might not be convinced by your strange tale of finding them in the muck of your trouser pocket." He scratched the side of his chin now, saying musingly, "I wonder where that lot got to? I'd give quite a bit to find out. But now this is the question: where do I stand? If you are picked up are you going to tell them my part in it?"

Freddie stared at Freeman and he knew that it would be unwise to make an enemy of this man: he mightn't be a good friend but he'd be a damn bad enemy. And so he said, "That wouldn't do me any good. I could say a man, a stranger, gave me the package and the instructions."

"That would be wise." But the tone in which this was said and the inference caused his natural repugnance to come out in a flash, as he said, "But don't take that as weakness, Mr Freeman, because believe this, I'm not afraid of you."

A slow smile spread over Freeman's face, and he gave a short laugh as he said, "No, you're not; and you're not telling me anything I don't already know. I've always realised that from when you were a nipper. But, as I've already indicated"—and now he almost voiced Freddie's thoughts—"I can be a tolerable friend but a very bad enemy. Anyway, we'll certainly keep in touch after this."

Freddie didn't confirm this statement but, rising abruptly, he said, "Good day to you, Mr Freeman." Then he went from the room, and as he did so he admitted to himself that he was now more troubled going out than when he came in, for whoever had sent that letter to the customs wanted him out of the way for some reason. The question was, who and why?

10

Maggie stayed in bed for five days, and the rest seemed to have done her good, for now she was up and in the sitting room and apparently free from pain; and during this time Belle's suitor had made two visits.

The first one was on the day following Freddie's visit to Freeman, the purpose of his visit being to ask formally for Belle's hand in marriage. Maggie gave it, and he put a ring on Belle's finger, kissed the palm of her hand, and then her lips, to which she had not really responded even though it filled her with excitement, because this was love, a different love that aroused emotions that were new to her and more than a little disturbing. This visit lasted five minutes.

But on his second visit their meeting was different. He had come accompanied by a servant in a hired cab, and the servant had borne in a large basket of fruit, and he himself had carried a bunch of hot-house grown flowers also for Maggie, and for Belle, a large box of crystallised sweets and a bottle of exclusive French perfume. He had also brought with him an invitation from his grandmother that they should all go to tea, not to his Newcastle home but to the house across the water. This was, as soon as Miss Hewitt was able to travel.

Maggie was up from her bed and sitting beside the fire in her bedroom, Belle and her future husband were alone in the sitting room. Freddie was at work.

And now Marcel kissed her. He began with a peck on her nose; then he kissed her brow, her eyes, her cheeks, and lastly her lips, and this time, and for the first time, her arms went about him and she held him almost as tightly as he held her. And when at last their faces parted, they stared at each other, their eyes bright, and when huskily he said, "I . . . I can't believe that you love me, Belle. Over the last few days I've had to stop myself from dashing down and begging you to say it. You haven't yet said it in words, but now I know that you do love me, don't you?"

And to this she answered, "Yes. Oh, yes, Marcel, I love you. From the moment I first saw you when you led me into the dance, I liked you. And, you know, Aunt Maggie says that the best way to start loving is to like. Do you like me?"

His head went back and he laughed, "Oh no, I don't like you, I love you and I adore you, and I know I can't live without you and I want you for myself alone; no one else in the world has to have any part of you. That is how much I love you. As for liking you, well, can one love without liking?"

"Aunt Maggie says you can."

"Your Aunt Maggie is a very wise woman, and I can say I like her, I like her very much but I don't love her. Well now"— his head was tilted slightly to the side—"it wouldn't be right, would it?"

They were both laughing now. Her head had dropped onto his shoulder and his arms drew her tightly into him again; and what he said now and very quietly was, "We must be married soon, very soon."

Her head jerked up. "Oh! Marcel, we've only become engaged, there'll be so much to do. The wedding . . . well, there's a lot of arrangements."

"Do you want a lot of fuss, all the parade?"

"Oh no." The statement was firm but not emphatic.

"Then it could be simple and soon by special licence."

She withdrew from his arms and turned from him, saying, "I don't think Aunt Maggie would agree to . . . well, rushing things."

He turned her towards him again. "Your Aunt Maggie, as you call her, my dear girl, is a very sick woman. You know that, don't you?"

She made no reply, only her eyes widened as she looked into his, and he went on, "I feel sure that she would like to see you settled, happily settled, while she's able to."

"What makes you think she's a very sick woman, Marcel?"

"Simply because, the other day when I was here, I had a talk with Jinny. Her prognosis wasn't good."

In her heart she knew herself that the prognosis wasn't

good, but when it was voiced it filled her with fear, and already she could feel the loss. Of a sudden she thought of Freddie and how he must be feeling now, and what would happen to him if she should die, for die she would.

When she voiced her thoughts, saying, "Freddie will be devastated when anything happens to her. He thinks the world of her and he owes her so much," he stared at her silently for a moment, then said slowly, "Freddie's a man and he has a mother of his own and a father and a brother and sisters, he won't be alone."

"Yes, you're right, Marcel. And I, too, love Freddie."

"Don't say that."

She was actually startled, for now he was gripping her arms and saying, "From now on I never want you to say you love any man but me." But almost as quickly his manner changed and, laughing gently now, he said, "Don't look like that. Isn't it natural? I must warn you I'll be a very jealous husband."

"I'll never give you reason to be jealous of me, Marcel, never."

"You promise that?"

"Yes, I promise that." She, too, was smiling now as if it was a joke.

Almost as soon as the tap came on the door it was opened and Jinny stood there, saying, "The cab man wants to know, sir, if he's still to wait? Your servant's in the kitchen, but the cab man wouldn't come in, not to have a drink. He's a surly bloke, he wants to get off."

Marcel had swung round and was looking down the room at Jinny, and it was evident he was about to make a sharp retort, but then, on a laugh, he said, "Tell him I'll be there in a moment," and, turning to Belle again, he said, "That's the last time I'll come to see you by cab. I'll be here tomorrow again. I want to talk to . . . Aunt Maggie about future arrangements."

"Marcel."

"Yes, my darling?"

"Will you also have a word with Freddie? because you see, Freddie. . . ."

"Yes, yes, I know; you owe such a lot to Freddie too. All right, anything you say, I'll have a word with Freddie. I'll say, please, sir, I want to marry your adopted daughter within the month."

"Oh no, no."

"Well, within two months."

"Oh, Marcel, it couldn't be arranged in. . . ."

"My dear, dear one, it could be arranged within the next two or three days if necessary." He now swiftly pulled her into his arms and his kiss was so breathtaking that when he released her she was left gasping. And now turning from her and in an almost boyish fashion he ran from the room.

Freddie had never known what it was to experience the feeling of fear since the night he had been chased by Gallagher, then witnessed his end. Of course, he had been worried when the Harpers got at him, but the fear that was filling him now was twofold. The main one was concerning Maggie and her illness which he couldn't believe was fatal because here she was going about on her pins like a lintie. And for the last three days she had been down at the office ordering everybody about and disproving the rumour that she was on her last legs. But the other fear was a niggling growing fear and it was gathering momentum now as he looked at John.

John had asked his employers for leave to take a journey in the middle of the week across the water to see his brother. He said it was important, and he was saying so now as he stood in the back room of Maggie's office. "I thought I'd better come, Freddie . . . I mean, as Cissy said, although they weren't in any kind of uniform they were officials. You know, she's cute, and she said she could smell them a mile off and the way they talked. Well, they wanted to know if we owned the cottage, and she bawled at them and said, 'Own the cottage! We pay two shillings and ten pence a week and it's kept off me husband's wages. You get nothin' for nothin' these days.' You know how Cissy goes on. It was then they asked if I got help from me brother? Wasn't he well off? And Cissy came back at them on that and said, 'Why should we expect help from him? He's workin' like the rest of us for his livin'.' Then one of them, she said, laughed, and said, 'Oh, but he lives pretty comfortably; I would have thought he would have looked after his own.' At this she had said, 'What the hell d'you want, the pair of you? If you want to know anything more, go up to the estate, me husband's workin' there. Who are you anyway?' she had asked. And one of them replied, 'We are making some enquiries about some lost property.' And to that she said, 'Well, what the hell d'you expect to find here? Would you like to dig up the garden?' They then went away laughing, she said." He now paused before ending, "What's it all about, Freddie? Are you in trouble?"

"No, no, John, not any more than I was when I was a runner. It all goes back to then."

"No! never."

"Oh, yes, yes. There was a lot of stuff went missing presumably, and they're still looking for it. I might as well tell you there's somebody determined to get me one way or the other. They sent, you know, one of those anonymous letters to the customs and the excise lot and this is what started it off. It's nearly sixteen years now since that all happened."

"Oh, time means nothing to the polis or to the excise. They're like that sayin' about the elephant, they never forget. Well, I must be off; I said I would be away two hours. I'll have to put it in the night. By! they get their pound of flesh, don't they?"

"I thought you liked it across there."

"It's a job, Freddie, it's a job. I like gardening, but when you're under an old fella like Bainbridge you get the muck and the grubbing jobs and he gets the smiles and the thanks for keeping the garden so lovely. D'you know somethin'?" He laughed now. "She complained, the mistress, because she saw a blade of grass sticking up atween the paving stones."

"Never!" Freddie was smiling too.

"It's a fact. Bainbridge took me almost by the scruff of the neck and bent me over that slab, saying, 'Look there! That's annoyed the mistress.'" He started to giggle now. "Me eyes were on a level with his bloated middle and I had a job to restrain me fist from diggin' it in." When he turned to go he said wryly, "If you've got a horde put away, Freddie, I wouldn't mind risk sharing it."

Freddie thumped him on the back, saying, "Same cell in the House of Correction?"

"Aye . . . aye, that's where we'll likely end. Goodbye, lad."

"Goodbye, John; and thanks for comin'."

"Freddie."

"Aye?"

"Be careful. Ma worries about you. Although you've been in clover all these years she still worries over you."

"I'm a big lad now, John. I've been a big lad for a long, long time. Go on with you. You've got plenty to worry about without puttin' me on your books. And keep those flags clean; don't annoy the missis."

The office to himself, Freddie sat at his desk and asked himself what was going to happen next? It felt as if a web was closing around him, a web of no silken threads, rather of steel hawsers. Since talking to Freeman he had racked his brains as to who might want him out of the way. He dismissed the Harpers: not one of them could write; although, like old Mr Wheatley they could have got someone to write the letters for them. That was a point. . . .

Maggie had left early and when he arrived home he didn't tell her what had transpired with John, but she in turn had something to tell him. "He's wanting to rush things," she said. "And she's more than half in agreement with him. All right, all right, all right"—her finger was wagging again—"I know what you're thinking, and your thoughts are the same as mine, I might as well tell you now. But she's young and headstrong and, as we've found out before, she's amenable up to a point only. Remember when she was fourteen and I wanted to move her from that school to what I thought was one of higher standard: she went missing for a day, and then she told me that if I insisted on sending her to this place she would just walk out again, and she would have done. So, we've both got to go steady and meet her half-way. And another thing, about this invitation across the water to that house. I could no more go into that house where he had lived than I could sprout wings and fly. You mightn't know it, Freddie, but I have night-mares still about that business. Many's the time I wake up in a cold sweat 'cos I can see him goin' down." When she put her hand across her eyes he immediately went over to her to allay her feelings and said, "As I've said before, it was either him, or you and me and her, because he certainly would have done for me with the child in me arms, he would have swiped me into the river, I knew that. Then you being a witness to it, you would have gone after me. It was self-preservation, so don't let it worry you. I had thought you had put it out of your mind."

She smiled wanly at him. "You don't put a thing like that out of your mind, lad. You take a life and the loss of it is with you for the rest of your days, be the victim good, bad, or indifferent. Anyway, you'll have to go over with her yourself."

"Not on your life." He was on his feet now. "Remember the fear in me about that man, well, believe it or not, like you it still comes back at times. It was as if he was two different beings: one minute he was an ordinary man, the next an evil devil. It showed in his face. And—" He turned about now and although he lowered his tone, he hissed, "And that fella's that man's son. There was a doubt about Belle's parentage but there's certainly no doubt about his, and that's why I'm not happy."

"Oh, I don't think you need worry on that score. He seems a nice enough fellow in his own way, and he's more than likely taken after his mother's side."

"Well, I don't care which side he's taken after, I'm not going across there. She goes on her own." And with this, he stalked out of the room.

11

Belle went across the river on her own. Freddie put her into a hire keel at the quay, and she was met on the Shields side by Marcel himself. He it was who handed her up to the quay and led her to the waiting carriage. The driver, in livery, placed a footstool for her to mount; and then they were sitting side by side bowling through Shields.

Holding her hand tightly in his now, he asked, "Excited?"

"Yes, very."

"Then you're not alone; I've hardly been able to contain myself for days. As I said to Grandmama, it won't be like showing you your future home, it's like bringing you home, to the house where you were born. It's amazing, isn't it?"

She remained silent. Yes, it was amazing. She had lain awake half the night thinking about it. You read stories that dealt with such tales but you knew they were the fanciful imaginings of the writer. Yet she had been and still was the main figure in this fanciful tale which was not fanciful at all but made up of stark reality.

She had realised over the past few weeks that her eyes had only of late been opened to reality. She traced this revelation back to when the man had been found dead in an alley way down at the Low Lights. His death was the result of foul play, but the culprit had not been discovered. The poor man had left a wife, and nine children all under eleven years old. They had been previously classed as a lucky family for they had managed to rear all but one child; now, however, they were all in the poor house. Maggie had been distressed about this.

That was reality, as Maggie had pointed out to her. And when the fishing fleet came into port with hardly enough herring among them to fill two creels and all those men had mouths to feed, that too was reality.

There was a lot of reality about, and she was just wakening up to it and realising more every day how sheltered she had been by that wonderful woman and that more than wonderful man who was now causing her pain, because she knew, no matter how he acted, he hadn't taken to Marcel.

Of course, when she used her reason on this matter it was understandable. He had known his dreadful father, the man who would have definitely murdered her had he had his own way.

Yet here was Marcel looking into her eyes, his face soft and beautiful . . . and he was beautiful. She had seen a number of pretty men but Marcel's looks went beyond that, he was beautiful.

He was saying, "You'll find Grandma ensconced on her chaise longue; she doesn't get about very much these days, but"—he leant towards her—"between you and me she loves being waited on . . . she's been waited on all her life, spoilt. I've told her that . . . you'll like her, and she'll love you as I do." She was in his arms now and he was kissing her long and hard until the carriage, going over a rutted stretch of road, rocked them both forward and almost onto the other seat, and they laughed like children.

"Where are we now?" She looked out of the window.

"Oh, entering the salubrious part of the town, Westoe Village. There used to be great fields between the village and the town proper but they're building like mad now all over the place. Still, I doubt if they'll get any further."

"They're lovely houses."

"Wait till you see yours." He turned her to him again. "Of course you won't remember anything of it, although if you did they would be pretty ghastly memories. I can recall when I first saw it I thought it was a dreadful place, so dark and dingy. But Grandmama performed her usual miracle with houses; she had it almost stripped bare inside, walls taken down, rooms extended, and then beautifully decorated. She's an artist of sorts is Grandmama, very clever in many ways. Oh yes, in many ways."

He turned now and looked out of the window, and when he didn't speak for some minutes she said, "Marcel." And she had to repeat his name before he turned to her, his lids blinking, and she couldn't stop herself from saying, "What is it? You look so sad." She could find no other word to express the look on his face.

"Sad? Nonsense!" And then he added, "Ten minutes more and we'll be there. My dear—" he took her face between his hands and there was a deep emotion in his voice as he said, "You are so lovely, breathtaking. I'll soon be the envy of every man in the world."

She did not contradict him for it was lovely to hear someone talk like this to her. No one had ever done so before. At times Freddie had teased her about her looks: When she had put on something new and asked him, "How do I look?" he had pursed his lips and put his head on one side, studied her, then said, "Passable, miss, passable." But then Freddie hadn't been looking at her through a lover's eyes. . . .

When the carriage drew up on the drive in front of the house and she stepped out of it, she stood and gazed about her. She had tried to imagine the house but her imagination had fallen short of what she was looking at now. The house was so much bigger, built of warm pinkish stone, with deep mullion windows and two tall stone pillars holding up the portico over the front door. His hand on her elbow, he led her up the three shallow steps to where another servant, in green livery this time, bowed slightly towards them, but Marcel Birkstead gave him no recognition. However, when a middle aged woman came across the hall towards them and said, "Good day, miss. Allow me to take your cloak," he said to her, "Is Grandmama upstairs, Cummings?"

"No, sir. She insisted on coming down into the drawing room."

"Oh, that's good." Then in an offhand manner he made a small motion with his head towards the woman, saying, "This is Grandmama's maid."

"How d'you do?"

"Very well, ma'am, thank you."

"Come along, dear." He again had his hand on her elbow, and she hadn't really any time to take in the splendour of the hall, only that it was beautifully warm and that the warmth came from a great wood fire in a recessed fireplace at the end of the room.

She would have liked to stand and look about her, because no matter how it had changed this was the hall that Freddie had carried her across and amazed the two women by the sight of her.

They were now entering the drawing room, and her first

231

impression of it was that everything was blue from the ceiling to the carpet.

He was leading her now towards where a lady was propped up on a chaise longue set some distance from but opposite another huge fire, and the next moment she was standing looking down into a face so delicately skinned it appeared like that of a china doll, and the round blue eyes helped the impression. And some part of her dared to be slightly amused when she realised that the lady was wearing a wig, because it was such a young looking wig in a beautiful brown shade, the hair lying in soft waves about the ears and supported on the crown by two pink bows.

Belle's impression of her was that of an elderly child, if that could have been possible; but only until the elderly child opened its mouth and the voice that said, "Well, my dear, so here you are," gave the lie to the appearance, for even in those words it conveyed a note of authority. And it went on, "And I can see the reason for all the fuss. Do sit down, my dear. Did you have a pleasant journey?"

As Marcel Birkstead placed a chair for Belle she answered, "Yes, it was very pleasant."

The old lady was staring at her now and her chin was moving in small jerks as if in agreement with her thoughts. And then she said, "Ring for tea, Marcel."

Belle watched him go to the side of the fireplace and pull on a thick red betasseled cord that apparently disappeared into the ceiling. Then returning to his grandmother's side, he said, "You're very naughty to come downstairs, you know that"; and she glanced at him sideways for a moment, then said, "My dear boy, I have never been naughty in my life, and you know that." When he laughed she laughed and Belle smiled.

At this moment and for the first time that she could remember in her young life she was feeling very ill at ease. She had imagined that the training she had received from Miss Rington had prepared her for all occasions: she knew how to enter a drawing room, and how to leave it; she knew the correct greeting with which to address a lady or a gentleman; but she knew now that that training hadn't taken into consideration an occasion such as this one, for she doubted if Miss Rington had ever met such a personage as she was now sitting beside.

The tea must have been ready and waiting for there came a

tap on the door and the butler entered carrying a heavily laden tray, and behind him a servant, in a grey uniform and wearing a tiny white frilled apron and a cap to match, pushed a trolley.

When the servants had departed the old lady said, "Are you used to pouring tea, my dear?" And Belle's answer was rather stiff: "Yes, quite used to it, madam," she said.

The delicate pencilled eyebrows moved upwards; the head inclined towards her, which was permission that she should go ahead and pour then. . . .

After two cups of highly scented china tea the old lady said, "Do eat a sweetmeat. I know it isn't usual to eat with tea but I have never stuck to rules, have I, Marcel?" She turned, as though for confirmation, towards her grandson, and he, smiling at her, said, "No Grandmama; you have never stuck to rules. You are a rule unto yourself."

She returned his smile as if he had paid her a compliment. . . .

The tea over, the bell again rung, the servants having taken away the trolley and the tray, the old lady turned to Marcel, saying, "I understand Yarrow thinks that Prince's leg has worsened. Would you like to go and see for yourself."

It was a veiled order and he smiled at her, saying, "Yes, of course, Grandmama; but you could have got me out of the way with a less subtle excuse."

The old lady's lips puckered, her hand wagged at him and he went out laughing. And now as if she had shed the wig and the enamelled face and definitely her autocratic manner, she held out her hand towards Belle, saying, "One can never be oneself in front of men, old or young, relations or not. Now, my dear, come and sit closer to me."

Belle drew her chair to the side of the couch and, taking the extended hand, she waited while the round blue eyes remained fixed on her in silence for a moment. Now, the voice low, the old lady said, "Let me say how glad I am that Marcel has chosen you to be his wife. I have never felt happy with any of his acquaintances before. But you, my dear, with this very, very, strange connection with this house, and the story is strange, isn't it?" She did not wait for an answer, but went on, "I found it at first quite improbable until I remembered the man Gallagher, and how I was against the marriage of my daughter from the first. Yet . . . yet, it must be said, that he loved her and loved her dearly. And such was she that she made a different man of him during the short time they were together. But recalling that he had no use for his own son, my dear, dear Marcel, it is understandable that when his second wife, your mother, did what she evidently did, his reaction should be horrific, even to the extent of destroying you. But it seems, and I have been thinking a lot these past few days, that destiny has turned the wheel and that you should come back into this house, your rightful place. Of course, my dear, as you see it now, it wasn't then, because from my daughter's death he had let it go to rack and ruin. And your mother must have found it so dreary. No wonder she sought consolation elsewhere. But, my dear"—Belle's hand was being shaken up and down now—"I want you to promise me one thing. You see, I love my grandson very much. He has been for the past twenty-one years or so my life-spring, and he is very precious to me, and I would do anything to bring him happiness. So, my dear, will you promise in a way to take my place, because you know"—she now took her free hand and, in a long sweep that started from her brow, drew it slowly down the shape of her body underneath the silken cover—"I am, a very old lady, but, as I said, I want a promise that you will always love him and care for him . . . yes and care for him as it says in the marriage service, in sickness and in health."

The blue eyes were staring straight into Belle's again, waiting for an answer, and Belle, her lips trembling slightly, said, "Yes; yes of course I promise, because, I . . . I love him very much."

"Oh, my dear, my dear, that is so good to hear. And he loves you. He adores you and he will never leave you, I can assure you of that, except when he may have to go to Harrogate on business. We have business interests there. Well, you know, our ancestral home is there. Oh yes"—she nodded at the expression on Belle's face—"the estate is now in my elder brother's hands. The old part of the house was two hundred years old when I was born there; it has been added to since; and our land covers quite an area." She now lay back on her satin pillow and, releasing Belle's hand, she went on, "I often, oh yes, so very often think of the old days, so wonderful yet so sad. My husband died in the hunting field, such a wasted life. I had no one else but my daughter. As you know"—she slanted her eyes towards Belle now—"families don't always agree, and when my dear child married Gallagher I was devastated, and more so by her death; but then God has a way of recompensing the ills of life: Marcel came into my charge and I seemed to be born again to a new form of happiness." Then the old lady made a movement that startled Belle: she gripped her hand again, and tightly, and as she leaned towards her, her whole expression was changed. It was no longer that of the wax doll nor yet of the kindly old woman that had been talking for the past few minutes, it was a face suffused with dark anger and hate, and the next words conveyed this: "You know something, child, I hate the very name of that man, Gallagher. When I think of what he has done to my. . . . Oh dear God in heaven!" She now fell back on her pillow, her hand to her throat.

The action brought Belle to her feet, apprehensively crying, "Oh! madam, are you ill? Shall I call. . . ?"

"No, no child; I'm all right. Forget this. I'm all right. I'm all right. Ah, here comes Marcel." The door was opening now, and as if the sun had suddenly come out and shone on her face her expression was now as it had been when Belle first saw her.

"Ah!" she was saying, "and how did you find Prince?"

"Not very good, I'm afraid, Grandmama; the leg is still swollen, the sinews strained. I think I'll get the horse doctor to him later, although I doubt he'll be able to do much more than Yarrow, as we've found in the past. Well, have you had your little chat, both of you?"

"Chat? Why should we chat? We have talked; only useless feather-brain women chat."

"As you say, Grandmama, as you say." He was smiling now at Belle, and she at him; she was feeling quite at ease. There were one or two things she might have questioned but they were of no importance. She knew that eventually she would come and live in this house and that she would have a champion, if she ever needed one, in this wonderful old lady who had so many sides to her, almost like a play actress, one who, she imagined, must have been very beautiful.

"Now I'm going to show Belle round the domain. Where do you suggest we start, Grandmama?"

"In the servant's quarters. This will give the lie to the fact that the gentry house their servants in less comfortable abodes than they do their cattle."

"Oh, Grandmama."

"Well, that is what the common people think; and they're right, perfectly right, for their kind are housed in hovels. My father was the first to point this out to me. And by the way, introduce her to them because she'll be ruling them ... er one day." She was nodding at Belle now; then as Belle was moving away with Marcel, the old lady said, "Strange, you don't blush."

"Excuse me, madam?" Belle had turned and inclined her head forwards.

"I said, you don't blush. You've just got to mention the word marriage to some girls and they blush and go all fey. Sickens me. I'm glad you don't blush."

In the hall they both stopped for a moment and Marcel said, "She's a character, isn't she?"

"She is indeed."

"She's taken to you. I knew she would; but she has, and in a big way." He caught at her arm and pressed it to his side as they walked across the hall, and he said softly, "I'm so happy, Belle, so very, very happy," which made her want to turn and fling her arms around his neck and say, "It's impossible for you to be as happy as I am at this moment."

They had reached a swing door, and as he went to push it open he said, "We haven't a large staff, eleven all told, but they have been with us for years, in fact, Benedict the butler, started in our family service when he was six; he is now in his sixties. And Grant, Alan Grant, who is my man, is Benedict's nephew. He is comparatively new: he joined the service at the same time as I went to stay with Grandmama, that's over twenty-one years ago. He was footman then; later he took me on." He smiled now. "Then there's Grandmama's maid, Sarah Cummings. You saw her in the drawing room. Oh, you'll see a lot of Sarah." He now pushed open the door and they entered a small hall from which a number of doors went off. Outside one, he said, "Now here we are," and opened it and she entered the kitchen, and a small round little woman was dipping her knee to her as Marcel said, "This is Mrs Welch, our cook."

Ada Welch said, "Ma'am."

"And this is Anderson." He pointed towards a woman well into her thirties. "Anderson is the kitchen maid. And there's Summers. She has something to do with the scullery." He laughed

236

then looked about him before asking, "Where are Chambers and Everton, cook?"

"Mary, sir, will be upstairs, and Linda, sir, in the dining room."

"Oh, yes, yes." Then turning to Belle, he said, "Now, as Grandmama dictated, I shall show you their quarters."

Belle hesitated just a second. He had not asked if it was convenient he should go into their quarters, but was walking away now towards the far door, and so, before following him, she turned and smiled at the cook and the kitchen maid, saying, "Thank you," then added, "It's a lovely kitchen you have, and so beautifully clean."

The little woman's knee went deeper now, and she said, "Thank you, ma'am. Thank you very much." And Rosy Anderson smiled broadly at her and dipped her knee almost to the ground and gave her a nod.

The servants' quarters were indeed different from those she had glimpsed in the school where two maids had slept in one bed, and that had taken up most of the room. There had been no wardrobe or dressing table, only hooks on the back of the door. She had told Maggie about the conditions, and Maggie had said, "Oh, child, that's the usual attitude: What are servants anyway? They're not human beings."

When she now remarked to Marcel, "You don't address them by their Christian names?" he turned sharply to her, saying, "Use the servants Christian names? No! No! Except Sarah, and that's because Grandmama calls her by her Christian name. But for the others, no, no; that would be too familiar."

"Oh, Marcel." Her laugh was a little derisory and, realising that he was displeased, she quickly endeavoured to alleviate his displeasure by saying, "But you see, of course, how would I know anything about it; we've only had Jinny to see to the house."

"Yes, that is right: how would you know anything about it?" He was walking ahead of her. "This leads to the dining room," he said.

After the dining room, he showed her the morning room, the library, the study, and the conservatory before mounting the stairs to a small gallery, where he said, "I think this is the part of the house Grandmama left untouched when she made the alterations, the stairs and this."

From the gallery two corridors led to seven bedrooms, all beautifully furnished, and three of them being very large. His grandmama's room, Belle saw, was like some pictures she had seen of grand boudoirs, silk lace and French furniture abounding.

They were now standing in another large room, at the end of one corridor and with windows on two sides looking into the garden. He turned to her and, pulling her into his arms, he held her almost fiercely while saying, "This will be our room. This will be our abode for the rest of our lives. Do you know that?"

"It's a lovely room."

"And you are lovely, and you will adorn it and I shall adore you."

She mightn't have blushed, but a heat had come over her body and it wasn't all pleasurable because a little pocket of her mind was saying, It's strange, the way he talks; Freddie would never say things like this; while at the same time she wanted to return the fierceness of his hold and the hard pressure of his lips as they traced every feature of her face. But when his hands began to move beneath her shoulder blades, she drew in a long breath and, putting her hands on his chest, she pressed him from her, endeavouring to make the action gentle even though she was having to use quite a lot of strength in order to separate them.

He was standing straight-faced now looking at her.

"You don't love me."

"Oh. Oh, Marcel, how can you say. . . ."

"You don't love me in the same way as I love you. It would be impossible. Perhaps it's just as well: we would burn up." He now drew her hands in between his own and gently placed them on his chest and, softly, he said, "We must be married soon, Belle, for so many reasons. As you see, my grandmama is an old lady and, as you know, your . . . Aunt Maggie . . . is an ill woman. What would happen if either of them should die? Decorum would demand that we put off the wedding, for how long? Oh, it would be torture. I'm going to come across and talk with Maggie."

Tentatively she said, "You . . . you must speak to Freddie too."

"*Freddie! Why Freddie? Always Freddie.* I don't see why darling."

"Oh . . . well, you know the whole story: I wouldn't be here now if it wasn't for Freddie."

238

"You might have been, and my father too, if it hadn't been for Freddie."

She stepped back from him. "What do you mean?"

"Well, as I see it, if he hadn't run off with you my father wouldn't have chased you and somebody wouldn't have caught him and done him to death. If he had left you where you were things would have worked out."

"In that!" She now pointed upwards; then put her hand to her head, saying, "I'd . . . I'd forgotten about that room. Is it still there?"

"No," his voice was harsh, "it isn't still there. It was stripped and blocked up."

"Marcel! Marcel!"—she put her hand out towards him—"Don't be angry. Please don't be angry. But you know I wouldn't have survived in there, or out of it. He . . . he must have been so vicious against my mother for what she did that he would have taken his revenge on me, as Freddie said."

"All right. All right, my dear, let us forget about it . . . about Freddie—yes, about Freddie—and everything. Come on, and I'll show you the rest of the place, and outside. But you must wrap up because the wind is cutting."

He had reached the bedroom door when he stopped and turned her towards him once again, saying, "I suppose you've realised by now that I'm a very jealous individual. I can't bear the thought of any man, father, brother, guardian or whatever capacity having anything to do with you. In the olden days I would have taken a sword and run them all through one after the other." He was smiling widely now, and she smiled, too, tolerantly as she said, "Oh, Marcel, you must have a very poor opinion of yourself if you think that I could even look at any one else or think of any one else when you are in my life."

Gently he brought her hand and cupped it against his cheek. It was such a gentle gesture that it warmed her heart and definitely decided her that when she returned home she would have a firm talk with Freddie and Maggie and tell them that she, too, wished to be married soon.

12

On the Wednesday following Easter Sunday they were married in South Shields by special licence in a church of no consequence except that it practised Christianity. The same kind of ceremony could have been performed in North Shields or, as Maggie wanted, at any of the fine churches in Newcastle. But no, it had to be in this little church because it should happen that Mrs Birkstead was acquainted with the Minister who happened to be the grandson of a friend of hers. At least, that is why she and, apparently, Marcel Birkstead had decided that the ceremony should take place there.

It was raining heavily and blowing a gale. The weather had reverted to that experienced in the early part of the year; the church felt cold and smelt damp.

After the opening words of the ceremony: Dearly beloved, we are gathered here together . . . Freddie asked himself once again how all this had come about. And why the rush? But more so, how could he bear to see her go to this fellow of all people. . . . But to this there were really two answers. . . .

"Therefore if any man can show any just cause. . . ."

Well, he knew of a just cause. This man was Gallagher's son: that was just cause enough surely. No; that alone couldn't stop the wedding. But the other impediment. . . . How could he name it? Only that he knew there was something wrong somewhere, and it was with this man, as charming as he was. And oh aye, he could be charming; it ran off him like hot butter at times. But there were other times when, taken off his guard . . . "Those whom God hath joined together let no man put asunder. . . ."

. . . It was done. It was done. And he didn't know how he would be able to bear it. He had kissed her pale cheek and her beautiful eyes had beseeched him, Be happy for me, Freddie, please. But he knew he would never be happy in his life again, nor know peace, because he had lost her and he was soon to lose Maggie. And God, that would be another kind of agony altogether. How many agonies could the mind tolerate?

It was arranged that they all return to The Towers for a wedding breakfast, after which the happy couple, and it was evident to all eyes that they were happy in each other, would take the train to London where they were to spend their honeymoon.

Why weren't they going abroad to France or Italy? That seemed to be the pattern of young wealthy married couples these days, and Belle had even put this to Marcel. But no; he had pointed out that his grandmama was very frail and he didn't want to be too far away from her. And of course she understood.

But now, standing outside the church with Marcel's two friends one of whom was the best man, Maggie said quietly to Belle, "My dear, I won't be able to make the journey. I feel I must return home."

"Oh! Aunt Maggie. Oh! do try."

"My dear"—Maggie forced a smile to her pain-filled face—"you wouldn't want me to cause an upheaval at your breakfast, now would you? I'm all right . . . really, but I feel I must get home and rest. I'll be anxious though to hear from you. Send me a letter. You will, won't you?"

"Oh! Aunt Maggie. Aunt Maggie." Belle was holding her tightly. "I hate to leave you like this. I feel. . . ." She didn't go on to say that she felt she shouldn't go away, that she was sorry it had all happened so quickly.

"Oh, Maggie, this is unfortunate." Marcel's tone was full of solicitude, especially when he added, "I tell you what we'll do, we'll come across and have a bite with you."

"You'll do no such thing. Now get yourselves away. Goodbye, my dear." She turned again to Belle who now hastily put in, "We'll only stay a week."

"Don't be silly. Go on with you, girl! Freddie"—Maggie turned to him—"let us away."

On this, he led her to the hired cab that had brought them to the church, and he helped her in, and was about to follow her but turned and looked to where Belle was looking at him, and she would have certainly made towards him but her husband was now firmly holding her arm.

After taking his seat beside Maggie he put his arm about her and pressed her gently to his side, but neither of them spoke; nor did they when they left the cab and took the ferry across the river. But once on the quay there, he said to her, "Would you like to go to the office and rest before you take the road up the hill?" And she replied quietly, "No; I can manage."

When at last they entered the house Jinny greeted them with, "Well, it's over then. It didn't take all that long."

Freddie made no reply, but Maggie said, "No; it didn't take all that long, Jinny; but how long it'll last, God only knows." And she added to herself, And I won't be here to see it.

In the sitting room, she said to Freddie, "Get me a glass of whisky, lad, a tall one."

"You sure? Don't you think you'd better take your pills?"

She looked up at him and said quietly, "A glass of whisky, Freddie."

A moment later he returned to the room carrying two glasses, and as he handed one to her he said, "Take it slowly."

She took two or three sips from the glass before heaving a long sigh; then she lay back in the chair. "Why is it I'm worried sick, Freddie?" she said. "She's in love with him and he seems to dote on her. Oh yes, I'm sure he dotes on her; but in spite of that I've got this awful feeling on me."

"You're not the only one."

"Oh, I know that." She nodded at him now. "I know what you've been going through these past weeks. But it wasn't to be, and I told you that from the first. She didn't see you in that way."

"She was never given the chance; at least, I didn't give her the chance, and I should have. I thought, being ten years older . . . but then he's nearly as old."

"It's done now, lad, and you've got other things to think about, and deeply I should say since this latest news from Nancy. My God! who would be on to this? We know for a fact it isn't Freeman, and we know for a fact too it isn't Connie Wheatley, and, as you say, she's scared the hell out of her father; and if you ask me, I think there's good reason there because I bet they feathered their nest before that old dame turfed them out. Not that I blame them. Odd, isn't it, how we've both managed to avoid meeting her? Yet I have a vivid picture in my mind of what she's like. An old autocrat by all accounts; yet Belle says she's got another side to her altogether and they seem to get on like a house on fire. Well, she'll likely need support. . . . Now why should I say that?"

Freddie looked at her, took a drink from his glass, and placed it on the table before he replied, "For the same reason I keep asking myself questions every time I think of him. Anyway, let's forget about them for the minute, if we can; and I would suggest you get yourself to bed."

"Oh no. As long as I'm in me own house, I'll be all right; I can trot about. And Freddie"—she held out her hand to him—"come here." And when he came to her side he dropped on his hunkers and took hold of her hand and her words seemed to pierce his heart as she said, "I'm not going to pop off today or tomorrow. I know all about this trouble: I'll have me good days and me bad, but I could go on for many months yet. And you know me, if I make up me mind to do something I do it, don't I?"

He dropped his head onto the arm of her chair as he muttered, "Oh, don't, don't Maggie, please, not today."

"We've got to face it, lad. We both have to face it. And I want you to know that I've left everything in order. Everything I have, every penny, every offshoot is yours. Before, I'd left half and half, but now she's settled, and money-wise she'll never want for anything. Only yesterday I altered the will, because yesterday was as near today as made no matter."

His voice was thick and broken as he muttered, "I don't want the money or the businesses, Maggie. Getting them would mean nothing to me. Oh no! If it would give you one extra day of life, I would give up a year of mine. I could get by without the businesses. I could take up running for a start." Maggie remained silent for a moment while she patted his bent head. Although she really knew what he meant when he denied the businesses, nevertheless the stark words saddened her somewhat; but then she gave a little laugh, saying, "Eeh! I can see you goin' up and down that quay. You always wore boots and no stockings. Your breeches were almost up to your backside. Who they belonged to in the first place I don't know because as small as you were they were too small for you. And you wore a jacket that was too big, you had to roll the sleeves back."

He lifted his head and looked at her through misted eyes, saying, "You remember that jacket?"

"Oh yes, I remember that jacket. Don't you recall I once said

243

to you, your trousers'll never trip you up but your sleeves will?"

"You said so many things to me. Jack the giant killer you used to call me."

"Yes, Jack the giant killer. Funny that. I used to wonder why I was interested in you, why you appealed to me, why I envied the woman who had borne you. Yet, I ceased to envy her years ago. But you know something else, Freddie? She still holds it against me, does . . . our Jinny."

"No, no, she doesn't."

"Oh, yes she does, and you know it. You've had to do a lot of placating in that quarter. And it's natural. My godfathers! if I'd been your mother and anybody had tried to take you from me I would have wiped the floor with them. So I understand Jinny's feelings, always have. And later on I think you should do something for them. Get them into a better place than they're in now, and set John up in something of his own. There'll be plenty to do that."

"Oh, Maggie, for God's sake! will you be quiet?" He got to his feet now. "And d'you know?" He turned to her, thrusting his arm out. "If the one who's onto me with those letters gets his way, I'll likely be along the line, never mind distributing largesse to the family. Have you thought of that?"

"Yes, I have, and I've thought of this an' all: they've got nothing on you, nothing at all. A lad of ten or twelve, you were. You can tell them everything that happened, but you told Freeman you wouldn't implicate him; tell them it was a man who gave you the package. And you could even go as far as to say, yes, you found the three stones in your pocket, and yes, I sold them. No, that would give old Taylor away. But then somebody's got to be given away; you're not going to sacrifice yourself. Just stick to the fact that you didn't see Gallagher after his servant said that the excise were coming. That's all you've got to do. Anyway"— she shook her head—"you were just a bit of a lad, not any bigger than two penn'orth of copper. If you had taken the stones you wouldn't have had the wits to keep silent about them; they would have shown up before now somewhere or another."

"Yes, I suppose you're right, Maggie. But, nevertheless, you can understand I'm worried. Strangely enough, not so much about the polis but about who's in on this that we don't know of. And I can tell you that Freeman is worried an' all. He hasn't said so, but it's in his mind. If the writer of this letter knows about these stones he's bound to know about other transactions that happened around that time and which Freeman himself was in up to the neck. But"—he paused—"what I can't understand is if they've been getting these letters and I must have definitely been mentioned in them according to Nancy's friend, why haven't they shown their hand before now?"

"There's still plenty of time. They'd have to feel sure before they accused anybody; and you're no longer a little nipper of no importance, you are known as Maggie Hewitt's lad or, in some quarters, man, and somebody to be reckoned with. So don't let's look for more worries to put on our plate. I think we've got enough at the moment, don't you?"

He didn't answer her but said, "I'll go and have a word with me mother; she'll want to know all about it."

She noticed that for the first time he had called Jinny his mother and not his ma. Odd that. In a way it only went to prove the distance he had moved from the far end of the town.

The new worry made itself evident on the Saturday morning at eleven o'clock when Jinny opened the door to two men who asked if they could speak to Mr Musgrave. One, she faintly recognised; the other was a complete stranger. She showed them into the sitting room.

Maggie had decided to stay in bed this morning. Freddie was down in the greenhouse in the garden, so she picked up her skirts and ran out of the back door and across the yard, through the shrubbery, over the lawn and down to the walled vegetable garden.

The door of the greenhouse was open and she could see him, and so she began to call: "Freddie! Freddie! There's two fellas here."

"What?" He'd come to the open doorway.

"One I seem to know, the other I don't. The one I know is from the quay, he's something down there."

"Maggie still upstairs?"

"Aye."

"Well, don't let on who's called yet a while."

"Oh, she'll be ringing down 'cos she heard the bell, you know that."

He dusted his hands, took down his coat from a peg, put it on, buttoned up the neck of his shirt, then followed her back to the house. But before entering the sitting room he pressed his shoulders further back, took a deep breath, then opened the door slowly and walked in. He immediately recognised one of the officers from the Customs House, but the other he hadn't seen before.

The two men were standing in front of the window and they turned but they didn't move towards him, while he made for the fireplace, to stand on the hearthrug before greeting them: "Well! gentlemen. You wish to see me?"

It was his tone that brought an exchange of glances between them; then they came forward and both of them stopped near the head of the couch, and the customs man said, "We would like a word with you, Mr Musgrave."

"May I ask what about?"

"Well"—there was hesitation now in the man's voice—"it will become clear during the course of our conversation. This is Mr Wilson."

Freddie refrained from replying, "Mr Wilson of what, the excise or the police?" Instead, he extended a hand towards the couch, saying, "Well, if we have to have a talk we might as well sit down."

It was evident that both Freddie's manner and his way of addressing them had taken them somewhat by surprise. One at least of the pair felt he had been misinformed about this man, and more so when the man spoke to him in the following manner, saying, "Well now, gentlemen, let's get on with this interrogation, for it appears that is what you're here for; but the reason escapes me."

"Well . . . sir"—the title was hesitant but nevertheless firm—"we will have to go back a number of years to when you were a boy."

"Yes, and what about that?"

"Now look here, Mr Musgrave." It was the customs man speaking, his tone showing some impatience. "Well now, Mr Musgrave, it's well known that when you were a boy you were used as a runner for a number of men who were breaking the law in bringing contraband stuff into this country at that time."

"A runner?" Freddie's eyebrows moved upwards. "That's simply another name for a messenger, and, yes, I ran messages for anybody who would pay me in those days. You may recollect, times were hard then for quite a large section of the people in

246

this town, and a penny was a penny. I would have run from here to Newcastle for sixpence, but unfortunately I wasn't able to pick my clients in those days."

The customs man was now looking down and to the side as if he was studying the carpet, and the stranger, with a more diplomatic approach, put in, "It is understood, sir, that on a certain night in late eighteen-forty-five a certain gentleman gave you a parcel to take across the water. Is that right?"

"Look, sir, we are going back all of sixteen years. I carried parcels and notes all over this town."

"This was a particular night, Mr Musgrave, when you were given a package that held some valuable jewellery and you went across in your little sculler." The man smiled now. "I saw it on the river this morning; it looks still in good fettle."

Freddie did not take up the pleasant tone nor reference to the sculler, but said, "I can recall a night when I was given a parcel, a small parcel, and I took it across the water and delivered it."

"To whom did you deliver it, Mr Musgrave?"

"To a man called Gallagher who lived out at The Towers."

Freddie knew that they were well aware of all this and that it was best to play them at their own game.

"You had taken packages to him before?"

"I don't recall. Perhaps I did; I took him messages."

"What kind of messages?"

Freddie now put his head to one side as if he was trying to remember; then shaking his head, he said, "Oh, they were bits of rhyme or some such. I couldn't remember back the very words I carried."

"You know who gave you the messages to carry?" It was the customs man again.

"Now you've set me a problem." Freddie had turned towards the man. "You deal with the customs, did you ever know who you were looking for?"

"Yes, we had a very good idea."

"Oh, well, that's your business; it wasn't mine as a child to remember the faces."

"But you remember who it was that passed you the parcel to be taken across to Mr Gallagher on that particular night?"

"No, I don't." He spat the words back at the man. "The only thing I recall was that it was black dark," which was true, "and

247

this fellow gave me a little parcel, not as big as the palm of your hand, and told me who it had to go to. But I didn't see his face."

"Perhaps you remember his voice?"

"Oh, man"—Freddie now made himself turn his head away as if in disdain—"asking me, a man of twenty-eight, did I remember a voice of someone who spoke to me in the dark when I was . . . what? eleven or twelve years old. Have sense."

When he turned back again to him the customs man's face was grim, his lips tight together, but the other man was smiling gently, and because of this it came to Freddie that this man was probably the more dangerous of the two: he was the kind that wouldn't lose his temper, he would probe gently until he caused you to trip yourself up. So, addressing him bluntly, he said, "Would you like to get to the point? Am I being accused of something?"

"No one is accusing you of anything, Mr Musgrave. We would just like some information. You see, we are not only dealing with the theft of some precious stones but we are also dealing with the murder of Mr Gallagher on that particular night."

"Well"—there was a touch of laughter in Freddie's voice now as he cast his glance from one to the other—"huh! you're not thinkin' that I did him in, are you? Remember, I was a kid at the time."

"No, we are not actually thinking that you . . . did him in, but we feel you may have knowledge of what happened to him."

"How would I know?"

"Mr Musgrave"—the pleasant man was nodding his head slowly now—"you know quite a bit about what happened that particular night. Now, I think it would be advisable if you would come down to the Court House with us where we can have further discussions because, as I understand it, there was more to the event that night than the theft of jewellery, now wasn't there?"

He stared back at the man and was about to say, "I'm comin' down to no Court House unless you have a warrant that states exactly why you're takin' me there," when he heard a movement up above, which meant that Maggie was getting out of bed. She must have got it out of Jinny that there were two male visitors. Getting abruptly to his feet, which caused the two men also to rise, he said, "I'll accompany you to the Court House only because Mag ... Miss Hewitt isn't well and I don't want her disturbed further in any way; but I fear she's already about to join us. Would you kindly wait outside? I'll join you in a moment or so."

At this, he hurried from the room, bounded the stairs and rushed into his own room. He put on a narrow tie that had been hanging over the back of the chair, and pulled a fresh coat from the wardrobe; then, hurrying out, he tapped on Maggie's door and called, "I won't be long; just popping down the town."

"Freddie! Freddie, wait!"

He didn't wait but ran down the stairs. Took up his hat from the hallstand, and joined the two men on the drive.

"We do appreciate your co-operation, Mr Musgrave."

Freddie cast a sidelong glance at the suave man and again he thought, He's a clever one ... do appreciate your co-operation.

He didn't know where they were bound for, nor did he ask, but, by the road they took, it wouldn't be the Customs House in Low Street; it was when they entered Norfolk Street he knew they were making for the Magistrates Court, and he could not help a slight tremor passing through him. He had known so many people who had passed through that court, especially after a customs raid, when the penalties were so harsh that the men wouldn't have been much worse off if they had attempted to murder someone: for what other crime were they manacled by the neck in the cellar of the Officers House?

As he entered the building between the customs officer and the suave gentleman, as he was now thinking of him, he told himself: Do what Maggie said in such circumstances, play dumb.

He was guided into a small room that had a form attached to one wall and six chairs in a row along another, and between them an oblong wooden table. The customs officer placed four chairs round the table; then he left the room, and the suave gentleman indicated that Freddie should sit; then he himself sat down, but he made no attempt to open a conversation. He didn't speak until the customs man returned with another man whom Freddie recognised immediately as the Chief Constable. For a moment he thought the man was going to give him a friendly smile, but his face quickly returned to its set pattern, and he too sat down. And it was he who first spoke. Looking at Freddie, he said, "Ah well, now for this little chat that might straighten things up, Mr . . . er . . . Musgrave." Then he added in a quite kindly tone, "There's nothing to be afraid of; we're just making some enquiries."

Before he could stop himself Freddie was slapping back: "I am not afraid because I have nothing to be afraid of. And I would thank you to let me know what all this is about. Moreover, I would ask if you have a warrant to bring me here."

"Oh. Oh." The Chief Constable wagged his head. "Don't let's talk of warrants. We just want a little conversation with you to get to the bottom of something."

"Well, would you kindly get on with the conversation and as quickly as possible because Miss Hewitt is far from well and I wish to be at home with her."

It was the customs man who was now stabbing his finger at him, only to be checked by the suave gentleman, saying to him, "Leave it. Leave it." And he himself, turning to Freddie now, said, "It's like this, Mr Musgrave: we will put it plainly to you, we have had information to the effect that on a night, many years ago now, you not only carried a message from, as you said, a man you didn't know, you didn't recognise, to a Mr Gallagher of The Towers beyond Harton village, and which you later realised was stolen jewellery; and there is a witness to your being seen landing on this side of the river in the dead of night with a strange bundle. But the most important point is, when did you really last see Mr Gallagher? Was it not on the dockside when he tried to prevent you taking his child?"

The man stopped talking, and Freddie stared at him, actually open-mouthed. How did he know all this? If it was old man Wheatley, he could have pieced together what had happened on yon side of the water; but he couldn't have known anything about their landing at this side, that would have come from Harper. But neither of them knew the full story, Harper very little of it except what he surmised. There was no one else. . . . When a thought entered his mind he flung it aside, then to the man he said, "I knew nothing about what happened to Mr Gallagher. You've probed so much why don't you work out the rest and find out who did him in?"

"Oh, we will find out who . . . did him in . . . never fear."

"You've taken a long time over it."

"Keep a civil tongue in your. . . ."

250

Freddie now swung round towards the customs man, crying, "Don't tell me to keep a civil tongue in my head! You have got me here without warrant or justice note. I can get up and walk out and you can't do anything about it. So *you* please keep a civil tongue in *your* head."

"Now, now, now!" The Inspector's hand was wagging. "Mr Musgrave, mind . . . mind your words."

"I am minding my words, sir. You tell your subordinate here to mind his words. I am not a prisoner."

"As yet."

It looked for a moment as if Freddie would strike out at the man sitting at the corner of the table, but he gritted his teeth and returning his attention to the suave man, he said, "You do realise that I was but a lad when all this happened? I can scarcely recall anything that took place."

"Then you wouldn't know what happened even to a very valuable hoard of jewels that you carried across the river to Mr Gallagher?"

"No, I wouldn't." Each word was emphatic. "Anyway, what would I, a lad in my position, have done with a hoard of jewels? I would have been terrified of handling them in the first place. And who in my family or neighbours could I have trusted them to? What could they have done with them that wouldn't have landed them right here or in the House of Correction or further up still? Jewels!" He tossed his head.

"I see your point, and believe me, Mr Musgrave, I take your word for it. But unfortunately there are more serious matters to go in to. For instance, you came across the river that night with Miss Hewitt, did you not?"

Freddie returned the man's stare but said nothing.

"All right, we will let that pass. But it is suggested."

"Who suggested?"

"Mr Musgrave." The suave man's voice spoke of patience. "And it has been suggested that Mr Gallagher was murdered that same night."

. . . "And you think I murdered him? a little strip of a lad twelve years old?"

"Oh, Mr Musgrave"—the man was smiling now—"I understand from those who remember you, you were a very spritely little strip of a lad with a lot about you, a clever mind, even in those days. You may not have done any such deed but you may be cognizant of the facts and perhaps could enlighten us as to what might have happened, I say might have happened, that brought about Mr Gallagher's death."

Cognizant of the facts. He hadn't heard that word before but he got its meaning. Oh yes, he got its meaning. Cognizant of the facts. Oh yes, he was that all right, and he was now feeling sick to the depths of his stomach. These fellas were clever. They had probed this far but they were stuck, and my God! they would have to remain stuck. He would have to be careful from now on of every word he ever uttered. And so, sighing, he looked at the man and said slowly, "Cognizant or aware of, or anyway you like to put it, I've told you when I last saw Mr Gallagher. I can tell you no more and I ask you one and all"—he now cast his glance around the other men—"can you remember back to things you did as a lad? I mean, to pinpoint things and to people you met?"

No one answered for a moment, but then the customs man spoke, saying, "Yes, if it was a time when there was a robbery, a murder, and an abduction. Yes, I'm sure we could all cast our memories back to that time; in fact, I'm sure it would have caused us some sleepless nights for many years after. Do you sleep well? . . ."

It was the suave man holding his hand up in the direction of the customs officer while he looked at Freddie, saying, "I think it would be best, Mr Musgrave, if we leave the matter in abeyance for a little while, don't you think? Perhaps if you talked the matter over with Miss Hewitt, she being an older person would be able to recall incidents . . . pertinent incidents that will refresh your memory and doubtless hers too." He rose to his feet now, adding, "I thank you very much for your co-operation. I'm sure you won't mind if I were to call on you at a later date, say Monday when we could have a ride into Newcastle."

"Newcastle?" Freddie was on his feet too now. "Why Newcastle?"

"Well—" The man gave a slight smile and his voice had even an apologetic note as he went on, "You see, my office is in Newcastle and it is more accommodating than here, although I thank the officer"—he inclined his head towards the man—"for the use of the Court House. I would rather we talked in Newcastle. Shall we say then Monday morning at ten o'clock?"

Freddie made no answer, he simply stared at the man, for now he was knowing real fear and it was creating a sickness deep inside him. All he wanted to do at this moment was to get back to Maggie, and yes, yes, talk to her, for no matter what happened she must be protected from an enquiry such as this. She wouldn't be able to stand it. God Almighty! What was happening to them? Why had this come about after all these years? And who was it who had supplied the information? Well, before Monday he'd pay a visit to Connie Wheatley and that father of hers. He dismissed the thought of the Harpers, theirs was only surmise created by what they had seen when the boat landed on the North side; they would know nothing whatever about what had taken place at the other side of the river. So who had started all this? After all these years the whole business had been forgotten, at least by him.

He was about to turn away when he forced himself to look at the man again and, in tones as firm as he could muster, say, "You'll get me to Newcastle, sir, when you can present me with a note from the Justices."

The man made no retort. And now Freddie went from the room, but not before he levelled his glance at the other three men. In the hallway he had to stand aside while two policemen dragged a drunken man in, and from the look of the man's clothes and the smell that emanated from him he had been dragged through the mire of some particular street.

Outside, he found that his stride was impeded by the shaking of his legs. He had the desire to run, to scamper as he had done when a lad when he sensed danger was imminent.

When he reached the house he fully expected to find Maggie dressed and downstairs, but it was his mother who greeted him, saying, "I had to put her back to bed"—she jerked her head upwards—"she was for gettin' into her clothes. But she had a spasm; it doubled her up. I've given her a dose. What's the matter anyway? What's happening?"

"Nothing at present, Ma." He stood before her, for a moment feeling the need of her strength, at least her physical strength. He had almost a childish feeling that he wanted her arms about him. He said slowly, "They're on to the business, Ma. Somebody's been writing letters, somebody who's been puttin' two and two together."

"About Belle?"

"Yes, and other things."

"What other things can they get against you and her?"

"They're probin' into where the jewels went that I was carrying that night and, more so, into how Gallagher met his death."

"My God in heaven! They don't think that you . . . ?"

"Ma, you never know what a policeman thinks much less a customs officer or excise man. Anyway, keep your tongue quiet, don't mention this to me da, 'cos you know how he gets chattin' to his cronies, and the less said from our side about this the better."

As he moved from her towards the stairs she said quietly, "This could be enough to polish her off." And as he mounted the stairs to Maggie's bedroom he thought to himself, Yes, she's right; it's enough to polish her off.

As soon as he entered the room she said, "Police and customs?"

He nodded once, then drew up a chair to the side of the bed.

"What happened?"

"They questioned me. There were four of them altogether."

"In the Court House?"

"In the Court House."

"Who could have done this? Look lad, I've been thinking: that Wheatley lot not only feathered their nest that night with a lot of loose change which could have meant a hoard of sovereigns, enough to get them started, but they likely took that bag of jewellery because it wasn't on him, was it, when he was taken from the river? And a thing like that doesn't float away out of a pocket or a body belt. When he got on his horse he had left that bag of stones behind, and they knew it."

"I can't think that Connie Wheatley would do anything like this, Maggie, she would be potching herself. Yet I've made up me mind to go and have a talk with her, 'cos there's her father and he's already opened his mouth to Freeman."

"Were the stones mentioned, I mean did they ask any questions about me taking those three stones to Mr Taylor?"

"No, no, that didn't come up; so let's hope they know nothing about that."

"Well"—Maggie pursed her blue lips now—"I bet your life that those Wheatleys picked the lot up and likely got rid of them in Scotland for not a crumb of their worth but enough to set them up, together with what else they took."

"I'm goin' to see her tomorrow."

"Yes, I would do that, but"—her hand came out and she clutched at his now—"about the other, they . . . they could never prove anything, could they? There were no witnesses, it's just all suspicion."

"Yes, Maggie, it's just all suspicion. There's nothin' for you to worry about, not a thing."

"Huh!" The sound seemed to come from deep in her throat. "I'm not worryin' about meself, lad, my time is so short. It wouldn't matter to me if they found out this minute, I'd be gone before they could carry me downstairs."

"Maggie, for God's sake!" He tried to pull his hand from hers. "Don't talk like that, woman, I can't bear it."

"All right, all right, calm down; but this is another thing you've got to face up to, as I've told you before. And anyway, we've all got to go sometime. That's an odd sayin', isn't it, we've all got to go? And where are we goin'? I've been lying here on and off these last few weeks askin' meself just that question, where do we go? Certainly not to the heaven that so many people are hanging their coats on, expectin' to be walkin' in flowered gardens with God. No, I threw that idea over when I was twelve because I reasoned out"—she gave a little chuckle now—"that if there were flower gardens up there the rain would sometimes fall the opposite way, it would have to keep them goin'."

"Oh, Maggie. Maggie."

When she saw the slight smile on his face she said, "Well, don't you think it is as good reasoning as any. Anyway, I've got a sort of assurance inside meself that wherever I'm bound for it will be peaceful, like a dreamless sleep. And after all, there's nothing more refreshing than a dreamless sleep. . . . But tell me, have they finished with you?"

"Oh, no; no, Maggie, they certainly haven't finished with me. He's comin' back on Monday to escort me to Newcastle."

Her breath caught in her throat, and as she attempted to heave herself up onto the pillows she brought out between gasps, "But . . . why? They . . . can't, they can't . . . have anything on you. You were . . . a bit of a lad."

"Don't agitate yourself, woman. Yes, I was a bit of a lad, but, as they say, I was a bright boy. Oh, yes, they stressed that, I was a bright boy."

"But not bright enough to murder a man."

He closed his eyes tightly, saying, "Maggie. Maggie, don't put it like that. If you hadn't done what you did, you wouldn't be here today, neither would I, nor Belle. It was he who meant murder."

"Yes, Freddie, I know; but who's going to believe that?"

"Nobody, 'cos it won't come out. It can only come out through me."

He didn't add what had just come into his mind: And I could be called an accessory after the fact, or some such, and be in for a long stretch. He didn't say it because likely the thought hadn't occurred to her, as it hadn't occurred to him until a minute ago. And once again there the feeling was of sickness in his stomach. To change the subject, he said quickly, "She was goin' to write straightaway when they got to London, wasn't she? If she had we would have received it this morning."

"They wouldn't get there till late on Wednesday, and if she wrote it on Thursday, it would be with luck that we got it today. You know what the post is like here on a Saturday."

He rose from the chair now, saying, "You've had your medicine?"

"Yes, I've had my medicine."

"Then you should be ready for a dose."

"I've already had the dose and woken from it." She smiled wryly. "Go on now and get something to eat, because your mother will want to get off home."

He stood looking down on her for a moment, then turned and left the room; but before descending the stairs he stood for a moment and covered his eyes with his hand.

Connie Wheatley opened the side door to be confronted by Freddie.

"May I come in?"

"Yes, yes, of course."

She led the way up the stairs; but as soon as they entered the sitting room she went hastily across to the door at the far side and closed it; then coming back to him, she said, "Sit down."

When he was seated he looked at her where she was perched

now on the edge of a chair, and he said, "There's trouble brewin', Connie."

"Yes, yes, I guessed that."

He stared at her for a moment before he said, "You wouldn't write an anonymous letter, would you?"

"Anonymous letter? Me, write an anonymous letter? What would I write about, if I could write? I can hardly write me name. I can reckon up figures; I'm good at that."

"No, I didn't think you would; in fact, I felt sure you wouldn't, Connie. But then, there's your father."

She glanced now towards the far door. "Yes," she said, "there's been me father and what damage he's done. He must have done it before three weeks ago because he's had a stroke."

"Oh. Oh, I'm sorry."

"Oh, you needn't be sorry because if I was speaking the truth the only one I'm sorry for is meself at the moment, because, I can tell you, since we left The Towers all those years ago he's been a trial. I think me mother would have been here the day if it hadn't been for the worry of him; at times I've even thought he would see me out. He was all right when he could keep off the bottle, but a couple of glasses of the hard stuff and God knows what he would say . . . what he has said. It got that way that the polis brought him back twice in the last few months. Once I understand he ended up in the polis station, the Central in the city, yelling his head off. God only knows what he came out with. For days I could hardly sleep expectin' a knock and somebody to walk in and say, 'Where did you get the money to start all this?' " She now looked straight at Freddie. "It could be the first question they would ask, couldn't it?"

He hesitated. "Yes," he said, "yes, I suppose so, Connie."

She drew in a long breath, then joined her hands tightly together in her lap and her voice was low as she now said, "They say that no one prospers from ill-gotten gains; but when we rifled through those places and the stuff he had stacked away, we all thought we had earned what we took." She now raised her head and said, "But we didn't clear the place, just took enough that we thought would start us up, except. . . ." She stopped abruptly and placed a hand on the top of her head as if she was trying to press it down onto her shoulders.

"Except what, Connie?" he asked her.

"It doesn't matter, it doesn't matter.... Can I get you a drink?"

"No, thanks. But can I ask you this: have you any idea of what your father let slip? Could he have told them about driving me and the child to the dockside?"

It was some time before she answered, "I don't really know, Freddie. I don't really know. The only thing I can say is that he came in here yelling one day that he had ... well—" her head wagged now before she finished, "potched you. And when he was sober I tried to get it out of him what he had said, but, you know, he couldn't remember a thing. And now he's lying there"—again she motioned her head towards the far door—"as helpless as any child, unable to speak or move. He's lost the use of everything except for one hand, and the doctor tells me he could lie there like that till God knows when. During the week I've got a woman who comes in and cleans him and washes him because I've got to be downstairs. But how long I'll carry on there, I don't know. You know"—she leant towards him—"I've got the feeling, a silly feeling as if I want to pick up me skirts and run right back into the past when I was a little lass, or more than a little lass. Anyway, before this happened"—she now tapped her face from one cheek to the other—"when I only had me eye to worry about and I was happy workin' in The Towers. . . . But we can't go back, can we?"

"No, Connie, we can't go back." He now rose to his feet and went over to her and put his hand on her shoulder, saying, "I suppose it's a silly thing to say, me being in the precarious position that I am, but if I can help you in any way you've just got to give me a shout."

She too rose to her feet and gripped his arm, saying, "I liked you as a lad, Freddie, and I like you as a man. And you know something—I can say this to you—I envy the woman you'll eventually take. I'm thirty-eight and past marriage, but you know"—she gave a cynical laugh now—"I had an offer and only last week. Yes, yes, I had. He's got a shoe business along the street, but it doesn't make quarter of the money that I do, and so he's willin' to put up with me face."

"Aw, Connie"—he was gripping her hand now—"beauty is as beauty acts and once anyone gets to know you they forget about the rest. And you say this fella has a shoe shop? Well, you know"— he brought his face down to hers—"that could have been me, because that was what I wanted more than anything else in life when I was a lad, to have a shoe shop, not a cobbler's mind, but a real shoe shop. I'd seen one in Newcastle full of boots and bonny ladies' slippers and things, and I used to dream about it at nights. Yes, that fella along at that shop could have been me."

"Oh, Freddie." She smiled now. "I wish to God it had been. But then you wouldn't have looked the side I was on."

"Don't you be so sure. I have me eye on the main chance; I'd have married you for your money."

"Not you, Freddie, not you. . . ."

As he walked into the street he thought: How strange! He had entered the house fearful but had come out laughing. And it was odd about the man in the shoe shop proposing to her. Funny, but he hadn't thought of his desire for the shoe shop for years. One thing, though, that had come out of his visit: Mr Wheatley was likely the man who, in his drunken state, had talked of the jewels and had undoubtedly insinuated, if not pointedly said, that the youngster, the runner, must have taken them. How other would the police have brought that up in the questioning? And if he said that, then he could also have hinted as to how his master died. But what about the letters? Connie had said her father couldn't write. But then there were plenty professional letter writers that would have done the job for him. Among these men would probably be some who, if this knowledge had come into their hands, would surely have used it in a form of blackmail.

A letter arrived on Monday morning from Belle. It was very short. It said,

> My very dear Aunt Maggie and Freddie,
> We arrived in the hotel at seven o'clock last evening. It is a very nice place. I am looking out of the window now and London seems vast. The sun is shining. We are to spend the day sightseeing.
> I miss you both so very much. I send you my fondest love.
> Belle

After reading the letter Maggie had handed it to Freddie, and he, now slowly folding it up, said, "Terribly informative, is how that could be described.

"Yes, that's right, Freddie, terribly informative. Not a word about how she feels."

"Oh yes there is: she says she misses us both terribly."

"And that shouldn't be on the first day of her honeymoon."

"She's merely being polite. You've paid a lot of money over the years to have her taught to be polite and, what's more, to hide her real feelings."

"You think I was wrong in doing that?"

"No, no, not at all. No, of course not. But"—he pointed to the letter now lying on the bed cover—"there you have the result, an educated young lady."

"She never hid her feelings when she was here at home."

"No, but she's not at home now, she's a married woman, Maggie." And God! how he knew she was a married woman, for on the first night of her marriage his imagination running rife had at one point almost driven him mad.

"Oh, it doesn't matter." She picked up the letter from the quilt and put it on the side table near the bed, then said, "There are more things to worry about. What time is it?"

"Quarter to ten."

"If they have a Justice's warrant, you'll have to go with them."

"Yes, but I won't otherwise."

"But, Freddie . . . if they have a warrant it will mean they've got something concrete to go on. What then?"

He sighed now, saying, "I don't know, Maggie; but don't worry, they won't get anything out of me, and that being the case they can't hold me."

"I wouldn't be too sure of that."

"I can't see how; there was no eye witness as to what happened on the dockside. As for that bloomin' bag of glass, because after all that's all they are, as Mr Taylor said, bits of glass. They'd have a job to trace that to me, the remainder of them anyway. They'll likely want to go through the house and I bet already they've been through my bank."

"I doubt if they would get any information from them what you have there. There's a kind of law. . . ."

"Oh, Maggie, you know as well as I do the polis can twist laws, especially the kind of polisman that is calling for me in a few minutes time. Anyway, I think that fella's lost in the polis force, he should be up in the government, in the Diplomatic

Service or something like that. He's so smooth, his words slide out of his mouth. Anyway dear." He bent over her and looked into her face for a moment before kissing her; and then her arms went round his neck and held him close. When she whispered something that he couldn't catch, and he said, "What is it?" she shook her head. But the tears were in her eyes and she pushed him gently from her, saying now, "Go on. But hurry back. D'you hear? Hurry back."

He nodded; then turned abruptly and went out.

His mother met him at the bottom of the stairs. "They're here, there's two of them," she said. "They got out of a cab; it's at the gate."

"Open the door; I'll be in the sitting room."

The men came into the room slowly, and he made himself rise just as slowly from a chair.

"Good day to you, Mr Musgrave." It was the same suave gentleman, as he called him; and he gave no reply to the man's greeting but waited. "I happen to be Inspector Mitchum," the man introduced himself; "and this is"—he pointed to the other man—"Police Sergeant Pringle. You know why we are here?"

Freddie knew why they were here; he also knew that the man's manner had changed, it was not as suave as it had been on their previous meeting.

"You stated, when we last met, that you would not accompany us to Newcastle unless it be on the order of a warrant. Well now, here is the required article." He withdrew a folded paper from his inner pocket and handed it to Freddie who, unfolding it, scanned it, picking out words here and there which ran:

> For questioning with regard to jewels that went missing. . . .
> . . . And being of knowledge with regard to the demise of one Roderick Gallagher on the same night. . . .
> You are requested to. . . .

"You will allow me to get my coat and hat?"

"Certainly."

It seemed now that the inspector put out his hand and stopped the sergeant from following Freddie into the hall.

A moment later when Freddie reappeared in the doorway he said, "If you are ready," and the men followed him, both eyeing the big boney woman standing to the side of the front door. And when she said, "When will you be back, lad?" he answered, "Later on in the day, Ma." She was glancing at the men and slowly she said, "You sure?"

"I'm sure. Don't worry, Ma." He put out his hand and touched her arm.

Outside, the inspector said in a polite enquiring tone, "Your mother?"

"Yes, my mother."

Seated now at one side of the cab, he looked at the two men who were looking at him. "We are not taking the train then?"

"No; out of consideration for you, we thought it would be less exposure."

"I see, out of consideration for me, not in case you've made a mistake?"

"We rarely make mistakes, Mr Musgrave. We do our homework first." The inspector said no more, only continued to look at him. It was the sergeant who leant forward, saying, "You wouldn't like to begin talking now to save time and trouble later?" only to draw back swiftly as if to avoid a blow because Freddie too had moved forward and was now sitting taut on the edge of the seat, his knees almost touching those of the sergeant as he cried at him, "Now listen here! Both of you listen here: I'll talk when I know what I'm accused of and it's put into direct words. And let me tell you this, you cannot stick any crime on me because I've never committed one, and by God! I'll see that there'll be a song and dance about this, and there'll be some people doing hornpipes. So, until I'm confronted by a magistrate or whoever's going to accuse me of what I haven't done, I'm saying not another word. Understand?"

Both men were now grim-faced, eyes narrowed, lips tight; and so was Freddie as he sat back against the smelly leather of the cab. The journey continued thus in an almost nightmare silence until they reached Newcastle.

The cab stopped outside the Court House. He had passed it dozens of times before on his meandering through the city but had never imagined that one day he'd be entering its doors almost as a prisoner, for that's what he felt he was already. Such was the turmoil in his mind that he only dimly took in the surroundings. There was bustle all about him, but it was a quiet sort of bustle, not like that in the Court House in North Shields;

but then this was a different kind of Court House altogether. He was guided across the spacious hall and up a staircase that was bordered by a fine balustrade—he always had an eye for wood—and to a sort of waiting room where the inspector indicated that he should sit. There was an officer in uniform standing by a door at the far end of the room, as if on guard. The inspector and the sergeant now went through another door leading from the room, and he was left alone, and, strangely, he was no longer feeling sick or fearful, rather he was experiencing anger, an anger that wanted to give voice to itself. And the longer he sat waiting the more fierce his anger became, until, after fifteen minutes, the sergeant returned.

Standing before him, he said, "Come along."

For a moment longer Freddie remained seated, then rose slowly and followed the man through the door at the end of the room and into another, a different room this. To one side were three wooden benches, at the other a desk with an officer sitting behind it. But in front and opposite the aisle between the forms and the desk was a long table, and behind this three men sat. And one of them was the suave inspector.

The sergeant pointed to the first form and indicated that Freddie should be seated, and when he sat on the end of it he saw that he was directly opposite the man seated between the other two. And it was he who now spoke to him, and the voice, Freddie recognised, indicated that the man was from neither North or South of the river, nor was he a Scot or Irish. He seemed not to have an accent at all, but his words were clear and his tone not unkind as he said, "You are Frederick Musgrave?"

"Yes, sir." When Freddie made to rise to his feet now, the man said, "It's quite all right, you may remain seated. This is just an informal enquiry, you understand that?"

Informal enquiry that took a warrant to bring him here. He could not stop giving voice to his thoughts as he replied, "I was brought here on warrant, sir."

"Yes, yes, I understand that; but nevertheless you are not being charged with any crime. All we want at the present moment is information about incidents that happened some years ago. The inspector has already questioned you at some length, I understand, but your answers have been rather evasive and not satisfactory. So shall we begin at the beginning and take your mind back to the night when you were given a small package to carry across the water to a certain Mr Roderick Gallagher at The Towers in the village of Harton."

"I can add no more, sir, to what I have already told the inspector."

"Come, come, Mr Musgrave. Let me now inform you that we have, from three separate sources, been given details of what transpired that night and these sources implicate you. On my part, I shall now be frank and tell you that, taking the third source first, this is of the least importance, yet it has its bearing, it deals with what you brought across in the sculler from the South side to the North side on the night in question, a bundle of some sort. You were also accompanied by the woman who was known as Miss Maggie Hewitt. Now for the second part of the information from another source. It is suggested that the packet of stolen jewels that you took and delivered to Mr Gallagher did not remain with him, for they were not found on his body when it was recovered from the river some days later. But it is suggested, only suggested, Mr Musgrave, that you know what became of that stolen property. The third information to us is of a more serious nature. It is the fact that you also know how Mr Roderick Gallagher came to meet his end. Now, do any of these things refresh your memory, Mr Musgrave?"

Freddie stared back at the man. His eyes were fixed on his alone although he knew that every other person in that room was staring fixedly at him, and his mouth became dry. His anger had left him as if drained through a sieve. This man was even more suave than the inspector and he appeared more kindly, which, he considered, made him more dangerous at this moment.

"Well, will you answer, Mr Musgrave?"

"I can remember nothing more than I've already said."

"Will you answer me just one question? What were you carrying when you came across the river that night? It was something bulky."

Before he could stop himself he answered, saying, "You don't think it was Mr Gallagher, do you?"

There was a single titter, but the expression on the man's face didn't alter and his voice remained the same as he said, "No, I don't suspect it was Mr Gallagher."

Sullenly Freddie said, "And it couldn't have been the jewels, because if I had been carrying such a notable bundle it must have been the Crown Jewels, all of them."

"No, I don't think they were the Crown Jewels, they would have been too heavy, wouldn't they for a boy of twelve to carry? But you admit to carrying something?"

He hadn't admitted to carrying anything, had he? No, he hadn't. The only one he had told that part to was Freeman, and after that talk Freeman wouldn't have said anything, he was sure. No, he hadn't admitted to anything, and he said so now: "I haven't admitted to carrying anything."

The man leant back in his chair, sighed, put his hand on what looked like a blotting pad in front of him and patted it. The action spoke clearly to Freddie of impatience. And so, now and in earnest tones, he said, "Sir, believe me, I have no knowledge of what was in the package I carried that night or what became of it and"—he had to swallow deeply before saying the next words—"I did not kill Mr Gallagher."

"Oh"—the flat hand came up from the blotter now and patted the air between them—"you are not being accused of stealing the jewels or of murdering the man you gave them to. But we feel you have knowledge of both events and that you are withholding this knowledge and so obstructing justice from taking its rightful course. You understand me, Mr Musgrave?"

"Yes, sir, I understand you very well, but I have said all I can say."

"All you can say, Mr Musgrave, but not all that you *could* say. I must impress upon you that this is a very serious matter that has come to light and that because it has come to light it will be pursued to its end. Again I ask if you understand me?"

Freddie wasn't absolutely sure if by this understand the man was meaning what he thought was meant by it. It was in his mind first, that they could keep him here until he told them something, or secondly, that they could definitely accuse him of the theft or the murder. And it was no use putting forth that a boy of twelve couldn't murder a man because it had been done before, if he was to go by what he read.

His eyes wavered from those of the man and his head drooped forward; and presently the man's voice came to him, saying, "Well, as you are seemingly determined not to be of help to us at the moment I can only hope that we will be supplied with further information very soon from one who was apparently a confederate of yours in those far off days, and who apparently does not wish you well. You know the saying, when thieves break up enemies are born. So until then I'm afraid you will remain in custody."

Freddie's head snapped upwards. "I . . . I have no enemies, not . . . not like that, and I had no confederates, as you call them, and . . . and I can't remain in custody. I won't. I have done nothing wrong, except act as a runner when I was a child. And then I would run for anyone who paid me, because . . . because I needed the money to help my family. I . . . I. . . ."

The man leaned slightly forward over the table, saying quietly now, "The matter is entirely in your hands, Mr Musgrave. And from the evidence that has been gathered I am afraid I cannot believe your statement when you say you know nothing further of what happened at that particular time. So, as I said, for the time being you will remain in custody."

"You can't do this. You can't."

There was a man now on either side of him. Each put a hand on an arm and when they went to turn him about he flung them off and, almost jumping the four steps to the desk, he bent over it and yelled at the officer, "I don't know anything about the jewellery."

He got no further for the men were now hauling him backwards out of the room and onto the landing again, but they didn't go down the stairs up which he had come but down a narrow stone stairway, so narrow that he was pushed forward and his arms wrenched behind him. They passed through a warren of passages until they came to a broad one which made him think that they were entering bedlam, such was the noise from the cells, then through this to a shorter passage, quieter here, even, you could say, quiet. A heavy door was opened and he was thrust inside, and when the door banged closed he beat on it and yelled until his throat was sore. Then limp, he turned and took stock of where he was: a narrow slit of a room, lit by a grating high up in the wall. The only article of furniture in the place was a pail and what appeared to be some wooden planks attached to the wall to form a bed. There was no bedding of any kind.

The anger had by now seeped from him and what came from his lips sounded like a whimper as he said, "Oh, Maggie. Maggie."

13

The pain was tearing at her. She wanted to cry out but she pressed her hands tightly on her stomach, the nails digging into the bare flesh as she waited for the door to open. When, a minute later, it did, Jinny stood aside and let the pock-marked woman, as she thought of Connie, enter the room.

There was no powder on Connie's face today; the pocks furrowed her cheeks as a miniature wind distorted landscape, making her nose, which was bare of signs of the disease, stand forth like a lone hillock; her bonnet shaded her brown hair but not her eyes. Maggie was experiencing an added and strange pain as she looked at the woman and said, "Thank you for coming."

Connie sat down on the chair that Jinny placed near the bedside and she thanked her with a muttered, "Ta"; then she looked towards the hand that was plucking the threads of the eiderdown before raising her eyes to Maggie. "I didn't know till last night about him," she said. "Eeh! it's awful. I was upset. I . . . I wanted to go and see him, but I didn't know if that would make things worse for him or not. I mean, they'd want to know who I was. They shouldn't have done it to him; he's never done anything but help people and be kind. . . ."

She stopped talking abruptly and brought out a handkerchief and blew her nose, and now Maggie said simply, "You *can* help him."

"I can? I'll do anything . . . well, I mean. . . ."

"Listen to me, my dear." Maggie was speaking to her now as if she were a young girl. "I can't get out of this bed or else I'd be with him at this moment, but I've done what I can. I've seen to it that he'll be cleared of one accusation. Jinny here is his mother."

The two women looked at each other now, then nodded, and Maggie went on, "His brother and Jinny saw him yesterday. He's being accused not only of"—she now closed her eyes for a moment and pressed the hand that was underneath the bed-clothes tight into her stomach before going on—"murdering or knowing who murdered your master, but also of being in possession of what he carried that night to him. They think he has them stored away some place. What did you say?"

Connie's head was bowed now, and what she had muttered was, "Oh my God!" But when she lifted her head again and looked at Maggie she said nothing further; and Maggie went on, "Can I ask you, my dear, if you know anything about those stones?"

Connie's lids were blinking rapidly. She looked from Maggie up to Jinny, then back to Maggie again, and she seemed to have to make an effort to speak, for twice her mouth opened then closed before she brought out what could not have been interpreted as either,"Yes" or "Nay," but then she said, "I . . . I'll be able to fix it so as he'll be all right."

Maggie's hand gripped hers now as she said, "Thank you. Thank you, my dear. When . . . when will you do this?"

Again Connie seemed to find difficulty in speaking, but eventually she said, "As . . . as soon as I get back. I'll . . . I'll go to them."

"To them? Who?"

"Those at the Court House."

Maggie's head now dropped back into the pillows, and with her eyes closed she lay quiet for a moment until Jinny said, "Would you like a drop of your medicine, dear?" and she answered, "Yes, Jinny. Yes."

Jinny now measured two teaspoonfuls of a clear liquid from a bottle into a glass and she placed her big hand between Maggie's shoulder blades, then put the glass to her lips. And Maggie's hand covered hers for a moment until she swallowed the bromide. Then, looking at Jinny, she said, "Would . . . would you like to make Miss Wheatley a cup of tea?"

"Aye, yes. Yes of course."

The moment the door closed on Jinny, Maggie said, "How will you go about it? Have you got them . . . I mean, to hand?"

Connie nodded, then said, "Yes, they're to hand, and I've never known an easy minute since they first came to hand. Me da would take them. We told him we could never do anything with them. The sovereigns and silver that we picked up was enough to get us going, but he wouldn't listen. I won't be able to tell them that, the authorities, that I've known about them all the time else I'd be in for it, wouldn't I? I've got a good little business going and I don't want to lose it in any way. Leave it to me." She bent forward and patted the eiderdown. "I'll . . . think up something, make up something convincing like about him having them hidden or stored away and he's just told me. Well, I could say, the day before he took the stroke. I could say they had got on his mind, that's what brought it on. Oh, don't worry, I'll say something. There's one thing sure, they'll get nothing out of him now for he's as dumb as a bell without a clanger. And I thank God for it. I've been worn out of late with him. He took to the drink you know. And when he was like that he split his mouth open. . . . Eeh!" Her head was moving from side to side now. "I'm sorry to the heart of me about Freddie. Oh dear! I've just thought of something else. It'll have to come out about Miss Belle, won't it?"

"Yes. Yes, I'm afraid so."

"Eeh! It'll be a nine days' wonder. It'll be in all the papers. Will she be very upset, d'you think?"

"Not as much as her husband will I fear, for her birth now will have to be brought into the open, otherwise there would be more complications, wouldn't there?"

"Yes, yes indeed. But that part'll be awful for her. I'm sorry for the lass, for she was so nice and bonny. And to think—" She paused. "You know"—she leant forward now—"there are nights I can't go to sleep. I just think back to the time when that young lass gave birth. That awful night when he acted like a maniac . . . Mr Gallagher, and I can see him now pushing that tiny scrap of a lad under the bed. It all started from then, didn't it?"

"If . . . if they question you about . . . about how you hid the child, will . . . will you tell them exactly what happened?"

"Oh, aye, aye I will. I've got nothin' to cover up there. I only thought of that bairn; she was so bonny and so full of life and kicking. I can remember the time as if it was yesterday when I knew what he meant to do so I played rough and said, 'Give her me here!' And I hauled her up roughly by the little nightgown neck and I said to me da, 'Get a shovel.' Then I yelled at him, the master, 'D'you want to come and see how deep we lay her?' I think now it was only me brazenness that stopped him from comin' with us at first, but come he did. You see I had pushed her into a box, but as soon as I got into the garden I took her out of the box, dropped off me petticoat, wrapped her in it and pushed her in the bushes. And it's as well I did for, not five minutes later there he was. He didn't come close up, but he watched me da digging, then me lifting the box and laying it gently in the bottom of the hole. And he stayed for some minutes until the soil was all pushed back, then he turned about and we heard him get on his horse and gallop off. You know, he often rode half the night. But as soon as he was out of the way I took the bairn and I put her upstairs in that room. Me da wasn't for it, he was scared, because, believe me, the master was a dangerous man, even when he wasn't in one of his turns. Me ma said that he had quite a bit in him that had been in his grandma, that's the one the room was built for. It only showed at times, but when it did, eeh! God, he raised skull and hair through that house. By the way, where is the young lass now?"

"She's on her honeymoon."

"So she won't know about Mr Musgrave and him being inside?"

"She will now. I sent her an express letter on Sunday. I don't think she'll even bother to write, she'll come straight back."

"Aye, yes, she would, 'cos she owes him a lot, she does."

Maggie's hand was again pressed tight on her stomach and her words came out between gasps now as she said, "You'll . . . you'll do something . . . right away . . . won't you?"

"Aye; yes, I will; and I'll get off now."

As she stood up she added, "I'm sorry to see you like this. Are you in much pain?"

"A . . . a little."

"That's a pity, it surely is. But some folks get off lightly; the doctor said me da's not suffering at all, he's just lying there like a log. Well, I'll go then and do me best, but—" she backed a step from the bed, then she paused before she ended, "I'm not goin' to say I'm not afraid, 'cos inside I'm all worked up. I know I've got to stick to the first thing I say and I'll get that pat in me mind. So, don't you worry; I'll . . . I'll do what I can. Ta-ra then."

Maggie inclined her head towards her for she was unable to speak at the moment; but as the door closed on her visitor she thought, Some people get off lightly . . . and that's true. But

God or the powers that existed somewhere had a strange way of working things out because if she hadn't been near her end, her end would have been either in jail for life or at the end of a rope, having done what she did this morning.

It was six o'clock the same day. The room where Freddie had been questioned seemed now packed with people. The same man with the accentless voice sat behind the table and on his right was the inspector, but at his other side sat a magistrate. And at the corner of the table sat a clerk, as also did one at the desk further back in the room.

The wooden seat on which Freddie had sat was now taken up by Maggie's doctor, her solicitor, Connie Wheatley and the doctor who was attending her father.

It was the magistrate who now addressed the man sitting on the edge of the form. "You say that the woman Margaret Hewitt is on the point of death and cannot be moved?" he said.

"I do, sir. Your men have already ascertained this."

"My men are not doctors, they cannot give a medical opinion."

"One of them was a police doctor." Doctor Wright's voice was terse, and the magistrate, nodding now, said, "Oh, yes, yes, of course, yes." He now leant forward and had a word with the man sitting next to the doctor. "You maintain, sir, she was in her right mind when she dictated this letter to you?" He patted some paper that lay to his hand on the table.

"I do, sir. She was in great pain but her mind was clear."

There was further whispered conversation; and then he was addressing Connie. "You have a very strange tale to tell, Miss Wheatley, and it would be quite unbelievable if it wasn't for the practical evidence you have brought here today." He now gently lifted up a small washleather bag. "But when your father confessed three weeks ago to having stolen and hidden these jewels, why didn't you then inform the authorities?"

"I've told you, sir." Her voice was weary because she had told the story three times in the last two hours. "I was frightened. I didn't know what to do with them. If he hadn't had the stroke I would have made him come and own up, at least I would have tried. He . . . he was a very dominating man." She hung her head as she congratulated herself once again on how she was putting this over. Then she added, "But when I

271

heard that Mr Musgrave was being charged with stealing them. . . ."

"Mr Musgrave was not being charged with stealing them. He was being held pending enquiries concerning them."

"As you say, sir. But remembering what a good little lad he was and how he was upset when he saw that bairn in that awful room and couldn't bear to leave her there, I knew I just couldn't keep me tongue quiet about them jewels. Anyway"—her voice took on a louder tone—"what could I have done with them?"

"I'm going to ask you now, Miss Wheatley, why all those years ago when Mr Gallagher's body was found that you didn't come into the open, you and your family, and explain about the child? It could then have been made a Ward of Court and given its rightful position."

"Well, sir, we felt that nobody would believe us, but . . . but I think I would have done something about it later only that I saw that she was in very good hands and being beautifully looked after at Miss Hewitt's and Miss Hewitt seemed to love her. So we decided to let sleeping dogs lie, sort of, and when Mrs Birkstead took over and brought all her own servants we were turfed out and went to Scotland and started a new life."

Connie now put her hand out to the back of the form to steady herself and this was no acting because she was tired and really sick with fear inside trying to remember to say the same things each time she was questioned.

"You can sit down and continue answering." The man motioned his hand towards her, and she sat down and when he said, "Where is the letter now that the young lady's mother wrote explaining the rightful father? . . ."

The man to the magistrate's side leant forward and was once more whispering; and now the magistrate said, "Oh, yes, yes, as has been said, it is in the possession of the young lady herself and she"—his head wagged in disbelief—"is now married, you say, to Mr Gallagher's son by his first wife?"

Connie nodded her head. "Aye, yes sir, she is."

"Amazing. Amazing." There was more whispering at the table and after a full minute the man in the middle stood up and said, "This is but a preliminary hearing but it is enough to allow Mr Musgrave to be freed for the present. This much I must say, his being in possession of information all these years of the said murder will have to be dealt with later. But for today we are finished now, but you will be called back to a full court at another date. You understand?"

They all answered by a motion of the head, and Connie finally ended the meeting by clapping her hand tightly over her mouth and making for the door, assisted now by a policeman. . . .

Fifteen minutes later Freddie was brought into the same room and, standing between two policemen, he faced the men at the table and was told briefly of what had transpired and also that he was free to go until a certain date when he would be recalled to answer the charge of withholding information. Did he understand?

He understood.

As he walked through the long corridor, then into the hallway and looked to where his mother and John, Nell and Nancy were waiting, he felt as if he were an old man returning home after years of absence.

He could find no words to say to them as they gathered round him: Jinny saying, "Oh, lad, lad. Thank God."

And John saying, "How are you feelin'?"

Nell said, "It's over. It's over."

Only Nancy said nothing but she gripped his arm with one hand and touched his face with the other.

They went into the street in a bunch. The twilight was deepening and Freddie stopped and looked upwards, his eyes travelling past the buildings and up to the sky. Then looking at John, he said in a broken voice, "I know how you used to feel, lad, down the pit"; and the next moment he gave his head a violent shake because he knew he was on the verge of crying, bursting out like a child, howling. He'd only been in that cell a matter of thirty-six hours but they had been like thirty-six lifetimes. And he had discovered himself in those lifetimes and knew there were great pockets of weakness in him and that he would never be able to stand a prison sentence without losing his mind. How did men ever survive, some of them manacled too? And those people back there who dealt out justice: they were a different kind of human being, their minds worked like machines. . . .

It wasn't until they were in the train that he looked from one to the other and realised what an effort it had been for them all to come up to the city to see him; they couldn't have known if he would be released or not. He said, "It was good of you to make the journey."

"Don't be daft. It's like a holiday ... well"—Nell's whole body seemed to wag—"you know what I mean, at least for me it is in a train. This is only the second time I've been to Newcastle, and I hope it's me last. Aw! lad." She leant forward and gripped his knee. "I'm pleased to see you."

"No more than I'm pleased to see you, Nell." And now he looked at John and said, "How did you manage to get off? It must have taken you nearly a day."

"Oh, I just gave him a sort of ultimatum, either he let me go or I went."

Freddie smiled weakly; then addressing his mother, he said, "Who's seeing to Maggie?"

"Oh, I got Mrs Carter. You know, she does nursing. She charges. Oh my! she charges. But she's very good." Her voice broke, her throat became full and she turned abruptly and looked out of the window; then after a moment she spoke again, saying now, "Your da said I had to give you . . . his best. He's very cut up. D'you think you could slip along and see him in the mornin'?"

"Yes, I'll do that, Ma."

They parted at the station, Nell going home with Nancy, for she was staying the night, John making his way down to the sculler ferry, and Jinny and Freddie hurrying now towards the house.

In the hallway, Freddie paused a moment. The lamps were lit, the house had its usual warm comforting, welcoming feeling, but in this moment it could have been like a portion of heaven except for one thing, there would be no agonizing pain in heaven. He threw off his coat and hat and went straight to the bedroom.

The sturdy middle-aged woman standing at the side-table, said, "Oh, you've got back then"; then she looked behind him, and when she saw Jinny beckoning her she went towards her, and they left the room together.

Maggie didn't say anything at his approach, but she held out her arms and he went into them, and in spite of the effort he endeavoured to make the tears sprang from his eyes and mingled with hers on her cheeks.

"My dear. My dear." She was stroking his hair and murmuring almost unintelligible words now till he raised himself from her, saying, "There, there, stop it. Stop it," and looking into her misted blue eyes he said, "You shouldn't have done it."

"What does it matter? They can't make me pay in any way. And you know something? I always meant to do it just in case something might come up. I thought about writing it out years ago; then got a bit fearful. But I thought today it was wicked of me to have put it off because I could have had a stroke, like Miss Wheatley's father, and then wouldn't have been able to say or write anything. That thought has made me sick all day."

He said now, "Have you heard from Belle?"

"No; and that's strange. Somehow, I've been expecting her to walk in the door."

"You sent the letter off on Sunday, didn't you?"

"Yes; she would get it yesterday morning, and if she expressed back I would have got it this morning. But what I'm thinking is perhaps they were out and didn't get back till late and that they're on their way today. Here it is, though, seven o'clock, so I doubt she'll be home tonight. I can't understand it."

"I can Maggie." He rose from the side of the bed now. "He's likely stopped her."

"Oh, I can't see that. If she thought either of us were in need she would have defied him and come, I feel sure of that."

"He's her husband, Maggie, and, to me, he's what you would call an unknown quantity. I've never been sure of him; I'm still not. Anyway, how are you feeling really? How's the pain?"

"Not too bad at all, not too bad at all, so don't worry. I've just got to pull a face and your mother pours more laudanum down me. I'll be floating in it next. Aw, Freddie"—she held out her hand—"I don't care about anything now as long as you're with me." She did not add: for as long as I've got left, which isn't very long; instead, she said, "The sight of you has given me a new lease on life. Go on now; Jinny, I know, is making you a meal. I bet you haven't had a decent bite in the past two days. I'm all right. Go on. And you could do with a wash, by the look of you, and a good shave."

He said nothing, but his eyes lingered on her for a moment longer before he left the room.

He didn't go down to the kitchen, but went into his own room; he didn't grope for the matches on the side table and light the lamp; but he made his way to the bedside basket chair and, dropping into it, he laid his head against the padded cushion attached to the top of it and muttered aloud, "Don't go. Don't leave me. I'm lost, Maggie."

14

It was three days later when Belle stood in the sitting room confronted by Freddie, and for the third time she ground out from between her teeth, "I've told you and told you! I didn't get a letter you sent on Sunday. I've never received any such letter. I wrote you both on Sunday. I've told you, haven't I, I knew nothing about it until last night when that wire came."

"Yes, I know you've told me, and told me you never got it, but what I'm saying is, somebody got it. There are very few letters lost in the post these days. I say again, *somebody* got it."

"What are you insinuating?"

"Well, you should have an idea by now what I'm insinuating."

"How dare you! If Marcel heard that he would. . . ."

"Yes, he would what?"

"He'd be very angry, to say the least."

"I wonder."

"What's got into you, Freddie?" Her voice was now soft, pleading. "It isn't like you. And do you think for a moment I wouldn't have come straight home if I had got that letter? And don't you think that Marcel would have had us return immediately if he had known anything about the letter?"

He remained silent, but he gazed at her. She was married yet she seemed not to have changed, and she didn't look happy. Well, she wouldn't, would she? with Maggie being in the state she was. But there was something about her. He couldn't lay his finger on it. He said, "Where is he now?"

Her chin worked up and down before she said, "He's had to go to Harrogate. His grandmama wanted some business done and she thought it best as I was coming across here and . . . and might stay for the night that he should take the opportunity."

"How long is he likely to be away?"

"I don't know. A day or two perhaps, perhaps as long as a week. His grandmama says there was some important business had come to light and it might take a little time."

"Why couldn't you have gone with him?"

Now she almost barked at him: "What would you have said if I had, instead of coming across here?" She could not say to him that no such invitation had been made and that her new husband had seemed at cross purposes with himself throughout the journey home, and more so this morning because he had scarcely given her a civil goodbye. She had thought that he must have been annoyed with his grandmama for making such a demand upon him at this time and also with herself for stating flatly that she must come across and stay the night, if not two.

His change of manner towards her had upset her and she felt deeply unhappy, and not only because of Maggie. But oh yes! she was unhappy about Maggie, and so she said now, "Please don't let us quarrel, Freddie, it will upset Aunt Maggie. Tell me truthfully, how much longer do you think . . . she will be with us?"

He turned from her and went towards the fire and, putting his hands on the mantelshelf, he bowed his head towards it as he said, "I don't know. It could be tonight, tomorrow, or next week, but it will be soon, and the sooner the better. God forgive me for saying it, but she's in dire pain and the laudanum is not touching it now."

She came swiftly towards him and put her hand around his shoulders as she said softly, "Oh, Freddie, I'll be heartbroken at the loss of her, but you, oh! you more so, I know, because she meant so much to you and you to her. She might have loved me. Oh yes, she did love me, but the word for the feeling she had for you couldn't be expressed in just love, it went so deep. When she used to speak of you it was as if she herself had created you."

He did not shrug her arm from his shoulder, he just turned his head away from her. But when she said softer still, "Freddie, I miss you so," he almost sprang away from her. And now his shoulders hunched and his head pushed forward, he cried at her, "You miss me so, you say. What does that mean? You should have thought about that before you married him."

"Oh! Freddie"—she backed from him—"I . . . I didn't mean. . . ."

"Well! what did you mean? You know what I could do at this moment, I could take this hand"—he thrust out his hand, his fingers spread and shaking—"and swipe you from the face of the earth with it, as far away as possible. I'm going to lose Maggie, but I want to lose you an' all. D'you hear?"

When he turned about and stalked from the room she dropped into a chair and, her two hands cupping her face, she whispered to herself, "Oh, my God! What have I done? What have I done?"

Maggie died at three o'clock the following morning. She did not have any last words of farewell; she did not die in Freddie's arms but she died while looking at him asleep in the chair to the side of her bed. She experienced one great flash of pain which seemed to cleanse her body of every vestige of discomfort and for a space she was aware of utter peace so wide, so deep, so high was the peace she was lying in she had the desire to put her hand out and tell Freddie about it. She wanted to say to him: The disease has gone, I am cured; but he had dropped off to sleep only minutes ago, so she would let him sleep and lie watching him while she rested in this floating peace. . . .

The face was that of a young woman, a smiling young woman. It was turned on the pillow and looking at him. There was a loud cry within him but it made no sound. He fell onto his knees by the side of the bed and laid his face on the pillow beside hers and, his voice calm-sounding, he said to her, "Goodbye my dear, dear Maggie. We'll meet up again and you will be as you look now, young and beautiful. And we'll be of an age to come together. Yes, we will. Oh yes, we will."

He now gently closed her eyelids, turned her head away, then went from the room to wake his mother and tell her that Maggie needed her for the last time.

15

The funeral took place five days later. It was said for a long time afterwards that most of the town attended Maggie Hewitt's passing: fishermen, longshoremen, keelmen, sailors of various nationalities, townsmen, councillors and even some dignitaries from Newcastle. This in spite of her having been denounced as a confessed murderess only a short time earlier.

It had been a story in the newspapers that people said was quite unbelievable and it had all begun with little Freddie Musgrave who used to act as runner when there was a lot of smuggling going on but who was now a highly respected member of the community. He, too, was due to face a charge of having kept the knowledge to himself of Maggie Hewitt's murdering Mr Gallagher. But the common sympathy was with him: he had been but a lad of twelve years old. And as it had said in the papers, Maggie Hewitt had emphasized that the man Gallagher had meant to kill the boy and the child, and herself into the bargain. It hadn't really been murder but self-defence because when she had struck out at him he had toppled into the water and the night was dark and she couldn't get him out. At least that's what the papers said, and she was supposed to have made a written confession to a parson and a doctor.

And then there was the business of this jewellery coming to light that the servant man had pinched it all those years ago, and his daughter just getting to know about it and bringing it to the police.

Oh, you didn't need pamphlets about the murders and the robberies that went on in London and other big cities, they were on your very doorstep. But who would have thought that Maggie Hewitt had carried that secret on her shoulders all these years.

Then, there was that nice kettle of fish wasn't there? That lass could have married her half-brother, couldn't she? But her mother had left a letter to say that his father wasn't her father. Now that was a mix-up, and, as some said, if you ask them that was too convenient to be real. What had happened was the two had fallen for each other and got spliced, then found out their relationship and the rest had been made up. Still, it was done now; they had been on their honeymoon. Anyway, it was nothing new. After all, they would only be half-brother and sister and there were lots of brothers and sisters doing what they didn't ought to do in this town, and lots of fathers and daughters an' all if the truth was known. And it *was* known in some quarters, but people minded their own business, especially mothers who were afraid of ending up in the workhouse. But wasn't it odd when you came to think about it that that young lass's husband, whether he be her half-brother or not, hadn't turned up at the funeral. But the lass was there walking alongside of Freddie Musgrave. And that was a bit of a disgrace too, wasn't it now, for a female to openly attend a funeral? That kind of thing wasn't done: women should know their place in matters like this.

And another thing, only a comparatively few people had been invited back to the house for a meal, not more than a dozen it was said. Of course it was well known there were always a lot of scroungers after a free tuck in at a time like this; they just attended the funerals for what they could get afterwards. But apparently Jinny Musgrave had given them short shrift, and there had only been ale for the pall bearers, no hard stuff at all. And it was wondered all about who would come into Maggie Hewitt's pile for it was well known she was a very warm woman. It wasn't very likely she would have left it all to Freddie Musgrave. Although he stayed up at the house a lot he was after all only a clerk.

The lawyer finished reading the will and he raised his eyes to look at Freddie where he was sitting next to Belle on the couch in the sitting room. And he said, "It was a simple will with no conditions. If Mrs Birkstead had not been married she would have inherited half of the estate, but as she is and undoubtedly well provided for"—the solicitor smiled in Belle's direction—

"there is no need for commiseration. I would wish that all wills were as simple, and I must congratulate you, Mr Musgrave, on becoming a very rich young man. Well now, that matter completed, I will take my leave, and I must thank you for that enjoyable repast and for your taste in wine."

Freddie made no reply to this, but he saw the man out. When he returned to the sitting room Jinny was sitting beside Belle holding her hand, saying, "There, there, lass. Don't upset yourself so. We'll all miss her. Oh yes, we'll all miss her." She turned to her son now who had taken a seat to the side of the fireplace and she said quietly, "I asked you yesterday what you intended to do and you said you wouldn't know until today. So do you know now?"

He looked at her for a moment or two before saying, "Well, what d'you expect me to do, Ma?"

"I don't know; that's why I asked. You did say a few days ago that you didn't think you could stay here, didn't you?"

"Well, there's one thing sure, Ma. I won't be able to leave the country as I'm due in court again, aren't I?"

"Yes, I'm well aware of that, but nothin' will come of it, it can't. And you're a man of means now and that makes all the difference. Oh, don't shake your head, because yes, it does, money calls the tune."

"Not when you're facing a judge, Ma."

"Well, I have me own opinion of that. Anyway, Belle here will have to get across the water before it gets dark. Are you goin' to take her over?"

"There's no need. I can go by myself."

He got to his feet and, looking down at her now, he said, "Don't be silly." Then he asked, "Have you had word that he's back?"

"No, no, nothing. I would have thought though that he would have come over had he returned."

"Get yourself ready. We'll get across while it's light."

She rose slowly from the couch, looked at him for a moment, then at Jinny, and went out without making further comment. And Jinny, looking at her son, said, "Now, I don't know what you think, but they've been married barely a week and he goes off on business an' not a scribe of a pen from him. I think it's funny an' that's sayin' the least. If I were you I'd do a bit of questionin' when you get across there. . . ."

"I'll do no such thing, Ma. It isn't my business and I'm not going into that house. I'll set her to the gates and that's as far as I'll go."

"Oh well, if that's how you feel, that's how you feel. I was only thinkin' that you might find out how the land lay with this granny of his."

"How the land lies or how it doesn't lie is no concern of mine now. She's a married woman."

She was on her feet now, her fingers stabbing at him: "You brought her up. Guardian, or brother, whatever you like to put a name to yourself, you brought her up. You were the man in her home, in her life, now you're washin' your hands of her. Well, as I see it I don't think that's anythin' to be proud of. She's still a bit of a lass an' that fancy school has left her still wet behind the ears. She hasn't been out in the world an' she knows nothin' about it. She's plunged herself into marriage, an' that, I can tell you, for any woman is a strange sea. My God! it is; and you've got to be tough to swim it."

"I take your analogy, Ma."

"Look, don't you come with any of your fancy words with me. Take me meanin', all right? Well, I think you would be wise to think on it an' don't throw her as if to the wolves."

"I wouldn't think that marrying into The Towers would be classed as being thrown to the wolves."

"Wouldn't you? Well, in my reckonin' it's equal to it. There was a mad woman there some years ago and her grandson was mad enough to try and murder a child, an' that child is married to that man's son. You might be smart up top, lad, but apparently you don't put two and two together."

He looked at her in silence and he could have said, "Right from the beginning, Ma, I've put two and two together, and that's what worries me, has worried me all along." But what he said was, "Can you stay here till I get back?"

Her tone softer now, she said, "Of course I can stay here until you get back. Your da thinks I've left him for months now, so one more night or two won't matter. But"—she smiled—"he seems to get on pretty well without me. Since he made himself that little pushchair he practically runs the house."

"That's something I want to talk to you about, Ma, the house. We'll go into it later, but I'd like you to move into a decent place."

She stared at him hard before saying, "Freddie, that house is as decent as I ever hope to live in; I'm happy in it. I've got good neighbours there, they're good to me and I'm good to them. I don't want to move to any better place where . . . well, let's put it frankly, I'd be looked down on. Oh, oh"—she raised her hand—"don't say it, nobody's goin' to look down on me, because I can say that, but it doesn't stop people from doing it. No, lad; thanks all the same. I appreciate it. I tell you what you can do though, if you can manage it: I would like to see our John set up in something and, if it's not too late, Nancy to have proper trainin', although she's dead set on this fella. I never thought she'd pick up with a customs bloke; but there, he picked up with her, she didn't have much choice, but she seems to care for him and he for her. But I don't suppose he'd object to her havin' her voice trained. And I know that those fellas, with all their posh uniform and classin' themselves above the rest, their wages won't bear their pockets down."

"Yes, I'll see to them, Ma, and glad to; and Maggie wanted it that way."

"She did? Well, I know she wanted it for you, but, you mean she wanted me to have a better place?"

"Yes; she put it into plain words, as plain as what I've said."

She turned away from him, and after a moment, her voice very small, she said, "That was nice of her, very nice, 'cos she knew, you know, that I was jealous of her; she couldn't help but. But oh dear God, I wouldn't have minded goin' on bein' jealous of her till she was a hundred-an'-one 'cos I miss her, already I miss her. Still"—the last word was sharp—"life's got to go on, you've got to go on. Once this business of the court is over what you want to do is to look round and find yourself a nice lass, or let's say a young lady, and. . . ."

"*Ma!*" The word was like a command. "Stop it! I'll marry when I want to, if ever I want to. Now have you got that?"

She stared at him, her lips working in and out; then she said in a voice that was harsh and firm, "Yes, Mr Musgrave, your ma's got that," and she flounced from the room, leaving the door open when she saw Belle approaching from the stairway. And Belle, noticing her expression, entered the room, saying, "You've upset your mother now. It's getting a habit with you, isn't it, upsetting people? . . . I'm ready."

He walked past her without a word, took up his knee-length coat from where he had left it earlier over the back of a chair, picked up his tall hat from the hall table and put them both on before opening the front door, saying, "Well, I'm ready too."

The small ferry boat was at the landing stage when they reached the Low Lights, and when he helped her onto it she sat on the slatted seat, her hands tightly joined in her lap, her back straight, and gazed before her while knowing she was at the centre of attention of the other passengers.

When they landed on the far side he said briefly, "We'll walk up to the market and take a cab from there." He was carrying her valise and when, putting out his other hand, he went to take her elbow to help her mount some greasy stone steps she shrugged off his hold, he moved sharply from her side and walked a step ahead of her until they reached the market place. And there, hailing a cab, he did not assist her into it but left her to arrange her skirt, then pull herself up and onto the seat.

He sat next to her in order that he wouldn't have to look at her, but they hadn't gone very far when she turned to him and caught his hand, saying, "Freddie. Oh please, don't be angry with me. I'm . . . I'm so unhappy at the moment."

He looked back into her eyes now and asked quietly, "Why are you unhappy, that is apart from losing Maggie? You broke your neck to get married and now you are married, why are you unhappy?"

"Because it is all so strange, the house and everything. Oh, it is beautiful. Everybody is so nice but it doesn't seem home. I've told myself that I'll get used to it; and it really is my natural home, isn't it? So it should come easy. But, somehow I can't see it. And madam has kept telling me in the short time I've been there that I am mistress of the house, but I'll never be mistress as long as she's alive. Oh, please, you know what I mean, I don't want her to go . . . to die, but everyone looks up to her so much. She reigns in the house like an old queen, and that is the point, she is old, very old I would say, but acts like someone young, her mind is so sharp."

"You are not married to her, you are married to him, and if you care for him so much, that's all that matters, or should be."

"Yes"—she nodded—"or should be. But, Freddie"—she looked into his face again—"if I could only think I was still welcome across the river as if Aunt Maggie was still there, I . . . I would feel happier inside."

Of a sudden he gripped both her hands and his voice shook slightly as he said, "Well, if that's all that's worrying you you're out of trouble because you know there'll always be a welcome there for you. That is still your home, the home I brought you to. Don't forget that, ever, Belle. It was me that brought you to that house, it was me that ran with you from the house you're returning to now and into the cart down to the river, and held you tight while Maggie had to commit murder in order to save us both. So, in a way you belong to me. I . . . I've never said this to you before, but that's how I feel about you, you belong to me. So whatever happens in the future, remember I'm there over the river and that it's your home, too."

"Oh, Freddie." Of a sudden she was in his arms and he was holding her tightly, and they swayed together until the cab, turning a corner, caused her bonnet to fall back from her head, and he put his lips into her hair.

Then they were apart sitting close looking at each other; and they seemed to continue to look at each other saying nothing, until the cab stopped, and the driver, from his box, shouted, "Is this the place, mister?"

And Freddie, looking out of the window through the open gates, called back, "Yes. Yes."

He had intended to go no further than this, but he did not alight and say to the driver, "Take your passenger to the door of the house and return straightaway; I'll be waiting"; he remained seated.

It was just before the cab stopped again that he said, "I won't come in." And she said, "All right, Freddie. And . . . and I feel better now."

He alighted and assisted her down to the ground, and stood watching her walk towards the main doors before he entered the cab again.

The door was opened by Benedict, and he peered at Belle for a moment before exclaiming, "Oh! the young madam," and looked past her beyond the door, saying, "Have you come alone, madam?"

"No. Mr Musgrave brought me, but he had to return home because of business."

"Oh, yes, yes. Let me take your coat, madam. I am so glad you have returned. The mistress will be so pleased to see you."

"Has she retired?"

"Oh yes, madam. She has been in her room these past few days. The weather has been anything but clement. Could I ask cook to get you a tray, madam, as dinner is over?"

"No, thank you; but I would be glad of a hot drink in my room."

"Very well, madam. Just leave your valise; I will see that it is taken up."

She wanted to say, Oh, I can carry it myself, but she knew that was one of the things she would have to learn; as madam had said, "Servants are there to be used." And she realised that if she didn't use them in this way they would consider her odd, perhaps not fitted to her position.

When she reached the room which she knew was hers and Marcel's but which she had not yet slept in, she looked about her. It was still light enough to take in each object in the room and, as she had realised the other day when she first saw it, it was all frills and furbelows, a replica of his grandmama's. She herself loved pretty things, or perhaps that wasn't the right word to use for her particular taste, rather she loved beautiful things. For instance, she would not have draped the head of the bed with yards of lace to look like a miniature waterfall, and the impression being strengthened by its pale blue colour. The bedcover, too, was blue, but made up of heavy quilted padded satin.

The four armchairs in the room were also upholstered in blue quilted padded satin, as was the small chaise longue at the foot of the bed. The walls she had noticed were not painted or papered but were made up of silk panels, these in an oyster colour, and a rose pink carpet covered the entire floor.

Mrs Birkstead had informed her that she was having the room decorated for her in a French style, and it was certainly that, overpoweringly French, she would say. And she wondered how long it would be before she could change what the grand old lady called the decor. But now she would have to go and see her.

She took off her bonnet and coat and as she was placing them on the bed there came a tap on the door. She called, "Come in!" and a housemaid entered and, bobbing her knee, said, "Good evening, madam. I . . . we didn't expect you or we'd have had the hot water up and the bed turned down."

"It's all right. Thank you. You are?"

"Mary, madam, Mary Chambers. I am the first housemaid."

"Of course, of course. Well, Mary, I'll be glad of some hot water, thank you; but in the meantime I'll go and pay my respects to Mrs Birkstead."

"Yes, madam, yes." She pulled the door wide and dipped her knee again as Belle passed her.

When Belle tapped on Madam Birkstead's door it was opened by her maid who smiled at her, then turned her head and looked back into the room, saying, "'Tis the young madam, mistress."

There was a considerable pause before the voice said, "Well, show her in."

Belle entered the room, and for a moment she hesitated in her step as she approached the bed for the person in it had no connection with the one who took court in her drawing room. Here was an old lady, a very old lady, wearing a pink nightcap made up entirely of plaited ribbons and bows. It was a high cap but its brim was not broad enough to hide the white streaks of hair that fell about the ears. The face beneath the nightcap was no longer covered with powder and paint but with what looked like grease, and when the mouth opened to smile, as it did, there was a gaping hole where the teeth had been. Hiding her surprise and not a little shocked at what she thought was a frightful sight, likening the face to that of an animated corpse, Belle said, "Good evening, madam. I hope I find you well."

"Good evening, child; and you don't find me very well. I'm somewhat changed from the last time you saw me, isn't that so? Oh, I'm not going to wait for your opinion. Sit down"—she pointed—"and tell me all that has transpired these past few days."

Belle took the seat Sarah Cummings placed for her while thinking that whatever was changed in the old lady's appearance command of speech certainly wasn't. And now she looked at her as she pointed to Sarah Cummings, saying, "Leave us now; you can do my massage later."

The woman gave a slight bend to her knee, then left the room, and Mrs Birkstead said, "Well, so you've buried her, have you, the woman who murdered my son-in-law?"

"She didn't murder him; it was self defence and in order to save me . . . and Freddie."

"Well, that's one version of it; but like all these cases the real truth will never be known, I suppose. But all that jewellery being

287

in the hands of those servants all those years. They're thieves, the lot of them! No matter how long they serve you they'll rob you. Remember that, girl. Although I must say mine are as faithful as dogs. Again though, only because it pays them. But the scandal, and how it was reported in that paper. I don't know how Marcel is going to take this."

"He was aware of most of it, madam."

"Oh no, he wasn't. Do you think he would have tolerated that woman for a moment knowing that she had murdered his father? No matter what kind of a man Gallagher was, he was his father. And then, he never thought for a moment that your parentage would be made public."

"He can be no more embarrassed than I was, madam."

The old lady now raised her hairless eyebrows, and then said, "Well, I suppose that's right enough. By the way, what did she leave you, that woman? From what I understand she was very rich."

"Nothing."

"What! Nothing?"

"No; it's all been left to Freddie . . . Mr Musgrave."

"Why?"

"Because she thought that, being married, I was well provided for."

"Oh, *did she? Did she?* But . . . but you were her ward, sort of, you should have been the one that inherited, for what was he? Just someone she took under her wing and, as Marcel says, a very common fellow at bottom."

"He is not a very common fellow." Belle rose to her feet and stared down into the wrinkled face that was visibly quivering with indignation, but before she could continue in Freddie's defence the cutting voice of the old lady forestalled her: "Girl! please remember to whom you are speaking. And if Marcel judged him to be a common fellow, then he is a common fellow. And it isn't right that he should have come into that woman's fortune."

"As I see it, madam, he has every right to her fortune: he has looked after her and been her right hand for years, and loved her and cared for her as he did for me."

The figure pulled herself up in the bed, the arm came out and the frilled nightdress fell away showing the loose sagging flesh; but it lacked no strength as the hand pointed towards the door and the voice commanded, "Leave me! girl."

Belle had no need to be told to leave the room. Her indignation carried her swiftly back to her own bedroom where she asked herself as she stood in the middle of it how she was going to put up with that changeable old lady who apparently allowed no opinion to be voiced, except her own. But it was enlightening to her in this moment that she didn't stand in awe of her. Everyone else in the house seemed to, for her name was mostly uttered in a reverential or revered tone. Oh, why wasn't Marcel here? What was keeping him?

Her nightclothes had been put on the bed and there was a copper jug of steaming hot water on the wash-hand stand in the closet. She opened the wardrobe door and saw that among her own clothes were arranged all the new ones that Marcel had bought her on the second day in London. They had spent most of that day shopping, and she recalled that it had taken her mind off things which had disturbed her but which she knew she must get used to, for marriage, she had found immediately, was not exactly what she had imagined it to be.

The bed was high and the bed tick was filled with feathers, which some people would have welcomed, but years spent sleeping on a dormitory bed, then at home on an ordinary flock-filled mattress, had given her no taste for this kind of luxury which she termed "smothering."

Having told herself she wouldn't sleep, nevertheless, she did sleep, and was utterly amazed when she heard a voice saying, "I have brought your early tea, madam. Have you slept well? It's a beautiful morning."

She pulled herself up out of the depths of the feathers and blinked at Mary Chambers who was smiling widely at her. And when she said, "Is it morning?" the maid laughed and said, "Yes, madam; it is morning and turned eight. I have brought your early tea; breakfast is at nine; and madam sends you her regards and hopes you have slept well."

This latter brought Belle into a sitting position. Was the maid just being tactful? And then she had the source of the message when Mary said, "And Miss Cummings said that the mistress would be pleased if you would call on her after breakfast."

The bed tray which Mary arranged across Belle's knees held a small tea service and a plate of four biscuits on it; and their appearance Mary now explained by saying, "Mr Marcel always liked biscuits with his early tea. I thought you might like them too."

"Thank you. Thank you, Mary; but I won't have anything to eat." She handed the plate back, and the woman seemed a little disappointed but said, "Is there anything you would like in place, madam, a light scone or toast?"

"Oh, no thanks, Mary; that would ruin my breakfast. No, I'll just have the tea. I'll enjoy that."

Mary now smiled; then pointing to the bell pull, she said, "If you should want any help with your dressing, madam, I'd be pleased to see to it. You just need ring."

Belle had already glanced at the bell pull; then she said, "I . . . I won't need you for that, Mary, but thank you."

After the maid had taken her leave, it was quite some minutes before Belle poured herself out a cup of tea and then lay back on the pillows against the shower of falling lace while comparing the difference in this present lifestyle with the one she had only recently left. And she knew at the moment which one she preferred. . . .

She presented herself at the mistress's bedroom door at half past nine, and was admitted to see the transformed old woman again, the wig in place, the powder and the paint applied, the silk negligée topped with a frill that covered the sagging flesh below the chin, and the voice too so changed from that of last night that she could hardly believe her ears as the greeting came to her, saying, "Good morning, my dear. Have you slept well? You look a little pale. What did you have for breakfast? Come and sit down by me." She patted the side of the chaise longue on which she was reclining.

Belle did not fully obey the order and sit on the edge of the chaise longue, but she sat on a dressing stool nearby and answered the questions one after the other: "I slept very well, thank you. And for breakfast, I just had toast and orange preserve."

"Oh, my goodness! That will never do. Breakfast is the main meal on which to start the day. Wasn't there any choice?"

"Oh yes." She was about to say, Too much of a choice, but deciding to match the old lady's manner with a change in her own, she smiled as she said, "The smell was most appetizing, but I wasn't hungry. I think I'll take a brisk walk this morning and that will give me an appetite for dinner."

"Oh, you can't go on till dinner time, my dear, on an empty stomach. You must have something at eleven o'clock. Cummings, you see to it. Give an order downstairs, young madam will have a light meal round eleven o'clock. That will serve until dinner at three."

Belle made no protest; she knew it would be a waste of words: this lady reigned in this house and her word was law. But there was one thing: she could order food but she couldn't make her eat. On the other hand though, by twelve o'clock she'd likely be hungry. Back home she could have eaten at any time of the day. Jinny used to laugh and say, "You make up for the mean years you had at that school, for, from what I hear, hard tack is nothing to what that must have been." Why was she still thinking of Maggie's house as home, and of Jinny and the warm. . . .

"When Marcel returns you must ride with him. That will put colour into your cheeks, and you'll eat like the proverbial horse then."

"When may we expect him, madam?"

"Oh . . . Oh." The boney hand now dusted an imaginary crumb or some such from the white-laced cover that was spread across the couch and reached to her waist, and she said, "Well now, it all depends on business. It is very unfortunate that it should happen at this time. I told you about my elder brother, didn't I? But of course, he is no use, it is his own son who is now in charge of the estate and . . . and the business. But . . . but I'm afraid Arthur hasn't got a head on him like Marcel."

"What is the business, madam?"

"Mm . . . er . . . what is the business?" the old lady repeated. "I should have said businesses; they are so varied. Now, let me see." She put her head back, then began to count on her fingers. "There is first of all the property; then there are the shops. Yes, there are the shops. When I was a girl there were seventeen shops and they were about to spread out further into the villages. But do you know, my dear, it was most difficult to set up shops in villages; they're so clannish, the people in villages. Their little industries have been established for years. Yes, so clannish." She shook her head now as if she couldn't fathom the reason for the clannishness. "Then there is the railway. But of course, there's only shares in that. That is quite a separate thing. Oh, my dear, I've forgotten how many businesses there are altogether. And from what he tells me things haven't been going very smoothly. So it could be another week, perhaps a little more before he returns. But you mustn't worry, my dear; he'll be all the more loving when you meet. And you know"—her voice dropped—"he does love you, and dearly. And you love him, don't you?"

She felt embarrassed to have to answer this question in front of the maid, but in just as low a voice, she said, "Yes; yes, I love him."

"Then everything is all right. Now it's such a lovely day I'm going down into the drawing room later, when we will have another chat. Perhaps you will bring your embroidery . . . you do embroider?"

"Oh, yes, yes."

"Do you paint or draw?"

"I like sketching, but mostly I like to embellish book plates."

"Oh, that is interesting and unusual. You mean you do the titles and things?"

"Well . . . well . . . yes, and enhance the fly leaves and the capitals."

"How interesting. Now that is a wonderful hobby. I am so glad you have things that will fill your time. Now you must take that walk which will make you ready for your meal later."

Dismissed, Belle went out and back to her room where she selected a plain straw hat and a dust coat. She did not, however, use the main staircase but went down a side one. Marcel had shown her this one because it led out near the corner of the house and right next to the big conservatory.

It was a lovely morning, and she walked through the gardens. She stopped and spoke to a man who was sweeping a grass path on which there were a few leaves: "It's a lovely morning, isn't it?" she said to him.

"Oh . . . oh yes, madam, 'tis a lovely morning."

"Are you the head gardener?"

"Oh no, madam!" He gave a deprecating smile. "Me, I'm the runabout. Well, Mr Victor is the head one and Dan Watson comes next."

"Oh, I see. Do you like gardening?"

"Yes, madam, I like it very much."

"I have never done any gardening. I must take it up sometime; I'm sure it's very interesting."

The young man laughed now as if at a joke and she laughed with him as she said, "Oh, I mean that." And still laughing, he said, "Yes, madam, yes."

Belle knew as she walked away that the man was still laughing at her statement.

She walked aimlessly for half an hour. She had seen another gardener in the distance but hadn't gone out of her way to have a word with him. Her ambling had brought her to another drive. This wasn't so well kept as the main drive and as she followed its winding way back she found a branching off which led to the stable yard, and from this a path that brought her out opposite the conservatory and the door from which she had emerged to start her walk and to which she now made her way with the intention of returning to her room.

She had almost reached the door when she imagined she heard Marcel's voice. She stopped and stepped back onto the path and looked into the conservatory. There was no one there. But again she heard the voice, and so, excitedly, she entered the conservatory.

The glass domed L-shaped conservatory was heavy with the scent of plants of all varieties and part of it was almost obliterated with greenery. At the far end was, she knew, the door that led into the drawing room, and she realised it was from there that the voice was emanating now. Almost at a run she started to move towards the door, only to be halted by the words: "You should not have come back so early."

Her eyes widened even further at her husband's reply, for it was undoubtedly Marcel's voice that said, "I had to. What do you think I am? You don't know how I feel." Then his grandmama answering, "Oh my darling, of course I know how you feel; and I feel for you. Haven't I always? But this was unwise, you should have given yourself another week."

Then his voice again, "I'm all right ... I'm perfectly all right. I know I am."

"How have you got here so soon?"

"I spent the night in the city."

"Alone?"

"No; Harry stayed with me."

"Oh, my dear, dear, you must be careful. And this business is bound to have disturbed you."

"Disturbed me! That's putting it mildly. My God! when I think of the exposure."

"What had Fuller to say?"

"I didn't bother calling on him because they would inform him soon enough. As for James, I'll knock him flat one of these days."

"Now, now, you must bear with James."

"Where is she?"

"Out in the garden. Be gentle with her, Marcel. She is very sweet but somewhat headstrong. But don't try to cope with that all at once."

Belle now backed down the aisle between the greenery, and immediately she emerged from it she turned and ran towards the door, out of it, then into the other door and up the stairs to her room. It was evident that he had already been there for a small leather portmanteau was on the floor near the couch.

Standing near the window, her hands clasped tightly in front of her, she asked herself if she had heard right? But what had she heard? Could she make sense of it? The only thing that had come out of it was that for some reason he'd had to go away and it hadn't been for business; and that his grandmama was surprised at his return and worried . . . as she herself was too. Even during those few days in London questions had arisen in her mind, but they had been swept away by his loving kindness, at least during the day, and the constant declaring of his love for her.

She wished she could rush out at this moment, down to the river and take a boat across to home and Freddie, and Jinny, and Nancy, and everybody on that side of the water, because here she was in a foreign land in which the language made her fearful, so fearful that she dare not translate it in her mind.

It was almost twenty minutes later when he came into the room and found her sitting at her dressing table. In a high voice he exclaimed, "There you are, my dear. Oh, my dearest dear." He came behind her and put his arms about her and tilted her head back and looked down into her face, asking softly, "Have you missed me?"

To this she could answer truthfully, "Yes. Yes, Marcel, I have missed you." Then having already made up her mind that she had a part to play until she managed to get to the bottom of why her husband had to take these mysterious visits to Harrogate, she asked, "Why did you stay away so long? Was business so pressing?"

He released his hold of her and, straightening up, said

flatly, "Yes, very pressing, very boring. But I think I have settled the affairs now for some time."

She turned on the seat and looked at him fully, and she paused before she said, "You are pale. Have you been unwell?"

"No, no." His voice was high again. "Unwell? No; but harassed; business can be very harassing. . . . But all that is past." He flung his arms wide; then taking two steps towards her, he pulled her into his embrace and pressed her jerkingly to him, once, twice, three times, until she gasped and said, "Oh! Marcel, you . . . you are hurting me."

"Oh, come now, come; you're not such a delicate little thing as to be hurt by a hug. What is it?" He pressed her from him. "It is you who don't look very well."

"Perhaps you are not aware that Aunt Maggie died and has been buried in your absence?"

"Yes, yes." His tone and manner altered now. "Since you bring it up, I am very well aware that your Aunt Maggie died and has been buried, and I should say it is fortunate for her she died as she did, because, being a confessed murderess, she would have died in any case."

"Oh no, she wouldn't! She wasn't a murderess." Here she was, going again. She must be careful for his expression was thunderous now and his voice matched it as he cried, "She killed my father, and all this business about one of the servants stealing those jewels is all poppycock. Your Freddie likely paid that woman to come up with that tale."

"Freddie would do no such thing. He would speak the truth, he always did."

For a moment she was fearful of what was going to happen next: she could see that he was making a great effort to control himself. He turned from her and walked to the far end of the room and stood facing the blank door of the wardrobe for a moment before once again turning around and, his voice now low and his tone appealing, he said, "Oh! Belle, please, please don't let us quarrel. I've . . . I've been very upset about that report in the paper and all the fuss. And there's still more to face, because, you know, people will not really believe that we are in no way related. But, oh my dear"—he approached her now, his hands extended—"don't . . . don't let us quarrel. I have missed you so much and longed to be with you. Be . . . be gentle with me, I beg; I need you, your gentleness."

She was overcome. Here she was being presented with two different natures within a matter of minutes. So, so like his grandmother. Yet she couldn't resist the appeal in his voice and his countenance, and so, her own voice soft, she said, "Marcel, my dear, I don't want to quarrel, but I want to understand; everything is so strange. You go away and you don't leave me a word. Why? Can't you tell me why?"

She watched him close his eyes and jerk his head backwards as he said, "I . . . I thought Grandmama explained everything to you, everything that you need to know. It's . . . it's my business, my dear, it's business, all business, business." His voice was rising; then again swinging round from her, he said, but in a more subdued tone, "I just want to forget about it, Harrogate and all in it. Quite candidly"—he was once again facing her—"I hate Harrogate and everything that drags me there. But look, my dear—" He bounced towards her now in boyish fashion and, catching her hands, he said, "Today we are going out riding."

"But I can't ride; I have never been on a horse, Marcel."

"Today you will be on a horse, my dear; you will have your first lesson. And from now on every day we shall ride, trot, gallop." His arms now were acting his words and when his legs, too, illustrated a gallop she forced herself to laugh, saying, "I'll never get to that stage; I'll be on the ground most of the time."

"Come on!" He pulled her hand. "Get into your coat and bonnet and winter boots. We must get you a riding habit. Yes, yes, that's what we must do. That's the next thing, we'll go into Newcastle and get you a riding habit. But not today. Today you will be just introduced to your horse, a gentle saunter. Oh, my love! my love!" She was in his arms again. "You have no idea how I feel when I am with you, when I can hold you, when I know that you love me."

He was holding her chin tightly with one hand now, his fingers pressing into the side of one cheek, the thumb into the other pushing her mouth out of shape. And there was a plea, yet a demand, in his voice when he now said, "Tell me that you'll always love me. Tell me. Say it."

Through her distorted lips she said, "You're hurting me."

"Oh! Oh, I'm sorry. I'm sorry. I wouldn't hurt you for the world." He was stroking her cheeks now with both hands. "But tell me that you'll always love me. Say it. I want to hear it."

As she looked into the face that had first fascinated her a

few months previously and continued to do so as recently as a fortnight ago, she would have then been able to answer without hesitation, but now she dared to say, "Always is a long time. We have just begun our life together; it . . . it depends on how we react on each oth. . . ."

She was almost thrust on her back. She stumbled and was saved from falling only by the low back of the dressing table stool. And he was yelling at her now, "I don't want philosophy! I want love. Do you hear? I want love."

She watched him throw himself on the chaise longue, his body bent almost double, his face in his hands, and although she was experiencing fear of him she was, at the same time, filled with compassion; and this drove her to him and, bending above him and putting her arm around his shoulder, she brought his head to her waist, saying, "You have love, my dear, you have love. What is it? What is the matter?"

He lay against her for some minutes, and when at last he looked up at her he asked softly, "Bear with me, will you? Please bear with me. I . . . I unfortunately have this quick turn of temper. I must try to control it. I will for your sake." And his voice still gentle, he said, "Come, let us get into the fresh air and ride. Yes, and ride, for you'll find the wind rushing through you is the most exhilarating feeling in the world. It clears your mind. It makes you a new being. Although"—he smiled gently now—"I don't want you ever to be a new being. It is me who must mend my ways. Come, my dear. Get into your things and let us go."

She did as he bade her and accompanied him downstairs for her first horse ride.

16

She did tolerably well with her first riding lesson. The following day she had another lesson, in which she did better. He also took her into Newcastle, and she was fitted for a riding habit. And then they called at his other house. It was only a small house, comprised of eight rooms altogether and situated at the very end of a very nice terrace on the outskirts of Jesmond. And there they found Marcel's friend Harry Benson. Apparently he was living there. As Marcel explained, he looked after the place and so it only needed one servant, and he a daily man.

Marcel's friend, Belle found, was what she termed a nice man, quiet, slightly aloof. He was a very big man, all of six foot two and broad with it, and that he was not only a friend but also a sort of superior servant she deduced from the fact that he asked Marcel if he would be needing him, did he think, within the next two days? And Marcel assured him that he wouldn't. He seemed to emphasize this. Then as she happened to glance back as they were leaving, she saw Marcel place a small chamois leather coin bag on the corner of the sideboard.

In the street a disturbing thought came into her mind, but she countered it by saying to herself, Well, there are some things that it's best not to know, only to attack this immediately: She should know; he was her husband.

The following morning she did not go down to breakfast, she felt very tired. Lovemaking, she was finding, was not only tiring, it was disturbing and distressing. She never expected it to be like this and therefore wasn't complying to Marcel's satisfaction. That he was annoyed with her was evident because he hadn't come back to see her after breakfast. It was eleven o'clock when she rose from the bed. She wasn't feeling at all well, and it didn't help matters when Mary Chambers came to the room and said that the mistress would be pleased if she would call in and see her before she went for her morning walk.

Was she expected to go for a morning walk? What she should be doing was go down and see the cook and arrange the meals. Part of her training at school had covered the running of a household and she had bought a book on it and so she knew the procedure. But she also knew she wasn't mistress of this house.

When she entered the old lady's room it was to find her in bed but adorned with wig, and paint, and powder, and wearing a different coloured negligée. Her greeting was rather cool. "Good morning, my dear. I understand that you have not been down to breakfast?"

"I did not feel hungry, madam, and I was feeling a little tired."

"Huh! Tired at your age, girl! You should never use that word. I myself have never used it."

Belle did not answer, but she thought, No, you've likely never done enough work in your life to feel tired. And for a moment she had a picture of Maggie's daily routine. Oh, she longed for Maggie and Freddie. Oh, yes, Freddie.

"You look surly. Why do you look surly?"

"I wasn't aware that I looked surly. Perhaps slightly bored. I have nothing with which to occupy my time. You can't embroider all day, madam, or take walks. I . . . I understood that I should be seeing to the household."

She thought for a moment that her words were going to cause the old lady to collapse but her voice gave no indication of this when she barked at her, "Young madam! let me put you into the correct picture. This is my establishment. I order it. I have always ordered it and I shall go on doing so. Do we understand each other?"

"Yes, madam; I think we understand each other very well. But can you advise me what I am to do with my time?"

"Yes, yes, I can advise you what to do with your time, and that is be a good wife to my grandson. Be his companion; and if you are a wise woman you would be entertaining during the daytime and—" She brought herself up from her pillows, leant forward and said, "And at other times." And now her voice was a low hiss: "A wife's duty is adaptation and sublimation of self.

These are the qualities that a wise wife aims at in marriage, and they are necessary for a successful marriage. Do I make myself clear?"

"Perfectly clear, madam, perfectly clear. And do I also make myself clear, madam, when I say I did not enter marriage to become an entertainer, nor a being who practises sublimation of self."

They were glaring at each other, Belle in pure anger, Mrs Birkstead in sheer amazement and indignation.

"Get out! Leave me, girl! And don't come near me again until I send for you. Do you hear?"

She was half-way across the room when she turned and said, "I hear, madam, I hear."

As she pulled open the door Sarah Cummings nearly fell forward into the room, and the woman's face was stretched, her eyes were wide, her mouth was open. But if Belle had had time to think and describe the expression she would have put the term "glee" to it.

On the landing she wavered whether to go back to her room or down to the kitchen and say to Mrs Welsh, "What are we having for dinner today, Mrs Welsh?" Then follow it up with, "I don't like that. Serve it to madam; but we will have so and so, and so and so."

But she went to her room, and there, going to the window, she beat her fists against the wooden stanchion. Adaptation and sublimation. She knew exactly the meaning of that old woman's words. Well, she couldn't adapt and she wasn't going to submit, not to things that had happened last night. That wasn't love, she was sure of it. She had known what to expect from marriage and had longed for it. Yes, yes, she had longed for it, but not for what was happening. Oh no, no. Oh, if she could only go across and talk to. . . . Who could she talk to? She couldn't talk to Freddie about this. No; but she could talk to Jinny. Oh yes, she could talk to Jinny; even more so than she could have talked to Maggie about this: Jinny had been married; Jinny had a large family: she was an understanding woman; she would tell her if she was right or wrong in her attitude towards her husband.

It came to her that she couldn't go across the water because she hadn't any money with her. Maggie made her an allowance all the years she was at school. And from the time she had come home she had given her one pound a month to spend on trifles; and, too, she had only to ask if she wanted more. And she had a small banking account of her own. Nor had she ever had to buy anything for herself in the way of clothes.

But now Marcel hadn't even mentioned a dress allowance. She had thought about it yesterday when they were in Newcastle because there were one or two things she had seen in the shops that she would like to have purchased. So she had made up her mind that she was going to put it to him.

She thought it must be miles from here to the ferry, and then she would have to hire a boat to get across the river. But what was she thinking about? If she could go over there alone he would certainly follow her and raise a scene; and oh, she didn't want that. She didn't want to have to prove to Freddie that he was right.

She swung round from the window. Had Freddie been right? Had his instincts been more clear than her own reasoning? She must get outside and walk. Not horse-riding. Oh no, she didn't like horse-riding and never would.

She walked for an hour or more, and when she returned to the house he was waiting for her. She was crossing the hall towards the stairs when he appeared and beckoned her imperiously towards him. And she followed him down the corridor and into the library, where he had a desk and did whatever business he might have to do.

He was well into the room when he turned to her and said, "You have upset Grandmama."

"Your grandmama upset me."

"Can't you understand"—he took two steps towards her but halted—"she is an old lady; and, what is more, she is a grand lady, and she has run her own establishments since before she was your age and is not used to being contradicted and bullied."

"Nor am I used to being bullied. Her manner towards me was outrageous."

"Look . . . look, Belle"—his voice had dropped back into his throat and each word was weighed now—"she is in a position to be as outrageous as she likes. You are not. It is a wonder she has received you into this house at all, let me tell you. It was only my affection for you and her affection for me that outweighed her first judgment, so, as long as you are in this house . . . and you are going to be a long time in this house, Belle, you will be subservient to her. *You* understand?"

She understood. Fearfully she understood. But she cried out against it, saying, "I shan't! As your wife I demand my rights."

"*Demand. Demand.*" His tone was scornful. "You—you can demand nothing. Anyway, what are you? You are a bastard. You realise that? You are a bastard. . . . Oh my God!" He put his hand to his head and flung round from her. "You're upsetting me." As quickly as he had turned from her he was facing her again, once more his hands outstretched: "I'm sorry. I'm sorry. But you make me say these things; and you never exasperated me like this before, you were so docile."

"I have never been docile. I'm not a docile person."

"Well, you were different when you were over there. You have changed."

"Me! changed? Have you seen yourself?"

A silence came between them; it fell like a heavy veil over them, and it seemed to emanate from his face. It was a figure of speech to say a person had a dark expression, but she saw that her husband's countenance was definitely dark. Yet there was a white line circling his mouth. For a moment his face appeared like that of a dark devil. Then he was gone from her, the heavy mahogany door crashing behind him.

She literally groped her way to his desk and dropped into the swivel chair. Then, putting her forearms on the table, she was about to drop her face onto her hands when the movement of the chair caused her elbow to slip on the pad and hit against a brass ink-stand and cause it to slide an inch or so on the polished surface.

The well must have been freshly filled with ink and a little of it spilt onto the table. So, grabbing at the rocker blotter, she dabbed at the spilt ink; but the blotter wasn't enough to sop it up.

Quickly but carefully now, she lifted the blotting paper from the slots in the pad and laid the edge of it on the remainder of the ink; it was as she went to replace the top blotter that she noticed that there were at least two blotters beneath it, this to form a softer pad on which to write, she supposed; she did this with her own writing pad. She had already inserted the ink-stained side of the blotter into the pad when her hand paused and she put her head to one side as part of a name caught her eye on the bottom blotter. It was, naturally, back to front but EVAR stood out in a large scrawling hand, then a squiggle, and the letters GSUM were quite plain.

Marcel had only ever written her one letter and the writing was small and neat. When he signed his name in the register his signature had been small; and the letter he had written to Aunt

302

Maggie had been in a small hand. But of course, you would change your style of writing when you wrote an anonymous letter, wouldn't you?

She stared at the letters; then turning her head sharply, she looked back down the room before she pulled out the blotter, folded it in four, and pushed it into the pocket of her dust coat. Then her whole body shivering as if from ague, she made her way back upstairs to her room. But she did not open up the blotter and look at it right away; she hung her coat in the wardrobe, went out of the room again and along the corridor and onto the gallery that overlooked the stable yard. And there he was, mounted, ready for a gallop. Hurrying back to her room again, she now took the blotter from her pocket, smoothed it out, then held it up to the mirror. And there she saw the word "Musgrave," and before that she could make out the word "Frederick," although it had other words blotted over it. Further up the blotter she made out the word, "Information," then what she took to be "authentic statement."

Of a sudden she dropped the blotter onto the dressing table and, turning from it, she began to pace the length of the room. How right Freddie had been. How right Maggie had been. And how mad she had been. What had she done? What kind of a man had she married? One minute like a child, the next like a fiend. And those letters to the police. He had wanted Freddie out of the way. She must get across to Freddie. She must go home. But she hadn't any money. It seemed impossible, but she hadn't any money. And she had no one to ask. That nice maid Mary. Yes, yes, that's whom she would ask. She rushed now to the dressing table, grabbed up the blotter, folded it into a small square, and put it in the bottom of her dressing case. And her hand was actually on the knob of the door when she heard her husband's voice from the far end of the corridor, calling, "Grant! Grant!"

She was standing at the window looking out when the door opened and immediately his voice came at her, saying, "You're coming riding."

She turned slowly and looked at him. "I am not up to riding. I don't feel at all well. What is more I don't like riding."

"You're coming riding." He was striding towards her. "Do you want me to drag you out?"

"Don't you dare!" She pressed herself back against the stanchion of the window.

"Don't dare what? Tell me what I mustn't dare now. You have two choices: one, to come quietly downstairs and get on the horse, or, I drag you down by the scruff of the neck."

She watched him straighten himself up, push his shoulders back and say, "Do you know who I am, or don't you know who I am? I'm somebody who must be obeyed. I am your husband. Now I shall count five, just five, in which time you will make up your mind."

"Oh dear God! Dear Father in Heaven!" She found she was praying. At school, when she had been forced to attend certain services it had been, "Dear Father, keep me a good girl. Don't let me hate Miss Lorimer. Oh, please Father, let me finish school this year. Persuade Aunt Maggie not to send me back." But now she was beseeching Him: "Oh, Lord, help me. Help me."

Slowly she walked past her husband to the wardrobe, and there she took down a coat and a form of bonnet with straps which she could tie under her chin, and with trembling hands put them on. Then, still without looking at him directly, she went before him out of the room, across the landing, down the stairs, through the hall and into the lobby, and so out onto the drive where the breeze cooled the sweat that was running down both sides of her face; in fact, her body was running with sweat bred by her fear.

It was Billy Martin the groom who helped her up into the saddle and put her foot into the stirrup before leading her horse forward until it was level with her husband's mount. Then at a word from him the horses moved forward and they walked down the drive and onto a bridle path. They walked thus for almost a quarter of an hour, and he hadn't spoken. Now he said, "Trot!" and when he put his horse into a trot hers followed.

He led the way through a narrow gap in a hedge and there, before them, was a wide hilly field, and perhaps because the horses were used to a routine once in the field they began to gallop.

She didn't cry out, but she hung on for dear life to the front of the saddle and was amazed when they reached the brow of the hill that she was still on the horse's back.

And apparently he was amazed too, for he said, "See what you can do when you try! Now if you do that every day for the next month you'll be a horsewoman."

She made no response; and again they were trotting. When the horses went into another gallop she still hung on.

They must have been out almost two hours, and when they returned to the yard she actually fell into the groom's arms when he went to assist her out of the saddle. And she had to lean on his arm for support for a moment before she could make her hips move.

She did not know how she managed the stairs, and her husband offered her no assistance; in fact he went before her and straight into his dressing room where his man was waiting for him with a hot tub ready as if he had timed his return.

In her own room, she made straight for the bed feeling she must collapse onto it when Mary Chambers appeared at the dressing room door. Her sleeves were rolled up and she had a large towel over an arm and, her voice different, she said, "When you were so long out, madam, I . . . we thought you might like a warm tub. It is ready at your pleasure."

Instead of throwing herself on the bed face forward, she slowly lowered herself down and, holding on to the bottom draped rail, she let out a long slow breath, then said, "Thank you, Mary. That will be very welcome."

A few minutes later, when she was partly undressed, Mary said, "You could sit in with your pantaloons and your camisole, madam, and I could massage your back."

"That . . . that is very kind of you, Mary, but . . . but I can manage."

The maid looked at her pityingly for a moment; then turning away, she said, "I hate horses, smelly things."

As Belle lowered herself into the long zinc bath she said almost aloud, "I don't hate horses . . . it isn't horses I hate."

She had made herself go down to dinner where she hardly touched any plate that was put before her. The first was a clear soup. She took three spoonfuls of it. Next, there followed rolled sole in sauce. She nibbled at this. But when there was placed before her a plate on which a small complete bird with a white frill around its stumped neck sat as if deep in a nest of varied vegetables, she felt she would vomit. She didn't know whether it was pigeon, grouse, pheasant, or wild fowl. She only knew she was disgusted by the sight of it and so pushed her plate away. But she had hardly done so when her husband startled even Benedict, who was pouring him wine, by bawling, "What is it woman! Not to your taste?"

She glanced from Benedict who was now approaching her, to Linda Everton who was at the sideboard and whose duty it was to help Benedict in the dining room, and the woman had turned and was looking at her. And when she forced herself to say, "I am not at all hungry," Linda hurried to the table and removed the plate, only to hear her master command, "Put that back!"

The maid put the plate back and retreated to the sideboard. And now Marcel was yelling at Benedict, "Inform the cook that my wife doesn't like her cooking. It's inferior stuff, not what she's been used to across the water."

She didn't recognise her own voice for it was loud and harsh as she cried down the table, "Sir! Please conduct yourself."

It was hard to say who was the most startled in the room. Then, a most surprising thing happened. She watched her husband slowly rise from the table and as slowly walk down the dining room and go out.

Benedict was now pouring wine into her glass and in a low voice he said, "The master is not well at the moment, madam. It will pass. Do try to eat a little. The pudding is light; it's sponge."

"No thank you, Benedict. I want nothing more; but . . . I will drink a little wine."

She wasn't fond of wine, but she drained the glass, telling herself she must be fortified in some way to help her through this day, for tomorrow, by whatever means, she would be gone. Oh yes, she was determined on that. As soon as he should leave the house, and a day never passed, she imagined, but he rode his horse, she would go, even if she had to walk all the way to the boat landing and then beg a creel man to take her across. She was sure most of them would know her, for had she not just recently made news in the newspapers.

The meal over, she did not return upstairs because she was afraid to be alone in her room with him; instead, she went to the drawing room where she took up her frame of embroidery and forced herself to sew.

For two hours she sat, and no one came near her, except Benedict who came in to see to the fire. But he himself did not build it up, he called Mary Chambers to bring in more coal and to blaze it with the ornamental blazer.

She had been expecting a summons from the lady of the house but none had come. Supper was to be at seven-thirty, and so, some time before, she went upstairs, washed her hands and face, changed her dress, as was the custom, and returned downstairs to find herself the only one in the dining room.

The supper consisted of hot broth, followed by a soufflé and a choice of cold meats, cold pie and cheeses.

As Benedict placed the broth before her, he said quietly, "The master asks to be excused. He is eating with the mistress tonight."

She inclined her head towards him; then, as much to please him and the cook, she endeavoured to eat some of the meal; and she found it easier, with her husband being absent from the table.

It was half past eight when she went up to her bedroom. The lamps were lit all over the house. She should have been saying to herself, "Doesn't it look beautiful," but the whole place was now appearing to her like a decorated cage from which she knew she must escape, or her reason, too, would become affected. . . .

Was his reason affected, or was his change of character just temper, like that of a spoilt child? And he had been a spoilt child. She knew that now. That old woman must have indulged him from the day he came into her care.

What she did when she reached her bedroom and made sure by listening that he was not in his dressing room was to put a few of her valuables she had brought with her into the dressing case. On top of these she placed a dress and some underwear, for that's all the case would hold. But she did not get undressed, for she did not want to take her things off and get into that bed; she would not be able to tolerate a repeat of last night.

So it was that she was still fully dressed at half past nine when he entered the bedroom from his dressing room. She had heard him there for the last quarter of an hour or more, and so she had sat near the side table where the lamp was and pretended to read.

He did not speak immediately he entered the room, but he stared at her till she raised her eyes and met his hard gaze.

"You are not undressed."

"I . . . I don't feel tired."

"It is time for bed . . . I am ready for bed"—he swept his hand down his dressing gown—"so, undress."

She rose from the chair, slowly laid the book by the side of the lamp, then looking at him and in a quiet, even placating, tone, she said, "I was unwell this morning; the horse ride did not help. I . . . I would feel obliged if you would allow me to sleep alone tonight. There is the couch in your bedroom. . . ."

So quickly did his hand come out and grab the front of her dress that she had no time to step back from him. And now he was actually shaking her as he said, "You telling me where to sleep! My wife telling me to get out of my own bed! We have scarcely been married a number of days. Get those clothes off, woman!" The last words were uttered as he thrust her back towards the bed, and as she fell onto her elbow she turned and cried at him, "No! no! I won't."

What happened next brought a loud cry from her, for he was actually tearing her dress from the neck downwards, ripping it from her body. It was belted at the waist, and he wrenched the buckle away from the band, and all the while she cried at him, "Stop it! Don't! Leave me be! Please! Please!"

She was swung round and thrown on her face. And now he was ripping the laces from the back of her corsets, and when she kicked out backwards he brought the side of his hand against the back of her knees and caused her to bury her face into the bedcover as she screamed.

By the time he had her naked she was too exhausted to resist him further, but not too exhausted to cry at him, "You're a fiend! I am leaving you. I am going home to Freddie tomorrow."

When his fists caught her one after the other between the eyes she screamed and fell back onto the bed. And then he was gone. She knew he had rushed from the room, but before she could pull herself upwards he was back standing over her, something in his hand, and through her blurred and tear-filled vision, she recognised that he was holding a razor strop. Freddie had one like that; it hung on a hook to the side of the fireplace and there was a little mirror above it. She could see him stropping the razor backwards and forwards; then his name was shouted down into her face, "Freddie! Freddie! You are going back to Freddie, are you? Not if I know it, madam, you're not. *Never. Never.* Do you hear me? I'll kill you first. You're a slut. That's what you are, a slut." When the strop caught her across her breast her screams mingled with his yelling: "Freddie! Freddie! Lusting after you and throwing yourself at him. Don't want to take your clothes off for your husband. But what did you take off for him?" Again the strop descended; and now she flung

308

herself onto her face and went to crawl over the bed, but one hand came on her neck almost pressing her face into the counterpane so that she could hardly breathe. But when a lash caught her across the shoulders her body jerked and she let out a higher scream and then another and another as the leather strop or the buckle tore at her flesh.

She wasn't aware that the door had opened and that Mary Chambers now stood on the landing, herself yelling, nor was she aware of Benedict and Alan Grant pulling the man from the bed and of Grant shouting, "Go get Billy and Roy!" Nor was she aware of the struggle that went on on the floor, when Benedict was knocked onto his back and Alan Grant was almost being over-powered, until he took his fist and landed it on his master's jaw.

Commotion followed commotion. At one time the room seemed to be full of people; then of a sudden everything went quiet. . . .

It seemed that everything had been quiet for a long time. She was in bed now, lying on her side, and there were voices about her murmuring. One said, "My God! When she comes to she'll be in agony. I've never known him go on like this."

Another voice said, "Oh, he went for a stable lad once, nearly did for him, all because the lad hadn't strapped the saddle tight or something. He shouldn't have come back last week. The mistress told him; but at times it's no good talkin' to him. Now she'll be upset again because it won't be just a week or two this time."

"How long has he ever gone without having to go to Harrogate?"

"Oh, six months, nine months, if he keeps off the drugs."

"I thought he had to keep takin' the stuff?"

"Yes, the white powder, but it's when he goes on to that brown stuff; that's the stuff that sends him over the hill."

"Well, why does he take it?"

"Don't ask me. . . . She's groanin', poor lass. Hand me that other bowl of fat."

"Anyway, the doctor'll have to pump him full of the horse that bit him to get him away this time. It's funny, isn't it, other times he goes on his own when he knows he's got a spasm comin' on. I'm sorry for him in a way."

"My God! I'm not. I'm not sorry for any man who can do this to a bit lass, and them not married for five minutes. You know what?" The voice dropped to a whisper; "I blame the mistress. She shouldn't have allowed it to happen. She knows what happens when he gets excited or anyone thwarts him."

"Shut up, Mary, and keep your tongue quiet. You know what happened to the last one that opened her mouth here, she got short shrift. And it's a good place: we do our work, we mind our own business, and let them get on with their lives, such as they are. Turn her over."

"How do you feel now, madam?"

She slowly opened her eyes and looked into Mary Chambers's face, but she could give her no answer. How did she feel? What was it like to feel you were in hell and your body was being consumed by flames, that the devil himself had set light to you. She must get away. She must. "Mary."

"Yes, madam?"

"Lend . . . lend me some money."

Mary Chambers looked at Linda Everton and whispered, "She must be ravin' a bit. She asked if I would lend her some money. Now, isn't that laughable."

"All right, madam; I'll lend you some money the morrow. All I've got I'll lend you. Go to sleep now." Mary turned her head away and whispered again to Linda, "Should we give her a dose of laudanum?"

"Can't see it would do any harm."

So they gave Belle a dose of laudanum, and she went into a fitful sleep.

The next morning she woke again in hell. When she couldn't open her eyelids fully and her face was so stiff and painful and her whole body burning as if she were in a white hot furnace, she knew she must be in hell.

"Will you try to drink this, madam? It's just warm, it's some tea."

As Mary dribbled the tea between her lips Belle moved them painfully and whimpered, "My . . . my face?"

"Yes, yes, madam; it's a bit of a mess, but it'll go down. Cook's sending up some steaks."

"Mary." She caught hold of the maid's hand. "Where is. . .?"

"Don't worry, madam, don't worry, he's gone. He went early this morning. You'll be all right now. Don't be frightened any more. It was a spasm he was in. He'll be different when he comes back."

"Mary."

"Yes, madam?"

"Will y'you loan me some m'money?"

The maid straightened up from the bed and stared down into the distorted features. Her mistress seemed to mean what she said; she was sounding sensible enough now. "What d'you mean, madam?" she asked.

"Mary, I . . . I have no money of my own. I . . . I want to engage a cab and to p'pay"—she had to swallow and wait before finishing—"the ferry. I . . . I'm going home."

"Yes, madam, yes. But just lie still now."

Eeh! she had thought she had come round but she hadn't, couldn't have. But she talked to her as though she had: "Me and Linda's goin' to see to your back again. There's nothin' like goose fat for healing—" She wouldn't say flagellating or flaying, so she said, "Sores like."

A moment later when Linda came into the room, Mary said, "She's still not right in the head; she asked me again to lend her some money."

"Well, the state she's in it's not surprisin'. She'll likely be like this for days. The mistress is coming along to see her later, so Miss Cummings said."

"Now I wonder if she'll be on her high horse, or will she be kindly? You never know with her either. You'd think in a way the master was from her side, wouldn't you?"

"Oh no! Her manner is the same as all the grand ladies. Mr Benedict says it's because she's an autocrat, the same as aristocrats you know. But there, I wouldn't have Miss Cummings's job for a pound a week."

There was a slight huh! before Mary said, "I wouldn't like to tempt you, Linda. But there, that's the last of that bowl of fat. Eeh! just look at the sight of her legs. He could have done her in."

"D'you think the mistress will call the doctor?"

"I doubt it. You know what she's like for hiding things up. What is it, dear?" She was now bending over Belle.

"I . . . I must go home. Will . . . will you get my clothes, please?"

"Oh, madam, you couldn't get into your clothes, you're not well enough yet. And . . . and you are home. Well—" Mary turned and exchanged glances with Linda, and Linda, now looking down at Belle, said softly, "You'll be all right now, madam. Things'll be all right now."

They didn't understand. Belle closed her eyes. They thought she was rambling but her mind was clear, so very, very, painfully clear. This wasn't her home and never would be and things would never be all right. Never again would things be all right; well, not until she got into the shelter of Maggie's home and Freddie's protection. Oh, Freddie, Freddie. If only she could be near Freddie. Why hadn't she valued Freddie? But she had, oh yes she had, but not in the way she should, not in the way he valued her. And it was clear to her now how he valued her. It was clear to her now, too, why he hadn't married May Harper.

When the sheet was drawn up over her body she wanted to cry out against its contact with her seared flesh. What had he done to her body besides abusing it?

The answer came from a faint voice in the middle of the room. It was saying, "By! he must have laid into her."

"Well he did; when you think her screams could be heard in the hall and they caused the mistress to interfere by ringing the bell. But she, of course, would have guessed what had happened."

The voices faded away, the door closed, and she was alone.

When she tried to raise herself up from the pillows she let out a low agonised groan of pain, but she persevered and pulled herself up into a sitting position. If she could only walk. She attempted to swing her legs from the bed, but the effort on her torn flesh was too much and she lay back gasping.

She'd have to wait. But how long? . . .

She did not know what time in the morning it was when she became aware of the tall, scented and perfumed figure standing by the side of the bed. But when she looked up into the face she saw no sympathy or pity there and there was certainly none in the voice that remarked, "You brought this on yourself, you know that?"

She made no effort to answer.

"When Marcel is handled properly there's not a kinder or more gentle person. You must have exasperated him in some outrageous way. I've been sadly mistaken in you; you're not a pliable person at all. But you will have to learn."

It was an effort to move her lips, but move them she did, and her own voice sounded to her like a growl now as she said, "I have no intention of learning, madam. How can one learn anything from a man who acts like a maniac. I have no intention of remaining his wife either; and you will kindly think on that, madam, and, believe me. . . ."

It gave her some satisfaction now as she watched the effect her words were having on the woman for she was clutching the front of her high necked gown and her voice had a strangled sound as she said, "Cummings! Cummings!"

Her maid took her arm now and turned her from the bed. And when the door had closed on them Belle lay back on the pillows gasping for breath: as if she had been running a race, her heart was pumping against her ribs.

Once more she pulled herself up into a sitting position. She knew now that definitely she must get away from this place, and soon, because in a way that old lady was as dangerous as her husband and would find ways and means of keeping her here, even going as far as to lock her in her room. Of a sudden she thought of the padded room in which she had spent her early life and from which Freddie had rescued her, and with the thought she brought her legs over the side of the bed. When her feet touched the floor she felt no pain in them; they at least had escaped the strop.

Clinging now to the side of the bed, she made herself walk to the foot of it; then she guided herself across the bottom by stretching painfully over the chaise longue to its ornamental back to come within a few steps of the dressing table. With difficulty she managed to take these, but as she lowered herself onto the seat she let out a smothered groan, only for the groan to die away on a gasp as she looked at her reflection in the mirror. The skin around her right eye was almost as black as her hair, and part of the left, too, was deeply discoloured. Her cheeks were puffed out and her mouth was swollen.

After a moment, she drew herself up from the chair and, her face twisting in agony, she now eased off the lawn nightdress that was stuck to her greased body. Then, seemingly unconscious and unashamed of her nakedness, she shuffled into the dressing room. But here, she could not find the clothes that she had worn the previous day.

Of course, she now told herself, they would have been removed last night. So, opening one of the press drawers, she took out a clean chemise, two waist petticoats and a pair of grey silk stockings. She did not take out any corset because she knew she would be unable to wear it.

Slowly and painfully she got into the garments, but when she pulled her garters on and they pressed against the weals behind her knees, she closed her eyes tightly, at the same time opening her mouth wide. But no sound was emitted.

In the bedroom again, she took down from the wardrobe a plain-fronted dress that was easy to get into. And she was sitting on the chaise longue when the door opened and Mary entered.

The maid stood gaping for a moment before hurrying towards her, saying, "Oh! madam, madam, you shouldn't. How on earth have you got into your clothes? Oh! madam, you're not well enough to be up. Come on." And she went to help Belle up from the seat, but Belle caught at her hand, saying, "Mary, close the door. I want to talk to you."

Mary ran back to the door, closed it, then returned to her. And once again Belle took her hand, and when she said, "I want to ask you a great favour. You see I have no money of my own, not even any coppers, would you loan me something, four or five shillings?" Mary's mouth became agape, and she said, "Eeh! madam, I thought you were . . . well, delirious like. But what do you want the money for, may I ask, madam?"

"I want to hire a cab to the dockside in Shields, then take a sculler or the ferry across to the North side and home."

"Oh, madam, madam. Eeh! if madam knew, she would. . . ."

"Please, Mary, don't say anything to madam, I beg of you. And . . . and I will return the money twofold. But in the meantime, I will—" She now pointed: "Would you please hand me my dressing case?"

When Mary placed the dressing case on her knee she opened it and from the bottom she took a small gold fob watch and, pressing it into Mary's hand, she said, "That is for your kindness to me, in any case, during the short time I have been in this house."

"Eeh! madam, I . . . I can't. Eeh! where would I say I got it? Eeh! madam. No, madam."

"Take it, Mary. You may not always be in service. But whatever you lend me I promise you I will return it with interest. Have . . . have you got four or five shillings?"

"Yes, madam, yes. But . . . but there's no way to get a cab out here; you would have to send a servant for it. And we never use cabs. There's the coach and the trap, or the store cart."

"Well, it is certain that I cannot use any of those things and, as yet, I'm unable to walk as far as Harton from where I might hire a cab." She lay back slowly now against the frame of the couch, and she stared helplessly through her narrowed vision at Mary. Then Mary, casting her eyes quickly towards the door and back to her again, bent close to her, saying, "Billy Martin the groom's had to go with Mr Grant to take the master to Harrogate, but there's Roy Yarrow. He's taking the cart into Shields for fodder and stuff this morning, well in half an hour or so I should say. But, madam . . . would you ride in a cart?"

Belle was sitting upright again and once more holding Mary's hand as she said, "Oh, Mary, I'd ride in any vehicle, no matter what it was. But . . . but do you think he will agree? Will it cost him his post?"

"He'll agree, madam; he'll do it for me 'cos we're walking out."

"Oh, I am pleased for you."

"I'll slip down now, madam, an' see him. But you won't be able to get in the yard; he'll have to pick you up somewhere down the back drive. D'you think you could walk that far? Cos you'll have to go on your own; you see, I can be on call any minute."

"I'll walk that far, Mary. Oh, yes, I'll walk that far."

"Well, I'll be back in a minute. In the meantime, madam, if you took to walking up and down the room to get your legs flexed sort of 'cos . . . 'cos they're in a state all round the back and you might find it difficult."

"Don't worry about that, Mary, only go, please, and try and make the arrangements." . . .

She walked up and down the room gritting her teeth against the agony each step brought her, and by the time Mary returned she had also donned her coat and chosen a bonnet with a large brim in the hope that it would hide some of her disfigurement.

"I've brought you six shillings, madam. If you wouldn't mind giving Roy a shilling when you leave him, I'd be obliged. And . . . and he says he can take you as far as the market place 'cos the Corn and Hay Chandlers warehouse is just beyond King Street."

Clutching the six shillings in her hand, Belle looked at Mary and, her voice trembling on the verge of tears, she said, "I'll . . . I'll never forget you for this, Mary. And if you are ever in need, you and your . . . fiancé, then you must come to me. Will you remember that?"

"I will, madam, and thank you. And may I say it would be a pleasure working for someone like you, it would that. One of the conditions of employment here, you know, is you keep your tongue quiet or else you're out without a reference. But now, madam, I'd be on your way. I'll go first and try to stall anybody that might be wanting to come along the landing. I'll keep them chatting until you've made your way down the side staircase, and it's only a few yards from there to where the back drive starts. Goodbye, madam, and good luck."

"Goodbye, Mary. And oh, I do thank you so much."

The maid, herself almost in tears now, hurried out; and Belle, picking up the small dressing case, followed her slowly, eased open the door, glanced along the corridor, then as quickly as her seared flesh would allow she did a shuffling walk to the staircase. But when she went to descend she felt she was going to topple head first down. It was one thing shuffling on the level, but another when she was forced to bend her knee. But she managed.

She paused by the door at the foot of the stairs and drew in a number of breaths. Then again she looked to right and left before stepping out onto the pathway that led to the drive.

She didn't know how far she had walked down the drive, she only knew she couldn't continue for much longer when she heard the sound of a trotting horse, and, turning, there came into view the high-backed cart.

When it drew up at her side Roy Yarrow jumped down and, taking her gently by the arm, led her to the back of the cart, saying, "I've put some horse blankets in it, madam; you'd be able to sort of . . . well lie down, if you wanted to."

"Thank you. Thank you, Roy."

He had to lift her up onto the back of the cart; and when she was settled on the blankets, he took another from the side and, putting it round her, said, "There now, madam. I'll go as careful as I can, but the side road's rough until we make the village."

"That will be all right, Roy. I don't mind. And . . . and thank you so much."

"That's all right, madam. That's all right. And let me say now what I think, madam, an' that is you're doin' the right thing, yes you are, in gettin' away from there. It's a pity you ever came, it is that. Mary's told me quite a bit about you, madam. Are you comfortable?"

"Oh, yes, yes, thank you."

"Well, we'll get goin' then." He nodded at her, then jumped down from the back of the cart and mounted the front seat again. And so for the second time in her life, she escaped from The Towers.

The first part of the journey she found excruciating, for her torn body registered every bump in the road. But once they reached the village the much smoother swaying of the cart almost lulled her into sleep.

Before they reached the market Roy descended from his high seat and, going round to the back of the cart, he said, "You all right, madam?"

She nodded, then said quietly, "Yes, yes, thank you, Roy."

"I've just thought, madam: seeing as Mr Martin won't be back from Harrogate the night there's nobody back there to check on me, how long I've been, and so I'm gona take you down to the ferry or where you can get a boat across. Which would you like to travel in, the ferry or the sculler?"

"Whatever comes first, Roy. And thank you so much, that will be a great help."

Again he took his seat and the cart now rumbled over the cobbled road that led down to the waterfront. Here he stopped it, and again hurried round to her, saying quickly, "We're in luck, madam; the ferry's just come in."

She now eased herself slowly forward from the blankets to the edge of the cart; and there he put his arms under her oxters and gently lifted her onto her feet. But she swayed and leant against him for a moment, and he said, "Just hang on there near the rail for a minute, will you, madam, till I tie the horse to the post? Then I'll take you down and see you set."

When, a moment later, he went to take her arm she put her hand out and pressed two shillings towards him, for she realised now that she would still have more than enough to see her across the river.

"Oh, madam, I don't want that. I haven't done this for money."

"No, I know you haven't, Roy; but I'm so grateful to you and to Mary. I'll never forget either of you. I've . . . I've told Mary."

"Mary thinks highly of you, madam. From the moment she saw you. Well now, d'you think you can walk to the ferry?"

"Oh, yes, yes."

She had said, yes, yes, but she found she was hardly able to put one leg before the other. It wasn't only the pain now, it was a great weakness that seemed to be overpowering her.

Not until she was seated, did he leave her; but just before taking his departure he bent down, put his lips close to her ear and said, "Could I say to you, madam, that you should see your solicitor. You've got a case. It's not right. They should have told you."

She didn't ask, Told me what? because she knew; but she was feeling so ill now that she could make no response to him, she could only hold out her hand and touch his.

The movement of the small ferry told her that she was on her way home; even so, she wasn't aware when it stopped until a voice said, "Well, we're here, missis."

When she lifted her head and looked at the man who was one of the small crew, he said softly, "Oh! my, my. Come on, lass," and he helped her to rise from the seat, calling to another man, "Give me a hand here, will you? This lady's not well."

She felt herself being lifted bodily onto the quay; then the man was speaking to her again: "Anybody to meet you, missis?" he asked.

She peered at him, but didn't answer. Then one of the passengers took the man aside, saying, "That's Maggie Hewitt's girl, the one that married and went across the water to live."

"My God! so it is. I didn't recognise her. Well, this is a to-do. Somebody's busted her up and done the job well. Poor lass." He turned to her again, saying, "I think you'd better rest on the quay, missis, and somebody'll go and tell Freddie Musgrave. That's where you're makin' for, isn't it?"

She was swaying slightly as she turned to the man who had been a passenger on the ferry: "Would . . . would you be so kind as to help me to Miss . . . Miss Hewitt's office on the quay?" she asked him.

"Yes, yes; of course I'll do that." The man took her arm, and slowly now they made their way past interested spectators along the Low Lights, and then there she was entering Maggie's office.

The sight of her brought Andy Stevens up from his desk and caused George Hooper to drop his pen to the floor.

When the man supporting her said, "The lady is not well, she needs seeing to," Andy Stevens came forward and, placing a chair, muttered, "Sit down. Sit down, miss . . . I mean missis. In the name of God! what's happened to you? I better get Mr Musgrave. You, Hooper, go and see if you can find him. He was to see Skipper Hanlon along at the fish quay. If he's not there he'll be at the top of the hill seeing what needs doing to that house. Go on. Go on, man."

Belle told herself she must not fall asleep. She did not put the name faint to the feeling that was overwhelming her, nor did she say she mustn't become unconscious, but she told herself that she must not fall asleep until Freddie came. And when Freddie came she would be able to rest. Freddie would look after her. Oh, Freddie, Freddie.

"What did you say Mrs Birkstead?"

She wanted to ask for a drink of water but the words wouldn't come. The men were talking over her head; the voices were low, and they went on and on and on. She felt her body falling forward, and then hands staying her and keeping her upright. But the voices went on, until there was the sound of pounding steps on the wooden pavement that ran along the front of the buildings, and then the door burst open. And there he was. She tried to open her eyes to see him but she could only dimly make out his face.

She spoke his name. Twice she said it: "Freddie. Freddie." And when his arms went about her she went to sleep.

17

And this sleep seemed to have taken over her life; for three days she floated in and out of it. At times she was aware of gentle hands on her and the familiar voice of Jinny saying, "Oh, me pet. Oh, me pet." And that other voice, that beloved voice, talking gently to her, talking her into the sleep again, telling her that never again would he let her go. Saying words to her that she never imagined he would utter . . . not Freddie.

Then there were other voices that impinged upon the sleep: The doctor's voice. Often she heard his voice. And then another strange voice and a word, "Horrendous." She hadn't heard that word before; she had read it, but she hadn't heard it spoken. What was "horrendous"? There was one time she became afraid, because they brought the police into the room and she had done nothing. She tried to tell them that she had only run away.

She came fully to herself one morning when the dawn was breaking. She had always been able to tell this through the chink in the curtains when they weren't pulled closely enough. Slowly she moved her head and looked to the side of her. There, seated in a chair close to the bed, was Jinny. Her eyes were closed and she was breathing heavily; but all of a sudden she snorted and sat up with a slight jerk, then exclaimed, "Ah! pet. Ah! pet. You're awake. You're really awake. D'you want a drink, hinny?"

"Yes please, Jinny."

"Oh, you look better, lass." She was bending over her now, stroking the damp hair from her forehead. "And your face has gone down. Aw, you'll soon be yourself again. Aw, I'll wake him."

"Oh, no, no, don't please."

"Oh, he'd want to know you're back along of us again. He's

320

been sitting up night after night, but he was all in. Now lie there still, pet, and I'll get you some tea. Oh my! am I glad to see you lookin' like that."

How was she looking? She didn't know.

How was she feeling? At the moment she felt nothing, no searing pain, nothing, her body seemed at rest and free. At least, it was until she attempted to turn on her side; and then she let out a low groan for it was as if her skin had turned to stiff hide and was cracking in various places with her movements.

She was lying fully on her side and gasping slightly when Freddie came in. His hair was wet and he was pushing it back from his forehead. It was as if his head had been immersed under the pump. She watched him grab a towel and dry his hands; then he was kneeling by the bed and his fingers were gently stroking her cheek.

"Hello, my dear."

"Hello, Freddie."

She could see his Adam's apple bobbing up and down in his throat. "Feel better?" he said.

"Yes, Freddie, so much better. . . . How long is it since I came home?"

"Four days."

"Four days!" She looked away from him for a moment; then softly she said, "It's a wonder I ever reached this side. I was helped by Mary and her young man."

She was looking at him again. "I must do . . . do something for them, Freddie."

"All right. All right. We'll do something for them. Whoever helped you out of there, oh yes, we'll do something for them. But don't talk now. Mam's bringing you a cup of tea; then I want you to go to sleep again."

"Freddie?"

"Yes, my dear?"

"You . . . you won't let them take me . . . I mean, I can stay with you, can't I? Freddie, I'll never go . . . go back."

He slipped his arm gently behind her shoulders and, holding her thus and his face close to hers, he said, "No. That's one thing you can be certain of, you'll never go back. And another thing you can be certain of, my love, is that I'll never leave you ever again. You are here to stay, always. . . . You understand?"

321

"Oh, Freddie, Freddie. Why . . . why did I do it? Why?"

"Well, you were a young lass, headstrong. You always were, you know." He smiled at her. "And it's my fault: I . . . I should have made myself plain long before now about . . . about how I felt for you."

"Oh, Freddie, Freddie, I wish you had, because . . . because I've always loved you. But . . . but I didn't know which way until recently. And now it's . . . it's too late."

"Oh no, my dear, my dear, my dear, it's not too late. You are never going back to that man. The witnesses who have seen the sight you're in will bear out that you have a case, and a very, very strong case, to prove that the marriage is at an end. But now, don't distress yourself. Lie back, that's it, and go to sleep. Ah, what am I talking about? Here's Mam with the tea."

He did not withdraw his arm from about her shoulders, but he took the cup and saucer from his mother with his free hand and held it while she slowly and thankfully drank the tea. Then when the cup was empty and he handed it back to his mother Belle put her hand out towards Jinny, and when it was clasped she said in a small voice, "You'll never know, Jinny, how glad I am to see you."

Jinny, deeply touched, now wagged her head, saying, "Well, the best thing you can do is to prove it an' get back on your feet an' be a nuisance to me runnin' in and out of that kitchen. D'you hear now?" Then she turned abruptly and left the room. And Freddie, touching Belle's face again with his fingers, said, "She's been sick with worry over you, and those simple words can explain her feelings; but I'll never find words to explain mine the minute I saw you down at that office. I'll never forget my reaction as long as I live, because in that moment I could have really done murder. Oh yes"—he moved his head slowly up and down—"that isn't an exaggeration. If on that day I could have found him in the house across the water I would have certainly done murder. It was just as well he was away. And that's another thing we'll talk about. I'm going to be away for a day maybe two, but you have no need to worry. John will be here all the time."

"John?"

"Yes, my brother John. I've got him and the family in the empty terraced house at the top of the hill. It was a fine little house, if you remember, and I've never seen a happier man. To be able to go and tell the head gardener to tell his mistress that, all right, he would forfeit the three weeks pay owing to him, made him, as he said, feel like a king. They moved their stuff in yesterday, and now he's working for me. And Mam couldn't be happier about it. So he'll be here night and day the time I'm gone."

"Where are you going?"

"Go to sleep now; we'll talk about that later."

"Freddie, please."

"Shh! Be quiet." He stared down into her discoloured face; then slowly and gently he lowered his head until his mouth hung above hers and then for the first time he really kissed her firmly but gently. And when her arms went round his neck he withdrew his lips from hers, saying, "There now, there now, no tears, no tears, not any more. We're together and nothing can part us, nothing or no one. Not any more."

"Nothing or no one. Not any more. . . . Freddie, he wrote those letters to the police. I found your name on the blotter; and you'll have to go to court again, won't you?"

"Yes; I guessed he did. But now be quiet and go to sleep. That's it, love, go to sleep."

18

He arrived in Harrogate at twelve thirty; quickly found an hotel, then ordered a cab to take him to Wellindean Hall.

It was an hour all but five minutes before he heard the cab driver call to someone to open the gates; and then they were bowling up a long winding drive. The cab came to a halt at the foot of a flight of broad stone steps leading to a wide balcony, the stone work of which was looking the worse for wear, with coping stones off here and there.

Bidding the cab driver wait, he crossed the balcony to the heavy oak door and pulled on the bell. It was some little time before the door was opened by a manservant who seemed to be almost bent double, so stooped were his shoulders; and so frail was he that he was unable to control two bounding dogs who barked and yelped all round Freddie's legs, but in a quite friendly welcoming way.

"Yes, what?"

"I would like to speak to Mr Fuller please."

The hand was cupping the ear and the voice was loud as it repeated, "What?"

Freddie moved nearer the man and in a louder voice said, "I would like to have a word with Mr Fuller."

The back endeavoured to straighten itself and the old butler said, "Colonel's in bed. See nobody. But Mr James, he's here somewhere."

"Could I have a word with him then?"

"In the stables likely." He put out his arm and, his hand held at an angle, he pointed it as if the stables were further along the balcony, then added, "If not there, down at the farm, West Side."

Freddie gazed at him in silence for a moment before saying,

"Thank you"; then turned to take the direction the hand had indicated to find, when he rounded the corner of the house, he was in the stable yard. He noticed straightaway that this was in parts overgrown with grass, and there seeming to be no one about, he stood in the middle of the yard and shouted, "Is anyone there?"

And then a head appeared over a horse box, the head of a lad, "Aye, yes, what's it you want?" he called back.

"I'm looking for Mr Fuller."

"Oh." The head disappeared, and Freddie walked across the yard to the box and saw the lad talking to a man who was attending to a horse; in fact, he was on his hunkers rubbing the animal's back leg. Freddie watched him straighten up, then rub his hands down his corduroy breeches before moving towards the half-door, saying in a voice that belied his attire, "Yes, what can I do for you?"

The voice and the manner both demanded that the person should be addressed as "sir," but Freddie said simply, "I would like to have a word with you."

"What about? I'm busy."

"It is rather important. I . . . I am young Mrs Birkstead's guardian."

He watched the man straighten up further and the chin sag just a little, then snap closed as he said to the young boy, "Keep rubbing in that liniment, Gerry; I'll be back." Then he pulled open the half-door and saying, "You'd better come in," he walked ahead of Freddie towards the house and a door that led into a long dark kitchen where a woman turned from a stove, saying, "You ready for a bite, Mr James?" But her voice trailed off when she saw that her master wasn't alone and he answered her, "Hold it, Peggie; I'll have it later." Then with a jerk of his head, he addressed Freddie again: "This way," he said.

After going through what seemed to be a maze of passages, they passed into a hall that appeared as dark and as untidy and dirty as the kitchen had. But when the man pushed open a door, they entered a smallish room which did show a little comfort, if only in a masculine sort of way. A fire was burning low on an open hearth and there were two leather chairs and a long couch which had presumably been used as a bed, and not too long ago, for there, on it, was a pillow and a blanket.

Pointing to one of the chairs, the man said, "You may as well sit down." And Freddie sat down; and the man did so, too, but he didn't speak until after he had reached out and taken a pipe from the rack, knocked the doddle out on to the dirty hearth to the side of him, refilled the pipe with shag and lit it from a spill that he had thrust into the low embers. Even then, he drew on the pipe three times before he said; "So he beat her up?"

Freddie was slightly taken aback, but he said, "Yes, if you put it like that, he beat her up."

"Well, she can't blame anybody but herself in the first place, and you, if you are her guardian, for letting the marriage take place. You must have noticed something odd about him, surely. Even when he's normal, he's odd; always has been since she brought him into this house when he was four years old. He was showing signs of it then. My God! the tantrums. Many a time I was for throwing him out of the top window. I'm talking about my aunt, you understand . . . Mrs Birkstead."

"Yes, I understand."

"Well, she's to blame in the first place I suppose." He now leant forward, took the pipe from his mouth and laid it on a stand; then with his forearms on his knees, he leant forward and looked from Freddie towards the fireplace before he went on, his tone low now, "The havoc that woman's caused in so many bloody ways. She's brought this house down, you know. Do you know that? You might think your ward's had the rough end of the stick. You know nothing about it. She's lucky: she can get shot of him now; I've heard what he's done to her. We thought we had got rid of him when she took him to Shields, but when he had his spasms, he'd be back here on the doorstep. He knew when they were coming on." He nodded to Freddie now. "Father put his foot down and made her send him to Havensford; but it was too late. She hated parting with her own money. And you know she's rotten rich. Birkstead was rolling in it and she got the lot. They hadn't been married five minutes. But do you think she'd part with a penny except what she spends on adorning herself and for her own comfort. You wonder why I'm telling you all this, don't you? Well, I'm just putting you in the picture. You've come here to complain, haven't you?"

"I've come here to find out exactly what is wrong with Marcel Birkstead."

"Oh, that's easily answered. He's mad. He's a maniac. Must have come from his father, the Gallagher man; and look at Annette, Annette Birkstead. But she's mostly cunning and possessive." He leant back in the chair now and, picking up his pipe again, he once more drew on it, having to pull hard to get it going now. Then as if to himself he said, "That a woman could get an old man to sign his estate away in dribs and drabs. That's what she did. I was in India most of the time. My father's been bedridden for years. He came out of the Army shot to pieces. Do you know if he lives till next year he'll be a hundred. Imagine that! He's lived for more than thirty years in bed . . . and she even ruled him long before he took to bed. They say she looks like a painted gargoyle. Well she's well in her eighties, too, and with her stamina she too could live to a hundred. Her daughter ran away and got married you know to Gallagher. She nearly went mad because she had reckoned to take her into the Aristocracy. Oh, yes." He was nodding his head briskly as if Freddie had denied the statement. "But when she died and Gallagher, being the kind he was, couldn't stand his son . . . well, likely he had already witnessed some of the traits in him, it gave her a new aim in life and she became obsessed with the lad and he with her. Weird. Weird."

He now rose to his feet, saying, "Can I offer you a drink?"

"No, thank you."

Freddie too got to his feet. "What I want to know is, has he been certified?" he said.

"Certified? No. He only has spasms."

He laughed now. "That's all he has, spasms. At first they were put down to just fits of temper, until he was round about seventeen or eighteen when he had grandiose ideas; he even started up companies here and there. But she put a stop to that. She got the solicitors on the job to state that she could not be held responsible for any debt he incurred and pointed out that he had no money of his own. He was cute enough to learn that lesson. And then she had him put on drugs. That's when she first contacted the clever Doctor Villiers at Havensford who's supposed to cure by nature. Nature be damned!"

"Couldn't he be certified?"

"Oh, yes; if anyone could stand up to her and get round the doctor and prove that his actions were abnormal. Oh now"—he was wagging his finger at Freddie—"you might be the very person. You might have a case. Was she really badly knocked about?"

"Yes, really badly, from head to foot."

The man sighed now and his tone changed and he said,

"Well, I'm really sorry because I understand she was nothing but a chip of a girl. And look, I'll tell you this much." He took a step nearer to Freddie and in a low voice he said, "If you were to take this to court I would bear witness for you. Yes . . . yes, I would, and be glad to. But I must admit it wouldn't be through pure altruism; no, because I would see it as a sort of recompense for what that bitch of a woman has done to this place." He waved his hand as if encompassing the whole estate. Then he added, "You know something? He still has the nerve to come here, very often after they let him out. Only a few months ago he stood where you are standing now, and when I told him to clear out and not to come back here again, do you know what he said? Oh, he would come back because when I died he would inherit and his grandmama would restore the place. Do you know, I nearly did for him. . . . You're sure you wouldn't like a drink?" He looked towards the corner of the room to a table on which were two decanters and some glasses, and he said, "That's one good thing we've got left, a few bottles in the cellar."

Freddie nodded as though agreeing with this statement, but said, "If you'll excuse me I'll be on my way. I've got to get back before nightfall."

"Well, all I can say is good luck to you. But don't forget, that was a promise I made: if you ever need a witness you have one."

"Thank you." For the first time Freddie smiled at the man, and the man smiled back and surprisingly held out his hand, and Freddie shook it. Then the man once again led the way, but to the front door this time; and after opening it he went out to the steps and remained there while Freddie walked down them to the cab; and before entering, Freddie turned and touched his hat to him, and the man raised a hand in salute.

John was tidying the garden near the gate when Freddie arrived back, and straightaway he enquired of his brother: "Well, how did it go?"

"All very enlightening, John. It proved at least one thing for me, that the fellow is mad. But now my job will be to find out if that constitutes what they call grounds for divorce."

"A divorce?"

"Yes, John, a divorce."

"Difficult things to get, I should imagine."

"Yes; but not impossible. . . . How is she?"

"Oh, Ma has her propped up in bed, and she's had some broth and beef jelly."

He left him and hurried into the house, and the first person he saw was Nancy. Her hand outstretched, she came towards him, saying, "Freddie?"

"Yes, dear. How are you?"

"I'm . . . I'm fine, Freddie; but Belle . . . her poor face and her back. Ma got me to lay my hands on her back, yesterday, and Belle said she found ease."

"You've got good hands, Nancy, always have had. Where's Ma now?"

"She's in the bedroom."

He patted her arm, saying, "Be seein' you."

"Freddie." He stopped. "I've . . . I've got something to tell you, but later on."

"Be glad to hear it, dear. Be glad to hear it." He hurried from her, but when he opened the bedroom door he paused for a second. Belle was propped up in bed. If anything she seemed to look worse than when he had last seen her. Her eyes looked to be great dark lumps in a puffed mass of yellow flesh.

Jinny turned to him, saying, "He walks in just like that as if he had been down to the fish market. Had a nice time then?"

"Excellent, marvellous holiday." He slapped her on the buttocks, and as she cried, "You look out now, lad!" she was smiling at what she would term a form of endearment; and when he said, "Ma, you know what I want? The strongest cup of tea you can brew," she answered, "Well, I'll think about it." She now patted the side of the bed, smiled at Belle, then went out. But only when the door closed did he bend down and gently kiss the swollen cheeks and then the lips. And she put her arms around his neck but she said nothing.

Pulling up a chair, he asked gently, "How are you feeling now?"

She drew in a long gasping breath before she answered, "If I was to speak the truth, Freddie, worse than I did yesterday. I seem to be coming more aware of every inch of my body. And yet you know something? When Nancy put her hands on my back yesterday the pain eased considerably. Do you think she could be what you call a healer?"

"She could, yes, I suppose so. She's gifted in many ways, is Nancy. But dear, listen; I want to ask you something. I want you to do something for me."

"Anything, Freddie. I would do anything in the world for you that was possible, except"—she smiled wanly—"get up at the moment."

"I don't want you to get up, my dear, not for another week, or for as long as you want to lie there, but this is what I want you to do for me. I want you to allow a photographer to come in and take a picture of all your cuts and bruises."

"You . . . you mean my body, my back and legs and . . . ?"

"Yes. He would do it in sections. You would be partly covered up. You see, it's this way, dear. That man is mad. He is a maniac but he is not certified and if you want free from him you've got to have proof that he's unsafe to live with. Now by the time you're on your feet and the case comes up in court, there'll only be shadows of the weals and scars on your body, and your face will be completely normal by then. Now if we can produce photographs of what he did to you and how your body looks even a week after the incident, then this will go a long, long way to proving his insanity or whatever is wrong with him. For I can tell you, my dear, there'll be a great deal of opposition from his grandmother. Oh yes, she'll fight you tooth and claw. But we have one ally, his second cousin. Oh, my dear, there's a story. I'll tell you about it later. But I met this man, a Mr Fuller in Wellindean Hall. That's the place you said the old lady bragged about. Well, you should see it now. And there's one thing certain, he hates his second cousin and has promised to help by standing as a witness if we ever need him. And we're going to need him, aren't we, dear?"

"Oh yes, Freddie. Yet at the back of my mind I have this fear that he could force me back."

"Not on your life! No one or nothing will get you back there. Now rest your mind easy on that. You know something? I never wanted Maggie's money, I felt guilty at taking it, at least half of it I felt should be yours, now all of it, every penny, can be used to fight this case. But . . . but about the photographer: you'll allow it?"

"Yes. Oh yes, Freddie, anything, anything you say."

For a moment he felt a great sadness overwhelming him: "Anything Freddie," she had said, "anything you say." All the

330

sparkle, all the spunk had gone from her. Never a day had passed for years, as a young child and then whenever she was home from school, when she hadn't teased him, contradicted him, or stood up to him. But now, 'Anything, anything you say, Freddie.' "

"Why do you look like that, Freddie?"

He smiled at her now and, gently holding her face between his hands, he said, "I'll never know real happiness again until I hear you cheek me and tell me to shut up, that I'm too big for me boots, and that I'm devoid of taste in all that really matters."

"Did I act like that?"

"You did, madam."

"Oh, I'm sorry, Freddie." She tried to smile and he said, "Don't be sorry. Don't you ever say to me you're sorry. Do you hear?"

The door opened and Jinny entered. "I've left your tea in the kitchen," she said; "Nancy wants a word with you. And you'd better prepare yourself."

"Why?"

"Oh, there's goin' to be another addition to the family."

When his eyes widened and his mouth fell into a slight gape she yelled at him, "You've got a bad mind you! She's goin' to marry that customs fella, at least she wants to, but she doesn't want to upset the lot of us."

"Why should she upset the lot of us by marrying him?"

"Well, you know yourself."

"I know no such thing, Ma. Anyway, it'll be a step up for her."

"You know what, Freddie Musgrave, you're gettin' too big for your boots. Something's turned your head."

He laughed at her now while looking towards the bed and saying, "Yes, I know; she'll tell you all about it." Then he went out.

In the kitchen John and Nancy were sitting having a cup of tea, and it was John who said, "You know what our Nancy here is just tellin' me? She's thinkin' about movin' up to the aristocracy of the town, the enemy's camp, me da would say."

"Well, you know what I would say"—he put his hand on Nancy's shoulder—"you couldn't be in a better or safer camp, nor a more respectable one. But I'm glad I'm not still a nipper, else I would have a bad time of it, wouldn't I, lass?"

She laughed, then stood up and, putting her arms around his neck, she kissed him. "He wants to come and see you," she said.

331

"Why see me? It's Da he's got to see."

"He said he would rather see you."

"Well, anytime tell him. Anytime."

"You know something? It was he who was on the ferry that day. He didn't tell me till last night. It was he who helped Belle to the office."

"Was it now? Was it now? Well, Nancy, that'll be in his favour. Oh yes, yes."

"Oh, by the way, Freddie," John said, "I forgot to tell you. A young fella, not from this side, well I mean by the sound of him, he said his name was Yarrow, he came askin' to see you. It was around four o'clock or so. I said I didn't know when you'd be back and he said he'd look in later the night. D'you know anybody called Yarrow?"

"Yarrow?" Freddie shook his head.

"Well, he seemed to know you, or Belle, 'cos he called her Mrs Birkstead. And he said something about one of the maids. He kept mumbling. He seemed upset, sort of."

"Just a minute." Freddie now went back to the bedroom again, silencing what was going to be a quip from his mother by raising his hand and saying, "Just a minute." He bent over Belle and asked softly, "What was the name of the young fella who brought you in the cart?"

"Roy . . . Roy Yarrow."

"Ah, that's it. And . . . and the maid?"

"Oh, I told you that was Mary . . . Mary Chambers. They are . . . I think they are close friends."

"Well, it must appear that he's in trouble of some kind because John tells me he called here just recently; but he's coming back. D'you think they were found out and they've got the push?"

"I . . . I shouldn't be at all surprised. But, Freddie, I . . . I promised Mary that if she ever needed a friend she . . . she had to come to me."

"Well"—he smiled broadly at her—"your friends are my friends. And I'll see to them both, never fear. Now what did you want to say, Mrs Musgrave?"

"Nothin' important, Mr Musgrave, only to repeat you're gettin' too big for your boots."

Belle made a queer sound in her throat and her discoloured eyelids closed as she murmued, "Oh, Jinny, don't . . . don't make

332

me laugh. I . . . I don't want to laugh. Don't make me laugh, Jinny. Oh! Oh! Freddie." As the tears sprang from her eyes he put his arms round her and held her, and as the sobs mounted his mother turned away, saying as she made for the door, "The best thing for her, better than the medicine. It'll wash it away."

But as he held Belle's shaking body and listened to her gasping breath as the sobs seemed to tear her apart, he wondered at the strangeness of old women's sayings: This tortured crying, the best thing that could have happened. Wash it all away.

He held her till her crying subsided, and he went on holding her, for that's what he wanted to do, hold her for the rest of her life, but legally.

Being unable to see into the future, he wasn't aware, at that moment, that the legal minds Mrs Birkstead would engage or those he himself would commission would not then be concerned with the matter of annulment of Belle's marriage nor with, perhaps, just a legal separation.

19

During the following days a number of things happened. Roy Yarrow had called again that particular night and told Freddie that both he and Mary had taken lodgings in Shields after being dismissed on the spot. It would appear that Mrs Birkstead hadn't been appraised of Belle's departure until the following day and that she herself had almost had a seizure when hearing of it. Both Mary and Linda had been summoned before her, and when neither of them would speak she ordered their dismissal. It was then that Mary owned up that she was the one. She did this, she said, because Linda had no one belonging to her, whereas she knew that Roy would stand by her. And Roy did stand by her; and he too was dismissed at a minute's notice with no reference. Apparently it wasn't so much the fact that they, like John, had to forego their wages but that they hadn't a reference to get another position. That was the important thing. And so the next day Roy brought Mary across to an emotional scene between her and Belle, whereupon Freddie, much to his mother's chagrin, engaged Mary as a maid. As Freddie said, his da was always complaining about his mother never being at home and she was always saying she would really have to cut her time down here; so what was she grumbling about? Anyway, Mary was a nice lass who had started her life in the workhouse; and this alone should endear her to her. Didn't she think so? For answer, Jinny had said that one of these days she would tell him what she really thought, and that would be that.

Nevertheless, Mary was happily installed, and Freddie found Roy temporary work doing necessary repairs on the property, until such time as they would build a stable and have, if not a carriage and pair, a horse and trap.

The second thing that occurred was Freddie's receiving a communication commanding him to appear in court in Newcastle in three weeks' time to answer the charge of withholding information all these years.

Then a photographer had come, commissioned as he put it himself, to take very odd photographs, but nevertheless very interesting. And as he could only take small parts of the body at one time it was a very long session, which Belle found tiring. The doctor had happened to call during the process, and after expressing his surprise had nodded his approval. His words were: a very clever move, one which would likely come in useful.

That it seemed the whole town was whispering again, they were all well aware, but nothing had appeared in the newspapers, not even under Probes column, a writer who ferreted out information and who, over the past year, had increased the circulation of his particular paper twofold. Before, it had been known as merely a political stirrer, and, as most people who were wise knew, politics were best left alone; only people with devious minds went in for such things; and if they didn't trouble the country the country wouldn't trouble them, and things would go on smoothly as they had done for hundreds of years. A war here and there, a famine, a few epidemics, and a bright note now and again with news of the Royal Family and the Queen herself and things like the Great Exhibition, which was still talked about, and, of course, there was Barge Day on Holy Thursday on the river. Now that parade would cheer anybody up, for all the towns on the river were turned topsy-turvy with merriment. . . .

The day Belle came downstairs for the first time she wore only her nightdress, a dressing gown, and a lace shawl, for as yet she could not bear anything close pressed against her skin.

It was in the early afternoon and the sun was shining, and when Jinny guided her through the door into the sitting room she stopped for a moment and, looking up into Jinny's face, she said, "I think it's the most beautiful room in the world."

"What!" said Jinny. "You still think that way after being in The Towers?"

"Oh"—Belle gave a little shudder—"that wasn't a home, Jinny; it was an enormous doll's house." Yes, she nodded to herself, that's what it was, an enormous doll's house. And that old woman was the big doll.

"Well, there's the couch all ready for you; and you know,

when his nibs comes in the first thing he'll do is bawl at me and say, 'Why did you let her come downstairs?' And then he'll come in here as soft as pie and say, 'How are you, dear? You're looking better.' "

Jinny's mimicry made Belle laugh. And as she sat on the couch she said to Jinny, "You know your son, Jinny, inside out."

And surprisingly Jinny answered flatly, "Oh, no, I don't, lass. No, I don't. There's things that's always gone on in his mind that I couldn't reach to or fathom. He's been different to the rest from the first, sharper you know, thinks ahead. Aye"—she nodded now—"too much ahead, and it gets him into trouble. But he's got a daft spot that contradicts all the rest of him, if you know what I mean. Like it was with May: how he let himself be caught and hung onto with that one, God knows, 'cos I don't. Except that for all his bawling and his big head he doesn't like hurtin' people."

"Well, you know, Jinny, you've given an exact picture of yourself."

"Go on with you, cheeky face. Exact picture of meself, indeed! Huh!" But as she repeated this apparent summing up of her feelings, her expression showed that she was not a little pleased at the compliment. Nevertheless, having to act like Jinny, she turned away, saying, "I'd better go and see what that one's doin' in the kitchen."

She was half-way down the room when she turned and said, "She might be all right with a duster and a mop but she's got a hand like an iron shovel when it comes to pastry."

"You'll soon alter that, Jinny, and"—Belle paused—"be nice to her, please. I'm here now because of her, otherwise I know I'd never have made it from that place. And as Mary says, that very afternoon the mistress ordered Miss Cummings to lock me in. I shiver when I think of it, Jinny. So, be nice to her. And she's never had a mother."

"Oh! Talk about soft soap, go on with you."

On this Jinny went out and Belle lay back against the cushions and looked about her. It was indeed a beautiful room because it was homely. She never wanted to leave this house. Suddenly she began to pray that nothing would happen to cause her ever to leave it again, and Freddie. She put her fingers to her face. The swelling had gone down but her eyes were still discoloured and her cheeks a muddy yellow colour. The doctor had assured her only this morning that in a week or so's time her colour would be back to normal.

When a shadow passed the window she started, then let out a slow breath. As she did so she saw John pause, look in on her and wave, and she waved back. Yet the sight of him outside didn't bring her a feeling of security; she wanted someone near her; she had this fear of being left alone. She just stayed her hand from going to the little brass bell on the table and bringing in Mary or Jinny again and asking one of them to stay with her until Freddie came in. It was odd, but once Freddie came into the house this fear would be subdued; it seemed not to matter if he wasn't in the same room with her as long as he was somewhere about. . . .

It was just on two o'clock when Freddie came in, and she had to hide both her relief and her anxiety for she wanted to say, "Where have you been? What's kept you? You weren't in for dinner," almost like a nagging wife might. What she said was, "Hello, my dear. Have you had a busy morning?"

"Busy morning." He sat down on the edge of the couch, her hand tight in his. "You wouldn't believe it. It must be almost two hours ago when I left to come home when Hopper came dashing after me. You know the cottage that became vacant on the road out and we had it spruced up ready for the people going in tomorrow? You wouldn't believe it, but some of the scum from the lodging house settled themselves in there, fourteen of them and it's only got two little bedrooms and a sitting room and a kitchen and the attic in the roof. Four kids, four women, and six men, thieves and vagabonds the lot of them. Anyway, I didn't want to get the polis at them again as the bairns would have landed up in the workhouse and the rest in the House of Correction, where they'll surely land in any case. I threatened to burn them out if they didn't open up—they had barred the doors inside. Now the people can't move in tomorrow. It'll take another couple of days to get rid of the filth they've left. You wouldn't credit it. Animals are cleaner. Anyway, that's today finished, at least the working part. How are you?"

"Feeling much better; so much better when you're here, but. . . ."

"But what?" He took her other hand. "What's worrying you?"

"Oh, I can't really explain but I seem to be waiting for them to make some move, because they will make some move won't they, Freddie? I feel any minute that there'll be a visit from her solicitor or one of her influential friends. You know, she was always talking about the influential friends, but for the time I was there, I know it wasn't very long, but there never was one caller. And . . . and Marcel only ever had that one friend, Harry Benson; at least, I thought of him as that, not as a guard. I couldn't have known that."

"Well, my dear, it doesn't matter; they can do nothing further to you. You're not to think about any of them again. Now that's an order from the boss, as Mrs Musgrave would say, that upstart, big-headed individual who happens to be her son."

"She's a wonderful woman, your mother, Freddie, and you know, you've been very fortunate, you've had two wonderful women in your life."

"Yes"—he answered her solemnly—"you're right there. I've had two wonderful women in my life. And you know, I've still got two wonderful women in my life."

When she looked at him softly, he said, "But tell me, how is the second wonderful woman getting on with the new maid?"

"Oh, I think it will work out. I told her not so long ago that Mary needed a mother . . . needed mothering, and I think that touched the right chord. You know, some women are made to do mothering whether they are married or not. But strangely, Maggie wasn't. She was the Auntie, she could have been the sister. She wasn't a mother to you, was she? What was she really to you, Freddie?"

He bowed his head and looked to the side. He couldn't say to her, she was my first love. It was a love that superseded the natural love for my mother or a man's love such as I have for you. It was a love that we both recognized but daren't put a name to, because we didn't know a name that would fit it. And so, looking at her again, he answered simply, saying, "I can't put a name to the feeling I had for Maggie because I owe all I am to her."

There was a tap on the door and Mary entered, pushing a trolley on which was set tea things and, on the lower shelf, a standing meat pie cut into slices, bread and butter, scones, and a ginger cake. And when, looking at Belle, she said, "Will I pour, madam?" Freddie answered her, "No, I'll see to it, Mary," and she replied, "Very good, sir," dipped her knee and went out.

"What are you laughing at?" Belle now asked softly, as she watched Freddie pouring the tea. And shaking his head he said, "Sir, madam, and a bobbing knee, it takes some getting used to.

She set my breakfast in the dining room this morning. I wanted to say to her, 'Lass, I always have it in the kitchen. And sit yourself down with me.' But somehow I knew that would embarrass her. On the other hand though she wasn't a bit embarrassed to sit down with me ma. But then nobody could be embarrassed with me ma. . . ."

The tea over, they chatted and then Freddie said, "I'm going upstairs to have a good wash and a shave. Now I can no longer do it in the kitchen, that puts me out a bit, you know." He pulled a face at her. "This arrangement has its drawbacks."

As he was about to turn away, she said, "You don't speak of Tuesday," and he, pausing a moment, said, "There's a saying, 'Sufficient unto the day is the evil thereof.' "

"What if things go against you, Freddie? I wouldn't be able to. . . ."

"I'm not going to stand here and listen to that sort of thinking, madam. Nothing is going to go against me. My life has changed, you're in it, so nothing can go wrong." He smiled at her, then went out.

Fifteen minutes later, as he was putting on Maggie's last present to him, a smoking jacket, he heard a scream, followed by another. Before the second one had echoed away he was taking the stairs two at a time. But when he burst through the open door and into the sitting room it was to come to a skidding stop, for there, standing at the head of the couch, a gun in his hand, was Marcel Birkstead.

Freddie stood as if he had suddenly become embalmed, unable to move or speak for a moment, so great was his fear of that gun pointing at Belle's head. Then Birkstead spoke, or growled out, "I've come for my wife. If she comes with me she may live, if she stays she'll be dead. It's up to you."

Freddie had to lever his tongue backwards and forwards over the roof of his mouth before he could say, "If you shoot her, that'll be murder and you'll die too."

He had hardly finished the word when Birkstead said, "Well, there won't just be two of us there'll be three because I'll see that you go before me. Oh, yes, I'll see to that. There are six bullets in this gun; I can afford to miss three times when dealing with you."

As if staring at a snake, Freddie's eyes were fixed on the gun. Six bullets. He had heard about a revolver that didn't need reloading. A colt it was called, first used in America. But he imagined it being only a tall tale, a sailor bragging about the wonders of the New World.

The cry came from Belle now: her head was being pushed into the corner of the couch by Birkstead's other hand. "I'll go, Freddie, I'll go. Just . . . just let me go."

"You'll not go, not with this madman who should never have been let out of that asylum. . . ."

It seemed for a moment that the world had exploded in the side of Freddie's head. As he staggered he put his hand up to his ear and his hot blood gushed over it. Mingled with the sound of the explosion there was Belle's scream, and as his right hand moved out for support against the table to his side his fingers touched the cherub.

The cherub was a foot high lead statuette. The fat arms of the boy were extended upwards to support a shallow dish above his head. He had often wondered why Maggie liked it so much because, to his eye, there was no beauty about it; being made of lead, the colour was a dirty grey. And he had recalled the time she had gone for him when he had used it as a door stop.

It could be that the movement his body made in throwing it saved him from the next bullet which struck the glass cabinet behind him sending glass and china spraying the corner of the room.

The cherub caught Birkstead on the shoulder, and as his body swayed and the gun dropped from his hand, Freddie leaped over the distance; and then they were grappling together. The blood was spreading into his mouth and almost choking him, but he aimed to get his hands around Birkstead's throat. Birkstead, however, was a strongly built man and his strength was increased with his madness. One moment Freddie was gripping his neck, the next he himself was almost stunned as he hit the wall to the side of the fireplace. But only for a second, for with his fist he caught Birkstead on the chin. The blow seemed to halt him for a moment. Then Freddie was grappling with him again, but with a difference now, for although Birkstead's arms were about him, there was no response from them. But the dead weight of the man brought them both to the floor by the side of the fireplace. And there they lay perfectly still, both now covered in blood.

Belle was moaning, and it was as she dragged herself from

340

the couch that Mary came scampering up the room, crying, "Oh! madam. Are you all right? Oh my God!" She looked at the two prone figures on the floor, then said, "Has he . . . has he killed him?" She did not make it clear who had killed whom, but gabbled on, "Oh dear! When I first saw him I sent Roy for the polis and Mr John. Oh, miss, you'll fall."

Belle now pushed Mary away and lowered herself painfully onto her knees at the side of Freddie. He was lying with his shoulders on the rim of the steel fender. His head was hanging slightly to one side and the hand of one outstretched arm was cupping Birkstead's shoulder as if in the act of patting it.

"Freddie! Freddie! Please." Inwardly squirming as she was at the nearness of Birkstead, she went to put her arms about Freddie when he opened his eyes, blinked twice and made an effort to move. His left hand covering his lacerated ear, he made as if to withdraw his other arm from the twisted position in which it was lying. But at this he let out a low groan, and Mary said, "He's hurt it, miss, his arm. Let's get him round on the mat." And it was she who now put her sturdy arms around Freddie and eased him, amid his groans, onto the hearth rug. And there, pulling a cushion from the couch, she put it under his head while saying, "We'd better do something, madam, to try and stop the bleeding."

Belle had already thought of that for she had taken off her shoulder shawl and formed it into a soft wool pad. And now she gently pressed it onto the lacerated flesh, yet cringed as she did so. Then turning to Mary, she said, "The little table cloth, bring it here."

Mary ripped off the fancy cloth from the side table and then, folding it into four, tied it round Freddie's head in an endeavour to keep the pad in place. Another time he would have looked laughable like a child with the toothache.

"Get Ma . . . and John."

"It's all right, dear, it's all right. Mary's seen to that. Are you . . . you all right?" She knew it was a silly question to ask because he wasn't all right, there was something wrong with his arm. Thinking that she might ease it back by laying it gently across his stomach, she went to do this, but a cry through his clenched teeth checked her and he said, "Leave it. Leave it." Then his eyes wide now he looked at the prostrate figure lying against the end of the fender. The cloak that Birkstead had worn was lying in a

341

crumpled heap to the side of him, and the bottom of his face and his white cravat shirt and great coat were saturated with blood.

Following his gaze, Mary said, "Will I straighten him, sir?"

"No, no, leave him till they come."

It then seemed to all three of them that no one came for hours. But John was there within ten minutes, the police within fifteen, and both Jinny and the doctor arrived almost at the same time.

It was the policeman who, after looking at the position of Birkstead's head, said, "Better leave him till the doctor comes."

A minute later, the doctor raised Birkstead's head from the fender, then felt for the beat of his heart. He looked up first at the policeman, then at Freddie who was now seated at the end of the couch, and he said quietly, "He's dead." Then he pointed down to the three spikes that protruded from the steel rim. They were of practical use: the middle one was the largest; it was used for holding the two foot steel tongs in place; the other two supported a steel shovel and a hearth brush. The doctor pointed to the middle spike, saying flatly, "It seems to have penetrated his jugular vein."

They all became quiet until the policeman appeared about to question Freddie, only to be interrupted by the doctor, saying, "I'm afraid you'll have to wait for that, constable. I must get this man to the surgery, or most likely to the hospital if we want to save any part of his ear. And then his arm that's apparently broken in more places than one." And nodding at Freddie now, he said, "You're a very lucky man, another fraction and that bullet would have done its job." He pointed down the room now to the wall, saying to the policeman, "Don't touch anything there. Nor that." He was now pointing to the gun on the table. "A lot of people are going to be interested in that, for more reasons than one."

"What about the body, sir?" The officer was asking now, and the doctor replied, "Well, that's up your street, isn't it? It'll have to go to the prison mortuary. But your inspector will have to see it first. Then of course you'll have to inform his people. But you, sir," he addressed Freddie now. "Do you think you're able to make your way to my carriage?"

At the moment? Freddie didn't feel he could make his way any place. He wasn't in any pain, not from his ear or his arm, but a great weakness was enveloping him. He was aware that his mother was standing to the side of him and he had a great desire to lay his head against her waist because life seemed to be draining from him and he wanted her sturdy support. He knew that Belle was on the other side of him, but it wasn't to her he put out his hand, but to Jinny. And when she clasped it she said brokenly, "Oh, lad; you are an unlucky swine, aren't you?"

When they lifted him to his feet and guided him out of the house and down the path and into the doctor's carriage, the words kept repeating in his mind, "You are an unlucky swine, aren't you?" And just before he passed out altogether on the doctor's table he asked himself why she had said that because he had always been lucky. He supposed it was because no two people saw the same things in the same way.

20

The first day of the inquest was over, and they returned to the house, each and every one slightly bemused at the happenings in the court.

On both sides of the river it had been prophesied a foregone conclusion. The newspapers, too, had been of that opinion. When the incident happened it made front page reporting for two days; it was also the main topic of conversation in every inn and hotel: There he was again, that Freddie Musgrave in the news. And here and there it was recalled that it was odd but he had always been mixed up in shady business right from the time he had been a runner not the size of two pennorth of copper. Then of course he had got in with Maggie Hewitt, and you couldn't say that Maggie's business was as straight as a die, now could you? She didn't just exchange money for those foreigners on the boats, there was underhand stuff slipping backwards and forwards there, if you asked them. There was that business, too, not five minutes ago, of his being brought up in court and just saved from standing trial for pinching jewels from that Mr Gallagher, then murdering him. He had been cleared at the last minute, oh yes, but only up to a point for he had known all along that Maggie Hewitt had done it. Hadn't he stood and watched her? That was likely why she had sort of befriended him. He had probably blackmailed her in a sort of way because he was always a sharp young 'un.

And so the discussions went on. But what did they think about the day's do?

And yes, that's what they were saying in the sitting room, each one of them, What did they think about today's do?

Freddie was sitting between his mother and Belle on the

couch, and John asked, "Could a blow to the jaw kill a man as he said? Do you think it could, Freddie?"

"Well—" Freddie let out a long sigh before he answered, "His jaw was broken and the doctor confirmed a blow to a certain point along there could kill a man."

"But he had shot you beforehand, fully intending to kill you." Jinny's voice was loud. "You've only got one ear, lad; you'll always only have one ear. Your man pointed that out and said if he had gone just the slightest fraction further you wouldn't be here now to tell the tale. He meant to kill you, not once but twice. Look what happened to the second bullet. It seems to me daft, it really does." Her head wagging now, she looked at John, then towards Nancy who was seated at the opposite side of the fire, then went on, "If the blow had killed him it was in self-defence; so why couldn't they finish the day?"

Freddie put his hand on her knee and patted it slowly as he said, "Because it's a case, Ma, and that's how justice works, at least so I'm told. My solicitor man said to me, they've got to put up a front, and"—he gave a derisive laugh—"he was what was known as a gentleman and that old gizzard of a woman is rich and influential."

"Eeh! I thought I would die when I saw them helping her into the court. She's like nothing I've ever seen before on this earth." Jinny now leant forward and looked at Belle. "Does she do up like that every day?"

"Yes, Jinny. Yes, she does, and at night too."

"My God! It must take her all her time to put the paint on."

"She doesn't put it on," said Belle flatly; "her maid does, and washes her, and dresses her, and practically feeds her. But she is quite capable of doing all those things for herself. She toddled into court today, but the last time I saw her she marched out of the bedroom like a soldier."

They all looked at Belle now. Her face was as it had been once: the scars on her body had healed and so she felt no pain except in her mind; Birkstead was dead and yet he haunted her: whenever she looked at the hearth she saw him lying there, his eyes wide, staring at her, and the intervening weeks since that night had not erased his presence from her mind. She doubted if time ever would.

Like everyone else, she too thought that the verdict at the inquest would be a foregone conclusion. And it must be, it must.

So why were they going to allow his grandmama to speak tomorrow? What evidence could she give; she hadn't been there. And oh, how that woman hated her. When, with Miss Cummings on one side and Mr Grant on the other, they had helped her into the courtroom she had stopped and glared at her. And everyone in that packed place had noticed it.

Freddie squeezed her hand now, saying, "Look, let's forget about it until the morning at least. What about a drink, eh Ma? and not tea, or cocoa, or coffee."

Pulling herself up from the couch, Jinny said, "I hadn't any of those in mind meself."

John, now bending forward towards Freddie, asked him, "Who was the pock-marked woman you were talking to?"

"Oh, that was Connie. She used to be one of Gallagher's servants. I told you about them, you know."

"Aye, but you didn't say that she looked like that. Poor soul."

Yes, poor soul, but she was a good poor soul. She had said to him, "Freddie, if you want me, I'll get up on that stand and tell them of the things that he did when he was four, that was before that old dame took him away. There was the instance with the cat and the curling tongs. We had to put the cat down." And he had answered her, "Thanks, Connie. If things get into a tight corner, I don't see how they can, but you never know with that lot, I'll be glad to call on you." She had patted his arm and said, "You'll be all right, lad. It's a foregone conclusion."

That saying, "It's a foregone conclusion." Everybody was so sure. And he had been, too, until he had got on that stand today. My God! How that man twisted things. And his voice had been so soft, so kindly, but so insistent in repeating and repeating a simple question: When he was pushed against the wall by the man in question and he had struck out with his fist, what had happened then? Three times he told him what had happened, at least what he thought had happened. He thought that Birkstead had come at him, but then had seemed to fall on him, and they both went down to the floor. And that's all he remembered for some minutes.

But did he think the man in question had collapsed from the blow he had delivered? Or did he think he was about to attack him again?

He didn't know, it all happened so quickly.

346

But did he struggle any more with the man in question when he fell against him?

No, not as far as he could remember. They both fell, as he said, to the floor. And it must have been he himself had passed out for a moment when his arm snapped. And what was more, he had then added somewhat angrily, he was losing a great deal of blood which must have made him feel weak. In consequence, things weren't clear in his mind.

He had then been reprimanded by the coroner because he had almost bawled at the old girl's barrister, saying, what was clear in his mind was that the man in question, as he was called, was out to kill him. His first bullet had found its target but hadn't finished him, so then he had tried again. Could anything be more clear than that?

When he was almost yelling the last words the coroner had cried, "You will kindly answer the questions put to you as briefly as possible. You will have time enough later to give a description of your feelings."

Whose side were these people on? Birkstead had been out to kill him, wasn't it evident to them all? Why were they keeping on? His solicitor had been against his allowing himself to be questioned, saying that the case against him in the first place was too complicated, being that it was suggesting he had arranged the abduction of his ward, Birkstead's wife. So it could be suggested the shooting was instigated by the act of the abduction. This, of course, was what had to be decided: whether Birkstead had died from the blow inflicted by the perpetrator of the abduction or by accidentally falling on a spike on the end of a steel fender.

So what if it was decided that Birkstead had died from the blow he delivered him, and what if they tried to prove that he had a hand in abducting his ward from her husband? Would they exonerate Birkstead for aiming to kill him?

He could give himself no answer because he had lost faith in justice. And, as his solicitor had pointed out, he still had to face a charge of being an accessory to the murder of Gallagher, which might have been understandable in the boy that he was when he witnessed the act, but not in the man that had withheld this knowledge.

John and Nancy had left the room with their mother, and

now he turned to Belle and, putting his arm about her, drew her head on to his shoulder, saying, "This time tomorrow night it should be all over."

"What if it isn't, Freddie? I wasn't fearful this morning for the outcome, but now I am."

"Well, if it isn't, it isn't. That's all about it. I don't think they can hang me nor put me away for life. I don't think they can put me away at all." He now looked away from her towards the fire and stopped himself from adding, At least that's what I thought this morning, but, like you, I'm not so sure now.

"Freddie. I love you so and I can't bear the thought of. . . ."

"Now be quiet. There's no thoughts to bear on that point, just let's not think about it. I tell you what, I've decided I need a holiday and you certainly do. So, tomorrow night we will sit here and plan where we are going. But of course," he lifted her chin up towards him, "that is after . . . the wedding ceremony."

She drew herself gently from him, but held on to his hand and in a low voice she said, "It's the first time you have mentioned marriage. You have said you loved me, oh many times, but you have never said we would be married."

"Well now I'm saying it. I didn't intend to until after all this business was over and you were really free, and me too. Oh yes, and me too. But now I say, Miss Belle Hewitt, *would* you *like* to be Freddie Musgrave's wife? But mind"—he smiled—"just if you'd like to be."

"Freddie. Oh, Freddie don't joke about it. I dream about being Freddie Musgrave's wife. I long to be Freddie Musgrave's wife. And if I can't be Freddie Musgrave's wife I won't be anyone's wife again. Oh, no, never again. But, Freddie, you . . . you won't be getting the girl that I once was. The girl that just a short while ago used to prance around this house, because I know I will never feel young again. I'm not yet twenty, but youth seems to have left me. I feel old inside myself as if in a matter of weeks I had run the whole gamut of life and it had left me empty except for my love for you. But it's a different love, I must tell you this, quite a different love. It's no longer gay, and joyful. . . ."

When the words seemed to stick in her throat he drew her gently into his arms and said, "I can promise you one thing and you've got to believe me, this feeling will pass. You'll be young and gay again, I'll see to it, and respected and looked up to, I promise you that too. Oh yes, you will, don't shake your head.

Once this is over we'll start a new life, a really new life. Just trust me."

It was two o'clock the following afternoon when those last words of Freddie's returned to Belle's mind and she said to herself, "You will be respected and looked up to," because now the court was all ears listening to that dreadful old woman evading the barrister's questions and gabbling on: "My grandson had a dreadful time with her. He was so patient. But what will a husband do when another man is flaunted to his face. The night he smacked her was because she deliberately bragged about her affection for the fellow Musgrave. That he smacked her face, yes, he admitted to me, but the flagellation, that is all nonsense. She did that to herself. I ask you, a woman who would allow pictures to be taken of her naked body to expose weals is not a proper person. And if she is capable of doing that she is capable, in the mind of any decent person, of preparing herself for those pictures to be taken. She did this in order to blacken my grandson."

The barrister was looking downwards, the coroner was looking at his desk, that was until the voice, high pitched now, almost at a scream, rang through the court and denying the frailty of the stance and looks: "She's killed my beloved boy! He was all I had in the world. She dares to blacken him and say he's of unsound mind. She's a whore, a whore, consorting from a child with her supposed guardian."

The coroner called, "Order! Order!" then motioned to her barrister to get rid of his witness. But the witness was now gripping the front rail of the box and was addressing him pointedly: "You have got to jail him for life, for life. That blow killed my darling grandson. You must do this. You see, I knew your father, I dined with him a number of times. I recall him very well because he never waited for his port. . . ."

She was being helped forcibly out, but still she went on, "He had it with his meal. Couldn't wait till after dinner. Very odd. Very odd."

Freddie's solicitor, sitting on the bench to his left, leaned across and said, "I should imagine it wasn't only from his paternal side that the mania came, if you ask me."

Two more people were questioned and both by Freddie's barrister. The first was a Mr James Fuller. He was asked his

349

relationship with Mrs Birkstead and her grandson. He was Mrs Birkstead's nephew and her grandson's half cousin.

What did he know of the deceased?

What he knew of the deceased caught the whole attention of the court. He went through his association with him from when, at ten years old, his grandmother took him from the ancestral home to live in The Towers, a house situated on the outskirts of South Shields. Then in later years when it was obvious he was about to have one of his spasms his aunt would call upon him to accompany Birkstead to Havensford Meade, which to his mind was a private asylum. Sometimes he would stay for only a week or two, but other times his stay might go into months.

The barrister now asked him if, to his knowledge, Birkstead was ever certified? And the answer was, No; his grandmother did everything in her power to prevent this. He went on to say that he had for some time now washed his hands of both of them and his aunt had engaged a man of good quality to act as a sort of warder while posing as a friend. They lived together in a small house in the city.

The barrister thanked Mr Fuller; then the next man was called. His name, he said, was Malcolm Villiers.

The barrister now said, "You call yourself a doctor. Are you a doctor?"

"Not in the medical sense of the word. I deal in herbs and natural medicine."

"Do you own a house that is run as a private asylum?"

"I own a house," the man said, "but it is not run as a private asylum, but for guests suffering from nerves."

The barrister now asked if he kept a record of the number of times guests visited him to be cured of their nerves; and after hesitating, he said he kept such a record.

Then how many times had Mr Marcel Birkstead been on such visits to his house?

He wasn't quite sure.

"Come come. You were asked to have this information ready. How many times, I repeat, did Mr Birkstead visit you?"

"Thirty-two."

"Thirty-two visits for nerves! Over what period of time?"

"Eleven years."

"And during any one of these periods did you have to restrain him?"

The man stared down at the barrister; then after a moment he replied, "Not restrained, just treatment with herbs."

"What was the longest period he stayed with you?"

"Nine months."

The barrister now turned from the box and, looking at the coroner and then the jury, he repeated, "Nine months for treatment with herbs." He then turned to the man again and, smiling gently, said, "That will be all." . . .

Freddie had his eyes now fixed on the coroner. He was summing up and if his last words had been, "I sentence you to ten years imprisonment," it couldn't have had a greater effect than when he finished, "I am recommending to the jury that there is no case to answer here. You Frederick Musgrave acted entirely in self-defence, therefore you can leave this court without any feeling of guilt."

He rose, the clerks and the usher rose, the court rose, then the family were around him. But he could make no answer to their relieved greetings, not even to Belle, for he felt he could be violently sick at any moment.

In the hallway he was surrounded by reporters and well-wishers. People he didn't know wanted to shake his hand, was he not famous? or infamous? whichever way you looked at it. By! with the way things had gone in there, with that old girl's barrister, he could have been brought up for murder.

His solicitor and barrister managed to extricate him from the crowd and his family and lead him into a small room. And there his solicitor did not congratulate him on the verdict, but reminded him: "You know, you'll be appearing here again in three days time; and I don't know if things will run so smoothly then for you, because, let me tell you, there are some disappointed officials in that courtroom. They were hoping this was just the beginning of your case. You were fortunate to get Mr Owen."

Knowing that this man's bill would be large enough already, Freddie chipped him: "Well, don't tell me you were one of them," at which the barrister put his head back and laughed: "It sounded so, didn't it?" he said.

Freddie looked at the man, this important man, the man who had the power to sway a case one way or the other and at this moment he looked so ordinary and sounded so ordinary, more so than the solicitor, and his voice and words were reassuring when he said, "Don't worry about the other business. They can't do anything. I've learned of all the ins and outs of the case." He laughed again now, saying, "By! you've had some experiences, haven't you? Have you ever thought of trying your hand at writing a book?"

"Writing a book? Me? Huh! That'll be the day. All I want, sir, is to get back home and live a quiet life out of the limelight. Oh, aye, out of the limelight. So if you want to read adventure, sir, there's always Mr Dickens or Wilkie Collins, or men like them."

"You read them?"

"Yes." Freddie's voice was flat. "Them and many more." Then he smiled at the man, saying, "And I'll keep it at that. But thank you for what you have done, sir."

The man now leant towards him and in a stage whisper he said, "Your note of hand will be all the thanks I need; I never do anything for love."

Freddie now actually laughed a deep, deep, laugh. He was a good fellow, he liked him. He now turned to his solicitor, saying, "Well, see you on Monday, Mr Roland."

And then he left to go home and start his new life with Belle, for that's what he wanted, all he had ever dreamed about, all that he craved for, a life with Belle, a life with Belle all down the years that were left to him: Belle by his side in the days and enfolded in his arms at night until death did they part.

to _____

from _____

Gratitude Works

*Each page has its own beautiful expression that gives
pause to reflect on blessings in one's life, big and small,
that we often take for granted. It's artfully and thoughtfully
presented, and has appeal for everyone.* — H. D.

*Each passage I read triggers a story from my past and
brings back memories.* — M. K.

Whenever I pick up the book, it's difficult to put down. — D. H.

*I like so much the ordinary things in life that you mention
in your book as being worthy of gratitude.* — J. O.

*It is very transparent and beautiful, something I seldom think
about. Very feminine, soft and warm. Full of ideals, bright
hopes and dreams. And courage. Old fashioned and clean
and bright as white kitchen curtains. Your poetry is the kind
of poetry I like because it tells me so much how you feel
about things from the heart. This is where you have found
a few answers, in enjoying what God has given you, and
not in lamenting for what you have not.* — R. D.

Gratitude Works

Christina,
Let gratitude
bring you joy.
Eileen Bodoh

Katherine Scheer

Gratitude Works

Open Your Heart to Love

Katherine Scherer & Eileen Bodoh

Cover and page design by Jack White Design, Inc. of Milwaukee, Wisconsin.

Editing by B. Kim Parsons of Milwaukee, Wisconsin.

Published by K & E Innovations LLP
6099 Oakwood Lane, W.
Greendale, Wisconsin 53129
414-421-8130

Website: gratitudeworks.com

Library of Congress Control Number 2003099770

ISBN 0-9748550-0-6

Printed in the United States of America, Second Edition.

Originally published by Trafford Publishing,
ISBN 1-4120-0147-1; 2003

Gratitude Works is available at special discounts for fundraising and charitable organizations when purchased in quantities. Contact the authors for details.

Appreciations

We would like to acknowledge and express our gratitude to:

Dr. Gisela Sannar, for her generosity and unconditional love.

Jo McReynolds Blochowiak, for encouragement to begin our work.

B. Kim Parsons, for her caring and timely editing.

Jack White and Bob Tambellini, for their incredible design work.

Robert Kalupa, for his ongoing patience.

Mary Sidello, for her creative assistance.

And the many teachers on our path of healing who have had a profound influence on our lives.

Themes

January	Reflection
February	Heart
March	Balance
April	Growth
May	Beauty
June	Love
July	Nature
August	Fun
September	Transition
October	Harvest
November	Thanksgiving
December	Gifts

Introduction

Gratitude Works is an easy way to access the power of counting our blessings. Through the eyes of gratitude we open our hearts and bring joy into our lives. There is an awesome force in the universe that steers the stars and guides the planets. We marvel at the wonders in our world and sometimes question where they all come from. It is said that we already have everything we need. Everything has been given and nothing is expected in return. Everything is a gift! What is often missing is our appreciation for it. Our inner world of thought creates our outer world. Words of thanks can change our thoughts, and by changing our thoughts, we can change our lives.

Gratitude Works is more than a pretty book to set on the shelf—it's a book to be used. This collection of three hundred and sixty-five short stanzas explores what we have to be grateful for in our lives. Each day focuses on one main thought, and the four lines that follow expand on that thought. The book can be read from beginning to end or opened at any page and used as a daily guide. It takes you through the seasons of the year month by month and inspires you to think of the things in your own life that you are grateful for.

Gratitude Works helps us stay in the present moment by being grateful for what we have now rather than dwelling on the past or dreaming into the future. It helps us learn to stop taking so much for granted. It reminds us to give thanks before our prayers are answered knowing that the blessings will come. When we realize how much there is to be thankful for and recognize the ways we are already blessed, we feel closer to God. When we feel gratitude for each moment, we enrich our souls.

Everything is an opportunity for us to expand, to learn, to grow, and to love. We hope the gratitudes we've written resonate with your life and prompt you to remember to be thankful. We hope being grateful for one thing leads to two and three and more until it ripples out and enhances your whole life with deeper meaning. We hope gratitude speaks to you and touches your soul. The world is rich when it's seen through the eyes of gratitude!

Katherine Scherer
& Eileen Bodoh

*May you begin each day
in the spirit of Gratitude*

*With Oceans of Love
and a kiss on each wave.*

January
Reflection

A sound wave, an image, a dazzling light
Opening the mind to new insight,
Musing thoughts remind me of when
Counting our blessings was so "in."

Keep your eye on higher things
Watching love's beauty spread its wings,
Live in the moment, be in the present—
Life is a reflection of the *I AM*.

I am so *Grateful*

for gratitude, a magical magnet.

A natural expression of a loving heart,
The power of gratitude recharges our souls,
In giving thanks we help heal the world
And increase our abundance of blessings
  unknown.

January 1

I am so *Grateful*

for another 24 hours.

*G*reeting each day as though it were the first,

God's presence is felt when the light shines in,

Looking in the mirror I like who I see

And affirm to live as fully as I can.

January 2

I am so *Grateful*

for simple pleasures of my senses.

My eyes that allow me to see
Snow-capped mountains glistening in the sun,
My ears that allow me to hear
Thundering wild horses as they run.

January 3

I am so *Grateful*

for valuing my time.

First I ask, do I spend my time well?
Or have I wasted it being envious of others?
Pausing to listen, observe and see—
I let go of the past and set myself free.

January 4

I am so

Grateful

for being open to feelings.

Good or bad, they are sure guides,
A barometer to measure what's going on inside,
Because our thinking determines our feelings,
It's best we learn how to direct our thoughts.

January 5

I am so *Grateful*

for an orderly routine.

Tiny messes are picked up early,
Cleanup happens before the house is too dirty,
Fully stocked cupboards store our goods,
And washing and ironing are done on time.

January 6

I am so *Grateful*

for creating with minimal effort.

A home is adorned with mementos from
    vacations,
A room is made over without spending a fortune,
What started as a hobby turns into a
    thriving business,
And Sunday leftovers become Monday's lunch.

January 7

I am so *Grateful*

for children with exceptional talent.

They skip grades with ease and are coordinated
    in sports,
They play musical instruments without learning
    to read notes,
Their open minds permit God to come through—
These humble peacemakers inspire the world.

January 8

I am so *Grateful*

for close friendships that continue to grow.

Best friends confide their most intimate thoughts,
Communicating to each other that it's okay
    to disagree,
They offer support for the dreams that they share,
And elevate each other's spirits when one is
    feeling down.

January 9

I am so *Grateful*

for the willpower to choose wisely.

Selecting nutritious foods when available,
Sitting in no smoking areas when eating out,
Using common sense when alcohol is served,
And exercising regularly for strength and
relaxation.

January 10

I am so *Grateful*

for a private space for reflection.

A corner of the room is designated as sacred,
A library is filled with meaningful books,
Aromatherapy candles glow in the stillness,
And an indoor fountain creates a peaceful mood.

January 11

I am so *Grateful*

for spiritual connections.

A mother is jubilant after giving birth,
A newborn infant cries its first breath,
Every day the presence of a miracle unfolds
Intricately uniting body, mind, and spirit.

January 12

I am *so* *Grateful*

for important people in my life.

Feeling loved by a significant other,
An uncle, an aunt, a sister or brother,
Blessed with parents and children who are there,
Along with true friends who show that they care.

January 13

I am so *Grateful*

for simpler times.

*S*tores were closed on Sundays,
TV shows seemed to make more sense,
Family members spent ample time with
    each other,
And people were valued more than things.

January 14

I am so *Grateful*

for memories of winter play.

We built snowmen with dark eyes of coal,
Swished angels in our neighbor's snow,
Skated perfect figure eights on the frozen lagoon,
And flew our toboggans down the biggest
   hill around.

January 15

I am so *Grateful*

for being remembered when ill.

The hospital room is filled with colorful flowers,
Timely visits are shared with family and friends,
Cards with genuine thoughts are sent by
    well-wishers
Along with a gift certificate to enjoy when I'm well.

January 16

I am so *Grateful*

for the healing power of laughter.

Victor Borge combined classical music with
    comedy for belly laughs,
Irma Bombeck's down-to-earth humor left us
    in stitches,
Norman Cousins wrote about using laughter
    as good medicine,
And Dr. Patch Adams' "clowning" around helped
    sick children heal.

January 17

I am so *Grateful*

for meeting challenges head-on.

We see mistakes as learning experiences
in disguise
And reach turning points in times of crisis,
We find serenity in the midst of turmoil—
It's not what happens *to* us, but what we
make of it that counts.

January 18

I am so *Grateful*

for messages from within.

Meaningful dreams stir up a memory,
A passage in a book is seen as a message,
An ache in the body alerts us to slow down,
And hearts pound when we fall in love.

January 19

I am so *Grateful*

for a lazy morning on a cold winter's day.

Snuggling up in flannel pajamas,
Thick fuzzy slippers cuddle my feet,
The icy wind rattles my window
As I lose myself in a gripping mystery.

January 20

I am so *Grateful*

for learning through board games.

*M*onopoly teaches us about owning property,
There's attack and retreat in a good game
    of chess,
Scrabble challenges our ability to spell,
And skills of deduction are tested in Clue.

January 21

I am so *Grateful*

for little things that matter.

Whether it's a shoulder to cry on
Or consoling words from another,
A great big bear hug or a soothing foot rub,
The smallest things make the biggest difference.

January 22

I am so *Grateful*

for time alone.

I schedule weekly dates with myself,
Vigorous walks help clear my mind,
Spending time in deep introspection
Prepares me to enjoy my own company.

January 23

I am so *Grateful*

for pursuing my interests.

Crocheting an afghan or knitting a sweater,
Mastering a language that is foreign to me,
Learning to dance a difficult step—
Experiences like these make my life rich.

January 24

I am so *Grateful*
for winter projects.

Organizing old photos in a new picture album,
Repotting plants that have become root bound,
Renewing my passport before it expires—
These simple chores become labors of love.

January 25

I am so *Grateful*

for feeling my feelings.

Crying the sadness,
Ranting the anger,
Shaking the fear,
And laughing the joy.

January 26

I am so *Grateful*

for living by my own standards.

No longer looking to others for validation
I expend my energies on what I believe in,
Accepting people for who they are
Makes my life much happier for me.

January 27

I am so *Grateful*

for a winter cruise.

Visiting ports of call bathed in warm tropical air,
Satisfying a hearty appetite at the captain's table,
Savoring a sentimental kiss on a moonlit night,
And a chocolate on my pillow—how sweet it is!

January 28

I am so *Grateful*

for a favorite beach.

Listening to waves gently breaking on shore,
Collecting delicate seashells the ocean left behind,
Squishing our toes in the warm, wet sand,
Walking miles and miles on this sun-soaked land.

January 29

I am so *Grateful*

for perking myself up.

Singing about sunshine makes me shine inside,
When I smile others seem to be smiling too,
Making others happy is what I try to do,
Giving back the joy that's been given to me.

January 30

I am so *Grateful*

for plain and truthful sayings.

Cheerfully saying, "Don't worry, be happy,"
Reflecting on, "It's a blessing in disguise,"
Suprisingly, "It's a small world after all,"
And, "Today is the first day of the rest of your life."

January 31

February
Heart

At the center of our innermost being
Heartache occurs, courage emerges,
Intellect directs with reassuring words,
Hearts soften, compassion stirs.

The longest journey with the shortest distance
Surrender head to heart, master resistance,
Make loving and giving an accomplished art
Become one song, one beating heart.

I am so *Grateful*

for caring people.

Always asking, how may I serve?
They've learned to give without taking credit,
Allowing what comes to come through the heart,
Changing something less into something more.

February 1

I am so *Grateful*

for love that expects nothing in return.

A baby's diaper is changed time and again,
Nurses cool the fever of a sick person,
A few dollars are given to a beggar on
   the street,
And people are seen through the eyes
   of compassion.

February 2

I am so *Grateful*

for tucking my children into bed.

Hearing a favorite bedtime story every night,
They cuddle their teddy bears with all their might,
Prayers are said to keep everyone safe,
And a comforting lullaby carries them to sleep.

February 3

I am so *Grateful*

for experiences of first love.

Dreamy-eyed glances say, "I love you,"
Goosebumps are felt when first they touch,
A dozen pink roses mark the beginning
Of couples embracing in unending love.

February 4

I am so *Grateful*

for heart-warming recollections.

The anticipation of a honeymoon destination,
And the thrill of holding a firstborn child,
A grandson receiving his college degree
Who just yesterday wobbled through his
    first step.

February 5

I am so *Grateful*

for an unruffled snowfall.

God blessed our city overnight
With a gentle hush of fluffy white,
Through wide-eyed wonder and glad surprise
Each one seems like it was the first.

February 6

I am so *Grateful*

for evenings in front of the fireplace.

Warming my body after a long day of skiing,
A mug of hot cocoa soothes my insides,
Charmed by the sound of crackling logs burning
And stories by grandfather of his early days.

February 7

I am so *Grateful*

for modern conveniences.

Breadmakers permeate the atmosphere with
    pleasing scents,
Microwaves warm food in a matter of seconds,
Hot pads and trivets protect a vulnerable spot,
And a teakettle sings when the water is hot.

February 8

I am *so* *Grateful*

for the world of books.

Writers toil at their art with devotion,
Libraries lend from their vast collections,
Just about everything can be learned from
    a book,
And it all began with, "See Spot run. Look
    Jane look."

February 9

I am so *Grateful*

for stolen moments.

Pushing the snooze alarm gives me an extra
    ten minutes,
And I finish a novel on the train ride to work,
While waiting for an appointment I catch
    a few winks,
And offer a short prayer on an afternoon break.

February 10

I am so *Grateful*

for heating up the kitchen.

Time is spared for whipping up goodies,
A creamy pudding or sugar cookies,
A steaming tin of muffins just out of the oven—
Blessed on this day with a little bit of heaven.

February 11

I am so *Grateful*

for oldies but goodies.

Bing and Bob traveled the road to nowhere,
Fred and Ginger were dancing everywhere,
Elvis Presley, was the *king* of rock and roll,
And shortly after, Beatlemania stole the show.

February 12

I am *so* *Grateful*

for live performances.

*D*ancers in unison are precise in formation,
There's a systematic rhythm in tap, tap, tap,
An a cappella choir sings in perfect harmony,
And a tricky magician holds an audience
spellbound.

February 13

I am so *Grateful*

for taking responsibility for myself.

Sometimes I've caught myself acting cocky,
And bragging often seemed to suffice,
Soon after noticing, I empowered myself,
And made a decision to change for the better.

February 14

I am so *Grateful*

for discovering my creativity.

Creating a treasure map uncovers hidden
 interests,
Drawing and painting what I feel is revealing,
Journaling on paper helps me become unstuck
And moves me to live from the inside out.

February 15

I am so *Grateful*

for the vision of our forefathers.

With foresight, they drafted the Declaration
of Independence,
With resolve and hope our Constitution
was authored,
Their serious efforts secured our freedom—
And documented ideals we believe in today.

February 16

I am so *Grateful*

for annual traditions.

Heart-shaped boxes enclose a perfect Valentine
gift,
Cleverly hidden, colored eggs add eagerness to
an Easter hunt,
Carved pumpkins glow hauntingly in the dark
on Halloween,
And mountains of beautiful roses float by on
New Year's Day.

February 17

I am so *Grateful*

for feeling content.

Waking up to the peace and quiet of the
early morn,
Today there's absolutely nothing on my agenda,
I spend my time in a tub full of bubbles
Giving no worry to yesterday or the next
day coming.

February 18

I am so *Grateful*

for humor in my day.

Playing an amusing tape while driving along,
Remembering a time when I wore shoes that
   didn't match,
Musing over those old "knock knock" jokes—
Thinking to myself, "Did I laugh enough today?"

February 19

I am so *Grateful*

for money saved for a rainy day.

A new furnace can be purchased if the old
   one fails,
The car can be fixed if it suddenly stops running,
The vet can be paid if a pet requires treatment,
And I can take time off just because I want to.

February 20

I am so *Grateful*

for free choice in America.

Whether it's selecting where I want to live
Or speaking up for what I believe in,
It's a privilege to worship at the church of my
    choice
And know that my vote counts in political
    elections.

February 21

I am so *Grateful*

for having it my way.

*M*oney is refunded for an item returned,
A parking spot is available in front of the store,
The catalog items I ordered are in stock,
And the dress that I love is the perfect fit.

February 22

I am so *Grateful*

for gracious treatment.

*B*eing served breakfast in bed on a wedding
   anniversary,
Unexpectedly, a friend picks up the check at lunch,
A casserole is delivered on the first day home
   following surgery,
And a neighbor listens to my story with an
   understanding heart.

February 23

I am so *Grateful*

for endearing kinship.

Husbands and wives set the example
For sisters and brothers to get along well,
Sons and daughters regard their parents highly
And use what they learn at home in the outside
world.

February 24

I am so *Grateful*

for the option of adoption.

Placing an unborn child into an unfamiliar home,
A birth parent makes an enormous sacrifice,
In loving so much she decides to let go,
She faces the toughest choice a mother
can make.

February 25

I am so *Grateful*

for the power of song.

*G*ondoliers serenade and romance escalates,
Spiritual lyrics instill inner strength,
Movie sound tracks brighten ordinary days,
And hymns communicate hope for eternal peace.

February 26

I am so *Grateful*

for ancient wisdom to ponder.

Biblical stories find Jesus teaching with parables,
Rumi explores the mystery of union with the divine,
The Torah and Bhagavad Gita, tho centuries old,
Underscore a lasting love more valuable than gold.

February 27

I am so *Grateful*

for being true to myself.

I measure my life in good deeds done,
Instead of how many years I've lived,
I live from my heart instead of my head,
Giving heed to the genius that lies within.

February 28

March
Balance

A life in balance, a desired effect,
Stability and composure lead to peace,
Unity, harmony, and simplicity in proportion
Make life smoother without question.

Thoughts and ideas float in our minds,
Creativity abounds, feelings combine,
A deep inner strength is gained through adversity,
Sound decisions and choices bring order to chaos.

I am so *Grateful*

for practicing mindfulness.

Relaxing and going with the flow,
Cherishing each ordinary moment,
Less worrying about what everyone else thinks,
Enjoying the process without being attached
    to the outcome.

March 1

I am so *Grateful*

for energy shifting techniques.

Graceful movements of Tai Chi reduce our speed,
Balancing the Chakras increases productivity,
Yoga breathing promotes deep relaxation,
And Sweat Lodges encourage purification and
    healing.

March 2

I am so *Grateful*

for means to calm my spirit.

Reading stanzas by a favorite poet,
Or quietly reflecting on current blessings,
Deep meditation lures me to solace
And an overshadowing awareness of lasting
peace.

March 3

I am so *Grateful*

for concepts of healthy living.

Forming a smile relaxes hundreds of muscles,
Anger used as fuel spends energy in a positive
   direction,
With an open mind we learn something new
   every day,
And exercise is the number one remedy for
   staying young.

March 4

I am so *Grateful*

for a happy-go-lucky disposition.

By choosing to see the brighter side of life
A positive outlook is ever present,
It's nothing more than a balancing act
And a trick keeping all the balls in the air.

March 5

I am so *Grateful*

for completing household tasks.

Furniture polished to a brilliant shine,
Clothes pressed for a neat, clean look,
Closets cleared out, getting rid of clutter,
Ah, simple things put our lives in order!

March 6

I am so *Grateful*

for breaking up daily routines.

Sleeping in till noon on a workday morning,
Or taking a vacation day in the middle of
   the week,
Going out shopping with no thought of time,
And having dessert first instead of waiting
   till after dinner.

March 7

I am so *Grateful*

for easy ways to enhance health.

Taking the stairs gains automatic fitness,
Parking the car in the farthest row forces a walk,
Avoiding unhealthy snacks maintains a good
    weight,
And refusing to sweat the small stuff eliminates
    worry.

March 8

I am so *Grateful*

for pampering at the spa.

A warm Jacuzzi loosens my muscles,
My body feels smooth after a massage with oils,
It's trendy to have a manicure and a pedicure—
It's about time that I splurge on myself!

March 9

I am *so* *Grateful*

for communication skills.

*S*tating the truth is healthier than holding it in
Yet it is wise to think twice before talking out
   of turn,
Say what you mean and mean what you say
Yet have consideration for another's point of view.

March 10

I am so *Grateful*

for team effort on the job.

Compliments and praise serve a meaningful
    purpose,
Associates work together in harmony and peace,
Being appreciated and valued for the work that
    is done
Conveys a feeling of accomplishment to everyone.

March 11

I am so *Grateful*

for special needs therapists.

They exercise composure with each individual
And explain situations in understandable ways,
They raise confidence without personal
    expectations,
And cheer on every attempted feat.

March 12

I am so *Grateful*

for the "Mozart Effect."

A remarkable phenomenon discovered through
   research,
Particular sounds, tones, and rhythms have their
   own power,
Known to strengthen the mind and rest the spirit,
Musical therapists use it for healing.

March 13

I am so *Grateful*
for workouts.

Treadmills keep going as we pound down
    the miles,
Jump ropes and trampolines give us a bounce,
Steam rooms and saunas sweat off excess
    pounds
After swimming laps, going round and round.

March 14

I am so *Grateful*

for toiletries.

Sweet-smelling soap cleanses the body,
Minty toothpaste freshens the breath,
Shampoo leaves hair shiny and clean,
And moisturizing lotions soften the skin.

March 15

I am so *Grateful*

for easing boredom on a rainy day.

I view black and white movies one after another,
And set the thousandth piece in my picture
    puzzle,
Hours fly by with an old friend on the phone,
And homemade soup slowly simmers on
    the stove.

March 16

I am so *Grateful*

for old photos.

Wedding pictures reveal youthful hearts,
Wholesome smiles, how the children have grown,
Family get-togethers featured pot luck sprees,
And road trip scenery sparks a memory.

March 17

I am so *Grateful*

for St. Patrick's Day.

Relishing root soup, soda bread and Irish stew,
Tender corned beef and cabbage, too,
Drinking spirits of cheer in green beer,
And kicking up heels to a fiddler's tune.

March 18

I am so *Grateful*

for honoring the "child" in me.

Eating all the brownies my heart desires,
Or teasing a kitten with a ball of string,
Smiling at puppies through the window of a
pet store,
And having a fit of giggles over something silly.

March 19

I am so *Grateful*

for the ease of doing laundry.

Hampers and baskets make sorting easy,
An automatic washer does all the work,
Soap and fabric softeners aid in the process
Before the automatic dryer finishes the job.

March 20

I am *so* *Grateful*

for unsolicited assistance.

A young man carries my groceries to the car,
A friend offers to drive on a weekend jaunt,
A door is held open when my arms are full—
These welcome acts hint at man's innate
goodness.

March 21

I am so *Grateful*

for feeling unconfined.

Dancing freely around the house,
Or skipping merrily down the street,
Acting footloose and fancy free,
Marching to the beat of my very own drum.

March 22

I am so *Grateful*

for the distraction of fantasy.

Dreaming of becoming an instant millionaire
Or an overnight movie star receiving an Oscar,
Maybe a financial guru revealing market winners,
Or an Olympic athlete receiving a gold medal.

March 23

I am so *Grateful*

for preserving our precious land.

*W*e conserve water when a shortage is
    threatened,
And place recyclables in marked containers,
We refrain from littering and pick up debris,
And join in community improvement projects.

March 24

I am so *Grateful*

for roadside relief.

A cell phone quickens my call for help,
A passing motorist stops to light a flare,
The car blanket warms me during the wait
For the flashing lights of the arriving tow truck.

March 25

I am so *Grateful*

for improved conditions for
the handicapped.

Motorized carts make shopping easier at the
grocery store,
Vans and autos are custom designed when
needed,
Accommodating bathroom facilities are available
everywhere,
And slopes at curbs allow wheelchairs to pass
with ease.

March 26

I am so *Grateful*

for committed activists.

Protesting injustice by standing up for a worthy
   cause,
Writing congressmen about important issues,
Volunteering time to organizations that need help—
Their actions are making an impact in our world.

March 27

I am so *Grateful*

for handicraft classes.

Sewing handmade quilts from scratch,
Painting my first tree with acrylics,
Writing in the ancient art form of calligraphy,
And wallpapering made easy, one, two, three.

March 28

I am so *Grateful*

for an evening at home.

Winning at solitaire is easy on the computer,
Albert Einstein's biography fills my head,
I play an old movie while resting in bed,
And munch hot buttered popcorn as my snack
    for tonight.

March 29

I am so *Grateful*

for the "good stuff" life is made up of.

Receiving an unexpected pay raise at work,
Running into an old acquaintance by chance,
Throwing a Frisbee for my dog on the run,
And sending flowers to a friend for no reason.

March 30

I am so *Grateful*

for the powerful effects of laughter.

Acting as a tonic and lightening our mental
   outlook,
Hearty laughs are contagious, a joyful approach
   to life,
By easing pain and benefiting the immune system
Laughter gives us the boost of energy we need.

March 31

April
Growth

Growing, growing, an ongoing process,
Seeds spring up, development evolves,
Surging, swelling, rising, increasing,
The love of life is never ceasing.

The human episode of innocent offspring
Silently expanding to arrive at full stature,
Physical, emotional, mental, spiritual—
This growing experience is surely a miracle.

I am so *Grateful*

for the rebirth of nature.

Icicles melt and ice-bound streams begin to flow,
A crocus peeps out through melting snow,
A fine tapestry of ivy creeps along a stone wall,
And days grow longer in this loveliest of seasons.

April 1

I am so *Grateful*

for trees.

Some bloom with flowers and bear edible fruits,
Others shade our earth and protect us from
    the sun,
They nest our birds until baby's first flight,
And provide plenty of paper for newspapers, write?

April 2

I am so *Grateful*

for spring waking up all over.

Gardens erupt even though it's cool,
Soaking rains moisten and nourish the flowers,
Bees carry pollen from one to the other,
And dewdrops twinkle in the morning silence.

April 3

I am so *Grateful*

for being open to change.

Embracing new ideas as they come my way,
Letting go of notions that don't seem to fit,
Praying for honesty, openness, and willingness,
And empowerment to deepen, heal, and create.

April 4

I am so *Grateful*

for spiritual practices.

Walking the sacred spiral of the labyrinth
Or participating in gentle, invigorating yoga
Or drumming in circles under a full moon—
My spirit is lifted to its own natural high.

April 5

I am so *Grateful*

for the body's continued renewal.

Muscle, bones, and hair replenish everyday,
Vitamins, minerals, and herbs are part of the
process,
It's all in the daily event of healthy development
As food is transformed into blood, cells,
and tissue.

April 6

I am so *Grateful*

for positive, front-page news.

A seed of hope is planted
Inspiring the whole community,
Turning an empty lot into a successful business,
Revitalizing neighborhoods draws national
    attention.

April 7

I am so *Grateful*

for spotless cleaning.

Special cloths are made for dusting,
Brooms and dust mops clean wood floors,
Powerful vacuums pick up every speck
And save us from doing tedious work.

April 8

I am so *Grateful*

for enriching my surroundings.

Hand-painted coffee mugs are lined up in the
kitchen,
A white lacy tablecloth dresses the dinner table,
Crystal candleholders sparkle in a curio cabinet,
And grandfather clock chimes on time everytime.

April 9

I am so *Grateful*

for tools of the intellect.

Drawing up a plan to create a desired experience,
Weighing, measuring, comparing, and analyzing,
Connecting pieces gives shape to an idea
And leads to clear thinking and a positive result.

April 10

I am so

Grateful

for sound financial habits.

I pay myself first by saving 10% of my wages,
A savings account adds to a good credit rating,
A credit card is used for emergencies only,
And delaying gratification pays off in the end.

April 11

I am so *Grateful*

for clever inventions.

An extra leaf enlarges the dining room table,
Handy twistems secure the freshness of bread,
Velcro sticks easily holding wallets closed,
And handy cup holders prevent spills that scatter.

April 12

I am so  *Grateful*

for exciting finds.

A unique picture frame holds a prized art
   possession,
An out-of-print book turns up at a second hand
   bookshop,
An airline accepts frequent flyer miles to a choice
   vacation spot,
And intrigue and magic are found in the Harry
   Potter stories.

April 13

I am so *Grateful*

for the chance to begin anew.

Eliminating words of worry and concern,
Lack and limitation are removed from our
    vocabulary,
Focusing on what we want instead of what
    we don't want,
Our vision is realized and paves the way for us.

April 14

I am so *Grateful*

for life-changing workshops.

*T*imeworn concepts become reinvigorated,
Repetition and sameness are released,
Practical applications smooth the pathway—
Moving us fearlessly into uncharted areas.

April 15

I am so *Grateful*

for conscious communication.

*P*olitical speeches are left to the politicians,
Religious sermons stay in church,
Dirty jokes are best left untold,
And gossip and rumors are nipped in the bud.

April 16

I am so *Grateful*

for shared purpose.

Communities unite during natural disasters,
Camaraderie is shown by the art of patience,
Group discussion gets to the heart of a problem,
And everything unfolds according to plan.

April 17

I am so *Grateful*

for pictures.

Videotaping children from their first step,
Taking posed snapshots before a high school
   prom,
Candid moments are developed instantly
And speak louder than words on a homemade
   greeting card.

April 18

I am so *Grateful* for mouth-watering smells.

Granny's beans baking in the oven,
Bacon and eggs sizzling in a fry pan,
Chocolate fudge hot off the flame,
And pink bubble gum, aah so sweet!

April 19

I am *so* *Grateful*

for warning sounds.

A blaring alarm shrieks before a tornado's wrath,
Fog horns alert ships of dangerous conditions,
Smoke detectors save lives by sounding off early,
And a siren forewarns of a speeding ambulance's
approach.

April 20

I am so *Grateful*

for novel technology.

A foreign language is translated by a software
program,
High tech devices allow the visually impaired
to read,
Electronically filed taxes return refunds in record
time,
And Global Positioning Systems furnish instant
directions.

April 21

I am so *Grateful*

for neatness.

Straightening drawers clears up disorder,
Shelves for knickknacks eliminate hodgepodge,
Bits and pieces in place are easy to find,
And a freshly ironed shirt suggests a tidy person.

April 22

I am so *Grateful*

for thriftiness.

Cutting corners wherever possible
Stretches a penny into three cents,
Paying attention to what's being spent
Moves one ahead financially step by step.

April 23

I am so *Grateful*

for fast food in a pinch.

Chinese carryout in a quart container,
Hamburgers and fries packed in a bag,
Chicken in a bucket with cole slaw on the side,
Or steaming hot pizza delivered to the front door.

April 24

I am so *Grateful*

for the American image.

Apple pie a la mode,
Hot dog stands on the corner,
Peanuts and Cracker Jack
On opening day at the old ball game.

April 25

I am *so* *Grateful*

for unforgettable sounds.

Church bells ring announcing Sunday services,
A whippoorwill calls to its mate in the distance,
Raindrops fall softly, pitter-pattering on the roof,
And a mom whispers reassuringly to her child.

April 26

I am so *Grateful*

for the sweet smells of spring.

Newly mowed grass spreads its aroma,
Lily of the valley release a pleasing scent,
Blooming lilacs deliver a powerful fragrance,
And flowering apple blossoms add sweetness
    to the air.

April 27

I am so *Grateful*

for garden tools.

Using shovels to dig and turn over the ground,
Wheelbarrows to haul excess dirt away,
Hoes and rakes to groom the plantings,
And hoses and sprinklers to govern the water.

April 28

I am so *Grateful*

for planted seeds that reach fruition.

The soil is tilled and the garden is planted,
The seedlings are watered day and night,
Unwanted weeds are pulled out at first sight,
And we reap the harvest that's been lavished
   upon us.

April 29

I am so *Grateful*

for wildlife in the city.

Rabbits bound across front lawns,
Raccoons peep out from their homes in the park,
Ducks team up to start new families,
And when the robins return, for sure it is spring!

April 30

May Beauty

Loveliness in life is fresh and flawless
Waking the perception of our senses,
Gracing artificial fashion or natural landscape
Beauty abounds in our fertile surround.

Beauty lures us with its charm
And its pervasive presence pleases the eye,
But by far the most beautiful thing to behold
Is inner goodness—a companion to the soul.

I am so *Grateful*

for tranquil beauty.

Perennial flowers return year after year,
Magnificent butterflies flutter delicate wings,
Tropical fish dart quickly amidst coral reef,
And the sky is colored in gentle, placid pinks.

May 1

I am so *Grateful*

for the colors of the seasons.

Yellow dandelions cover green, grassy meadows,
Puffy, white clouds drift across a deep blue sky,
Vibrant red and orange leaves call us to autumn,
And deep evergreens glisten with new fallen snow.

May 2

I am so *Grateful*

for gentle sounds.

The rippling gurgle of a flowing brook,
A miniature chime tinkling in the wind,
A tranquilizing purr from a contented cat,
And baby's first word tickling me pink.

May 3

I am so *Grateful*

for ancient beauty.

Bristlecone pines grasp craggy peaks,
Twisted in silhouette against the setting sun,
Hundreds of years old, stooped over and bent—
What inner depth does such beauty hold?

May 4

I am so *Grateful*

for the beauty of our elders.

Aged with wrinkled skin and arthritic hands,
Full of wisdom often left unspoken,
Like a pearl inside an oyster,
True beauty is more than its outer shell.

May 5

I am so *Grateful*

for several styles of decor.

Early American sets the period,
Contemporary is in the now,
Some like the country look,
And others create their own unique style.

May 6

I am so

Grateful

for the finer things in life.

Clear-cut diamonds and mother-of-pearl,
14 karat gold and fine art jewelry,
Silver goblets and crystal glassware,
And imported china ages old.

May 7

I am so *Grateful*

for reaching out to others.

Lending an umbrella on a rainy day,
Being a better listener by talking less,
Tithing 10% of earnings to charity,
Giving is more satisfying than receiving.

May 8

I am so *Grateful*

for unexpected happenings.

A violin-gram is received in celebration of
Sweetest Day,
A favorite recipe is published in a monthly
magazine,
My boss lets me off early when I'm expecting
guests,
And a seemingly hopeless failure ends in success.

May 9

I am so *Grateful*

for musical excursions.

Attending the concerts of a local symphony,
Swing dancing to a 20-piece orchestra,
Cruising down the river with a Dixieland band—
Its lively beat "picks you up and sets you down."

May 10

I am so *Grateful*

for pleasant memories.

Blowing out candles on a birthday cake in one
breath,
Driving in the country with the top down on
a warm day,
Spotting pelicans swooping down on an
unsuspecting fish,
Or watching a performance of the Blue Angels'
precision flying.

May 11

I am so *Grateful*

for dependable people.

Dads master the role of breadwinner,
Teachers detect a unique gift in each student,
Support groups are there for people in need,
And mothers wipe noses and dry tears.

May 12

I am so *Grateful*

for thoughtfulness.

Canned goods are gathered for a homeless
    shelter,
A cake is baked for a co-worker's birthday,
A complimentary letter is sent to a company
    manager—
A little bit of kindness goes a long, long way.

May 13

I am so *Grateful*

for our parks.

Birdies fly fast in a hot game of badminton,
A paddleboat ride cools you down quick,
Picnics are set up on a red, checkered tablecloth—
It's a privilege to be a visitor at the park.

May 14

I am so *Grateful*

for the time to smell the roses.

Lying in a hammock between two shade trees
Or wandering through a multicolored rose garden,
Sitting quietly and communing with nature
Beholding something beautiful in each person
  I meet.

May 15

I am so *Grateful*

for lovers.

A handsome man spreads his charms
Striking a delicate woman's delight of attention,
A breathtaking moment gives way to excitement
Creating the beautiful sight of two people in love.

May 16

I am so

Grateful

for beauty only I can see.

My old apartment has creaky floors and crooked
   walls,
And sometimes the radiators bang as they warm,
It's just a one-bedroom overlooking the main
   street,
But when I walk through the door, I know I'm home.

May 17

I am so *Grateful*

for traveling without a hassle.

Hotel reservations are made in advance,
Planes and trains arrive on schedule,
The rental car is credit card ready,
And subway systems are fast and easy.

May 18

I am so *Grateful*

for favorable results.

Making it through bad weather on a bumpy
   plane ride,
Finding one motel room left after an exhausting
   day of driving,
A car in the fast lane lets me slip in front of it,
And I leave the doctor's office with a clean bill
   of health.

May 19

I am so *Grateful*

for natural beauty around the house.

African violets look pretty on a bookshelf,
Yellow daffodils brighten up a kitchen,
A window box is full of perky-faced pansies,
And flowers in the garden wave to passersby.

May 20

I am so *Grateful*

for unique sounds of music.

The mournful notes of Swiss Alpine horns echo
off distant mountains,
A humpback whale moans in the background
of a meditation melody,
A soprano solo soars high above the orchestra
in a moving aria,
And a beginning violin player's bow moves
cautiously over the strings.

May 21

I am so *Grateful*

for old-fashioned hospitality.

A neighbor collects the newspapers when I'm
out of town,
A thank you note is received for a project's
completion,
My spouse calls to say he'll be a few minutes late,
And borrowed items are returned before they
are forgotten.

May 22

I am so

Grateful

for locating misplaced items.

I spot my car in the parking lot after a long,
hard look,

Theatre tickets are found a day before the
performance,

I discover a missing piece of my china set at a
local garage sale,

And the mate to a pair of socks shows up under
the bed.

May 23

I am so *Grateful*

for a holiday in Europe.

Gold-stenciled ceilings beautify spiral-topped
cathedrals,
Prestigious opera houses reflect a glamorous
lifestyle,
Glowing cherry paneling radiates old-world charm
In exquisite historic restaurants serving fine
cuisine.

May 24

I am so *Grateful*

for artists who fill our world with beauty.

Artisans create magnificent sculptures of ice,
    stone and sand,
Talented craftsmen restore paintings hidden
    by years of grime,
Workers labor to preserve historical buildings
    from ruin and decay,
And the artwork of masters decorates galleries
    throughout the world.

May 25

I am so *Grateful*

for a walk with no destination.

A choice pair of tennis shoes cushions my feet,
Pretty plantings in the neighborhood catch my eye,
A leisurely chat provides a welcome, short break,
And a nonchalant jogger says, "Have a nice day."

May 26

I am so *Grateful*

for a nourishing downpour.

Heavy rains fill brooks, lakes and streams
And replenish our water supply up to the brim,
A natural growth of plant life occurs,
And birds find shelter in full-leafed trees.

May 27

I am so *Grateful*

for slow-motion photography.

A flower bud opens to its full bloom,
A hummingbird hovers in midair,
A butterfly emerges from its cocoon,
And a baby develops in its mother's womb.

May 28

I am so *Grateful*

for the magnificence of the Universe.

Majestic mountain peaks glisten with snow-topped
   beauty,
Towering pine trees stretch toward heaven,
The moon beams brighter than a million stars—
There's not a spot where God is not.

May 29

I am so *Grateful*

for unexplained mysteries.

Crop circles appear in an overnight charade,
Unidentified flying objects still make us wonder,
Stonehenge megaliths tower in a circle
Enchanting us all with their magic spell.

May 30

I am so *Grateful*

for matter in its proper place.

For single stars placed in the heavens,
And every fish that swims in the sea,
Each of us shines in our very own light
Dazzling others with who we've become.

May 31

*June
Love*

The tender passion of our desires
Is prompted by an enthusiastic flame,
Unselfishly giving of talent and time
Produces results of lasting fulfillment.

Strong affections for one or another
Fancy a yearning for warm attachment,
Terms of endearment stroke a beloved
Enhancing loving connections to each other.

I am so *Grateful*

for love in action.

Family members are quick to reconcile
    differences,
Romances are rekindled following long absences,
The renewal of wedding vows strengthens a
    marriage,
And happy couples hold hands walking side by side.

June 1

I am so *Grateful*

for affectionate touch.

Cradling an infant to my breast
Or fitting a child's hand snuggly in mine,
Tenderly planting a kiss on the cheek,
And holding tight to those I love.

June 2

I am so *Grateful*

for hearty gestures.

Placing a cold wash cloth on a feverish brow,
Giving a pat on the back to express support,
A firm handshake can be a warm welcome—
Pick-me-ups like these can't be bought.

June 3

I am so *Grateful*

for young love.

Whisker rubs remain after a morning smooch,
Impromptu hugs are traded throughout the day,
Hello kisses are an intimate greeting—
Abounding love makes the world go round.

June 4

I am so *Grateful*

for traditional weddings.

Old, new, borrowed and blue
Makes me remember saying "I do,"
Cheery-eyed guests sniffle through joy
As they shower newlyweds rushing out the door.

June 5

I am so *Grateful*

for treasures worth their weight in gold.

Museums exhibit ancient finds from archeological
digs,
Recitals give voice to romantic love sonnets,
There is wisdom to be found in the great books
of literature,
And a mystical meaning in "Footprints," a prayer
of hope.

June 6

I am so

Grateful

for bridging the gap between
humanity and divinity.

I deepen my experience of the sacred self
By following God's agenda instead of mine,
I love and accept myself for who I am
And find awesome power in saying, "It's all right."

June 7

I am so *Grateful*

for benevolence.

In adverse situations I offer my hand,
The "other guy" deserves the benefit of the doubt,
I extend congratulations to honor your success,
Love goes beyond words when compassion is
shown.

June 8

I am so *Grateful*

for hospice personnel.

*P*atients are given a voice in their care,
Medicine is administered to manage their pain,
Leniency and mercy do a good turn,
And unconditional love stops time for a moment.

June 9

I am so *Grateful*

for doting parents.

*L*auding children with lots of affection
And audibly commending extra effort,
Cherishing exemplary behavior early on
Teaches kids all about loving themselves.

June 10

I am so *Grateful*

for recalling childhood grins.

Chasing ice cream wagons down the street
Hooked by the piercing, popular jingle,
Welcoming a frenzied greeting from my dog
Who licked my face and jumped up and down.

June 11

I am so *Grateful*

for objects that protect us.

Visors shield me from the sun's powerful rays,
Extinguishers put out a flash fire in the kitchen,
Raincoats and galoshes repel chilling rain
and slush,
And flashlights and candles light our way
after dark.

June 12

I am so *Grateful*

for guiding road signs.

Detours for road construction provide directions,
Food, gas and rest areas are fast approaching,
Drive slowly through school crossing zones,
And use caution for the deaf and blind in the area.

June 13

I am so *Grateful*

for yesteryear.

A mother's love, a father's care,
A rocking horse, a baby chair,
The scent of clean clothes drying on the line,
An old rope swing for a child to climb.

June 14

I am so *Grateful*

for proud fathers.

*A*lways patient and never too busy,
Hanging in there with little recognition,
Foresight and good judgment offer fair counsel,
Setting an example for young ones to follow.

June 15

I am so *Grateful*

for the sounds of summer.

A bicycle beeps a warning from behind,
A hard hit baseball implants a resounding whack,
Lawn mowers drone while cutting the grass,
And booming fireworks light up the night sky.

June 16

I am so

Grateful

for a trip down memory lane.

Musty hallways of days we knew,
Seize the moment of a nostalgic mood,
Old times and old scenes of smiles and tears,
Classmates reunite after many a year.

June 17

I am so *Grateful*

for carryalls and holders.

A cookie jar contains tempting sweet treats,
Podiums hold speeches during a talk,
Carts carry our groceries until we check out,
And belts and suspenders, we can't do without.

June 18

I am so *Grateful*

for people who serve us.

The waitress pouring our morning coffee,
Mailmen delivering our daily mail,
Bus drivers traveling back and forth across cities,
And dog sitters walking and feeding our pets.

June 19

I am so *Grateful*

for friendly responses.

An endearing message is left on the answering
    machine,
A letter is received from a pen pal far away,
My apology is accepted after I've acted offensively,
And a companion replies, "Thanks so much
    for asking."

June 20

I am so *Grateful*

for doing what I love and loving what I do.

Choreographing a new dance to favorite music,
Collecting stamps from all over the world,
Preparing an English trifle for a dinner party,
Or flying to the Bahamas to swim with the
    dolphins.

June 21

I am *so* *Grateful*

for places to store things.

I carry clothes and sundries in a backpack or
  duffel bag,
And store bigger things upstairs in the attic,
My favorite books are stacked on shelves by
  my bed,
And handbaskets carry my potential purchases.

June 22

I am so *Grateful*

for privacy.

Closing a door that can be locked,
"Do not disturb" is hung on the handle,
A fence keeps out unwanted intrusions
For times when solitude is desired.

June 23

I am so *Grateful*

for the good old days.

Growing up in the era of front porch swings
And grandfathers who welcomed, "Fix it, please,"
One by one our troubles slipped away
As we listened to tall tales told for fun.

June 24

I am so *Grateful*

for the lazy, hazy days of summer.

The click of croquet balls rebound across
  manicured turf,
The cool tingle of a root beer float satisfies a
  deep thirst,
Straw bonnets tug against their ribbons on
  a breezy day,
And barbershop quartets harmonize in the
  good old summertime.

June 25

I am so *Grateful*

for useful advice.

*S*et boundaries when someone offends you,
Be assertive and ask for what you want,
Delegate simple tasks to free up your time,
And sign up for projects that interest you.

June 26

I am so *Grateful*

for the future before us.

Give up your resistance to change,
Put your heart into it and do not lose faith,
Carve out anything that you can imagine—
No matter what happens the sun always rises.

June 27

I am so *Grateful*

for feeling needed.

A committee member asks for my opinion
Telling me I have so much to offer,
My partner says I am the light of his life,
And the grandchildren climb up for a
little TLC.

June 28

I am so *Grateful*

for a relationship with pizzazz.

Horsing around in jest recharges batteries,
A pinch of kookiness is a recipe for fun,
Romantic interludes unleash amazing energies—
It's marvelous to love and be loved in return.

June 29

I am so *Grateful*

for wholesome connections.

Touching each other links us together
As one piece of a puzzle connects to another,
Extending love to our neighbors and friends
Expands our community out into the world.

June 30

July
Nature

Though cosmic energy mystifies man
Earth demonstrates a creative universe—
Like a shooting star crossing the dark night
The glories of every day shine in the light.

A dynamic force in each individual
Sends seemingly inborn talents forth,
The inherent character of every person—
The simple presence of love's beginning.

I am so *Grateful*

for the forces of nature.

Splendid, towering trees bend with the wind,
Rushing rapids thunder a melody over jagged
    rocks,
Lightning cracks with electricity through the
    night,
And an ocean of mammoth waves roll ashore.

July 1

I am so *Grateful*

for a drive in the country.

Sunflowers hold their faces up to the sun,
Baby pine trees are growing up for Santa,
Wildflowers bow in unison with the breeze—
A city girl feels at home in the country.

July 2

I am so *Grateful*

for animals in character.

Cattle graze undisturbed in a farmer's field,
Elegant swans glide gracefully on a calm lake,
A deer drinks without caution at the river's edge,
And an eagle spreads his wings and soars
    overhead.

July 3

I am so *Grateful*

for acts of patriotism.

Singing the "National Anthem" at every sports
event,
Displaying the American flag on pertinent holidays,
Reciting the "Pledge of Allegiance" from memory,
And shedding a tear at the majestic strains of
"America the Beautiful."

July 4

I am so *Grateful*

for history preserved in our land.

Red granite in the Grand Canyon tells a deep
story,
The Crazy Horse Memorial stands tall in
South Dakota,
Custer's last stand took place in Montana,
And in the south of Texas we "Remember the
Alamo."

July 5

I am so *Grateful*

for the flowers that grace our earth.

Morning glories climb their trellis in silent
    ascension,
Desert cactuses add a splash of color to the
    barren sands,
A thousand varieties are strewn throughout
    the countryside,
And occasionally one pokes through a crack
    in the sidewalk.

July 6

I am so *Grateful*

for exhilarating moments.

Glorious rays of sunshine filter through a lifting
  fog,
A multicolored rainbow appears during a
  summer shower,
A spouting whale surfaces off the bow of a boat,
And streaks of brilliant yellows turn a blue sky
  into gold.

July 7

I am so *Grateful*

for refreshing water.

Strolling in a misty rain cleanses the psyche,
A plunge in a swimming pool sends chills up
    the spine,
A playful balloon fight works up quite a thirst
That water quenches better than any other drink.

July 8

I am so *Grateful*

for tiny delights.

Finding a forgotten twenty-dollar bill in a jacket
      pocket,
Threading the eye of a needle on the very first try,
Sniffing a bouquet of pretty, pink peonies,
And sitting after twilight watching fireflies glow.

July 9

I am so *Grateful*

for handy packaging.

Trash bags close with zippers and ties,
Foils and clear wraps mold and cling to any dish,
Glass bowls and plastics have covers and lids—
There's the right size container for every need.

July 10

I am so *Grateful*

for cleanliness.

Washing the car demonstrates pride of
    ownership,
A warm shower rinses frothy soap down
    the drain,
Snug in bed between sheets still warm from
    the dryer
One wonders, "Is cleanliness really next
    to godliness?"

July 11

I am so *Grateful*

for professional hairdressers.

I can pick from many colors to cover the gray,
The perfect cut puts me in shape,
I love stylish wigs both curly and straight—
I take my cue from a friend, "You look just great!"

July 12

I am so *Grateful*

for fabrics to mix and match.

Silk and satin are sleek to the touch,
A taffeta piece adds a bit of crispness,
Fine linen is cooler for the summer—
So many pretty patterns and colors to
choose from.

July 13

I am so *Grateful*

for a relaxing weekend.

Spending idle time "people watching" from a
sidewalk cafe,
Lunching at an out-of-the-way inn with fabulous food,
Exploring a street that takes me off the beaten
path,
And tossing a coin in a fountain while making
a wish.

July 14

I am so

Grateful

for being a step ahead of the game.

A rain scarf in my purse is ready for an
   unexpected shower,
The soothing ointment in the cabinet eases
   a cut or a burn,
Lawn chairs stay in the trunk in case of an
   unplanned outing,
And a delicious stew in the Crock-Pot is ready
   on my return.

July 15

I am so *Grateful*

for the circus parade.

Costumed clowns comically romp down
    the avenue,
Ladies in flowing silks sit atop splendid horses,
A man on stilts waves at youngsters in awe,
And show wagons are beautifully carved
    and painted.

July 16

I am so *Grateful*

for spectacular spots in the U. S.

Liberty greets the world at the gates of
New York,
Niagara roars mightily, what a beautiful sight,
Massive faces are carved into Mount
Rushmore—
This larger-than-life monument is history
in stone.

July 17

I am so *Grateful*

for timely reminders.

I wake to the pleasant music of my clock radio
And take the cake out of the oven when the
    timer signals,
The service rep calls before arriving to do a repair,
And a phone call reminds me of my appointment
    tomorrow.

July 18

I am so *Grateful*

for office supplies.

I use pens and pencils to put my thoughts down
on paper,
And scotch tape and scissors are handy when
wrapping,
I use clips and staples to hold it all together,
And binders keep my papers neatly in one place.

July 19

I am so *Grateful*

for the performing Lipizzans.

Magnificent stallions prance an elegant gait,
Superior strength shows in their sleek form,
Dancing and executing maneuvers with refined
    grace,
Horse and rider are a moving ballet.

July 20

I am so

Grateful

for picturesque postcards.

Incredible rock formations span the state of Utah,
Old Faithful spouts off in Yellowstone National
  Park,
Photos capture breathtaking beauty in natural
  settings
Providing a closeness to nature that enriches
  the soul.

July 21

I am so *Grateful*

for wild animals at the zoo.

Lions and Siberian tigers strut their stuff,
Elephants are massive and giraffes are tall,
Playful monkeys have no care at all,
And giant guerrillas are as scary as ...?

July 22

I am so *Grateful*

for nights around the campfire.

Sharing sing-a-longs by the warmth of a fire,
Roasting marshmallows to a rich golden brown,
Crawling into a sleeping bag long after dark,
Looking up and wishing upon the brightest star.

July 23

I am so *Grateful*

for a stroll through the park.

Skateboards hum as they roll down the sidewalk,
Live music fills the air at an outdoor concert,
Shrieks erupt when a Little Leaguer hits his first
   home run,
And hands clap in unison to the beat of the band.

July 24

I am so *Grateful*

for living with gusto.

*L*earning the hula on vacation in Honolulu,
Hooking a marlin while deep sea fishing,
Sinking a twelve-foot putt wins the match—
Each episode in life is a new adventure.

July 25

I am so *Grateful*

for untamed voices.

A morning dove coos to its mate,
A lone wolf howls beneath a full moon,
Geese honk as they trail their way home,
And chirping crickets command our attention.

July 26

I am so *Grateful*

for nature's processes.

*G*randiose waterfalls tumble down a mountainside.
Billowing clouds drift along in slow motion,
Unnoticed changes flow one season into the next,
And daylight subtly returns after the night.

July 27

I am so *Grateful*

for a thunderstorm after a dry spell.

The grass greens up as the pavement darkens,
Tiny roots spread out in the once hard ground,
Worms crawl in and out—what ingenuous irrigation,
And people stay inside letting nature do her thing.

July 28

I am so *Grateful*

for contemplating stillness.

When the birds become still
And a dog's barking stops
And a downpour ends
And a baby's crying ceases.

July 29

I am so *Grateful*

for wonders of creation.

A forest of redwoods shades a woodland floor,
Clusters of cattails sway lightly on a riverbank,
A sharp-eyed hawk glides effortlessly through
    the air,
And a sweet-smelling flower is kissed by a honey
    bee.

July 30

I am so *Grateful*

for relaxing under an oak tree.

A bird's sweet song murmurs in my ears,
Children's laughter drifts through the air,
Before dozing off for an afternoon siesta
I think to myself, "It's a wonderful world."

July 31

August Fun

Indulging in play or light amusement,
Mischievous action or boisterous speech,
What provides enjoyment or entertains us more
Than a fun-loving person who's refreshing to be with?

A jester, a wisecracker, full of tricks and wit,
A spirited jokester delights with light teasing,
Adding humor to a party's merriment and gaiety—
Contagious laughter yields glee and joyfulness.

I am so *Grateful*

for a sense of daring and adventure.

Riding a cable car high above the mountains
Or a hot air balloon at the mercy of the wind,
Grips tighten as the roller coaster plunges
    downward—
It's simply impossible to have too much fun!

August 1

I am so *Grateful*

for lighthearted play.

Twisting and turning, rolling around,
Playing hopscotch—touching the ground,
Ring-around-the-rosey, musical chairs,
Are those London Bridges still falling down?

August 2

I am so *Grateful*

for my mischievous puppy.

Throwing his toy brings me great joy,
He fetches the ball and returns when I call,
With boundless energy he chases his tail,
Going round and round, his antics prevail.

August 3

I am so *Grateful*

for a playful self.

Frolicsome wrestling raises energy,
A trip to the magic shop peaks curiosity,
Borrowing a bike and taking a ride
Hints at the "little kid" inside.

August 4

I am so *Grateful*

for slap-stick comedy.

Charlie Chaplin started it all,
Laurel and Hardy carried it on,
The Marx Brothers and The Three Stooges
Led us to the first lady Lucy—we had a Ball!

August 5

I am so *Grateful*

for treats of sweets.

A chocolate bar provides instant energy,
Lemon drops burst with a tart, tangy taste,
Animal crackers tide us over till lunch,
And after dinner mints calm the tummy.

August 6

I am so *Grateful*

for small favors.

A loan from a friend when I'm in a bind,
Making it to the gas station before running
   out of gas,
A garage loaner when the car is in the shop,
And a stranger who plugs an expired parking
   meter.

August 7

I am so *Grateful*

for little girl's pastimes.

*I*ntroducing Barbie to a daring new doll outfit
Or drinking tea with imaginary characters,
Arranging furniture in a well-kept doll house
Or dressing up in Mommy's high heel shoes.

August 8

I am so *Grateful*

for aquatic diversions.

Wading knee-deep in a crystal clear lake,
Floating in an inner tube to a waiting raft,
Paddling a canoe down a winding river—
I'm a kid at heart for just a bit longer.

August 9

I am so *Grateful*

for "chilling out."

Screens and fans allow the air to circulate,
Air conditioners lower the temperature,
Ice cubes chill a tall glass of lemonade
While I sit outside shooting the breeze.

August 10

I am so

Grateful

for backyard barbecues.

Brats soaked in beer, grilled to perfection,
Hot roasted sweet corn, dripping with butter,
Grandma's potato salad never tasted better,
And ripe watermelon—"life is go-ood!"

August 11

I am so *Grateful*

for graceful sports.

High jump skiers fly motionless through the air,
Dancing figure skaters mirror each other,
Gymnasts flip easily across a padded floor,
And skilled high divers plunge in without a splash.

August 12

I am so *Grateful*

for ecstatic dance.

Using free-form movement
Body, mind, and emotions are in motion,
Humans express by their playfulness
Connecting with the One through universal
    rhythm.

August 13

I am so *Grateful*

for formulating my own music.

*H*umming a catchy tune softly,
Singing off-key, unheard in the shower,
Listening to an almost forgotten old favorite,
And happily whistling while I work.

August 14

I am so *Grateful*

for satisfying immediate needs.

Finding shelter in a sudden downpour,
Quarters in my purse for an urgent phone call,
An extra role of scotch tape so I can finish
    wrapping presents,
And batteries in the drawer when a flashlight
    goes out.

August 15

I am so *Grateful*

for throwing my own party.

I get so excited addressing invitations,
And I tear open the R.S.V.P.s as they're returned,
I prepare delicious food a day ahead of time,
And happily I live my life to the hilt.

August 16

I am so

Grateful

for special touches at dinner.

Ice water is freshened with a slice of lemon,
Napkins are encircled with decorative rings,
A cut glass vase of fresh flowers beautifies the
    table,
And a delicate china cup is filled with steaming
    flavored coffee.

August 17

I am so *Grateful*

for advanced electronics.

Digital cameras record movement in stop action,
Marketplace sales bring the public up to speed,
Tips and tricks are necessary info
Enabling us to shoot videos like a pro.

August 18

I am so *Grateful*

for scientific progress.

Man's persistence opens doors for
　　advancement—
Telescopes draw the twinkling heavens closer,
Spacecrafts took the first men to the moon
And it's not made of cheese after all!

August 19

I am so *Grateful*

for recreational athletics.

Engaging in a tennis match with friendly
   competition,
Tossing a volleyball back and forth on the beach,
Running for a touch down playing free-for-all
   football,
Or driving a hole-in-one straight from the tee.

August 20

I am so *Grateful*

for man's best friend.

Watch dogs protect us,
Guide dogs lead us,
Hunting dogs retrieve for us,
And playful puppies keep us young.

August 21

I am so *Grateful*

for great food.

Farm fresh fruits and vegetables at a roadside
   stand,
Homemade cherry pie still warm from the oven,
Gourmet food prepared by a famous chef,
And leftovers fixed more beautifully than the
   day before.

August 22

I am so *Grateful*

for fairs and festivals.

Country-and-western music sends us a message,
A stage is set for a live opera performance,
Cream puffs and specialty foods, there's plenty
    around,
And a band's oom-pah-pah blares o'er the grounds.

August 23

I am so *Grateful*

for itty-bitty things that please me.

A traffic light turning green when I'm in a hurry,
Or finding a seat on a crowded bus,
Filling in all the blanks of a crossword puzzle,
And tacking up my child's first piece of art.

August 24

I am so *Grateful*

for biting into wholesome fruits.

A luscious strawberry straight from the patch,
A scarlet purple plum, succulent and sweet,
A juicy peach before it reaches the bushel,
And a vine-ripened tomato still warm from
the sun.

August 25

I am so *Grateful*

for my beach bum character.

The wind rustles my once neatly combed hair,
The rush of the surf splashes over my hot feet,
I sip a frosty, ice-cold piña colada,
While the sun shines down on my smiling,
     tan face.

August 26

I am so *Grateful*

for simple pleasures.

Playing Bocce ball with longtime pals,
Finding a jewel in an unknown antique shop,
Posing for silly pictures in a 25¢ photo booth,
And riding in a horse-drawn carriage under
  the city lights.

August 27

I am *so* *Grateful*

for children's games.

Captain May I gives you permission,
Simon Says you can do it,
Olly Olly Oxen sets you free,
And boys chase girls, tiddely dee.

August 28

I am so *Grateful*

for permitting myself to act childlike.

G My face lights up as I smile from ear to ear,
Uttering oohs and aahs over a new experience,
Setting aside fears, risking, being daring
Brings about a sense of wonderment I thought
    I had lost.

August 29

I am so *Grateful*

for amusement sites in America.

Zipping down water slides at the Dells in Wisconsin,
Partying hardy at the Mardi Gras in New Orleans,
Shaking hands with Goofy and Mickey at Disney
    World,
And strolling through the glitz and glamour in Reno
    and Vegas.

August 30

I am so *Grateful*

for humor that tickles the funny bone.

A top-notch comedian has the audience rolling,
A funny sitcom makes us cackle out loud,
The German word "Ausfahrt" means "highway
      exit"—
A good laugh deserves to be shared with a friend.

August 31

September
Transition

Embracing life's most difficult moments
New challenges erupt, new skills unfold,
Change is the only thing that never changes
Truly life flows best when we adjust to it.

Passing through one stage to another
Sometimes takes a gentle shove,
Difficult times can only get better
When transformation occurs with love.

I am so *Grateful*

for positive transformations.

An alcoholic joins AA and recovers from addiction,
A shy child accepts the lead role in a school play,
Helen Keller is the perfect example
Of the seeds of greatness just waiting to emerge.

September 1

I am so *Grateful*

for differences.

*S*ome things we want and don't have,
Some things we have and don't want,
Some things we never want and another
    person does,
One man's junk is another man's treasure.

September 2

I am so *Grateful*

for eternal optimism.

Always searching for the good in the bad,
Seeing the glass half full rather than half empty,
It's wise not to judge a man's worth by comparing,
Because most of us are doing our best.

September 3

I am so *Grateful*

for living with integrity.

*L*eaving the scene before an argument starts,
Refusing to react to another's bad mood,
Not taking everything said to me personally
Cultivates my practice of self-control.

September 4

I am so *Grateful*

for changing my perspective.

Employing cooperation instead of competition,
Practicing the art of skillful negotiating,
Compromise clears up unfinished business,
And life becomes much easier for me.

September 5

I am so *Grateful*

for being free of unwanted habits.

No longer buying unnecessary items
Or chatting on the phone way too long,
Giving up vegging out in front of the TV
Or wasting time feeling sorry for myself.

September 6

I am so *Grateful*

for self-discovery.

Developing character beats impressing others,
Magic moments identify hidden talents,
It's never too late to try something new
Or take a risk to expand our capabilities.

September 7

I am so *Grateful*

for the ability to express myself.

Composing and delivering a meaningful speech,
Freely communicating what's important to me,
Daring to speak out on a controversial issue—
Competence and skill become second nature.

September 8

I am so

Grateful

for impressions that come easily.

After an upsetting discussion clarity comes
    without asking,
Exciting new thoughts arise during a brainstorming
    session,
Issues are resolved by asking the right questions,
And answers appear at times when I'm still.

September 9

I am so *Grateful*

for interludes in distant places.

Gazing upon Michelangelo's masterpiece at the
    Sistine Chapel,
Drinking a tall beer at a Bavarian festival,
Musing at the wonder of the leaning tower of Pisa,
And kissing a lover underneath the Bridge
    of Sighs.

September 10

I am so *Grateful*

for broadening horizons.

*A*ttending a lecture on a topic new to me
Or attempting a complex task I haven't tried before,
Beginning a business career after years of raising
    kids,
And living my life as if I had only one month to live.

September 11

I am so *Grateful*

for creating with words.

*I*n weaving a story with pen and paper
A personal voyage through life is taken,
A trip back in time or a look into the future,
Writing is an adventurous thing to do.

September 12

I am so *Grateful*

for modern bookstores.

A diverse selection of books is displayed,
Space for reading is a refuge for learning,
Popular authors sign their latest publications,
And refreshments are served in a tiny cafe.

September 13

I am so *Grateful*

for a well-decorated home.

Tasteful accessories are used when rearranging
And beautiful pictures are hung on the walls,
Feng Shui principles instill balance and peace,
And a welcome mat invites company in.

September 14

I am so *Grateful*

for stay-at-home moms and dads.

Tender bonds build minds and bodies,
Sound principles are more important than "stuff,"
Respect and honor begin early on,
Responsible parenting teaches right from wrong.

September 15

I am so

Grateful

for safeguards for little ones.

Unsafe toys are removed from the market,
Car seats and bike helmets provide protection
    for individuals,
Crossing guards guide youngsters across busy
    streets,
And after dark lighting illuminates scary places.

September 16

I am so *Grateful*

for order when the school bell rings.

Competent, compassionate instructors
Establish new rules that benefit learning
Beckoning us to places we've never been
Asking: "Who, what, where, why, and when?"

September 17

I am so *Grateful*

for guided tours of old cities.

Cultural images of the past meet the eye,
City halls are often as impressive as churches,
Local people prance nobly in historical costume,
And outdoor markets create a small town feeling.

September 18

I am so *Grateful*

for annals of wisdom.

*F*amous quotations inspire us,
Historians record meaningful events,
Libraries hold our presidents' memoirs,
And heritage is uncovered in genealogical
    studies.

September 19

I am so *Grateful*

for astonishing finds of anthropologists.

Relics of the past are uncovered and pieced
    together,
Stories that go way back are brought to life
    carefully,
Dinosaurs and cave men are priceless antiquities
    preserved,
And "Before Christ" is one way to date ancient
    times.

September 20

I am so *Grateful*

for dedicated inventors.

The light bulb makes our life fuller and simpler,
An inventive partnership created the airplane,
The phonograph was just the beginning—
Devices like these have changed our world forever.

September 21

I am so *Grateful*

for the bravery of the disabled.

One-legged downhill skiers have courage beyond
measure,
Paraplegics create art holding a paintbrush with
their teeth,
Little boys without legs have been known to
play football—
Daily problems of the average person seem pale
in comparison.

September 22

I am so *Grateful*

for practitioners who save lives.

Paramedics arrive first on the scene,
Emergency room staff stand ready to serve,
Surgeons perform necessary transplants
Of organs bequeathed long before death.

September 23

I am so *Grateful*

for composure in a tragedy.

When tension is high and anxiety increases,
The calm of another can sweep over you,
Without question that person can put you at ease,
The presence alone of a professional can help.

September 24

I am so *Grateful*

for insight in the midst of sorrow.

Seek out proper help and assistance,
Call someone who does not give in to their grief,
Get back to a normal life, the faster the better,
And remember a smile is the best antidote.

September 25

I am so *Grateful*

for highs and lows.

Dips into valleys precede the experience
Of reaching a peak every once in awhile,
It's impossible to live only on the peaks,
And great to know there's value in the valleys.

September 26

I am so *Grateful*

for Twelve Step programs.

Sometimes it's difficult to move beyond denial,
We wish we could go back and make some
    changes,
For those that have hurt you, there are others
    to help them,
Take no time for pity, waste not one more minute!

September 27

I am so *Grateful*

for taking the initiative to apologize.

When I've been hurtful, I say I'm sorry,
Forgiving daily is a beneficial practice,
I like myself more after the air has been cleared,
And feel much better for being honest.

September 28

I am so *Grateful*

for a positive result.

*K*nowing that defeat is only adversity
Serving as a challenge to elicit greater effort,
Developing wits and moving forward,
Flexibility and strength are gained through
struggle.

September 29

I am so *Grateful*

for an "aha" moment.

*G*rasping an idea that seems to come from
   nowhere,
A light bulb goes on, my awareness is peaked,
A sudden realization tells me "I get it,"
And empowering myself, I make a life shift.

September 30

October
Harvest

The year is coming to its end
As autumn's harvest is gathered in,
All has been grown in one single season
And provides a feast without special reason.

The miracle of seeds having reached fruition
Is like a child achieving full potential,
The love we put in is the love we get out
Indeed what we sow is what we shall reap.

I am so *Grateful*

for the bounty of a season's end.

Mighty oaks drop acres of acorns,
Milk pods open, scattering cotton,
Orchards teem with fruit ready for picking—
A harvest is gathered from vine, field and tree.

October 1

I am so *Grateful*

for the brilliant hues of fall.

Trees experience spectacular changes,
Dry leaves crackle underfoot,
Ripe pumpkins are lined up row by row,
If only Indian Summer would never go!

October 2

I am so *Grateful* for a hike in the woods.

The scent of smoldering embers lingers in
    the air
While wild turkeys gobble warnings to their
    mates,
The call of the loon echoes off the water,
And an unexpected fawn comes into view.

October 3

I am so *Grateful*

for a master plan at work.

Roosters crow when the sun comes up,
Farmers head toward the milking barn,
Newborn kittens snuggle in the corner—
A dairy farm day begins at the crack of dawn.

October 4

I am so *Grateful*

for the Big Sur.

Climbing high on a California ridge
Reveals a perfect picture of a rugged coastline,
A panoramic vista of cool, tree-lined valleys,
A flourishing landscape filled with giant sequoias.

October 5

I am so *Grateful*

for cameras attached to sea mammals.

*G*iving view to the secret world of colossal
    underwater creatures
Like whales, the monstrous masters of the
    deep, dark ocean,
Critter Cams show us mysterious creatures
    such as the giant squid,
And science has a better picture of the
    spectacular world under the sea.

October 6

I am so *Grateful*

for our feathered friends.

Squawking parrots or loudmouth macaws,
Singing canaries or trickster parakeets,
Pink flamingos and blue herons in the wild—
Their marvelous coloring catches the eye.

October 7

I am so *Grateful*

for the beauty of the turning woods.

Red maples burst into gorgeous scarlet hues,
Greens turn to gold, seasonal change is near,
Pick a fallen leaf and hold autumn in your hand,
An artist couldn't paint a canvas as beautiful.

October 8

I am so *Grateful*

for our precious earth.

The outdoor world is an abundance of resources
And there is much healing potential on our planet,
Our lakes, rivers and oceans beg for purity
And totally deserve our utmost attention.

October 9

I am so *Grateful*

for personal comforts.

A lumbar cushion accommodates my achy back,
The plush bathroom rug absorbs my shower
    drips,
My tattered bathrobe is a warm, old friend,
And the wicker sofa on the veranda is my favorite
    place to relax.

October 10

I am so *Grateful*

for freebies and discounts.

Free tickets admit us to dress rehearsals,
Money is saved by attending afternoon matinees,
Factory discounts are received when shopping
     direct,
And a borrowed outfit saves both time and money.

October 11

I am so *Grateful*

for being a part of the action.

Tailgating with buddies at the first football
   game
Or riding a bicycle built for two with my honey,
Socializing with club members at a wine
   tasting party
Or raising money for charity by running a
   marathon.

October 12

I am so

Grateful

for a visit to the big city.

Attending a taping of a popular TV show
Or visiting a well-known planetarium,
Shopping in stores on the Miracle Mile
Purchasing pricey presents for family
and friends.

October 13

I am so *Grateful*

for common necessities.

Clocks help me to be on time (sometimes),
I pat myself dry with large fluffy towels,
Deep dresser drawers hold all my winter
    sweaters,
And needles and threads keep me from
    becoming too "holey."

October 14

I am *so* *Grateful*

for ready-made assistance.

A dictionary and thesaurus are for checking
    accuracy and meaning,
"How to" books teach us what we want to know,
Printed directions guide us with a new product,
And over-the-counter health aids bring us
    quick relief.

October 15

I am so *Grateful*

for the news media.

Radio and television report current events,
Newspapers print stories of local interest,
Reporters and announcers bring it about,
And National Public Radio talks it all out.

October 16

I am so *Grateful*

for serious conversation.

Talking with someone who's interested in me,
I proceed uninterrupted when it's my turn to talk,
We state our truths in an eye-to-eye discourse,
And keep each other's confidences to ourselves.

October 17

I am so *Grateful*

for financial planning.

Pennies in a piggy bank are a beginning,
Government bonds accrue for the future,
Interest bearing savings accounts grow
without attention,
And free seminars help us make wise
investment decisions.

October 18

I am so *Grateful*

for the American dream.

Returning to college to earn a degree,
Becoming a boss of a private company,
Purchasing a home when it's affordable,
And changing a career to realize a dream.

October 19

I am so *Grateful*

for lost and founds.

*M*isplaced luggage is returned by the airlines,
A glance at the scale shows a loss of pounds,
A clerk might ask, "May I help you find
   something?"
And a wandering child is found safe and sound.

October 20

I am so *Grateful*

for my independence.

No longer a "wanna-be" in another person's life,
The grass isn't greener on the other side,
Not expecting others to fill me up
Compels me to be fully accountable for myself.

October 21

I am so *Grateful*

for men who pursued their dreams.

Taking us to places we would never have known,
Their strong determination withstood the test,
Never knowing where an inspiration would lead,
They explored new frontiers in pursuit of their
quest.

October 22

I am so *Grateful*

for interesting viewpoints.

Some say the issue is always the same,

Others preach, "It'll work when you make it work,"

Say it the best way you know how

And stop waiting for permission to live your life.

October 23

I am so *Grateful*

for helpful tools that keep me on track.

I keep addresses and phone numbers in
    my rolodex,
And schedule my days with appointment books
    and calendars,
I plan out short and long term goals in a
    notebook,
And prioritize the day's tasks with my "to do" list.

October 24

I am so

Grateful

for an attitude adjustment.

When everything seems to be falling apart
A darn good idea is to turn to the Self,
Feel the chaos for only a moment
And understand that life is readjusting itself.

October 25

I am so *Grateful*

for compositions of famous composers.

Beethoven's "Moonlight Sonata" amplifies a
    rippling wavelet,
Chopin's poetic nocturnes are a sentimental
    journey,
Tchaikovsky's "Nutcracker" is a fanciful piece—
Such music is alive and will be with us forever.

October 26

I am so

Grateful

for the search for truth.

There's great potential in this material world,
Your principles and ideas create reality,
Finding heaven and earth on the inside,
Reduces the span of uncertainty.

October 27

I am so *Grateful*

for the lasting impression of change.

A touch of crispness penetrates the air,
Indian corn ripens to an intricate design,
Crimson and brown leaves turn into a bonfire—
Autumn's golden days are drawing to an end.

October 28

I am so *Grateful*

for yields from the fields.

The fields are ripe and rich with plenty,
Cut hay lays drying in the sun,
Crops are gathered before winter sets in,
And harvest bins are filled to the brim.

October 29

I am so *Grateful*

for the alluring charm of fall.

A scarecrow stands watch among aged yellow
cornstalks,
Costumed ghosts and goblins ring doorbells
for treats,
The orange-red harvest moon casts its magic
spell
Over the hayride planned after the barn dance
tonight.

October 30

I am so *Grateful*

for the last days of autumn.

Flower beds are cleared and readied for spring,
Bushel baskets of apples are stored in the cellar,
Busy squirrels are scurrying for fast falling nuts
Hiding them before Jack Frost's deep freeze.

October 31

November
Thanksgiving

A day set aside for giving thanks,
A fitting way to voice our appreciation,
A wonderful loving thing to do
Expressing a prayer of gratitude.

Rediscover your sense of awe—
Heeding the words of Meister Eckhart,
"If the only prayer you ever say in your whole life
Is thank you, that would suffice."

I am so *Grateful*

for a fitting time to express gratitude.

We bow our heads in silent prayer,
Remembering our loved ones far away,
For freedom, friends and work we do well,
Thankful we have lived yet another year.

November 1

I am so *Grateful*

for participating in prayer.

On my knees, standing up,
Sitting down, and in song,
With my family or my friends,
Together at church or home alone.

November 2

I am so *Grateful*

for a tug on my heart strings.

I keep a loving memory in my heart
Of the very last hug my mother gave me,
The older I am the more appreciative I become
Remembering my dear ones and how much
I love them.

November 3

I am so *Grateful*

for spiritual community.

*U*plifting sermons have a long lasting effect,
Meaningful conversations occur after service,
Retreats are restful and life transforming,
All in the company of like-minded people.

November 4

I am so *Grateful*

for the mystery of One.

Birds swoop and swerve appearing invisibly
   connected,
Schools of fish swim together as if in concert,
Sparkling diamonds reflect one unending light,
The air we breathe sustains all life.

November 5

I am so *Grateful*

for humanitarians.

*W*anting to share something from deep within,
A gift of service straight from the heart,
These higher motives of unselfish men
    and women
Bring sunshine into the lives of others.

November 6

I am so *Grateful*

for turning a bend in the road.

Suffering has ended,
Pain has ceased,
Victims have survived,
And hope is renewed.

November 7

I am so *Grateful*

for one woman's mark on the world.

She provides a studio for the artwork of
    unsettled teens
Who paint their future with acrylics and
    watercolors,
Writing press releases and learning how to sell—
It's incredible to watch their greatness unfold.

November 8

I am so *Grateful*

for demonstrations of concern.

Mothers take a stand against drunk drivers,
Companion animals are shared with the elderly,
Professional athletes visit children in the hospital,
And prayer circles meet weekly to pray for
the sick.

November 9

I am so *Grateful*

for natural attributes of children.

Their innocent curiosity charts a new path,
Loving smiles are strewn along the way,
Their helping hands have a softening effect,
And we are humbled by their willingness
    to forgive.

November 10

I am so *Grateful*

for deserving accolades.

An unexpected compliment is paid after a job
   well done,
A standing ovation applauds an accomplished
   performer,
An employee is recognized at a company banquet,
And a gallant serviceman deserves the Medal
   of Honor.

November 11

I am so *Grateful*

for a talented boy's choir.

Giving young men a voice gives them a future,
Music as a tool teaches love and fellowship,
Reaching new heights through musical
achievement
Increases one boy's respect for another.

November 12

I am so *Grateful*

for mature teenagers.

They take the right to drive very seriously
And maintain an acceptable grade point average,
They live authentically without putting on airs—
Making it easier for mothers to let go.

November 13

I am so *Grateful*

for special greetings.

Singing "Happy Birthday" at a surprise party,
Lifting a glass of cheer at a holiday function,
Welcoming a hug after exiting an airplane,
And receiving a grin on the return back
        to work.

November 14

I am so *Grateful*

for words of encouragement.

I'm proud of you," follows a decision,
"Shoot for the moon," if taking a chance,
"Bravissimo," is heard after a solo performance,
While "Way to go!" signifies approval.

November 15

I am so

for easily staying connected.

I follow the business news in the Wall Street
Journal
And make calls anywhere, anytime from my
cell phone,
I can fax forms and messages anywhere
in minutes
And use e-mail to communicate all over the world.

November 16

I am so

Grateful

for a friendly computer.

It can research information in a matter of
    minutes
And contact many people all at the same time,
Its ability to perform depends on the software
    installed—
It is much easier to use than I thought it would be.

November 17

I am so *Grateful* for well-known restaurants.

Bananas Foster at Brennan's in New Orleans,
Kaffee and strudel at Demel's in Vienna,
Tea at three at the Breakers in Palm Beach,
And dinner at Tavern on the Green in New York.

November 18

I am so *Grateful*

for famous works of art.

The water lilies of Monet seem to float quietly
   on a still morning,
The ballerinas of Degas make me wish I'd been
   a dancer,
The talked-about Mona Lisa looks ahead with
   a fearless smile,
And Rembrandt's "Night Watch" is housed
   in its very own room.

November 19

I am so *Grateful*

for a day's work.

Success is preceded by extra effort,
Dedication and loyalty pay off well,
Opportunities arise to push us beyond
    boundaries—
The only real failure is in not trying.

November 20

I am so *Grateful*

for slowing down and nestling in.

Rocking in a rocker gazing out the window,
Or napping in a recliner in the late afternoon,
My head rests on a fluffy pillow at night—
The comforts of home are such a delight.

November 21

I am so *Grateful*

for a jaunt in the car.

Buckling up is how we begin,
Speed limits are set with us in mind,
Traffic lights protect us from oncoming cars,
And our destination is reached without a hitch.

November 22

I am so *Grateful*

for a safe haven.

A roof and four walls shelter me from the
    elements,
A private backyard acts as a retreat,
A plaque on the wall calls for God's blessings—
Home is the place where my worries disappear.

November 23

I am so *Grateful*

for the ritual of Thanksgiving.

Our forefathers hunted wild game and planted
   the land,
Loading their tables with the bounties of
   the earth,
Remembering that first meal shared by the
   Pilgrims and Indians
Reminds us that giving thanks has long been
   the way.

November 24

I am so *Grateful*

for savory foods on Turkey Day.

Stuffing prepared with apples and raisins,
Cranberries gleaming atop a table set with
    white linen,
Spiced pumpkin pie fragrant and flaky—
One day is not enough to count all our blessings.

November 25

I am so  *Grateful*

for valiant guardians.

Police officers deal with dangerous situations
on any given day,
Fire fighters battle blazes saving lives and
property,
The armed services are trained and ready
when called—
All have given us heroes who died for a cause.

November 26

I am so *Grateful*

for caregivers.

Home care workers administer to shut-ins,
Seeing Eye dogs guide the blind,
Foster parents look after abandoned children
And often give more than what is expected.

November 27

I am *so* *Grateful*

for strong emotions that stir us.

*I*ntense anger can motivate us to leave a
     harmful situation,
Heroic shock may result in an unearthly godsend,
Out of the depths of misery "Amazing Grace"
     was born,
And one child's wish preceded the "Make-a-Wish"
     Foundation.

November 28

I am so *Grateful*

for the melody of "Taps."

With a lump in his throat and a tear
     in his eye
A loving father grieves for his son,
A lone musician plays his polished bugle
Rousing self and others, "God is nigh."

November 29

I am so *Grateful*

for prayer.

The Serenity prayer encourages acceptance,
A higher power leads us, guides us, and directs us,
Grandmother Earth provides protection and
    nourishment
With enough for the entire world to live together
    in peace.

November 30

December Gifts

Longing for the goodness of the season
A gift, a present, curious, fanciful things,
Expecting happiness from something we get
Forgetting that happiness is something we give.

Giving and receiving are said to be the same,
Through giving we seek only the joy of another,
True gifts are those we do not see,
True gifts are acts of unconditional love.

I am so *Grateful*

for the closeness of God.

Readily receive the gift of this day,
Look for beauty right where you are,
Acknowledge every breath of life you take,
And know that silence is the way that
    God speaks.

December 1

I am so *Grateful*

for my wonderful hands.

So intricately connected, fingers and thumb,
Palms facing up, I look at each one,
Holding them together before each prayer,
Reminds me to be thankful they are there.

December 2

I am so *Grateful*

for gifts often taken for granted.

Lungs breathe without conscious thought,
Hearts maintain a steady, rhythmic beat,
Brains think without us telling them to—
Clearly, the human body is a walking miracle!

December 3

I am so *Grateful*

for genuine qualities.

The strength of a man,
The gentleness of a woman,
The innocence of a child,
All hail from up above.

December 4

I am so *Grateful*

for a soul journey.

Life is full of twists and turns,
Each of us has a unique path to follow,
Read the signs beyond doubt and fear,
Love alone is the true healer.

December 5

I am so *Grateful*

for the call of Spirit.

The ocean needs the waves,
The waves need the ocean,
There are many rivers to the sea
And many paths to the mountain.

December 6

I am so *Grateful*

for rediscovering my sense of awe.

Something wonderful happens each and every day,
Never grow too dull to wonder at a single moment,
Fill a heart with gladness by sharing another's load,
The essence of God is in everyone—peek-a-boo!

December 7

I am so *Grateful*

for enrichment through giving.

Saving useful clothing for the underprivileged
Or tutoring a child who has fallen behind
   in school,
A small donation can improve someone's life
And have a major effect in ways we'll never
   know.

December 8

I am so *Grateful*

for vital, dynamic living.

God, give me the courage to live by
The wisdom of Dr. Martin Luther King, Jr.'s
    words:
"I have decided to stick with love,
Hate is too great a burden to bear."

December 9

I am so *Grateful*

for the Golden Rule.

*L*et kindness become a second language,
Make a concerted effort to be fair and square,
When tempted to speak harshly count to ten,
And in retrospect ask, "What good have I done?"

December 10

I am so

Grateful

for efforts toward peace.

A diplomat maintains composure in a heated
   discussion,
A third person attempts to facilitate a meeting
   of the minds,
Searching for ways to bring more meaning into life
We might adopt Mahatma Gandhi's philosophy
   of peace.

December 11

I am so *Grateful*

for a conscientious community.

Blood banks are filled to capacity,
Meals are delivered to housebound elders,
Housing is provided for families of sick children,
And money is collected by ringing Salvation
      Army bells.

December 12

I am so *Grateful*

for positive events that
improve our world.

When walls come down broken countries are
    united,
Friendship extends to all parts of the world,
There are peaceful exchanges between diverse
    peoples,
And one nation extends a helping hand to another.

December 13

I am so *Grateful*

for scholars.

Wit and wonder are theirs to share,
Words are blended to make sense to me,
Each one has something important to say,
Sharing hands-on experience is their way.

December 14

I am so *Grateful*

for skilled craftsmen.

Wood carvers whittle novel creations,
Delicate glass sculptures are blown with care,
Colorful stained glass artwork hangs in a store
    window
Where the gifts of talent are proudly shown.

December 15

I am so *Grateful*

for winter clothing.

Furry earmuffs and soft wooly mittens,
Coats filled with down or lined with sheepskin,
Waterproof boots keep feet warm and dry
As we play in the snow until our rosy cheeks
glow.

December 16

I am so *Grateful*

for holiday cards.

Coming from places near and far,
Weeks ahead or in the nick of time,
A simple verse, a timely rhyme,
A personal message from friends of mine.

December 17

I am so *Grateful*

for holiday goodies.

Licking spoons from candy making,
Gingerbread men slowly baking,
Sticks of peppermint placed in a jar,
Fruitcakes ready and waiting to be cut.

December 18

I am so *Grateful*

for the feeling of love at Christmas.

Mom decorates cutout cookies with red and
green sprinkles,
Shimmering, shiny tinsel adds a finishing touch
to the tree,
Willing hands wrap each present with pretty
bows and love—
These are the most priceless gifts, these are
the gifts of the heart.

December 19

I am so *Grateful*

for musical talent.

*L*ifting music to lofty levels of accomplishment
Professional artists celebrate through sound,
Leading crowds in an electrifying performance
Enhances each listener's personal experience.

December 20

I am so *Grateful*

for a show of Christmas spirit.

Decorative lights set houses aglow,
Shoppers are caught in the hustle and bustle,
Carolers sing a note of seasonal joy,
And kisses are shared under the mistletoe.

December 21

I am so *Grateful*

for a snowfall's delight.

Snowflakes piled high cover the landscape,
Crusted banks glisten under a rising moon,
A frosted pane holds winter at bay
As we sit undisturbed in our comfy room.

December 22

I am so *Grateful*

for receiving thoughtful gifts.

*T*ime was spent in careful selection,
Handpicked with thoughts only of me,
A generous present beautifully wrapped—
A thank you card will surely be sent.

December 23

I am so *Grateful*

for the greatest gift of all.

The nicest present Santa has
Of all he places under the tree
Is the gift of love that sharing brings
In the cookies and milk I'm excited to leave.

December 24

I am so *Grateful*

for the sounds of Christmas.

The piercing sweetness of a well-tuned organ
Echoes and reechoes in the hearts of all,
The sudden blare of a French horn so golden
Trumpets the announcement: a child is born!

December 25

I am so *Grateful*

for angels.

*P*ositioned atop a Christmas tree
Or simply worn on a lapel,
Some that pose in human form
Are merely guardians in disguise.

December 26

I am so *Grateful*

for a candle's glow.

A brilliant flame in the night,
Steady, flickering, unfailing light,
Burning in our hearts so bright,
God's love shines tonight.

December 27

I am so *Grateful*

for reconnecting as night draws near.

Pondering trying moments without motive
    or pretense,
Hidden possibilities appear at long last,
Increasing my belief in the spiritual world,
Conceding that God has something better
    planned.

December 28

I am so

Grateful

for a gleam of hope.

*L*Light, love, peace and joy
Flow continuously on our earth,
Gifts like these are there to see,
If only we pause to behold and be.

December 29

I am so *Grateful*

for the joyous anticipation
of the New Year.

The lessons I've learned from past experience
And the plentiful opportunities I've had for
    exploration
Bless all the circumstances of my life
With the expectation of much happiness
    in the coming year.

December 30

I am so *Grateful*

for having a deeper appreciation for life.

Within the creative process time stands still
    while hours are passing by
An empty canvas awaits its masterpiece—
It's the *"I AM"* expressed and confidently believed
That sets the stage for finishing touches and
    perfect endings.

December 31

Gratitude Works

May gratitude cause you to reflect and follow your heart.

May you find balance in your life and grow in spirit.

May beauty surround you and may love embrace you.

May you find serenity in nature and experience the joy of having fun.

May you transcend your troubles and harvest the goodness within.

May your prayers of thanksgiving be answered kindly.

May the gifts of prosperity and abundance follow you every day.

And, most importantly, may you be grateful for who you are.

Gratitude Works **Order Form** Please photocopy

Name

Organization

Address

City   State   Zip

Phone   Email

Quantity ordering: _____ x $11.97 = $ _____

WI Sales Tax: Add 5.6%   = $ _____

Shipping and Handling – $4.00 first book
        $1.00 for each additional book = $ _____

| ISBN: 0-9748550-0-6 | **TOTAL** $ _____

All orders pre-paid please!

☐ By check, payable to: Orders may be submitted by mail,
                            or through our secure website:
K & E Innovations, LLP   www.gratitudeworks.com
6099 Oakwood Lane, W.   Email: gratitudeworks4u@aol.com
Greendale, WI 53129   Phone: 414-421-8130